SYMBOL	DESCRIPTION
j	Sometimes used to represent subscripts in a double summation: $$\sum_{j=1}^{m}\sum_{i=1}^{n} X_{ij} = (X_{11} + X_{21} + \cdots + X_{n1})$$ $$+ (X_{12} + X_{22} + \cdots + X_{n2})$$ $$+ (X_{1m} + X_{2m} + \cdots + X_{nm})$$
L, L_1, L_2	Contrast used with analysis of variance
$L(D)$	Unit normal loss function
L_j	Lower limit of class interval
LCL	Lower control limit
$\log \hat{Y}(X)$	Logarithm to base 10 of $\hat{Y}(X)$; used in regression to find curve, $\hat{Y}(X) = ab^x$
λ (lambda)	Mean rate in a Poisson process
λ_A, λ_S	Mean arrival and service rates used in queuing applications
M	(1) Median of population (2) Monetary amount for calculating utility
MSA	Mean square (between columns) in a two-factor analysis of variance
MSAB	Interactions mean square; used in two-factor analysis of variance
MSB	Mean square (between rows) in a two-factor analysis of variance
MSCOL	Mean square (between columns) in an analysis of variance using a Latin square
MSE	(1) Error mean square; used to calculate the F statistic in analysis of variance (2) Mean squared error in exponential smoothing
MSR	Regression mean square
MSROW	Mean square (between rows) in an analysis of variance using a Latin square
MSTR	Mean square; used to calculate the F statistic: (1) (between columns) for the treatments in a one-factor analysis of variance (2) (between letters) in a three-factor analysis of variance using a Latin-square design
m	(1) Sample median (2) Number of variables used in multiple regression and correlation analysis (3) Number of smoothing parameters in exponential smoothing
μ (mu)	Arithmetic mean of a population
μ_0	Value of the population mean assumed under the null hypothesis
μ_0, μ_1	Prior and posterior expected means
$\mu_1, \mu_2, \mu_3, \ldots$	Population means in analysis of variance
$\mu_{11}, \mu_{12}, \ldots$	Means of treatment combination populations; used in analysis of variance
$\mu_{\cdot 1}, \mu_{1 \cdot}, \mu_{\cdot \cdot}$	Population means for factors or overall; used in analysis of variance
μ_b	Breakeven level for mean
μ_A, μ_B	Means of populations A and B, which are compared using two samples

SYMBOL	DESCRIPTION
$\mu_{Y \cdot X}$	Conditional mean for Y for a specified value of X; used in regression analysis, where $\mu_{Y \cdot X}$ represents the height of the true regression line
$\mu_{Y \cdot 12}$	Conditional mean for values of Y for specified values of X_1 and X_2; used in multiple regression analysis, where $\mu_{Y \cdot 12}$ represents the height of the true regression plane
N	Number of observations in a population
n	(1) Number of observations in a sample (2) Number of trials in a Bernoulli process
$n!$	n factorial, or the product $n \times (n-1) \times (n-2) \times \cdots \times 2 \times 1$
n_A, n_B	Sample sizes for two-sample tests comparing the parameters of two populations A and B
n_a, n_b	Number of observations of type a and type b obtained in a sample; applicable to the number-of-runs test
$O_1, O_2 \ldots$	Outcomes in a decision structure
P	(1) Proportion of sample observations having a particular characteristic (2) Proportion of successes from a Bernoulli process
$\Pr[A]$	Probability of event A
$\Pr[A\|B]$	Conditional probability of A given B
$\Pr[A \text{ and } B]$	Probability of the intersection of events A and B; event occurs only when both A and B occur (also called the joint probability)
$\Pr[A \text{ or } B]$	Probability of the union of A and B; occurs when either A or B occurs, or when both A and B occur
$\Pr[X = x]$	Probability that the random variable X assumes one of several particular values
$\Pr[X \leq x]$	Cumulative probability that X assumes any value less than or equal to X
$P*$	Critical value for P
P_A, P_B	Proportions of observations having a particular characteristic for samples from populations A and B
P_C	Combined sample proportion; used to compare two population proportions
P_r^n	Number of permutations of r items taken from a collection of size n when different orders of selection are counted
$\bar{P}$	Combined sample proportion
p_n, p_0	Prices per unit of an item in year n and in base period 0; used to find index numbers
π (pi)	(1) Proportion of a population having a particular characteristic (2) Probability of a trial success in a Bernoulli process
π_0	Value of the population proportion assumed under the null hypothesis
$\pi_1, \pi_2, \pi_3, \ldots$	Values of population proportions in testing for equality of several population proportions

Statistics for Modern Business

A FIRST COURSE

33
49
69

LAWRENCE L. LAPIN
San Jose State University

THE DRYDEN PRESS
Harcourt Brace College Publishers

Fort Worth   Philadelphia   San Diego   New York   Orlando   Austin   San Antonio
Toronto   Montreal   London   Sydney   Tokyo

Acquisitions Editor	Scott Isenberg
Developmental Editor	Millicent Treloar
Project Editor	Emily Thompson
Art Director	Brian Salisbury
Production Manager	Ann Coburn
Permissions Editor	Shirley Webster
Product Manager	Scott Timian
Marketing Assistant	Kathleen Sharp
Indexer	Lisa Lapin
Compositor	GTS Graphics, Inc.
Text Type	10/12 Times Roman
Cover Image	© M.C. Escher/Cordon Art—Baarn—Holland

Address for Orders
The Dryden Press
6277 Sea Harbor Drive
Orlando, FL 32887-6777
1-800-782-4479 or 1-800-433-0001 (in Florida)

Address for Editorial Correspondence
The Dryden Press
301 Commerce Street, Suite 3700
Fort Worth, TX 76102

ISBN: 0-03-007786-9

Library of Congress Catalog Card Number: 94-69026

Credits appear on page 668, which constitutes a continuation of the copyright page.

Printed in the United States of America

4 5 6 7 8 9 0 1 2 3 032 9 8 7 6 5 4 3 2 1

The Dryden Press
Harcourt Brace College Publishers

THE DRYDEN PRESS SERIES IN MANAGEMENT SCIENCE AND QUANTITATIVE METHODS

PREFACE

This book was written in response to an increased need for a single semester course in statistics for business and economics majors. As with my earlier book, the overriding goal is to enliven statistics, to make it more interesting, relevant, and easier to learn. This gives the book a *decision making* flavor and, at the same time, emphasizes *data analysis* as a topic having equal footing with deductive and inferential statistics. This modern thrust is reflected in the estimation chapter, which includes an optional section on statistical *bootstrapping* and in the multiple regression presentation, which has a *model-building* flavor.

All topics are introduced by carefully chosen examples illustrating more than technical mathematical concepts. The stage is set, the motivation is provided, and the rationale is given as each new concept is presented. Many of the examples and exercises clearly relate to present-day issues, such as health, the environment, and global enterprise. Several examples of each major area of business and economics—such as accounting, marketing, finance, production, forecasting, and consumer behavior—serve to richly illustrate the applications of statistics.

A course in high school algebra is the only prerequisite. Although this textbook should prove more accessible than most statistic books, the relevant nature of its presentation is achieved by addressing some reputedly difficult material. Probability, hypothesis testing, and various more difficult topics receive generous explanation, often from several viewpoints. Only the essentials are included, with just enough probability to support statistics. The reader is encouraged to rely more on intuition than on rote memory. Computational demands are kept manageable, with the role of the computer amply illustrated throughout the text.

This book reflects the computer's dominant role in statistical evaluations. Several popular software packages are used in the many illustrations. My experience, however, teaches that knowing a software package does not equate to a good understanding of the topic itself. The computer does not eliminate the need for a minimal amount of number crunching—by hand with calculator assistance. (It is possible to effectively use this book without ever booting up a computer!) Some hand computation has proven to be an effective way to master underlying concepts. Working small problems by hand not only facilitates a better understanding of the underlying procedure, but it also gives added incentive to seek out computer help with bigger problems. This book's balanced mix of small and large problems makes that a practical reality. To further enhance computer applications, several large data sets are available on disk.

There are several user-friendly features of this book. Students will find several problem sets falling at the ends of sections within chapters, as well as a comprehensive review problem set at the end of the chapter. These have all been class tested and graded in terms of difficulty. Each chapter has three special problem sets as well. The Real-Life Statistical Challenge section utilizes *real* data with its own questions. This section is followed by a Statistics in Practice problem set emphasizing analysis of the student's *own* data. Each chapter ends with a medium-length case providing questions that exercise concepts and tools in a *realistic* setting. Every chapter opens with a list of prerequisite concepts important to understanding the material to be presented and a series of major questions that the chapter will answer. The answers are given in the end-of-chapter summary section.

Course enrichment and variety are facilitated by *optional* sections appearing in several chapters that cover useful topics which some instructors might easily skip to save time. Each optional section has a self-contained problem set. Complete solutions to all exercises and questions are provided in the Instructor's Manual, which also provides answers to case questions and example solutions for problems involving student-generated data. Nearly 100 additional exercises and 300 examination questions and their solutions are available in a Testbook.

Also available to accompany this book is the *Guide to EasyStat,* a computer manual that incorporates a complete software package called *EasyStat,* all included on a diskette that comes inside every manual. *EasyStat* is a user-friendly program for any IBM PC-compatible system. The computer manual is keyed to the text and contains its own detailed examples and hundreds of problems. A special feature of *EasyStat* is a master data set comprising U.S. Decennial data for 1,000 urban employed homeowners. Students can select their own random samples from 14 different categories and analyze them separately. Class results can be pooled to illustrate concepts of sampling error.

The new end-of-chapter features, "Real-Life Statistical Challenge" and "Statistics in Practice," were written by my colleague, Jerome Burstein, of San Jose State University. I wish to thank Jerry for helping to make my book more relevant, interesting, and functional. I am greatly indebted to the many people who have assisted me in preparing this book. Special thanks go to Janet Anaya of San Jose State University, who contributed some of the practice exercises and who carefully checked the manuscript for accuracy. I also wish to thank my colleagues whose comments were invaluable in setting the tone and the reviewers of this edition: Raymond J. Ballard, East Texas State University; Roger Even Bove, West Chester University; Douglas P. Dotterweich, East Tennessee State University; Jim Knudsen, Creighton University; and Richard M. Smith, Bryant College.

Finally, thanks go to the book team at The Dryden Press: Scott Isenberg, acquisitions editor; Millicent Treloar, development editor; Emily Thompson, project editor; Ann Coburn, production manager; Brian Salisbury, art director; Scott Timian, product manager; Kathleen Sharp, marketing assistant; and Shirley Webster, permissions editor.

I am deeply grateful to my students, who over many years of debugging the book helped identify the problems a reader might face.

Lawrence L. Lapin

CONTENTS IN BRIEF

CONTENTS

PART I

BASIC STATISTICAL

CONCEPTS

AFTER READING THIS CHAPTER, YOU WILL UNDERSTAND:

The meaning of "statistics."

The role of data in statistics.

Data classifications and the basic statistical building block.

The distinctions between the population and the sample.

The types of statistical data.

Two essential types of modern statistical methodology.

Statistics plays a major role in modern lives. It is impossible to read a newspaper or watch television news without encountering statistical information, such as the latest presidential approval percentage, the present month's annual inflation rate, the level of the Dow Jones Industrial Stock Index, or the drop in SAT scores. It is obvious that such statistics permeate the decision-making process. Presidents and other politicians make crucial policies based on the latest opinion poll results. The U.S. Federal Reserve System bases far-reaching monetary policy choices on trends in inflation, while important investors continually monitor their actions, which are anticipated by stock prices. SAT scores serve as a barometer for assessing the quality of public education, affecting not only daily policy but school board elections and local taxing decisions.

We are all affected by statistical information, and some truly informed people are immersed in statistics. Regardless of your chosen career path, your educational experience will be greatly enhanced by knowing how to look beyond everyday numbers and how to generate and report statistical information. Such knowledge will enable you to cope with the unavoidable potential for errors that underlie so much survey information. Through study of statistics you will become aware of the opportunity for statistical misapplications—ranging from unintentional bias to manipulation or fraud. You will also become familiar with the tremendous opportunities that a statistical approach can offer investigators and decision makers.

1-1 THE MEANING OF STATISTICS

Although the word "statistics" commonly brings to mind masses of numbers, graphs, and tables, these play a limited role in modern statistics, in which the focus is placed on *making decisions in the face of uncertainty*. This book describes some of the more useful methods and procedures that can be applied to numerical evidence to facilitate decision making in the face of uncertainty. Certain basic principles are explained within a theoretical framework to enable you to achieve a greater appreciation and understanding of how and why they work.

A concise statement summarizing the subject of this book is the

DEFINITION: **Statistics** is a body of methods and theory that is applied to numerical evidence when making decisions in the face of uncertainty.

This definition treats statistics as a separate academic field, just like physics, history, or biology. As a discipline, statistics has advanced rapidly during the twentieth century to become recognized as a branch of mathematics.

Partly due to the relative newness of statistics as a subject of study, the word *statistics* has acquired several meanings. In its earlier and most common usage, statistics means a collection of numerical facts or data. In sports, for example, batting averages, rushing yardage, and games won or lost are all statistics. Closing prices from the New York Stock Exchange, figures showing sources of income and expenditures for the federal budget, and distances between major cities are also statistics. Your reported income on last year's tax return is a statistic. Examples of this usage are the **vital statistics**—figures on births, deaths, marriages, and divorces—and the contents of publications listing population and economic data, such as the *Statistical Abstract of the United States*. The main distinction

STATISTICS AROUND US

From the Bushman to the Space Scientist

Everyone—from such remote people as the Bushman in Africa's Kalihari desert to space scientists who plan grand tours of the planets—uses statistics. A successful Bushman locates water in a manner that puzzles some geologists. He sucks through a reed stuck in the sand in what his experience tells him is a likely spot, as if he were drinking a thick milkshake from a straw. Sometimes no water is found, but often enough the Bushman does find a "drink hole." His very survival depends on his skill at locating drink holes—on using his experience to cope with uncertainty.

Similarly, scientists depend on experience to determine an optimal space-vehicle configuration that will withstand the rigors of an environment far more hostile than earth's atmosphere and that will survive long enough to fly past Jupiter and eventually to even more distant planets. If the communications system fails, the mission itself will be a failure. The system must be super-reliable—designed so that its chances for survival are high. Millions of hours of human experience can contribute to design decisions. Even so, there are no guarantees that the chosen design will function as intended. Again, decisions must be made in the face of uncertainty.

Both the Bushman's and the space scientist's mechanisms for making choices utilize limited experience, and in this respect they are not substantially different. The remaining element that makes their mechanisms statistical is that *both use numerical evidence.* To evaluate the reliability of communications equipment, components must be tested under stress to determine the number of hours they can function before failing. The scientist's evidence is numerical. But what about the Bushman's? He knows that one set of conditions favors the presence of water more than another. Every wet hole reinforces his knowledge of factors that are positive to water, and each dry hole strengthens his awareness of the negative factors. Thus, the Bushman's numerical evidence is the *frequency* of successful drink holes he finds under various prevailing conditions. Even though the presence of water is a qualitative factor, frequencies of occurrence are themselves numerical.

between our definition of statistics and this usage of the word is its form: singular versus plural. Statistics (singular) *is* a subject of study; statistics (plural) *are* numerical facts.

THE ROLE OF STATISTICS

Our definition of statistics is particularly appropriate for readers who are primarily interested in applications to business and economics, where there is a high incidence of decisions made under uncertainty. Business decisions involving both numerical data and uncertainty are encountered at all levels of business. Consider the following list:

The Decision Maker	The Decision	The Uncertainty
Manager	Whom to hire	Employee performance
Planner	Facility locations	Volume needed
CEO	Set policies for:	
	Pricing	Demands
	New products	Market shares
	Financing	Costs
Federal Reserve	Interest rate targets	Effect on:
		Inflation
		Employment
		Growth
Sales manager	Customer communication	Order size
Investor	Stock to buy	Rate of return

TYPES OF STATISTICS:
DESCRIPTIVE, INFERENTIAL, AND EXPLORATORY

The emphasis on the decision-making aspects of statistics is a recent one. In its early years, the study of statistics consisted of methodology for summarizing or describing statistical data.

DESCRIPTIVE STATISTICS

This area is known as **descriptive statistics** because it is concerned with summary calculations and graphical displays, such as those in Figure 1-1. Descriptive statistics is often just a small part of two more sophisticated types of statistics: inferential and exploratory.

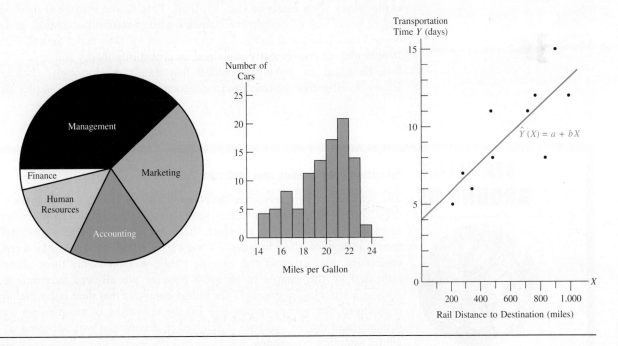

FIGURE 1-1 Graphical displays to describe statistical data.

INFERENTIAL STATISTICS

sample

Descriptive statistics contrasts with the modern statistical approach in which generalizations are made about the whole (called the **population**) by investigating a portion (referred to as the **sample**). Thus, the average income of *all* families in the United States can be estimated from figures obtained from a *few hundred* families. Such a prediction or estimate is an example of an inference. The study of how inferences are made from numerical data is called **inferential statistics**.

Inferential statistics acknowledges the potential for error in making generalizations from a sample. This still does not guarantee that correct conclusions will be reached, since samples may deviate from the underlying population. Such discrepancies are called **sampling errors**. But sampling errors may be insignificant when sampling is done randomly. Statisticians use **probability** to assess the likelihood of making large sampling errors.

Inferential statistics acknowledges that the potential for error exists in making generalizations from a sample. Because of the important role it plays in statistical inference, we will discuss probability in Chapter 5, after we examine descriptive statistics for populations having *known* properties. This will prepare us for developing statistical inferences about populations whose characteristics are *unknown*. Our formal definition for the field of statistics applies to both its descriptive and its inferential forms. This book emphasizes inferential statistics because it can play such a dynamic role in decision making. But first we will focus on descriptive statistics in Chapters 2 and 3.

EXPLORATORY DATA ANALYSIS

For many years statistical procedures have been classified primarily as either descriptive statistics or inferential statistics. The borders between those original statistical realms are becoming blurred, as a third major statistical area, **exploratory data analysis**, has evolved. This newer statistical methodology makes heavy use of descriptive statistics while extending statistical procedures beyond their traditional forms. Exploratory data analysis is not limited to circumstances that are conveniently explained by probability theory and need not, therefore, be based on convenient models that simply do not apply. Data analysis allows investigators the freedom to systematically utilize small samples and "ill-

STATISTICS AROUND US

Television Programming and Statistics

The seasonal controversy over decisions made by television networks to drop certain programs illustrates some of the principles and problems involved. The information on which these decisions are based is obtained from a sample of a few hundred TV viewers who are believed to be a representative microcosm of the viewing public at large. Only those shows indicated by the sample to be most popular are allowed to continue. Although articulate segments of the public complain that their tastes are not represented, the agency responsible for the collection of sample data has demonstrated that its audience is selected in accordance with accepted scientific sampling procedures.

behaved" data in reaching meaningful conclusions, even if the conclusions would not otherwise qualify within the known inferential framework.

Throughout this book opportunities will be explored for using exploratory statistics to complement traditional methods.

1-1 For each of the following decisions, give an example of potential numerical data that might be helpful in making the choice.
  (a) in which magazine to place an ad
  (b) where to locate the pet food in a supermarket
  (c) screening job applicants
  (d) number of retail feet for gifts in a card shop

1-2 Consider the following numerical data. Suggest for each a decision situation where the data might be used in reaching a choice.
  (a) batting averages of players on your favorite softball team
  (b) earnings per share for companies in an industry
  (c) average starting salaries for students in various majors
  (d) examination scores from two statistics classes taught by different methods

1-3 From the first section of your favorite newspaper, identify four instances of numerical data which may be used for making a decision under uncertainty.
  (a) List each item.
  (b) Indicate for each example (1) the potential decision maker, (2) what choices might be considered, and (3) the uncertainties involved.

1-2 STATISTICAL DATA

A collection of data is referred to as a **data set**. To illustrate, consider the following daily temperatures (low, high) reported at 10 P.M. by a Channel 11 weather forecaster.

(52,73)	(47,81)	(55,79)	(57,75)	(46,80)
(56,64)	(54,73)	(52,77)	(53,72)	(49,69)

Each of the above temperature pairs applies to a single location. They are the elements of the data set referred to as **data points**.

A statistical evaluation usually involves one or more **variables**. In the above set the daily *high* temperature is one variable. A second variable is the daily *low* temperature. From those two, a third variable, the daily temperature *range*, may be determined.

CLASSIFICATIONS FOR DATA AND VARIABLES

Data sets involve two classes of data. **Quantitative data** involve numerical values. To illustrate, consider the data sets in Figure 1-2 representing the current payrolls of three Central City employers. Hourly rates of pay and the hours worked are quantitative data. Each employee record constitutes a data point, with the amounts and specific types varying among employers. The second class of

Ace Widgets	Name	Born	SS#	Class.	Hours	Rate	Exemps . . . .
	Adams, A.	10/65	521-48-0237	DB	42	11.25	02 . . .

DanDee Assemblers	SOC SEC	NAME	GRP	RATE	HRS	COM . . . .
	471-22-1189	B. Johnson	H	8.50	37.5	25.50 . . .

Central City	Dept	Name	ID	Hrly	Hours . . .
	Power	Smith T.	9258	11.35	46 . . .

FIGURE 1-2 Data sets for hourly worker payrolls of three Central City empployers.

data is **qualitative data**. The payroll data include employee department or classification and are examples of qualitative data, which is ordinarily categorical in nature.

A variable need not be limited to a single data set. Following the same designations as the respective data type, a variable may be either quantitative (hourly pay) or qualitative (sex, classification). Levels for quantitative variables are called **variates**. In the payroll data, the hourly earnings (dollars per hour) for the three persons listed are $11.25, 8.50, and 11.35. The counterparts to level for a qualitative variable are **attributes** or **categories**. For those same persons, the employee classification (or group or department) variable lists attributes DB, H, and Power.

TYPES OF QUANTITATIVE DATA

Four types of quantitative data are encountered in statistical investigations.

1. **Nominal data** arise when numbers are used to represent categories or attributes. Such values often arise when information is coded for data processing. Thus, a university might designate majors by numbers, so that a 5 might apply to an accounting student, a 37 for finance, and a 51 for marketing. Such data should not be treated as numerical, since relative size has no meaning.

2. **Ordinal data** are often encountered when items are ranked by importance, strength, or severity. One example is provided by the Beaufort wind scale, which assigns numbers to wind forces at sea. A gentle breeze is rated at 3, a strong breeze at 6, and a strong gale at 9. The increasing severity of winds is reflected by the Beaufort numbers, so that 3 is less than 6, since gentle breezes are less forceful than strong ones, while 6 lies below 9 because strong breezes

are weaker than strong gales. Simple arithmetic operations are not meaningfully applied to ordinal data. Even though $6 - 3 = 3$ and $9 - 6 = 3$, it would be wrong to conclude that the increase in wind severity between a gentle and a strong breeze is identical to the change in force between a strong breeze and a strong gale.

3. **Interval data** provide ranking, and the arithmetic operations of addition and subtraction are meaningful. For example, each degree level on the Celsius temperature scale reflects that a constant amount of heat is necessary to raise the temperature of water one notch, regardless of the starting level. Thus, the same amount of heat is used to raise water from 30 to 40 as from 60 to 70, since $40 - 30 = 10$ and $70 - 60 = 10$ are the same differences. But 0, achieved at the freezing point of distilled water, is arbitrarily chosen. (The Fahrenheit scale has a zero defined differently.) Thus, 60 is not twice as hot as 30, and the ratio 60/30 has no meaning.

4. **Ratio data** allow for all basic arithmetic operations, including division and multiplication. Typical business data, such as revenue, cost, and profit fall into this group. Physical measurements and time increments are usually ratio data.

Most statistical procedures are based on arithmetic operations, limiting them to applications involving interval or ratio data. A limited class of statistical methods may be used with ordinal data. With nominal data, statistics is primarily concerned with counting frequencies of occurrence.

EXERCISES

1-4 Publications, such as *Business Week, Fortune,* and *Forbes,* contain data sets. Find an example of a data set. Then do the following.
   (a) Identify the data points.
   (b) Determine useful variables, indicating whether each is quantitative or qualitative. Identify for that data point the level or attribute for each variable found.

1-5 Give an example of each of the following data types.
   (a) nominal   (c) interval
   (b) ordinal   (d) ratio

1-6 Indicate for each of the following situations which of the four types of quantitative data applies.
   (a) Survey questions that ask you to scale a product from 1 (extremely poor) to 10 (absolutely wonderful).
   (b) ZIP codes used in sorting mail.
   (c) Richter scale used to express earthquake energy.
   (d) Supermarket checkout times.
   (e) Daily high temperatures.

1-3 THE POPULATION AND THE SAMPLE

The basic element of statistics is an **observation**; it represents what we actually see. An observation may be a physical measurement (weight or height), an answer to a question (yes or no), or a classification (defective or nondefective). Observations relevant to a particular decision constitute a **population**. Stated more formally, we have the following

DEFINITION: A statistical **population** is the collection of all possible observations of one or more variables.

In most applications we will encounter, the population will ordinarily involve a single variable. But a population may be *multi-dimensional*. As with variables, populations may be quantitative, qualitative, or even both (when there is more than one dimension).

Note that a statistical population exists whether all, some, or none of the possible observations are actually made. It may be real (such as the height of 30-year-old males in Schenectady in June 1992) or hypothetical (such as the longevity of laboratory rats fed a special diet that is not yet widely used). Because it consists of all possible observations, a population is often referred to synonymously as a **universe**.

In contrast to the statistical population, which consists of all possible observations, the **sample** contains only some of the observations. We make the following

DEFINITION: A **sample** is a collection of observations representing only a portion of the population.

DISTINGUISHING BETWEEN THE DATA SET, POPULATION, AND SAMPLE

The statistical population and sample may encompass portions of several data sets. Figure 1-3 may be helpful in sorting things out. There we consider the population of hourly pay rates for all workers in the Central City area. Every payroll in town applies, so that numerous data sets are needed to define the population data. Although the individual data points involve other types of information, only the hourly pay from each applies to the population of interest. The number of elementary units in a population can involve fewer data points than the entire data set. That would be the case if an investigator were interested in wages of only a portion of the city workers—for instance, just the employees of the Power Department.

The population consists of all the possible observations that might be made. It exists whether or not those observations are actually made. (It may be too expensive to gather all of the population data.) The sample contains just a portion of the population observations. The levels of the variable are actually found for each sample observation.

Thus, the population is usually not totally *known* (but it will be precisely *defined*). Only the sample observations are actually made. The sample results are the basis for making generalizations about the population.

Statistical methodology is mainly concerned with evaluating sample information. Ordinarily, only a few randomly chosen observations are made, and the resulting sample then provides information for drawing conclusions about the population. A population can even exist in theory only, and only the sample observations would then be real. Such a grouping is called a **target population**. Testing situations give rise to target populations. For example, attitude toward a prototype package design might be determined only for a sample group, unless that design is later chosen for final product distribution.

in theory

FIGURE 1-3 Relationship between data sets, the population, and the sample.

ELEMENTARY UNITS

A statistical population consists of **observations** of some characteristic of interest associated with the individuals concerned, *not* the individual items or persons themselves. Suppose that the state legislature needs to know the hourly wages of Central City workers in order to analyze proposed changes in labor laws. To find these, the employee records for all companies might be searched and the wages determined. Each number obtained constitutes an observation of the wage

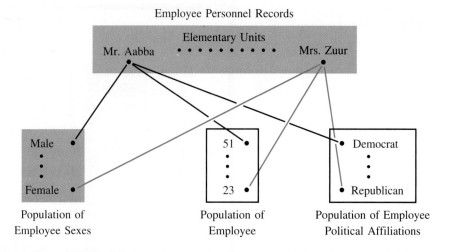

FIGURE 1-4 Illustration of how several different populations may be obtained from the same elementary units.

variable. The entire collection of numbers so obtained is the population; the employees themselves are referred to as the **elementary units** of the population.

A limitless variety of different populations may be obtained from the same elementary units, depending on the characteristic of interest. This principle is illustrated in Figure 1-4. Thus, a company could have different populations for political affiliation, sex, marital status, years of education, height, weight, eye color, job classifications, and years on present job, where each population is composed of observed characteristics of the same elementary units—the employees.

WORKING POPULATION AND THE FRAME

frame helps to define population

How do we define the elementary units of a population? The employer can define the employees as those persons on the payroll, so that the names of all employees may be obtained from payroll records. Such a source of elementary units is called a **frame**.

The frame is important in statistical studies because it helps to define the population. Suppose that a sample of voter preference toward candidates is taken to predict the outcome of an election. The sample should represent the population of votes to be cast for a specific office. In selecting the sample of voters, the only frame available to the opinion surveyor is the roll of registered voters. The elementary units listed in this frame may differ from those of the population, because some people who are registered will not vote. The votes that would be cast if all those who are registered voted constitute the **working population**, because its frame is the only one currently available. The sample must be drawn from this population.

QUALITATIVE AND QUANTITATIVE POPULATIONS

As with the variables used to define them, populations may be **quantitative** or **qualitative**. In our presentation of statistics, we will discuss these two kinds of populations separately but in parallel. Different methods are required to describe

TABLE 1-1 Illustration of Possible Observations for Various Quantitative and Qualitative Populations

Quantitative Population Observations

Elementary Unit	Characteristic of Interest	Unit of Measurement	Possible Variate
person	age	years	21.3 yr
microcircuit	defective solder joints	number	5
tire	remaining tread	millimeters	10 mm
account balance	amount	dollars	$5,233.46
employer	female employees	percent	35%
common stock	earnings per share	dollars	$3.49
operator	errors	proportion	.02
light bulb	lifetime	hours	581 hr
can of food	weight of contents	ounces	15.3 oz

Qualitative Population Observations

Elementary Unit	Characteristic of Interest	Possible Attributes
person	sex	male, female
security	type	bond, common stock, preferred stock
building	exterior materials	brick, wood, aluminum
employee	experience	applicable, not applicable
television	quality	defective, nondefective
firm	legal status	corporation, partnership, proprietorship
patient	condition	satisfactory, critical
student	residence	on-campus, off-campus

and summarize each type of population: Arithmetic operations can be performed on numbers, so that, for example, we can calculate the average height of a collection of 30-year-old men; other procedures must be employed to summarize a qualitative population.

We refer to a particular observation of a qualitative variable as an **attribute** or category. Thus, for the variable marital status we might observe any one of the following attributes: single, married, divorced, or widowed. An observation of a quantitative variable such as hourly wage will be a particular numerical value or **variate**, such as $8.40, 12.15, or 10.50. Table 1-1 presents examples of observations from various quantitative populations.

DEDUCTIVE AND INDUCTIVE STATISTICS

An important dichotomy underlies statistical reasoning. This concept is illustrated in Figure 1-5, in which two kinds of sampling situations with coins are presented.

DEDUCTIVE STATISTICS

Deduction ascribes properties to the specific, starting with the general. For example, probability tells us that if a person is chosen by lottery from a group containing nine men and one woman, then the odds against picking the woman are 9 to 1. We deduce that in about 90 percent of such samples the person will be male. The use of probability to determine the chance of obtaining a particular kind of sample result is known as **deductive statistics**.

DEDUCTION

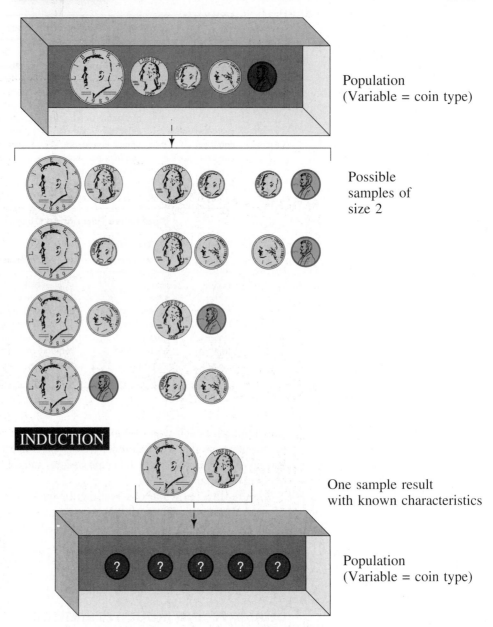

Population
(Variable = coin type)

Possible
samples of
size 2

INDUCTION

One sample result
with known characteristics

Population
(Variable = coin type)

The population ought to represent the sample. But it
may differ in unknown ways. Possible conclusions are:
• 2 halves and 3 quarters (credible)
• 3 quarters and 2 halves (credible)
• at least 1 half and 1 quarter (most credible)
• some coins of each type (least credible)

FIGURE 1-5 Illustration of deduction and induction using coins.

Figure 1-5 shows how we may deduce what kinds of samples might be obtained when two coins are randomly selected from a box containing five coins. Ten equally likely sample outcomes are presented.

INDUCTIVE STATISTICS *drawn from sample*

In Chapters 5, 6, and 7 we will learn how to apply deductive techniques when we know everything regarding the population in advance and we are concerned with studying the characteristics of the possible samples that may arise from *known* populations. In much of the remainder of the book, we will reverse direction and use **inductive statistics**. Induction involves drawing general conclusions from the specific. In statistics this means that inferences about populations are drawn from samples. The sample is all that is known; we must determine uncertain characteristics of the population from the incomplete information available.

Figure 1-5 illustrates this principle when only the sample result is known and a conclusion must be drawn about the entire population of coins. The statistical challenge is to draw a meaningful conclusion that is also credible. Inductive and deductive statistics are completely complementary. We must study how samples are generated before we can learn to generalize from a sample. The role of deduction in statistical analysis is a limited one and the pragmatic aspects of statistics are largely inductive. But we cannot understand inductive statistics unless we first study deductive statistics.

STATISTICAL ERROR

Statistics is characterized partly as art and partly as science. It is an art because we must rely heavily on experience and judgment in choosing from the vast number of procedures available for analyzing sample information. But statistics embodies, to various degrees, all elements of the scientific method—most notably the element of **error**. Because statistics concerns uncertainty, there is always a chance of making erroneous inferences. Statistical procedures are available both to control and to measure the risks of reaching erroneous conclusions. To illustrate this point, consider television-viewer opinions.

Television networks use *sample* information to help make the hard choices about which programs to drop. Those who disagree with the network choices also base their arguments on a sample—the opinions of their own friends and acquaintances. The problem here is that such a sample is **biased** in favor of persons who have similar tastes, education, and social experience. The validity of opinion surveyors' claims is supported by a random selection from the public at large in which everyone has an equal chance of representation. As we will see in Chapter 8, the survey agency chooses a sample large enough to minimize the chance of error.

The survey agency cannot be legitimately criticized, unless it can be shown that its samples were not random and were therefore biased in favor of specific groups. Even when large samples are taken, bias can be introduced by statistical errors due to improper procedures. We will discuss some of the more serious sources of bias in Chapter 4.

EXERCISES

1-7 Consider a group of your friends. Comment on the suitability of using one person's GPA in attempting to make conclusions regarding the academic performance of the entire group.

1-8 For each of the following problem situations, (1) provide an example of an elementary unit; (2) provide an example of a characteristic of interest; and (3) state whether the population would be qualitative or quantitative.
  (a) An aircraft manufacturer's investment plans will be affected by the fate of a congressional appropriation bill containing funds for a new fighter plane. The company wishes to conduct a survey to facilitate planning.
  (b) A politician plans to study the voter response to pending legislation to determine her platform.
  (c) The California Public Utilities Commission is seeking operating cost data that will help it establish new rates for the San Francisco-Los Angeles airline routes.

1-9 For each of the following situations, discuss whether the suggested frame would be suitable.
  (a) An insurance company is using home-theft claims processed in the past year as its frame to determine the number of thefts from its policy holders of items valued below $50.
  (b) A public health official uses doctors' records of persons diagnosed as suffering from flu as his frame to study the effects of a recent flu epidemic.
  (c) A stock exchange official studying the investment attitudes of owners of listed securities uses the active accounts of member brokerage firms as her frame.

1-10 Fred Fox collects old Monopoly markers. He will select items at random from a box containing one each of the slipper, hat, dog, thimble, and car.
  (a) A sample of two markers is selected. List the possibilities.
  (b) Suppose that three markers are chosen. List the possibilities.

1-11 For each of the following situations, indicate whether deductive statistics or inductive statistics best categorizes the investigation.
  (a) A listing is made of all the possible number outcomes from tossing a pair of dice.
  (b) Ten randomly chosen students are tested in order to determine how well economics principles are understood by university students.
  (c) A pharmaceutical researcher gives super doses of an experimental substance to rats in order to assess side effects.

SUMMARY

1. What is the meaning of "statistics?"

As an area of academic study, **statistics** is a body of methods and theory that is applied to numerical evidence when making decisions in the face of uncertainty. The topic may be subdivided into three main groups: **descriptive statistics** is concerned with summary calculations and graphical displays; **inferential statistics** involves drawing conclusions about a complete **population** by using the information contained in a **sample**; and the third area, **exploratory data analysis**, is the newest type of statistics. The word statistics has other meanings, most notably numerical facts.

2. What is the role of data in statistics?

Data are the central focus of modern statistics. Fundamental to any investigation is the **data set**, a grouping comprising one or more **data points**. A statistical investigation is concerned with one or more **variables**.

3. **How are data classified and what is the basic statistical building block?**
   Statistical data may be **quantitative** or **qualitative**. The basic building block is the **observation**, a measurement or classification of an **elementary unit**.

4. **What are the distinctions between the population and the sample?**
   Statistical investigations involve **populations** or **samples**. The population includes the totality of observations that *might* be made, while the sample is just that portion where observations are *actually* made. Population observations may never be completed, which is the case for the **target population** (e.g., the recovery times of patients who would have been treated by a drug never released). They might instead be part of a **working population**, having an accessible **frame** (source of elementary units) that does not coincide with the population of interest.

5. **What are the types of statistical data?**
   We ordinarily encounter quantitative observations that are **ratio data**, like distances, times, or monetary units, where all arithmetic operations may be meaningfully applied. But observations might involve **interval data**, like temperatures, where addition and subtraction are the only meaningful operations. **Ordinal data** convey size ranking only, while **nominal data** are arbitrarily chosen categorical numbers.

6. **What are two essential types of modern statistical methodology?**
   In developing methodology for or in explaining statistics, an important dichotomy is **deductive statistics** versus **inductive statistics**. Deductive statistics considers what types of samples might be generated from a population of *known* characteristics. Probability concepts are used for coping with the uncertainties involved. Inductive statistics is concerned with the process of making generalizations about the *unknown* population using known sample results. Inferential statistics is largely inductive. A key concern in drawing conclusions from samples is minimizing **error** and avoiding **bias**.

deductive
– known population
(probability)

inductive
– known sample
about unknown population

REAL-LIFE STATISTICAL CHALLENGE

Collecting Data about the Homeless

In the 1990 Census of Population, government planners attempted to count the total number of homeless in the United States. Government and social agencies were unsure how many people were homeless or even how to go about counting them. Estimates ranged from 50,000 to over 3 million.

In the spring of 1990, the U.S. Bureau of the Census attempted to count all the homeless. Over 22,000 census takers visited over 11,000 shelters and 24,000 "preidentified street locations." A total of 178,282 people were found at overnight shelters and 49,793 at the street locations for a total of 228,075 individuals. Most groups, including the census takers themselves, believe this figure still underestimates the true number of homeless people. The results of their findings for selected cities are found in Table 1-2.

Aggregate data helps cities and nonprofit organizations know roughly how many homeless people exist in a given city. However, to truly assist individuals, much more information is needed.

REAL-LIFE STATISTICAL CHALLENGE

TABLE 1-2 Estimates of the Homeless Population in Selected U.S. Cities, 1990.

Rank City	State	Number in Shelters	Number Visible on Street	Total
1 New York	NY	23,383	10,447	33,830
2 Los Angeles	CA	4,597	3,109	7,706
3 Chicago	IL	5,180	1,584	6,764
4 San Francisco	CA	4,003	1,566	5,569
5 San Diego	CA	2,846	2,101	4,947
6 Washington	DC	4,682	131	4,813
7 Philadelphia	PA	3,416	1,069	4,485
8 Newark	NJ	1,974	842	2,816
9 Seattle	WA	2,170	360	2,530
10 Atlanta	GA	2,431	60	2,491
11 Boston	MA	2,245	218	2,463
12 Houston	TX	1,780	151	1,931
13 Phoenix	AZ	1,710	276	1,986
14 Portland	OR	1,553	149	1,702
15 Sacramento	CA	1,287	265	1,552
16 Baltimore	MD	1,144	387	1,531
17 Dallas	TX	1,200	293	1,493
18 Denver	CO	1,169	100	1,269
19 Oklahoma City	OK	1,016	234	1,250
20 Minneapolis	MN	1,052	28	1,080
Total		68,838	23,370	92,208

Sources: U.S. Bureau of the Census, 1991; and the *Universal Almanac 1992*: 215.

How to gather data about the homeless has usually been controversial. Advocates for the homeless disagree (at times quite vigorously) about which questions to ask people. Some data elements on a form may be used for aggregate statistical purposes; others address concerns of abuse—child, spousal, and substances (alcohol and drugs). Some of the data elements may be hard to gather, and in some cases completely forthright and honest answers require a degree of trust not easy to develop during the brief intake process[1].

The form shown in Figure 1-6 is used in Santa Clara County, California, to help process incoming homeless individuals in its Winter Shelter at the National Guard Armory in San Jose. Once collected, the data is transcribed onto magnetic cards (similar to an ATM card). Using this magnetic card system speeds up check-in on subsequent nights. The clients at this shelter are primarily single adults, although some adults with children also stay at the facility. Similar forms (but with different questions) are used for shelters targeted toward migrant farm workers, battered spouses, and single parents and couples with childern.

While the details requested on the form seem very intrusive, clients can decline to answer most of the questions with which they feel uncomfortable. The demographic details are summarized for reporting purposes, and the summary data is provided to funding groups such as county and state agencies and private foundations.

[1]Discussion drawn from Project SHARE Prototype, Jerome Burstein, Principal Investigator.

REAL-LIFE STATISTICAL CHALLENGE

Emergency Housing Consortium
91/92 Winter Shelter Intake Form

Reference Number: _____   Date: _____

First Name: _____   Birthdate: _____

Family Name: _____   Veteran: ☐ Yes ☐ No

SSN: _____   Discharge Date: _____

Last City: _____   Shelter: _____

Last State: _____ Last Zip: _____   Intake by: _____

Individuals
Adult Male: _____
Adult Female: _____
Child Male: _____
Child Female: _____
Total: _____

Ethnicity
White: _____
Black: _____
Hispanic: _____
Asian: _____
Native American: _____
Other Ethnic: _____
Unknown Ethnic: _____
Total: _____

Age
Under 5: _____
5 to 12: _____
13 to 17: _____
18 to 20: _____
21 to 30: _____
31 to 44: _____
45 to 59: _____
60 & Older: _____
Unknown: _____
Total: _____

Employment
Full Time: _____
Part Time: _____
Unemployed: _____
Training: _____

Benefits
AFDC: _____
GA: _____
SS: _____
SSI: _____
Veteran: _____
SDI: _____
Unemployment: _____

Parentics
Couple: _____
Female Parent: _____
Female Single: _____
Make Single: _____
Male Parent: _____
Two Parents: _____

Emergency Information
Name: _____
Address: _____
_____
City: _____
State: _____
Phone: _____

Income
None: _____
Below Very Low: _____
Very Low: _____
Low: _____
Moderate: _____

Personal/Medical
How long homeless? _____
Date last employed? _____
Skills: _____
Disabled? ○Yes ○No
Sick Now? ○Yes ○No
Medical Problems? _____
Allergic to? _____
Taking Medicine? ○Yes ○No
What Medicine? _____

FIGURE 1-6 Sample Intake Form.

Discussion Questions:

1. What difficulties might census takers have in locating the homeless in or near your community?

2. Refer to the form in Figure 1-6. Indicate examples of nominal, ordinal, interval, and ratio data. Which questions would you feel uncomfortable answering?

REVIEW EXERCISES

1-12 You are assisting the brand manager for a new household product to devise a marketing plan.
   (a) List four questions for which numerical data might be helpful in making the choice.
   (b) For each question in (a), provide (1) the source of data and (2) the type of data.

1-13 You have been asked to assist an accountant to prepare a detailed routine for auditing a chemical company. Suggest where you might find data for the following.
   (a) Freight costs for shipments of various sizes.
   (b) Number of orders of various quantities for chosen products.
   (c) How salaries compare to similar jobs in other companies in the same industry.

1-14 Indicate for each of the following situations whether the type of statistics involved is primarily inductive or deductive.
   (a) Assessing the chance that a particular ticket will win the lottery.
   (b) A quality assurance manager rejects shipments of parts when more than 2 items in a sample of 25 are defective, since the evidence then strongly indicates that the shipment is of poor quality.
   (c) A professor knows the exam scores of all 30 students in her class. She wants to know the possible levels of the average test score for five randomly selected students and how likely each possibility is.
   (d) The government uses experimental results in deciding whether or not a new drug would have excessive side effects with all potential users.

1-15 For each of the following quantities, indicate whether the data would be classified as (1) nominal, (2) ordinal, (3) interval, or (4) ratio.
   (a) movie ratings, 1 to 10   (e) employee payroll code numbers
   (b) heights of men   (f) Richter earthquake intensity scale
   (c) daily high temperatures   (g) task completion times
   (d) football player jersey numbers   (h) GMAT test scores

1-16 For each of the following statistical investigations, identify a potential source of error and suggest how it might be remedied.
   (a) As he shakes hands with potential voters, a congressional candidate asks how he or she will vote.
   (b) A software company asks persons to evaluate EZ-Calc against competing packages. The questionnaire is on the backside of the EZ-Calc warranty registration card.
   (c) A telephone survey firm makes calls only between 9 A.M. and 5 P.M. This minimizes overtime costs.

STATISTICS IN PRACTICE

1-17 How are statistics used where you work? If you do not have any work experience, ask a relative or friend how statistics are used at their workplace. What are the elementary units? Provide an example of the frame and the working population.

1-18 How are statistics used in a nonwork environment such as a social club or religious organization? You may want to ask a relative or friend how statistics are used at organizations they are familiar with. What are the elementary units? Provide an example of the frame and the working population.

1-19 *Collecting a master class data set.* A class project, create a list of class data using the following variables:

Case Number	Sex	Age	Height	Major	Favorite Food	State/Province or Country of Birth
1	F	26	57	Aviation	Pizza	Georgia
2	M	19	71	Accounting	Hamburgers	Mexico

To help organize the data and to facilitate future evaluations, assign each successive student a case number, starting with 1.

1-20 *Developing a data set.* List several types of data to gather from your classmates, along with the questions you would ask in eliciting the data. Include both qualitative or quantitative variables, and include among your quantitative variables at least one of each type: nominal, ordinal, interval, and ratio. Indicate for each of your variables which type it is. Indentify any questions that people might feel uncomfortable answering.

1-21 *Collecting a group's class data set.* Form small groups and compare your list, adding or deleting variables as needed, until you arrive at a group consensus regarding what data to collect. (Your instructor may suggest some ideas.) Then collect your group's data, getting one observation from each member of the entire class for every variable. Use as his or her case number the student's position on your group's list.

CHAPTER 2

DESCRIBING AND DISPLAYING STATISTICAL DATA

BEFORE READING THIS CHAPTER, MAKE SURE YOU UNDERSTAND:

The various meanings of "statistics."

The role of data and the distinction between quantitative and qualitative data.

The distinction between samples and populations.

The types of statistical data.

The dichotomy between deductive and inductive statistics.

AFTER READING THIS CHAPTER, YOU WILL UNDERSTAND:

How statistical data are organized in terms of frequency of occurrence.

What kinds of numerical and graphical displays are used for data.

How to compare data sets and make further summaries.

What common forms are taken by statistical data.

How to display data when two or more variables are present.

What special data displays may be useful for important statistical applications.

The arrangement and display of statistical data are important elements of descriptive statistics. Raw numbers alone do not provide any underlying pattern from which conclusions can be drawn. For example, we might believe that doctors generally have high incomes and that younger people usually earn less than older people. But even if we had access to all the tax returns on file with the Internal Revenue Service, without arranging, sifting and sorting the original income data, we would not be able to determine if doctors earn more than dentists, if some lawyers earn more than most doctors, or if greater experience in a particular occupation increases salary. Only by organizing the data can we gain information to use in career planning.

Such descriptive statistics sets the stage for everything else.

2-1 THE FREQUENCY DISTRIBUTION

FINDING A MEANINGFUL PATTERN FOR THE DATA

The ages of a sample of 100 statistics students are given in Table 2-1. If we wish to describe this sample, how should we proceed? The values in Table 2-1 have not been summarized or rearranged in a meaningful manner, so we refer to them as **raw data**. We might begin by grouping the ages in a meaningful way.

A convenient way to accomplish this is to group the ages into categories of two calendar years, beginning with age 18. Each age will then fall into one of the categories 18.0–under 20.0, 20.0–under 22.0, and so on. We refer to such groupings of values as **class intervals**. Now if we summarize the raw data simply by counting the number of ages in each class interval, we should be able to identify some properties of the sample.

First we list the class intervals in increasing sequence, as in the first column of Table 2-2. Then, reading down the list of raw data for each successive age, we place a tally mark beside the corresponding class interval and a check mark beside the number on the original list so that it will not be counted twice. When the tally is complete, we count the marks to determine the total number of observations in each class interval. The final result indicates the **frequency** with which ages occur in each class interval and is called a **frequency distribution**. In Table 2-2, we find that 10 of the 100 statistics students fall into the interval 18.0–under 20.0.

TABLE 2-1 Ages of a Sample of 100 Statistics Students

				Age (years)					
20.9	33.4	18.7	24.2	22.1	18.9	21.9	20.5	21.9	37.3
57.2	25.3	24.6	29.0	26.3	19.1	48.7	23.5	23.1	28.6
21.3	22.4	22.3	20.0	30.3	31.7	34.3	28.5	36.1	32.6
33.7	19.6	18.7	24.3	27.1	20.7	22.2	19.2	26.5	27.4
22.8	51.3	44.4	22.9	20.6	32.8	27.3	23.5	23.8	22.4
18.1	23.9	20.8	41.5	20.4	21.3	19.3	24.2	22.3	23.1
22.9	21.3	29.7	25.6	33.7	24.2	24.5	21.2	21.5	25.8
21.5	21.5	27.0	19.9	29.2	25.3	26.4	22.7	27.9	22.0
23.3	28.1	24.8	19.6	23.7	26.3	30.1	29.7	24.8	24.7
23.5	22.9	26.0	25.2	23.6	21.0	30.9	21.7	28.3	22.1

TABLE 2-2 Frequency Distribution for Student Ages

Age	Tally	Number of Persons (class frequency)
18.0–under 20.0	ⅢⅢ ⅢⅢ	10
20.0–under 22.0	ⅢⅢ ⅢⅢ ⅢⅢ |||	18
22.0–under 24.0	ⅢⅢ ⅢⅢ ⅢⅢ ⅢⅢ |||	23
24.0–under 26.0	ⅢⅢ ⅢⅢ ||||	14
26.0–under 28.0	ⅢⅢ ⅢⅢ	10
28.0–under 30.0	ⅢⅢ |||	8
30.0–under 32.0	||||	4
32.0–under 34.0	ⅢⅢ	5
34.0–under 36.0			1
36.0–under 38.0	||	2
38.0–under 58.0	ⅢⅢ	5
	Total	100

The number 10 can be referred to as the **class frequency** for the first class interval.

Each class interval has two limits. For the first interval, the **lower class limit** is 18.0 and the **upper class limit** is "under 20.0." (We use the word *under* to distinguish this limit from 20.0 exactly, which serves as the lower limit of the second class interval.) No matter how precisely the raw data are measured, this designation prevents ambiguity in assigning an observation to a particular interval. For example, the age 19.99 years is represented by the first class, whereas 20.01 years would fall into the second class (20.0–under 22.0). The **width** of a class interval is found by subtracting its lower limit from the lower limit of the succeeding class interval. For example, the width of the first class interval is $20.0 - 18.0 = 2.0$. All intervals except the last class interval have the same width. As we will see, beginning and ending class intervals must sometimes be treated differently.

GRAPHICAL DISPLAYS: THE HISTOGRAM

A visual display can be a very useful starting point in describing a frequency distribution. Figure 2-1 graphically portrays the frequency distribution of student ages. Age is represented on the horizontal axis, which is divided into class intervals of two years in width. The classes are represented by bars of varying heights, corresponding to the class frequency (the number of observations in each interval). Thus, the vertical axis represents frequency. Such a graphical portrayal of a frequency distribution is called a **histogram**.

Since 23 of the ages are 22.0–under 24.0, the corresponding bar is of height 23. Only one person is between 34.0 and 36.0 years old, so the height of that bar is 1. Neighboring bars touch, emphasizing that age is a continuous scale.

Note that the highest class interval, 38.0–under 58.0, is 20 years wide—ten times as wide as the standard intervals. With only five ages falling between 38.0 and 58.0, there is, on the average, one-half an observation every two years in this interval. This bar therefore has a height of $\frac{1}{2}$. Treating the two-year width as a

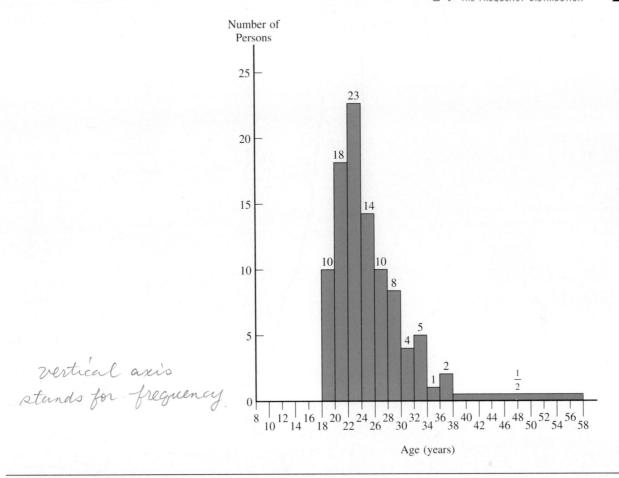

vertical axis stands for frequency

FIGURE 2-1 Histogram for the frequency distribution of student ages.

standard unit, *the area inside any bar* (its height times its width in standard units) *equals the number of observations in the corresponding class interval.* Thus, the area inside the first bar is $10 \times 1 = 10$, and the area inside the last bar is one-half the number of standard two-year class intervals, or $\frac{1}{2} \times 10 = 5$, which is the number of observations in that category.

GRAPHICAL DISPLAYS: THE FREQUENCY POLYGON

An alternative graphical portrayal of a frequency distribution is the **frequency polygon**, shown in Figure 2-2 for the same sample of student ages. In Figure 2-2, each class interval is represented by a dot positioned above its midpoint at a height equal to the class frequency. Each midpoint is typical of all values in the interval and is defined by the average of the interval's class limits. Thus, the midpoint of the first interval is $(18.0 + 20.0)/2 = 19.0$; the midpoint of the second interval is 21.0; and so on. The midpoint of the last interval is $(38.0 + 58.0)/2 = 48.0$. The dots are connected by line segments to make the graph more readable. To complete the frequency polygon, line segments are drawn from the first and last dots to the horizontal axis at points one-half the

dot above midpoint

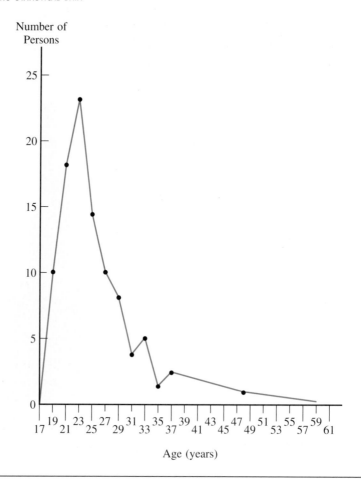

FIGURE 2-2 Frequency polygon for sample of student ages.

width of a standard class interval below the lowest and above the highest class intervals, respectively (in this case, touching the axis at 17 and 59).

DESCRIBING A POPULATION: THE FREQUENCY CURVE

A frequency distribution, similar to that found for student ages, may be constructed for any quantitative data set. In many statistical applications, the only data available are *sample* observations. The nature of the complete population remains *unknown*. The unobserved population values may be represented in a general sense by a **frequency curve**, like the one in Figure 2-3, which might apply to the original *population* of student ages. The basic shape of a population's frequency curve is usually suggested by the histogram or frequency polygon originally constructed from the sample data. Because populations are usually quite large in relation to the number of observations in a sample, the frequency curve would resemble a frequency polygon or a histogram with many class intervals of tiny widths. If these intervals were individually plotted, the entire collection of population data would present a less jagged graph than one obtained from the sample data alone, and this graph would be almost totally smooth (like the curve

FIGURE 2-3 Suggested shape of a smoothed frequency curve for the entire population.

in Figure 2-3). Later in this chapter, we will examine some forms of the frequency distribution that are commonly encountered for populations.

DESCRIPTIVE ANALYSIS

We have managed to translate the confusion of our raw data on student ages into a pattern based on frequencies. The frequency distribution tells us two things: It shows how the observations cluster around a central value, and it illustrates the degree of dispersion or difference between observations.

We know that no student is younger than 18 and that ages below 28 are most typical. Of these, the most common age is somewhere between 22 and 24, which (from general information obtained from the registrar's office) we know to be higher than usual for the student who enters college right after high school and graduates at about age 22. The students in the sample are generally older, but we can rule out the possibility that they might be graduate students because of the substantial number of younger persons. It is possible that the population could be made up of night students and that the older persons work on their degrees on a part-time basis while holding full-time jobs.

The appropriateness of this conclusion may be substantiated by the incidence of persons over 30, who are most likely to have financial burdens and thus not be full-time students. Although predominantly young, the sample is peppered with

TABLE 2-3 Fuel Consumption Achieved by 100 Large-Sized Cars (raw data)

Fuel Consumption (mpg)									
19.0	20.8	22.0	22.7	20.0	18.9	16.6	16.8	20.8	14.7
15.1	21.8	21.1	21.5	21.1	15.5	19.3	15.1	20.6	16.8
18.2	20.5	15.3	16.2	16.3	22.8	22.7	21.9	22.5	17.1
19.1	21.6	19.0	18.3	18.6	22.1	17.5	22.9	21.7	18.7
21.9	20.2	14.5	14.1	22.9	20.2	17.3	22.6	19.3	21.7
21.5	22.6	18.7	19.2	22.8	21.6	21.7	20.5	22.7	20.4
18.8	15.1	16.5	20.5	19.1	17.4	19.7	19.2	16.4	21.9
14.3	19.2	19.7	17.1	21.4	21.9	21.7	19.2	23.9	19.6
20.9	18.5	20.2	18.2	20.2	22.4	20.4	21.6	21.3	22.4
20.5	18.1	20.7	21.3	16.9	20.3	23.9	18.8	21.1	21.9

persons approaching or exceeding the age of 40. Five students are relatively so much older that they have been put into a special group—the "over 38s." Their ages (41.5, 44.4, 48.7, 51.3, and 57.2) are spread so thinly along the age scale that it is more convenient to lump these more extreme ages into a single special category.

This descriptive analysis provides us with an image of the student sample that is not immediately available from the raw data. The entire description is based on frequencies of occurrence—the heart of all statistical analysis. As we will see in Chapter 5, frequency is the basis for probability theory and as such plays a fundamental role in all procedures of statistical inference.

CONSTRUCTING A FREQUENCY DISTRIBUTION: NUMBER AND WIDTH OF CLASS INTERVALS

A frequency distribution converts raw data into a meaningful pattern for statistical analysis. In doing this, detail must be sacrificed to insight.

The first step in constructing a frequency distribution is to specify the number of class intervals and their widths. No totally accepted rule tells us how many intervals are to be used. Between 5 and 20 class intervals are generally recommended, but the number is really a matter of personal judgment. When all intervals are to be the same width, the following rule gives the required

CLASS INTERVAL WIDTH

$$\text{Width} = \frac{\text{Largest value} - \text{Smallest value}}{\text{Number of class intervals}}$$

EXAMPLE: DESCRIBING FUEL CONSUMPTION DATA

Using the 100 observations of fuel consumption in miles per gallon (mpg) for the fleet of cars listed in Table 2-3, suppose we wish to construct five class intervals of equal width.

TABLE 2-4 Frequency Distribution for Fuel Consumption of 100 Cars Using Five Class Intervals

Miles per Gallon	Number of Cars
14.0–under 16.0	9
16.0–under 18.0	13
18.0–under 20.0	24
20.0–under 22.0	38
22.0–under 24.0	16
Total	100

SOLUTION: We find the required width by taking the difference between the largest and smallest values, $23.9 - 14.1 = 9.8$, and dividing by 5 to obtain 1.96 mpg. To simplify our task, we can round off 1.96 to 2.0 for the width and 14.1 to 14.0 for the lower limit of our first class interval. The frequency distribution is provided in Table 2-4 and graphed in Figure 2-4(a).

Figure 2-4 also contains histograms for the same fuel consumption data using 10 class intervals (b) and 20 class intervals (c). Notice that the histogram profiles become progressively "lumpier" as the number of classes increases. Both the 5-interval and 10-interval graphs provide concise summaries of the data, but a pronounced "sawtooth" effect occurs with 20 intervals. The poorness of the 20-interval summary reflects the large number of intervals in relation to the size of the sample. One way to decide how many class intervals to use would be to try several—plot a histogram for each and select the one that provides the most logical explanation of the underlying population pattern. A large number of class intervals will provide more data, but too many will produce meaningless oscillations.

STEM-AND-LEAF PLOTS

As a preliminary step in constructing a frequency distribution, the data may be conveniently arranged in a **stem-and-leaf plot**. This display organizes the raw data in tabular form by locating each observation on a "tree." This is done by separating the values into **stem digits** and **leaf digits**.

To illustrate, consider again the fuel consumption (mpg) data in Table 2-3. On a blank piece of paper begin by listing the possible miles per gallon in whole numbers followed by a decimal point.

```
14. |
15. |
16. |
17. |
18. |
19. |
20. |
21. |
22. |
23. |
```

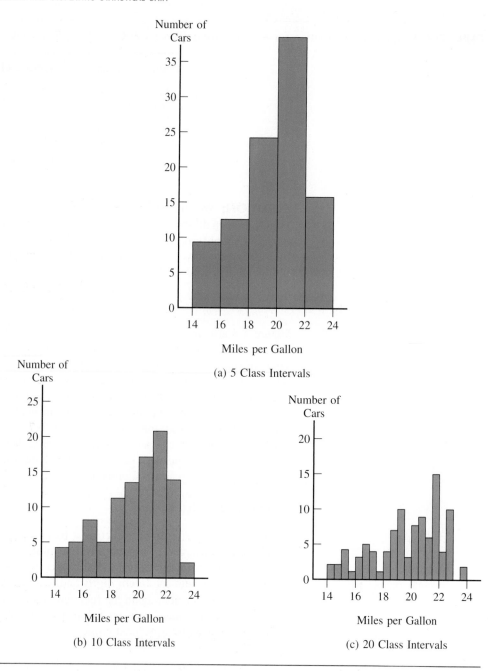

FIGURE 2-4 Histograms for fuel consumption of 100 cars using three different sets of class intervals.

The list constitutes the *stems* of the plot. A vertical line is placed directly to the right of the listed entries to separate those quantities from the leaves. There will be one leaf for each observation of fuel consumption in Table 2-3. Consider the first three entries in column one: 19.0, 15.1, 18.2. Detaching the last digits, we get 0, 1, and 2. These digits determine the first three *leaves* on the plot and are placed directly after their respective stems. The following is a display of the plot at this stage of construction.

```
14.
15.  | 1 ←——————— 15.1
16.
17.
18.  | 2 ←——————— 18.2
19.  | 0 ←——————— 19.0
20.
21.
22.
23.
```

The fourth entry in column one of Table 2-3 is 19.1 miles per gallon. This establishes the second leaf on the 19. stem.

$$19. \mid 0 \quad 1 \leftarrow\text{——————} 19.1$$

Proceeding down the successive columns, the remaining leaves are placed onto their respective stems. The completed stem-and-leaf plot is provided below.

```
                              Leaf
                          (last digit)
          14. | 3 5 1 7
          15. | 1 1 3 5 1
          16. | 5 2 3 9 6 8 4 8
          17. | 1 4 5 3 1
          18. | 2 8 5 1 7 3 2 6 9 8 7
    Stem  19. | 0 1 2 0 7 2 1 3 7 2 2 3 6
          20. | 9 5 8 5 2 2 7 5 0 2 2 3 4 5 8 6 4
          21. | 9 5 8 6 1 5 3 1 4 6 9 7 7 9 6 7 3 1 7 9 9
          22. | 6 0 7 9 8 8 1 4 7 9 6 5 7 4
          23. | 9 9
```

A compelling advantage of the stem-and-leaf plot is that it contains essentially the same information as a histogram. (To see this, rotate the page counterclockwise 90 degrees. If you then add a frequency axis having one tick per leaf and highlight each leaf digit with a magic marker, you will have the histogram in Figure 2-4(a).) No information is lost, since the complete set of raw data is readily available, but in a more useful form. In Chapter 3 we will see how the stem-and-leaf plot enables us to compute more quickly certain summary data measures.

The stem-and-leaf plot can be cumbersome when the number of observations is large. (Imagine a stem with 105 leaves.) Also, the tree may not be very useful if the data range is wide and expressed to more than three significant figures. If this is the case, the potential stems could outnumber the leaves.

ACCOMMODATING EXTREME VALUES

Class intervals of equal width will facilitate comparisons between classes and provide simpler calculations of the more concise summary values to be discussed later in this chapter. But, as we noted about the distribution of the age data in Table 2-2, it is sometimes better to lump the extreme values into a single category.

This becomes quite evident during the construction of a frequency distribution for individual annual earnings. Most persons earn incomes of less than $50,000, and a few earn between $50,000 and $100,000. But the rare, extremely well-to-do have substantially higher incomes. A frequency distribution graph with equal intervals of income width of, say, $5,000 would be hard to draw and difficult to read. The resulting histogram would be analogous to a few mountain peaks (representing frequencies for the lower income levels) sitting to the left of many successively smaller anthills (representing the number of persons in each progressively rarer, higher income category). This difficulty can be avoided by grouping the higher incomes into a single class interval of, say, "$100,000 or more."

COMPUTER-ASSISTED CONSTRUCTION

Today we are fortunate to have statistical software packages widely available for personal computers and time-sharing operations. Such computing power greatly aids constructing frequency distributions and graphical displays. The greatest effort is data input. Once the sample data are in computer memory, an investigator can try various interval widths and numbers of class intervals, plotting on the terminal screen a histogram for each combination. The analyst can then print out for permanent use that frequency distribution judged to achieve the best balance between summarizing the data and preserving detail. Figure 2-5 shows such a histogram for the fuel consumption data in Table 2-3, constructed on an IBM PC using EasyStat.

QUALITATIVE FREQUENCY DISTRIBUTIONS

When the data are qualitative, each attribute is like a class interval. The following frequency distribution was obtained for the majors of 100 Beta Gamma Sigma members.

Major	Frequency
Accounting	17
Finance	4
Management	38
Marketing	27
Human Resources	14
Total	100

The data are summarized graphically in Figure 2-6. Each category is represented by a bar or spike. These do not touch, emphasizing that the attributes are qualitative categories. A similar graphical display, called a **bar chart**, could be constructed for the frequency distribution of a **discrete variable**, such as family size or the number of rooms at home, where only whole numbers or integers serve as the categories.

The Statistics Around Us box on page 34 shows how frequency of occurrence can reduce the confusion of raw data.

THE PIE CHART

A common graphical display of qualitative data is the **pie chart** shown in Figure 2-7 for the student majors described earlier. The pie chart is a highly intuitive

```
Interval                                    Frequency
                                 ------------------------------------------
                                 0    10   20   30   40   50   60   70
      14.0 under 16.0      9     :*****
      16.0 under 18.0     13     :*******
      18.0 under 20.0     24     :************
      20.0 under 22.0     38     :*******************
      22.0 under 24.0     16     :********
      24.0 under 26.0      0     :
```

Note: Figure generated on an IBM PC using EasyStat.

FIGURE 2-5 Histogram for fuel consumption data.

display in which the size of each slice is proportional to the frequency of the category. Although some drafting skill is required to construct a proper pie chart by hand, many computer software packages will generate a finished pie chart from supplied categories and frequencies.

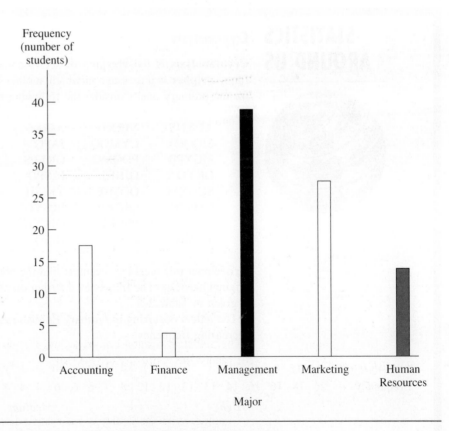

FIGURE 2-6 Bar chart for frequency distribution of Beta Gamma Sigma members' majors.

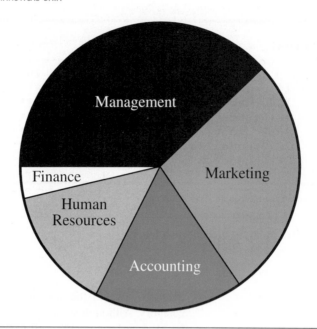

FIGURE 2-7 Pie chart for student majors.

STATISTICS AROUND US

Cryptanalysis

Cryptanalysis is the breaking of secret codes or ciphers. In its simplest form, a **cipher** is a message in which another alphabet has been substituted for the ordinary one. Consider the following message.

AOYNS	YIRXJ	AJRRS	OOYIR	YGDYP
MQQCY	CYMOQ	JAPQM	QDPQD	RMGMI
MGXPD	PDQMG	GRVPS	PQJRO	YMQYJ
OKYOA	OJHRJ	IASPD	JIHYM	IDIBA
SGGXM	OOMIB	YKISH	UYOPR	MIQYG
GSPMP	QJOXM	IKCYG	LSPRC	JJPYH
YQCJK	PMIKL	OJRYK	SOYPA	JOBYI
YOMGD	ZDIBM	UJSQL	JLSGM	QDJIP

To decipher this message, we must find the counterparts to the letters in the original message. The frequency distribution of letters in the cipher message is given in Table 2-5.

The letters occurring in ordinary English may be arranged in sequence of decreasing frequency.

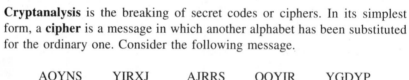

English letters	e	t	a	o	n	i	r	s	h	d	l	u	c	m	p	f	y	w	g	b	v	j	k	x	q	z
Frequency	26	18	16	16	14	13	13	12	12	8	7	6	6	6	4	4	4	3	3	3	2	1	1	1	$\frac{1}{2}$	$\frac{1}{2}$
				High										Medium										Low		

A similar arrangement of the ciphertext letters may be made.

Ciphertext	Y	M	J	P	O	I	Q	G	S	R	D	A	K	C	H	B	L	X	U	N	V	Z	E	F	T	W
Frequency	21	18	17	16	16	15	14	12	11	11	10	7	6	5	4	4	4	4	2	1	1	1	0	0	0	0

It would be highly unusual for this particular message to provide an identical match—letter for letter—strictly on the basis of frequency. But the frequencies can help us to find the more likely possibilities. By trial and error (for instance, substituting e for Y or M and t for one of the other high-frequency letters), portions of the original words can be found. This is a slow process at first, but as each letter is identified, it becomes easier to match the remaining ones.

The complete key for our message is

Ciphertext	M	U	R	K	Y	A	B	C	D	E	F	G	H	I	J	L	N	O	P	Q	S	T	V	W	X	Z
Original text	a	b	c	d	e	f	g	h	i	j	k	l	m	n	o	p	q	r	s	t	u	v	w	x	y	z

The cipher is constructed by using the word MURKY for the first five original text letters and listing the remaining ciphertext letters in alphabetical sequence. The text of the full message reads

Frequency of occurrence lies at the heart of statistical analysis. It allows us to create order from confusion. Meaningfully arranged, numbers can tell us a story and help us choose methods and procedures for generalizing about populations.

TABLE 2-5 Frequency Distribution for Letters in the Cipher Message

Letter	Tally	Number of Letters	Letter	Tally	Number of Letters
A	|||| ||	7	N	|	1
B	||||	4	O	|||| |||| |||| |	16
C	||||	5	P	|||| |||| |||| |	16
D	|||| ||||	10	Q	|||| |||| ||||	14
E		0	R	|||| |||| |	11
F		0	S	|||| |||| |	11
G	|||| |||| ||	12	T		0
H	||||	4	U	||	2
I	|||| |||| ||||	15	V	|	1
J	|||| |||| |||| ||	17	W		0
K	|||| |	6	X	||||	4
L	||||	4	Y	|||| |||| |||| |||| |	21
M	|||| |||| |||| |||	18	Z	|	1
				Total	200

2-1 For each of the following sample arrival times, determine the class interval widths for constructing frequency distributions.

	Largest Value	Smallest Value	Number of Intervals
(a)	6.04 min	.54 min	11
(b)	2.50 hr	.10 hr	6
(c)	38 sec	3 sec	5
(d)	45 min	10 min	7

2-2 The following sample levels of precipitation (inches) have been obtained for selected U.S. cities during the month of April.

2.9	3.7	3.2	4.0	3.9	2.1	2.9	2.9	1.1
0.4	3.0	3.2	1.0	2.2	5.4	3.5	3.6	4.0
0.7	2.8	1.8	1.5	4.0	4.0	0.3	2.2	3.3
3.8	2.6	2.2	4.2	5.4	4.8	3.3	2.7	1.8
4.4	2.6	2.9	2.0	1.2	3.6	3.9	0.8	3.1
3.1	3.7	0.3	3.7	4.1	4.5	2.3	1.5	3.4
3.4	3.3	1.2	5.9	3.6	3.8	4.0	3.6	
5.0	3.4	2.6	3.3	5.8	0.6	2.9	2.4	
1.6	3.6	0.7	2.9	3.1	2.9	2.0	3.2	
1.2	1.8	3.6	2.7	3.4	2.9	0.5	2.4	

Source: *The World Almanac and Book of Facts,* 1988 edition, © Newspaper Enterprise Association, Inc., 1987, New York, NY: 181.

(a) Construct a stem-and-leaf plot.
(b) Construct a table for the frequency distribution that has intervals of width 1 inch. Use 0 as the lower limit of the first interval.
(c) Plot (1) a histogram and (2) a frequency polygon for the frequency distribution you constructed in (b).

2-3 Sample weekly sales receipts for McBurger franchises are provided below.

$ 3,145	$15,879	$ 6,914	$ 4,572	$11,374
12,764	9,061	8,245	10,563	8,164
6,395	8,758	17,270	10,755	10,465
7,415	9,637	9,361	11,606	7,836
13,517	7,645	9,757	9,537	23,957
8,020	8,346	12,848	8,438	6,347
21,333	9,280	7,538	7,414	11,707
9,144	7,424	25,639	10,274	4,683
5,089	6,904	9,182	12,193	12,472
8,494	6,032	16,012	9,282	3,331

(a) Construct a table for the frequency distribution that has six class intervals of equal width. Round the width to the nearest $1,000 and use $3,000 as the lower class limit of the first interval.
(b) Plot a histogram of the frequency distribution you constructed in (a).

2-4 Refer to the sales receipt data given in Exercise 2-3.

(a) Construct a table for the frequency distribution that has 12 class intervals of width $2,000, with $3,000 as the lower limit of the first interval.

(b) Plot a frequency polygon of the frequency distribution you constructed in (a).

(c) Do you think a more accurate data summary could be obtained by using a fewer or a greater number of class intervals? Discuss the reasons for your choice.

2-5 The following sample temperatures (°F) have been obtained for selected U.S. cities during the month of April.

47°	49°	51°	49°	60°	46°	50°	58°	46°
55	45	47	42	42	68	53	56	56
35	43	54	76	55	50	68	49	46
56	37	38	69	62	60	50	70	72
62	66	49	46	62	52	43	61	53
51	49	30	52	57	69	50	55	52
54	48	60	65	37	53	48	80	
63	51	69	68	63	18	59	38	
43	66	52	39	75	58	45	66	
49	47	46	55	45	60	46	49	

Source: *The World Almanac and Book of Facts,* 1988 edition, © Newspaper Enterprise Association, Inc., 1987, New York, NY: 181.

(a) Construct a stem-and-leaf plot.

(b) Construct a table for the frequency distribution that has intervals of width 10°. Use 10° as the lower limit of the first interval.

(c) Plot (1) a histogram and (2) a frequency polygon for the frequency distribution you constructed in (b).

2-6 The following heights (inches) have been obtained for the female staff at the *Daily Planet*.

62.4	63.7	65.1	64.8	66.2
64.4	63.9	60.5	64.8	64.8
61.2	59.7	62.8	63.4	61.4
63.8	63.3	63.0	58.9	65.6
62.1	63.6	61.3	62.7	61.3
58.8	63.1	64.3	63.7	62.5
60.3	64.8	63.6	65.0	61.7
67.2	60.9	64.7	64.9	59.9
66.3	61.1	63.7	62.7	61.7
63.2	60.8	65.4	62.5	64.9

(a) Construct a table for the sample frequency distribution that has ten class intervals of width 1 inch. Use 58 inches as the lower limit of the first interval.

(b) Plot a histogram of the frequency distribution you constructed in (a).

2-7 Second National Bank obtained the following frequency distribution of automatic teller transaction times. It has too many classes. Construct a table for the frequency distribution with half as many intervals, each twice as wide.

Class Interval (seconds)	Frequency	Class Interval (seconds)	Frequency
10–under 15	5	45–under 50	21
15–under 20	13	50–under 55	39
20–under 25	25	55–under 60	28
25–under 30	32	60–under 65	59
30–under 35	33	65–under 70	37
35–under 40	27	70–under 75	11
40–under 45	32	75–under 80	1

2-8 Using a separate category for each alphabetical character and treating upper- and lower-case letters as equal, construct a table for the frequency distribution of the first 200 letters of Abraham Lincoln's Gettysburg Address.

> Fourscore and seven years ago our fathers brought forth on this continent a new nation, conceived in liberty, and dedicated to the proposition that all men are created equal.
>
> Now we are engaged in a great civil war, testing whether that nation, or . . . .

Compare your distribution with the first one listed on page 35. Do you think that Lincoln used "ordinary" English? Explain.

2-9 Refer to the women's heights data given in Exercise 2-6.
(a) Construct a table for the frequency distribution that has five class intervals of width 2 inches. Use 58 inches as the lower limit of the first interval.
(b) Plot a histogram of the frequency distribution you constructed in (a).

2-10 Criticize each of the following designations for class intervals of monthly household electricity bills.

(a)	(b)	(c)
$10–15	$11–22	$10–under 15
15–20	21–32	16–under 20
20–25	31–42	21–under 25
etc.	etc.	etc.

2-11 A sample of 100 engineering students has been categorized by sex, marital status, and major. The number of persons in each category is summarized below.

Sex	Marital Status	Major	Number of Students
male	married	electrical	14
male	married	mechanical	16
male	married	civil	10
male	single	electrical	5
male	single	mechanical	19
male	single	civil	4
female	married	electrical	5

(continued on next page)

Sex	Marital Status	Major	Number of Students
female	married	mechanical	12
female	married	civil	0
female	single	electrical	5
female	single	mechanical	8
female	single	civil	2
		Total	100

Construct a table for the frequency distribution characterized by (a) sex, (b) marital status, and (c) major.

2-12 The following sample data have been obtained for the number of professional women employed (thousands) in the United States in 1986.

Profession	Number of Women
Engineering/Computer science	347
Health care	1,937
Education	2,833
Social/Legal	698
Arts/Athletics/Entertainment	901
All others	355

Source: Bureau of Labor Statistics.

Construct a bar chart.

2-13 Comment on the appropriateness of each of the following class interval widths for a frequency distribution of pay rates for a sample of 100 hourly workers in a metropolitan area.
(a) $.05　(b) $.25　(c) $.50　(d) $1.00　(e) $2.00

2-2　RELATIVE AND CUMULATIVE FREQUENCY DISTRIBUTIONS

Two useful extensions of the basic frequency distribution are the relative and the cumulative frequency distributions.

RELATIVE FREQUENCY DISTRIBUTIONS

A **relative frequency** is the ratio of the number of observations in a particular category to the total number of observations. Relative frequency may be determined for both quantitative and qualitative data and is a convenient basis for the comparison of similar groups of different size. For example, consider comparing family incomes in sparsely populated Nevada with those in California, the most populous state. It would not be very meaningful to say that only 6,000 families in Nevada have achieved a particular level of income and that 250,000 families in California receive the same income. But if we say that 1% of the families in Nevada and only .8% of the families in California have achieved this income level, we can make a realistic comparison between family incomes in the two states. We must compare the *proportions* (percentages)—not the total frequencies—of families who have achieved this income level in each state.

TABLE 2-6 Calculation of Relative Frequency Distribution for Age of Accounts Receivable

(1) Age (days)	(2) Number of Accounts (frequency)	(3) Relative Frequency
0–under 30	532	.330
30–under 60	317	.196
60–under 90	285	.176
90–under 120	176	.109
120–under 150	158	.098
150–under 180	147	.091
Totals	1,615	1.000

The relative frequencies are calculated by dividing the number of observations in each category by the total number of observations. Once the frequency distribution itself is obtained, the relative frequency computations are a matter of simple arithmetic. This is illustrated in Table 2-6 for each class interval of data on the age of department store accounts receivable (accounts 180 days or older are written off as uncollectible). The relative frequency of accounts less than 30 days

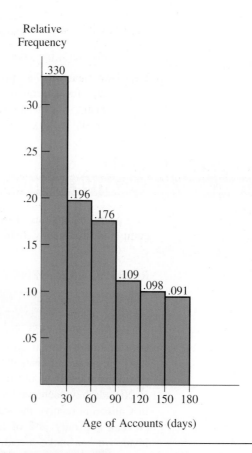

FIGURE 2-8 Relative frequency histogram for age of department store accounts receivable.

TABLE 2-7 Frequency Distributions for Students by Sex

Large University		Small College	
Sex	**Frequency**	**Sex**	**Frequency**
male	6,000	male	400
female	4,000	female	100
Totals	10,000		500

old (the class interval of 0–under 30) is 532/1,615 = .330, which means that 33% of all accounts are less than 30 days old. The other relative frequencies are also calculated by dividing the class frequency in column (2) by the total number of accounts.

The sum of all the relative frequencies must always be 1. Columns (1) and (3) constitute the **relative frequency distribution** for these data. The histogram for this distribution is shown in Figure 2-8. A histogram constructed using relative frequencies will have the same shape as one constructed using original tallies, or absolute frequencies. Only the scale on the vertical axis will change.

Analysis of relative frequencies can sometimes be useful when analysis of absolute frequencies is not. A department store's credit sales will fluctuate considerably over the seasons, but the same seasonal patterns will generally persist from year to year. If the credit worthiness of the store's customers remains about the same as it has been in the past, then the relative frequency distributions for the ages of accounts receivable obtained during the same calendar month in two successive years should not be noticeably different when growth is steady. A substantial difference in relative frequencies may be due to erratic growth or to a change in the quality of credit customers or in collection procedures. Absolute frequencies cannot isolate the effect of sales growth from the effect of changes in credit procedures.

Relative frequency may also be used to compare two qualitative populations. Table 2-7 shows the frequency distribution by sex of students on two campuses. The number of men competing for dates at the large university is 6,000, whereas the number at the small college is only 400. The relative frequency distributions are provided in Table 2-8. In terms of relative frequency, there is less competition at the university, where the proportion of men is smaller (.60 at the university versus .80 at the college).

TABLE 2-8 Relative Frequency Distributions for Students by Sex

Large University		Small College	
Sex	**Relative Frequency**	**Sex**	**Relative Frequency**
male	.60	male	.80
female	.40	female	.20
Totals	1.00		1.00

CUMULATIVE FREQUENCY DISTRIBUTIONS

A **cumulative frequency**, used only when the observations are numerical, is the sum of the frequencies for successively higher class intervals. For example, we might find that 8,439 men in a population of 10,000 are less than 6 feet tall; stated differently, 84.39% of the population is shorter than 6 feet. Cumulative frequencies can provide useful descriptions of a population, especially when they are expressed relatively as percentages or proportions. We can judge our chances of being accepted by a graduate school, for example, partly by the percentage of persons who obtained lower scores on the admissions examination. (Cumulative frequency is relative to some probability concepts we will encounter in Chapter 6.) The cumulative frequencies are determined by adding the frequency for each class interval to the frequencies for preceding intervals.

EXAMPLE: SALES OF TELEVISION SETS

Table 2-9 contains data from a sample of 100 annual sales figures for television sets sold by retail stores. We will construct cumulative frequencies for these data.

TABLE 2-9 Frequency Distribution for Unit Television Set Sales

(1) Units Sold	(2) Number of Stores (frequency)
100 – under 200	0
200 – under 300	5
300 – under 400	39
400 – under 500	31
500 – under 600	16
600 – under 700	6
700 – under 800	3

SOLUTION: The cumulative frequency for sales under 300 units is found by adding the frequency of sales at or above 100 (but under 200) to the number of stores having sales at or above 200 (but under 300), or $0 + 5 = 5$. The remaining cumulative frequencies are shown in Table 2-10.

TABLE 2-10 Calculation of Cumulative Frequencies for Unit Television Set Sales

(1) Units Sold	(2) Number of Stores (frequency)	(3) Cumulative Frequency
100 – under 200	0	0
200 – under 300	5	$0 + 5 = 5$
300 – under 400	39	$5 + 39 = 44$
400 – under 500	31	$44 + 31 = 75$
500 – under 600	16	$75 + 16 = 91$
600 – under 700	6	$91 + 6 = 97$
700 – under 800	3	$97 + 3 = 100$

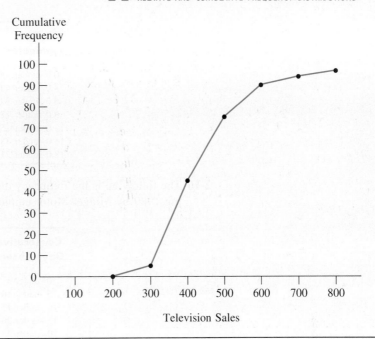

FIGURE 2-9 Ogive for cumulative frequency distribution of television sales.

The cumulative frequency for a class interval represents the total number of observations falling in or below that interval. In the preceding example, columns (1) and (3) of Table 2-10 constitute the **cumulative frequency distribution** for the television sales data. Likewise, **cumulative relative frequencies** are found by adding successive relative frequencies, and these results determine the **cumulative relative frequency distribution**. The largest cumulative relative frequency is 1.0.

Sometimes it is desirable to plot the cumulative relative frequency distribution in a graph, as shown in Figure 2-9. The ordinate (vertical height) of a plotted point represents the cumulative frequency for values less than the abscissa (the horizontal axis value). Such a curve is called an **ogive**.

EXERCISES

2-14 Refer to the fuel consumption data in Table 2-4.
   (a) Construct a table for the relative frequency distribution.
   (b) Construct a table for the cumulative frequency distribution.

2-15 Ingrid's Hallmark Shop obtained the following frequency distribution of times between arrivals of customers.
   (a) Construct a table for the relative frequency distribution. Then plot a histogram for the distribution.
   (b) Construct a table for the cumulative frequency distribution. Then plot an ogive for the distribution.

Time (minutes)	Number of Customers
0.0–under 3.0	210
3.0–under 6.0	130
6.0–under 9.0	75
9.0–under 12.0	40
12.0–under 15.0	20
15.0–under 18.0	15
18.0–under 21.0	10

2-16 The following is the frequency distribution of consecutive days absent during 1989 by Midget Motor employees.

Consecutive Days Absent	Number of Employees
0–under 5	3,100
5–under 10	810
10–under 15	510
15–under 20	320
20–under 25	120
25–under 30	30
30–under 60	110

(Employees absent a total of 60 or more consecutive days are reclassified as inactive. Each employee is counted just once, being placed in the category corresponding to his or her longest absence.)
(a) Construct a table for the relative frequency distribution.
(b) Construct a table for the cumulative *relative* frequency distribution.
(c) Plot an ogive using the data obtained in (b).

2-17 Copymat orders occasional spot checks of tardy and absent employees. A particular audit of payroll records resulted in the following sample frequency distributions.

	Number of Employees by Office				
	A	**B**	**C**	**D**	**E**
Tardy	60	60	10	56	2
Absent	60	30	20	24	15
On job and on time	1,080	510	270	720	233
Totals	1,200	600	300	800	250

(a) Determine the relative frequency distributions for each office.
(b) Using office *A* as a standard, which regions have an excessively high number of tardy employees?
(c) Compared to office *A*, which regions have an unusually large number of absent employees? Do you think that the managers of these regions are necessarily "softer" than the manager in region *A?* Explain.

2-18 The cumulative relative frequency distribution for the number of shares owned by each of the 1,000 shareholders of Kryptonite Corporation is provided below.

Number of Shares	Cumulative Proportion of Shareholders
0–under 5,000	0.36
5,000–under 10,000	0.63
10,000–under 15,000	0.81
15,000–under 20,000	0.90
20,000–under 25,000	0.97
25,000–under 30,000	1.00

(a) Construct a table for the relative frequency distribution.
(b) Determine the original frequency distribution using your answer to (a).
(c) Determine the cumulative frequency distribution using your answer to (b).

2-3 COMMON FORMS OF THE FREQUENCY DISTRIBUTION

Statistical methodology has been developed to analyze samples taken from populations having various general forms. By placing populations in various categories, we can increase our analytical powers considerably by using techniques that apply to all populations in the same **distribution family**. All quantitative populations have some form of distribution. Most populations can be classified into a few well-known distributions, although the mathematical equations describing them may be complex. The shape of the sample histogram usually indicates the form of the population distribution.

In the following figures, some of the more common general shapes of frequency curves appear beside representative sample histograms. Figure 2-10 represents the relative frequency distribution of the diameters of a production batch of 1-inch-thick steel reinforcing rods. Note that the histogram is fairly symmetrical about the interval .995–1.005 inches, with frequency dropping for the next higher and lower intervals. The histogram bars on the left and right become progressively shorter, tapering off at about .91 and 1.09 inches, respectively. The smoothed frequency curve beside the histogram is bell-shaped and belongs to a class of

FIGURE 2-10 Sample histogram (left) and population frequency curve (right) for steel rod diameters.

FIGURE 2-11 Sample histogram (left) and population frequency curve (right) for television sales.

populations having the **normal distribution**. We will have more to say about normal curves in Chapter 7. A large number of populations have frequency distributions in this category, including many physical measurements.

Figure 2-11 shows the histogram for the television sales data given in Table 2-9. Here the data are **skewed** to the right, because a few stores had sales levels that were quite high. Beside the histogram is a frequency curve in which the right "tail" is longer than the left. This general shape corresponds to a class of skewed distributions in which there are a few small observations and in which proportionately more large observations fall over a wide range of values.

Another type of skewed distribution is provided in Figure 2-12, where the fuel consumption frequency curve has a longer left tail. In this case, the smaller values are widely spread from 14 through 18 miles per gallon, and the rarer large values fall into the single class 23.0–under 24.0.

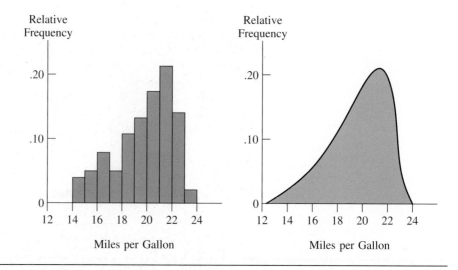

FIGURE 2-12 Sample histogram (left) and population frequency curve (right) for fuel consumption.

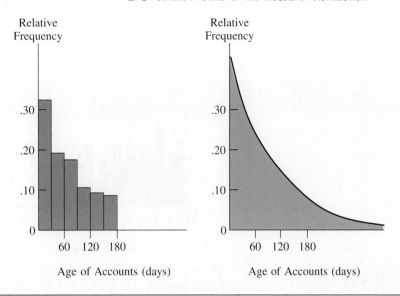

FIGURE 2-13 Sample histogram (left) and population frequency curve (right) for the age of department store accounts receivable.

involves items that exibit changes in status over time

The distribution given in Table 2-6 for the age of department store accounts receivable is plotted in Figure 2-13. Here, the smoothed frequency curve has the general shape of a reversed letter J. This type of distribution is sometimes called the **exponential distribution**. Such a frequency curve approximates a great many populations in which the observations involve items that exhibit changes in status over time. Exponential distributions have been used to characterize equipment lifetimes until failure. They are also used to describe the time between successive arrivals by cars at a toll booth or by patients in a hospital emergency room and are therefore useful in the analysis of waiting-line or queuing situations.

The left portion of Figure 2-14 is the histogram for the lengths of pieces of scrap roofing lumber from a construction job. Any piece shorter than 20 inches (the width between studs) cannot be used. Because the lumber arrives from the mill in various lengths, a piece of scrap is likely to be any length between 1 and 20 inches. (Scrap shorter than 1 inch is not counted.) The histogram is therefore approximated by a rectangle. Because no particular width is favored, such a population is a member of the **uniform distribution** family.

Later we will encounter other, less common shapes, and we will discuss how one particular shape—the bimodal—can help identify nonhomogeneous population influences. Classifying the various shapes of frequency distributions enables us to obtain better population descriptions and to be selective in choosing statistical techniques for analysis.

EXERCISES

2-19 For each of the following populations for the *ages* of persons, sketch an appropriate shape for the frequency distribution and explain the reasons for your choice.

(a) Science-fiction novel readers.
(b) Persons who do not work full-time.
(c) Persons who have false teeth.
(d) Children in a grammar school.

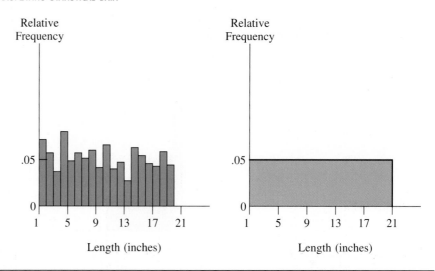

FIGURE 2-14 Sample histogram (left) and population frequency curve (right) for lengths of scrap pieces of lumber.

2-20 For each of the following populations, sketch an appropriate shape for the frequency distribution and explain the reasons for your choice.
(a) The times required by a pharmacist to fill new prescriptions.
(b) The last two digits in numbers assigned to telephones in a metropolitan area.
(c) The number of persons employed by manufacturing firms.
(d) The duration of stay of patients hospitalized with nonchronic diseases.

2-4   DISPLAYING DATA IN MULTIPLE DIMENSIONS

Statistical investigations may involve two or more variables, such as income, years of education, and age; production cost and quantity; or type of degree and salary. Statistical investigations attempt to uncover relationships between two or more variables, such as how income levels relate to different educational backgrounds and ages, or how degrees differ in salary level. A starting point is often a data display.

QUANTITATIVE DATA DISPLAYS—THE SCATTER DIAGRAM

Figure 2-15, generated on an IBM PC using Minitab®, shows a data display for two quantitative population variables. The **scatter diagram** relates total production cost to the production lot size. There is one asterisk for each sample production run. The asterisks are located at the coordinates for the observed cost and lot size for a particular sample run. (The "2"s indicate that two observations have nearly the same coordinates.) A visual inspection indicates that cost should increase with lot size. Chapter 10 shows how a line or a curve can be used to summarize that relationship.

QUALITATIVE DATA DISPLAYS—THE CROSS TABULATION

When both variables are qualitative, a two-dimensional counterpart to the scatter diagram may be used. Table 2-11 shows a **cross tabulation** for the sample of

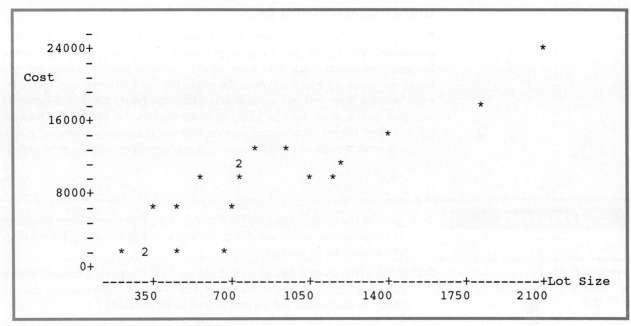

Note: Figure generated on an IBM PC using Minitab.©

FIGURE 2-15 Scatter diagram for total cost versus size of production run.

Beta Gamma Sigma members encountered earlier. Each member is counted into the total of a particular cell. There is one row for each major (5 levels) and one column for each sex (2 levels).

A cross tabulation is a logical starting point for evaluation of qualitative data. From a quick examination of Table 2-11, we can determine that the sexes are not evenly represented among the majors, even when we account for fewer female members. Chapter 16 shows how a similar cross tabulation with sample data might be used to test whether various occupational categories in an overall population have disproportionate representation of the sexes.

TABLE 2-11 Cross Tabulation for Beta Gamma Sigma Members

Major	Sex		Total
	Male	Female	
Accounting	8	9	17
Finance	3	1	4
Management	22	16	38
Marketing	16	11	27
Human Res.	9	5	14
Total	58	42	100

HIGHER DIMENSIONAL DATA

When there are three or more variables, it can be challenging to display the data graphically. The scatter diagram concept extends to any number of dimensions. In three dimensions, each data point would resemble marbles suspended in a room, one corner of which serves as the origin for two horizontal axes where the walls join the floor and one vertical axis where the two walls join. Chapter 11 describes how a *plane* may be found that summarizes the relationship between the variables. Higher dimensional relationships are not usually portrayed graphically. Instead, statistical procedures seek a mathematical expression to explain them.

2-21 Refer to the student data given in Exercise 2-11. Construct a cross tabulation of marital status versus sex. What can you conclude regarding the tendency of each sex to be married?

2-22 Refer to the student data given in Exercise 2-11. Construct a cross tabulation of major versus marital status. What can you conclude regarding the tendency of students in the various majors to be married?

2-23 The following checkout times and purchase amounts were obtained by a student during one Saturday morning at a local supermarket.

Time	Purchase	Time	Purchase
2.5 min	$29.75	13.5 min	$136.05
1.0	11.15	9.0	68.50
7.6	42.14	2.1	9.14
8.5	94.07	3.4	25.23
4.6	33.01	5.7	53.18

Construct a scatter diagram using checkout time for the vertical axis and purchase amount for the horizontal axis.

2-24 The following sample data have been obtained for automobiles driven in the United States.

Year	Average Distance (miles)	Average Fuel Consumption (gallons)
1960	9,450	661
1965	9,390	667
1970	9,980	735
1975	9,630	712
1976	9,760	711
1978	10,050	715
1979	9,480	664
1980	9,140	603
1981	9,000	579
1982	9,530	587
1983	9,650	578
1984	9,790	553
1985	9,830	549

Source: Energy Information Administration, Annual Energy Review, 1986.

Construct a scatter diagram. Use average fuel consumption for the vertical axis and average distance for the horizontal axis.

2-25 Refer to your graph from Exercise 2-23. Use a straight-edge to draw a line that seems to fit the data points.

(a) According to your line, find the checkout time expected when the purchase is (1) $20, and (2) $70.

(b) The checkout time level where the line crosses the vertical axis represents the *fixed* component of time required for every transaction, regardless of purchase amount. What is this time?

(c) The *variable* component of checkout time is the slope of the line, in minutes per dollar of purchase. Compute this by dividing the difference between (2) and (1) from part (a) by $50.

(d) Using only your answers from (b) and (c), compute the checkout time expected for a purchase of $100.

2-5 SPECIAL DATA DISPLAYS

② when you need to take immediate action

① when number of data is small — don't use histogram

The histogram is an important display for quantitative data partly because it dovetails with mathematical concepts relating probability concepts to the sampling process. Alternative displays are sometimes used when the number of data points is small or when the purpose of the statistical investigation is to take an immediate action rather than make a generalization.

THE BOX PLOT

When the amount of data is limited, a clear pattern may not be distinguishable with a histogram or frequency polygon. Consider the results obtained by a production supervisor who wishes to calibrate the control mechanism for filling jars of instant coffee. A proper calibration should accomplish two things: (1) provide contents of jars close to 16 ounces and (2) yield little fluctuation in contents from jar to jar. Over a trial period, successive samples are taken, with adjustments made after each. The following data were obtained.

	Sample 1	Sample 2	Sample 3	Sample 4	Sample 5
	15.1	16.3	16.0	15.9	15.9
	16.5	15.8	15.8	16.2	16.1
	14.7	15.7	15.5	16.0	16.0
	15.5	16.7	16.2	16.1	16.1
	13.8	16.3	16.2	15.9	15.9

Percentiles					
25th	14.25	15.75	15.65	15.9	15.9
50th	15.1	16.3	16.0	16.0	16.0
75th	16.0	16.5	16.2	16.15	16.1

Figure 2-16 shows a box plot for each sample. The borders of the box are positioned at the 25th and 75th percentiles, while the box is divided at the 50th percentile. Chapter 3 gives a detailed discussion of how to obtain these summary values. The line segment at the left of each box is a "whisker" extending to the minimum observed value for the respective sample, while the line for the right whisker stops at the maximum sample observation. Notice that the successive boxes become narrower and that the middle becomes closer to the desired 16 ounces.

Once the regulator valve is calibrated, only minor adjustments will be required for day-to-day operations. Another display is useful for this purpose.

THE CONTROL CHART

Each day the foreman in charge of instant-coffee filling takes a sample of jars. The mean values for 28 days are plotted in the **control chart** in Figure 2-17. On Day 11 and Day 18 the filling process was "out of control," and the regulator

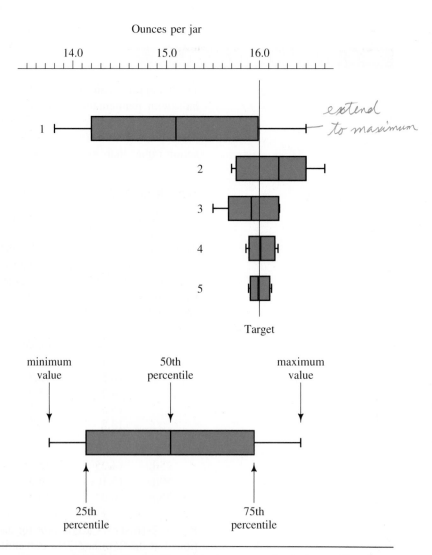

FIGURE 2-16 Box plots obtained from successive samples of instant coffee jar contents, made during calibration of regulator.

FIGURE 2-17 Control chart used to monitor process for filling instant coffee jars during production.

valve was then cleaned and readjusted. Chapter 13 describes how to find the limits for control charts. That is a procedure of **statistical quality control.**

THE TIME SERIES PLOT

Perhaps the most common data display in business applications is the **time series plot**, shown in Figure 2-18 for Ingrid's Hallmark Shop (an actual store). The sales for each month are plotted for the five-year period 1986–90. Notice the pronounced seasonal pattern reappearing every year, with maximum sales in December, followed by a dramatic January dropoff.

The time series plot is very similar to the control chart. But instead of locating points that are out of control, the time series plot is useful for identifying meaningful patterns. Chapter 12 describes in detail various statistical procedures for evaluating time series data. The ultimate objective of **time series analysis** is in **forecasting** the future levels of one or more variables.

EXERCISES

2-26 Construct a box plot for weekly closing prices of DanDee Assemblers shares.

Prices $18.50 19.85 19.25 18.25 17.75 16.50 17.25 17.25 18.25 19.00
Percentiles 25th–17.25 50th–18.25 75th–19.06

2-27 Construct a box plot for the number of daily orders generated by a telemarketer selling newspaper subscriptions.

Subscriptions 5 2 7 8 11 15 7 6 4 13
Fractiles 25th–4.75   50th–7   75th–11.5

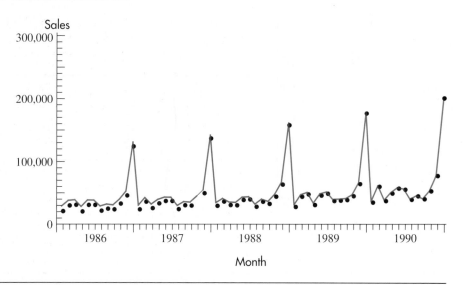

FIGURE 2-18 Monthly Sales by Ingrid's Hallmark shop.

2-28 The following data apply to the mean contents of five-pound cans of ground coffee.

Mean	5.1	4.8	5.5	5.6	5.3	5.6	5.1	4.9	4.6	4.9	5.0	5.0
Day	1	2	3	4	5	6	7	8	9	10	11	12

Plot these data on a control chart. Use 4.75 pounds as the lower limit and 5.25 pounds as the upper limit. On which days (if any) is the process out of control?

2-29 Consider the average driving distance for autos in Exercise 2-24.
  (a) Plot the time series on a graph.
  (b) What can you conclude regarding how average driving distance has changed over the 1960–1985 period?

2-30 Consider the average fuel consumption for autos in Exercise 2-24.
  (a) Plot the time series on a graph.
  (b) What can you conclude regarding how average fuel consumption has changed over the 1960–1985 period?

SUMMARY

1. How are statistical data organized in terms of frequency of occurrence?
A first step in organizing the **raw data** obtained from a statistical investigation is to establish the **frequency distribution**. All observations are classified by category or size. Numerical values are placed into **class intervals**. The number of observations in a particular group is the **class frequency**.

2. What are the kinds of numerical and graphical displays of data?
Two graphical displays are commonly obtained from sample data. One is the **histogram**, a chart having a bar for each class; each bar is as tall as the number of observations found for that group. A similar picture is provided by the **frequency polygon**, which is applicable only when the data are quantitative.

Another display is the **stem-and-leaf plot**, which maintains the raw data and arranges the numbers more conveniently. A **pie chart**, in which each slice is proportional to the category frequency, is a common display for qualitative data.

3. How do we compare data sets and make further summaries?

Comparisons are best made using **relative frequencies** instead of the original tallies. A complete collection of these constitutes the **relative frequency distribution**. Another useful set of values applicable to quantitative observations are the **cumulative frequencies**. Even more helpful are the **cumulative relative frequencies**, which collectively provide a table called the **cumulative relative frequency distribution**.

P.42-3

4. What are the common forms of statistical data?

Frequency distributions are not ordinarily known for populations, since a census is not usually taken. Nevertheless, the form of the underlying distribution may be known. Populations are often represented by familiar **frequency curves**, such as the bell-shaped **normal curve**.

Several shapes for the histogram or frequency curve are important to statistics. In addition to the normal curve, important shapes include those **skewed** positively or negatively and representatives of distribution families, such as the **exponential distribution** or the **uniform distribution**.

5. How may data be displayed when two or more variables are present?

Multidimensional data displays are important for assessing the relationships between variables. The **scatter diagram** exhibits quantitative data points in two-dimensional space, with one axis for each variable. A counterpart with qualitative data is the **cross tabulation**, with rows for the levels of one variable and columns for the levels of the other. Each data point is counted in a cell total, with one cell for each level combination of the two variables. Statistical procedures extend to higher dimensions, even when graphical displays may be impossible to construct.

6. What are some of the special data displays that are useful for important statistical applications?

Special displays are encountered in statistical applications: the **box plot** is an alternative to the histogram when there are few data points; the **control chart** is useful in statistical quality control; and the **time series plot** is helpful in forecasting evaluations.

REAL-LIFE STATISTICAL CHALLENGE

Selling to the Personal Computer Marketplace.

The information age of the 1990s has brought a maturing of the personal computer market. Personal computer systems, consisting of a microcomputer, a printer, software or programs, and other accessories are a multibillion-dollar business. Sales in this market offer great rewards. Successful selling requires specific and accurate information to design a successful sales strategy. For example, in which newspapers or trade journals should a computer equipment company advertise?

REAL-LIFE STATISTICAL CHALLENGE

InfoWorld, a data-gathering division of IDG, keeps track of the sales of personal computers throughout the world. They provide advertisers and distributors with data concerning where people are buying their products. Table 2-12 shows the total sales by metropolitan statistical area (MSA) for the top ten personal computer markets in the United States. *InfoWorld* found that "as of 1991, there were 53,887,000 personal computers installed in the United States for a value of $92.2 billion."

Other data can be combined with the total sales data to help marketing strategists develop winning approaches. For example, adding census data to the original data in Table 2-12 allows us to learn more about each of these markets. Using population data for each MSA presented in Table 2-13 helps us determine the per capita (per person) dollar value we might expect to see in each community. The per capita values are shown, and the metropolitan areas have been reranked by these per capita figures.

These ten markets account only for about 24 percent of the total market. Table 2-14 summarizes the data for other MSAs.

Discussion Questions:

1. Calculate the cumulative relative frequency for the ten MSAs in Table 2-12.

2. What types of visual displays might provide understandable presentations for the data in Tables 2-13 and 2-14? Create the displays.

TABLE 2-12 Top Ten Computer Markets

Rank	Metropolitan Statistical Area	Installed Units	Percentage of U.S. Units	Value of Installed Base (000s)	Population	Per Capita Installed Base
1	Los Angeles-Long Beach, CA	2,137,643	4.0	$3,658,370	8,863,164	$413
2	New York, NY	2,110,269	3.9	3,611,522	8,546,846	423
3	Washington, DC-MD-VA	1,832,859	3.4	3,136,761	3,923,574	799
4	Chicago, IL	1,455,488	2.7	2,490,927	6,069,974	410
5	Boston, MA	1,222,103	2.3	2,091,511	2,870,669	729
6	Philadelphia, PA-NJ	1,203,674	2.2	2,059,972	4,856,881	424
7	Detroit, MI	834,817	1.5	1,428,709	4,382,299	326
8	San Jose, CA	825,387	1.5	1,412,570	1,497,577	943
9	Minneapolis-St Paul, MN-WI	756,412	1.4	1,294,526	2,464,124	525
10	Anaheim-Santa Ana, CA	733,941	1.4	1,256,069	2,410,556	521

Source: InfoWorld, an IDG company, "The Personal Computer Market by Metropolitan Statistical Areas, 1991."

TABLE 2-13 Top Ten Computer Markets Ranked by per capita Dollar Value

Rank	Metropolitan Statistical Area	Installed Units	Percentage of U.S. Units	Value of Installed Base (000s)	Population	Per Capita Installed Base
1	San Jose, CA	825,387	1.5	$1,412,570	1,497,577	$943
2	Washington, DC-MD-VA	1,832,859	3.4	3,136,761	3,923,574	799
3	Boston, MA	1,222,103	2.3	2,091,511	2,870,669	729
4	Minneapolis-St Paul, MN-WI	756,412	1.4	1,294,526	2,464,124	525
5	Anaheim-Santa Ana, CA	733,941	1.4	1,256,069	2,410,556	521
6	Philadelphia, PA-NJ	1,203,674	2.2	2,059,972	4,856,881	424
7	New York, NY	2,110,269	3.9	3,611,522	8,546,846	423
8	Los Angeles-Long Beach, CA	2,137,643	4.0	3,658,370	8,863,164	413
9	Chicago, IL	1,455,488	2.7	2,490,927	6,069,974	410
10	Detroit, MI	834,817	1.5	1,428,709	4,382,299	326

Sources: InfoWorld, an IDG company, "The Personal Computer Market by Metropolitan Statistical Areas, 1991" and U.S. Bureau of the Census, release 1991.

3. What other business factors (for example, local manufacturing or service industries) should we consider when we study this data?

4. Which other types of high-technology equipment (for example, mobile telephones and fax machines) might we expect to have similar patterns?

TABLE 2-14 Cumulative Totals for Top 150 Markets and the Remainder of the U.S. Markets

Metropolitan Statistical Areas (MSAs)	Installed Units	Percentage of U.S. Units	Value of Installed Base (000s)
Top 10	13,112,593	24.3	$22,440,937
Top 25	21,905,822	40.7	37,489,701
Top 50	29,086,856	54.0	49,779,347
Top 75	33,143,843	61.5	56,772,490
Top 100	36,009,714	66.8	61,627,151
Top 150	39,782,020	73.8	68,083,087
Remainder of U.S.:			
MSA 151-333	5,079,011	9.4	8,692,235
Not in MSAs	9,025,969	16.8	15,447,078
	14,104,980	26.2	24,139,313

REVIEW EXERCISES

2-31 A sample of MBA students has been selected. The students' ages have the following frequency distribution.

Age (years)	Number of Students
20–under 25	18
25–under 30	23
30–under 35	15
35–under 40	13
40–under 45	7
45–under 50	6
50–under 55	5
55–under 60	5
60–under 65	8
Total	100

Construct a table for the relative and cumulative frequency distributions.

2-32 Refer to the student data given in Exercise 2-11. Construct a cross tabulation of major versus sex. What can you conclude regarding the prevalence of each sex within the majors?

2-33 Sky King provided the following incomplete fuel consumption data for its delivery fleet.

Miles per Gallon	Number of Vans	Relative Frequency	Cumulative Frequency
6.0–under 8.0	—	—	—
8.0–under 10.0	23	—	29
10.0–under 12.0	—	.34	—
12.0–under 14.0	17	.17	—
14.0–under 16.0	—	—	92
16.0–under 18.0	—	—	—
Totals	100	1.00	

(a) Determine the missing values.
(b) Plot the cumulative frequency ogive for this population.

2-34 The following heights (inches) have been obtained for the male staff at the *Daily Planet*.

73.1	66.0	65.9	72.0	67.5
69.9	69.1	68.4	74.3	69.9
72.1	69.4	71.0	70.1	71.5
61.5	70.0	63.4	71.0	66.2
68.3	74.2	68.9	73.8	69.3
71.3	74.6	66.9	69.8	68.8
73.0	65.0	63.7	70.9	76.6
69.7	64.8	71.2	70.7	67.5
75.1	71.5	72.0	76.1	68.2
66.8	72.0	69.7	73.0	70.6

(a) Construct a table for the frequency distribution that has sixteen class intervals of width 1 inch. Use 61.5 inches as the lower limit of the first interval.
(b) Plot a histogram using your answer to (a).
(c) Add a column of relative frequencies to the table found in (a).
(d) Add a column of cumulative relative frequencies to the table found in (a).
(e) Plot the cumulative relative frequency ogive.
(f) What proportion of the sample lies (1) under 70.5″, (2) under 75.5″, and (3) under 66.5″ tall?

2-35 Hops Brewery has two divisions, one in the South and the other in the North. Separate frequency distributions for the hourly wages of workers in the South and North are provided below.

South		North	
Hourly Wage	Number of Workers	Hourly Wage	Number of Workers
$ 5–under 6	150	$ 5–under 6	0
6–under 7	300	6–under 7	0
7–under 8	150	7–under 8	0
8–under 9	100	8–under 9	0
9–under 10	50	9–under 10	50
10–under 11	50	10–under 11	150
11–under 12	50	11–under 12	150
12–under 13	50	12–under 13	200
13–under 14	50	13–under 14	100

(a) Plot frequency polygons for each division separately but on the same graph.
(b) Combine the South and North data into a single table for the all-company frequency distribution.
(c) Plot a frequency polygon using the data obtained in (b).
(d) Comparing the graphs in (a) to that in (c), which presentation do you think provides more meaningful managerial information? Explain.

2-36 A sample of 350 persons has been categorized by sex, marital status, and occupation. The number of persons in each category is summarized below.

Sex	Marital Status	Occupation	Number of Persons
male	married	blue collar	75
male	married	white collar	37
male	married	professional	12
male	single	blue collar	55
male	single	white collar	38
male	single	professional	3
female	married	blue collar	13
female	married	white collar	32
female	married	professional	2
female	single	blue collar	12
female	single	white collar	66
female	single	professional	5
		Total	350

Construct a table for the frequency distribution by (a) sex, (b) marital status, (c) occupation.

2-37 The following sample data have been obtained for the number of monthly trades in portfolios managed by Ponzi Trust Company.

17	25	32	41	43
31	28	27	39	36
25	19	21	28	26
30	32	26	27	34
21	24	20	25	31

(a) Construct a stem-and-leaf plot.
(b) Construct a table for the frequency distribution that has six class intervals of width 5 transactions. Use 15 transactions as the lower limit of the first interval.
(c) Determine the relative frequency for each class using your answer to (b).
(d) Determine the cumulative frequency distribution for each class using your answer to (b).

2-38 Refer to the sample data given in Exercise 2-36. Construct tables showing the following cross tabulations.
(a) sex versus marital status
(b) marital status versus occupation
(c) sex versus occupation

STATISTICS IN PRACTICE

2-39 Use the master class data from Exercise 1-19.
(a) For the height data, find the frequency, cumulative frequency, relative frequency, and relative cumulative frequency distributions.
(b) Use the frequency distribution for heights and to construct a histogram.
(c) Separate the class by sex, compare the height distributions, and create a chart to illustrate your findings.
(d) For one nominal variable, create an appropriate visual display.
(e) Categorize the class data by place of birth. Create one category for the state, province or country where your school is located and one for all others. Create a cross tabulation using place of birth by major or favorite food.
(f) Use the student age variable in a grouped format, and compare against favorite food or state of birth.

2-40 Using your group class data list developed in Exercise 1-21, perform the following operations for describing and displaying statistical data.
(a) For one quantitative variable (having an interval scale) find the frequency, the cumulative frequency, relative frequency, and relative cumulative frequency distributions.
(b) Use the frequency distribution from part (a), to construct a histogram.
(c) Create an appropriate visual display for one qualitative variable.
(d) Create a cross tabulation with two nominal variables.

2-41 *The Last Cold War Olympics.* Consider the best way to organize the medal total data from the 1988 Summer Olympics presented in Table 2-15. With the merger of East and West Germany and the breakup of the Soviet Union, can the data be reorganized? Why or why not?

TABLE 2-15 Olympic Medals Earned at the 1988 Summer Games for the Top Six Countries

Country	Gold	Silver	Bronze	Total
USSR	55	31	46	132
East Germany	37	35	30	102
United States	36	31	27	94
West Germany	11	14	15	40
Bulgaria	10	12	13	35
South Korea	12	10	11	33
Others	76	104	95	275
Total	237	237	237	711

2-42 Table 2-16 shows the twenty most populous countries for the years 1991 and 2100.
(a) Can you meaningfully calculate the cumulative frequencies? Discuss.
(b) Calculate the cumulative relative frequencies for these two lists.
(c) In illustrating the populations for the *continents* listed, would there be any ambiguities?

TABLE 2-16 World's Twenty Most Populous Countries: 1991 and 2100 Estimates

	1991				2100		
Rank	Country	Population	Continent	Rank	Country	Population	Continent
1	China	1,151,300,000	Asia	1	India	1,631,800,000	Asia
2	India	859,200,000	Asia	2	China	1,571,400,000	Asia
3	United States	252,800,000	N. America	3	Nigeria	508,800,000	Africa
4	Indonesia	181,400,000	Asia	4	Indonesia	356,300,000	Asia
5	Brazil	153,300,000	S. America	5	Pakistan	315,800,000	Asia
6	Russia	147,400,000	Europe/Asia	6	United States	308,700,000	N. America
7	Japan	123,800,000	Asia	7	Bangladesh	297,100,000	Asia
8	Nigeria	122,500,000	Africa	8	Brazil	293,200,000	S. America
9	Pakistan	117,500,000	Asia	9	Mexico	195,500,000	N. America
10	Bangladesh	116,600,000	Asia	10	Russia	180,400,000	Europe/Asia
11	Mexico	85,700,000	N. America	11	Ethiopia	173,300,000	Africa
12	Germany	79,500,000	Europe	12	Vietnam	168,100,000	Asia
13	Vietnam	67,600,000	Asia	13	Iran	163,800,000	Asia
14	Philippines	62,300,000	Asia	14	Zaire	138,900,000	Africa
15	Thailand	58,800,000	Asia	15	Japan	127,900,000	Asia
16	Iran	58,600,000	Asia	16	Philippines	125,100,000	Asia
17	Turkey	58,500,000	Europe/Asia	17	Tanzania	119,600,000	Africa
18	Italy	57,700,000	Europe	18	Kenya	116,400,000	Africa
19	United Kingdom	57,500,000	Europe	19	Myanmar (Burma)	111,700,000	Asia
20	France	56,700,000	Europe	20	Egypt	110,500,000	Africa
	Total	3,868,700,000			Total	7,014,300,000	

Source: *1992 Information Please Almanac*

2-43 *Scholastic Aptitude Test Results.* Table 2-17 contains the average SAT verbal and math scores for college-bound high school seniors from 1970 to 1993.

TABLE 2-17 SAT Verbal and Math Scores for College-Bound High School Seniors (minimum score 200, maximum score 800)

Year	Verbal			Math		
	Total	Male	Female	Total	Male	Female
1970	460	459	461	488	509	465
1975	434	437	431	472	495	449
1980	424	428	420	466	491	443
1985	431	437	425	475	499	452
1987	430	435	425	476	500	453
1988	428	435	422	476	498	455
1989	427	434	421	476	500	454
1990	424	429	419	476	499	455
1991	422	426	418	474	497	453
1992	423	428	419	476	499	456
1993	424	428	420	478	502	457

Source: *The World Almanac and Book of Facts, 1994.*

(a) Create an appropriate visual display of the total SAT verbal scores.
(b) Create a single graph that compares male and female verbal SAT scores.
(c) Comment on your graph in (b).

2-44 Using the data in Table 2-17, repeat parts (a)–(c) of Exercise 2-43 for the SAT math scores.

2-45 *Television Viewing Time.* Table 2-18 shows the average television viewing time, by age group and time period, for 1993.

TABLE 2-18 Television Viewing Time by Age Group and Time Period for 1993

Age	Mon–Fri 10 AM–4:30 PM	Mon–Fri 4:30–7:30 PM	Mon–Sun 8–11 PM	Sat 7 AM–1 PM	Mon–Fri 11:30 PM–1 AM
2–5	4:47	2:52	4:19	1:11	:20
6–11	1:40	2:56	4:58	1:06	:19
12–17	1:57	2:58	6:10	:44	:44
18–24	4:55	2:56	6:32	:32	1:12
25–54	4:33	3:09	8:32	:34	1:24
55+	7:48	5:55	11:46	:42	1:35

Source: *The World Almanac and Book of Facts, 1994.*

(a) Prepare an appropriate visual display for each of the five time periods.
(b) Comment on the television viewing habits of the age groups during the different time periods.

2-46 *Political Party Affiliation.* Table 2-19 shows a partial demographic profile of the 1990 voting population (in percent).

TABLE 2-19 Political Party Affiliation for the 1990 Voting Population (in percent)

	Republican	Democrat	Independent
Overall	**32.0**	**40.0**	**28.0**
Sex			
Male	33.4	36.5	30.2
Female	30.9	42.1	27.0
Region			
East	29.8	43.6	26.6
Midwest	30.8	35.0	34.2
South	32.4	41.1	26.5
West	36.4	36.7	27.0

Source: *The World Almanac of U.S. Politics, 1991–93.*

(a) Prepare a pie chart that shows the overall political affiliation for the 1990 election.
(b) Construct a bar graph showing political affiliation by region.

CASE   Ingrid's Hallmark Shop I

Ingrid's Hallmark Shop, a 2,000 square foot card and gift shop, is located next to a large supermarket in a suburban town of nearly 20,000 residents. The stores are among others in a small strip center.

Ingrid has fine-tuned her business by adapting the type and mix of gifts to the needs of her clientele. She has learned, through experience, to drop slow selling items and to expand merchandise breadth and depth for the faster selling lines of goods. She can never be sure which items will do well, however, because of ever-changing tastes and trends. It is necessary for Ingrid to constantly try new things.

In deciding on specific gifts to order, Ingrid has developed a few guidelines. For example, she avoids bulky items, preferring small gifts of high value for their size. But, since Ingrid's customers typically choose gifts on impulse while shopping for Hallmark staples, there is a price threshold above which gifts move very slowly. Ingrid has learned to limit her gift buying to items with a retail price that falls in the fast-moving range.

Ingrid wants to improve her gift buying by taking a more active stance. She wants to be able to anticipate specific customer needs. Although she knows a great deal about individual customers, Ingrid needs to gain an overall perspective. To do this, a small marketing research firm has been retained to make a statistical evaluation of Ingrid's customers.

Using public domain data for the census tracts covering and contiguous to the town where Ingrid's Hallmark Shop is located, a sample of homeowners has been selected from Ingrid's market. Table 2-20 shows a partial listing of the sample data obtained. (There is one row for each sample customer.)

TABLE 2-20 Sample Data for Customers of Ingrid's Hallmark Shop

Age	Income	Home Value	Age	Income	Home Value
30	$17,005	$ 37,000	35	$25,110	$156,000
49	35,505	88,400	46	52,510	117,200
36	10,005	44,300	45	36,050	133,800
35	30,445	60,000	33	23,005	80,300
30	10,200	34,700	45	10,805	38,200
39	18,915	83,100	47	35,005	72,300
42	21,005	61,300	51	28,005	69,600
43	22,295	43,600	30	9,745	45,300
28	7,010	53,600	30	34,080	101,800
39	17,505	59,300	59	8,505	58,700
49	4,050	55,000	48	25,505	14,900
35	21,430	56,400	57	14,505	36,000
40	21,005	45,200	44	23,005	78,900
20	11,005	131,400	35	23,940	159,300
40	20,005	69,900	39	18,005	48,500
45	47,015	71,400	36	49,515	67,900
34	3,005	77,700	34	25,060	73,100
35	18,005	103,700	37	12,510	45,600
65	13,080	40,500	32	13,005	40,900
52	30,010	85,600	34	18,265	105,200

Questions

1. Comment on the appropriateness of using census tract data to help Ingrid formulate her strategy for buying gifts. Give any suggestions for improving the sample data in terms of (a) identifying the target populations, (b) choosing the sample customers, and (c) completing the observations.

2. Consider the ages of the sample customers.
   (a) Construct a stem-and-leaf plot.
   (b) In three sentences, describe the homeowners as a group.
   (c) Assuming that the sample is representative of all of Ingrid's customers, what type of gifts do you believe Ingrid might want to concentrate on when making her buying decisions? Explain.

3. Consider the incomes of the sample customers.
   (a) Determine a meaningful class interval width. Use the width to construct a table for the frequency distribution.

(b) Plot (1) a histogram, (2) a frequency polygon, and (3) a cumulative frequency ogive using your answer to (a).

(c) Based on the income profile suggested by the sample, suggest to Ingrid a few price points for gift items. Explain.

4. Consider the home values of the sample customers.
(a) Recommend a display that would meaningfully summarize the data.
(b) Prepare the display.

5. If a follow-up survey were taken, what sample data or information—other than age, income, and home value—do you think would be helpful? What arguments would you present to convince Ingrid to follow your recommendations?

CHAPTER 3

SUMMARY DESCRIPTIVE MEASURES

BEFORE READING THIS CHAPTER, MAKE SURE YOU UNDERSTAND:

The distinction between quantitative and qualitative data (Chapter 1).

The types of data displays and how to construct them (Chapter 2).

The common forms taken by statistical data (Chapter 2).

AFTER READING THIS CHAPTER, YOU WILL UNDERSTAND:

How to evaluate statistical data.

How to measure central tendency.

How to obtain and use percentiles and related measures.

How to measure central tendency.

How together the mean and the standard deviation provide added descriptive power.

How to summarize qualitative data.

We have seen how the frequency distribution arranges raw data into a meaningful pattern. Now we are ready to investigate further ways to summarize statistical data. Knowledge of the frequency distribution alone is not sufficient to answer many statistical questions. For example, in evaluating a new drug, researchers must establish whether it improves patient recovery. The new drug must be compared in some way with the drug in current use. Sample data can provide recovery times for the two treatments, but a direct comparison of histograms would be cumbersome. Instead, the **average** recovery times for the two drugs would more clearly establish whether the new treatment is better. If the new drug significantly speeds up the average patient's recovery, it should replace the old drug.

This chapter considers a variety of summary measures. Each is a number precisely measuring various properties of the observations. There are two major classes of summary numerical values for quantitative data. One measures **location**. Measures of location may be concerned with **central tendency**, a value around which the observations tend to cluster and which typifies their magnitude. The **arithmetic mean** is one of the more commonly used measures of central tendency. A second grouping of location is concerned with **position**. Not limited to the center, measures of position are placed according to frequency of occurrence. Another broad category of numbers provides measures of **dispersion** or **variability** among the observation values. These measures indicate how observed values differ from each other. Conceptually, the simplest of these is the **range**, which expresses the difference between the largest and smallest observations. A useful summary measure for qualitative data is the **proportion**, which indicates how frequently a particular attribute is observed.

Summary data measures are ordinarily computed from *sample* data, since all of the parent population is not usually observed. A computed summary measure is referred to as a **statistic** and conveys a property only for the data actually observed. Sample statistics, such as the arithmetic mean, have their counterparts in the population. The mean of all potential observations is a type of **population parameter**. Exact values for population parameters are not ordinarily computed, since observations are rarely made of the complete population.

central tendency

3-1 THE ARITHMETIC MEAN

The arithmetic mean is the most commonly encountered and best understood of the measures of central tendency. Consider the cash balances (thousands of dollars) of five manufacturing firms: 101.3, 34.5, 17.6, 83.4, and 52.7. The mean 57.9 is calculated by adding these values and dividing the sum by the number of firms (5).

$$\frac{101.3 + 34.5 + 17.6 + 83.4 + 52.7}{5} = \frac{289.5}{5} = 57.9$$

SYMBOLIC EXPRESSIONS FOR CALCULATING THE ARITHMETIC MEAN

Since the arithmetic mean is calculated in the same way for any group of raw data, it is convenient to express this calculation symbolically. Because we may not yet know the value of a particular observation, we may also have to assign a special symbol to each observation. Traditionally, the letter X is used to represent an observed value. To distinguish each observation, we use the numbers 1, 2, 3, ... as **subscripts**. Thus, X_1 represents the first observation value; X_2, the second; X_3, the third; and so on. The symbol X_1 is referred to as "X sub 1." Another advantage of expressing observation values symbolically is that algebraic expressions can be used to state precisely how each statistical measure is calculated, so that the same procedure can be applied to any set of data.

The mean is represented by the special symbol $\bar{X}$, called "X bar." To calculate the mean, we divide the sum of the values by the number of observations made, which is represented by the letter n. The following formula is used to calculate the

MEAN

$$\bar{X} = \frac{X_1 + X_2 + \cdots + X_n}{n}$$

In our previous illustration, the sample size was $n = 5$, and the observed values were $X_1 = 101.3$, $X_2 = 34.5$, $X_3 = 17.6$, $X_4 = 83.4$, and $X_5 = 52.7$.

Sometimes it is convenient to use an even more concise formula for the mean. Just as we use a plus sign ($+$) to add two quantities together, we can represent the sum of several values by a **summation sign**, which takes the form of $\sum$ (the uppercase Greek **sigma**). The mean can then be expressed as

$$\bar{X} = \frac{\sum X}{n}$$

THE POPULATION AND SAMPLE MEAN

If the five cash balances represent only a sample from a population of observations of all medium-sized companies in the nation, then the result of the calculation is a *sample* mean of 57.9 thousand dollars. If, instead, they are the entire set of observations for the population of cash balances at the foundries in Marlborough County, then 57.9 thousand dollars is the *population* mean.

The symbol $\bar{X}$ often represents a level for the sample mean, with n then denoting the **sample size**. A major application of statistics is using a sample to draw conclusions regarding the *unknown* population mean, which is traditionally represented by μ (the lowercase Greek **mu**). μ is the equivalent of "m," the first letter in mean. (Several other population parameters are also represented by Greek letters.) Generally, we do not compute μ directly, because the entire population is not usually observed. Ordinarily, the value of μ remains unknown; only $\bar{X}$ is calculated, and this value serves as an estimate of μ.

USING A COMPUTER TO CALCULATE THE MEAN

When the number of observations is large, it can be time consuming to calculate the mean by hand—even with the assistance of a calculator. Consider the sample

TABLE 3-1 Sample Temperatures (°F) for Selected Cities

Temperatures (°F)								
58	59	62	59	67	59	62	68	54
64	56	58	52	53	75	63	66	65
46	55	64	78	64	61	77	59	57
63	50	50	75	71	68	60	76	77
69	73	52	57	65	62	53	63	62
60	59	48	63	65	75	57	58	62
63	58	68	73	50	62	58	79	
70	61	75	74	71	36	67	50	
55	74	62	48	79	67	56	73	
57	57	58	65	55	68	55	55	

Source: *The World Almanac and Book of Facts,* 1988 edition, copyright © Newspaper Enterprise, Inc., 1987, New York, NY: 181.

temperature (°F) data in Table 3-1 obtained for selected U.S. cities during the month of May. These data were entered into an IBM PC using Minitab and double checked for accuracy. Most computer software allows for quick correction of any data input errors.

Figure 3-1 displays the printout generated on a computer using the temperature data. A variety of statistical measures are provided. The mean is computed by averaging the 86 temperatures. We find it to be $\bar{X} = 62.244$. (The other descriptive statistics will be explained later.)

DECISION MAKING WITH THE MEAN

The mean plays an important role in decision making. A product manager can use the mean cost per 1,000 readers as a guide in selecting magazines in which to place advertisements. A student might select his or her major based partly on the mean starting salaries of graduates in the respective fields. The following Statistics Around Us box on page 68 shows how useful the mean can be in production management.   *70*

```
MTB > describe c1


            N     MEAN    MEDIAN   TRMEAN    STDEV    SEMEAN
Temp.      86    62.244   62.000   62.333    8.598    0.927


           MIN     MAX      Q1       Q3
Temp.    36.000  79.000   57.000   68.000
```

Note: Figure generated on IBM using Minitab.

FIGURE 3-1 Computer printout for sample temperature data.

STATISTICS AROUND US

Deciding When to Adjust Bottle Filling Controls

The quality control manager for Astronic Tonics uses the arithmetic mean for deciding when to shut down production for equipment maintenance. She is establishing a policy that will tell workers when to adjust the filling controls for 6 oz bottles of mineral water.

Under ideal conditions, the population mean contents for all filled bottles should be exactly $\mu = 6$ oz. Unfortunately, over time the controls tend to drift, so that the true value for the population mean might be some smaller amount, like $\mu = 5.85$ or $\mu = 5.91$ oz. It might also be greater, so that population means like $\mu = 6.15$ or $\mu = 6.22$ oz are possible. In any of these cases, the filling process would be so far off target that the controls need to be adjusted. Unfortunately, it would be too expensive to precisely measure the contents of every bottle, and *the true value for μ at any time can never be known*.

Nevertheless, the process can be monitored by means of *samples*. Every fifteen minutes a sample of $n = 20$ bottles is removed from the production line, the content volume of each is precisely measured, and the sample mean contents $\bar{X}$ is then computed. The following **decision rule** is applied.

CONTINUE filling operations whenever $5.90 \text{ oz} \le \bar{X} \le 6.10$ oz.

STOP and adjust control valves if $\bar{X} < 5.90$ oz or if $\bar{X} > 6.10$ oz.

In using the above rule, the manager knows that the computed $\bar{X}$ may be above or below the true level for μ. Thus, sometimes abnormally extreme sample results will give a "false" signal, and production will be stopped for unneeded adjustment. Conversely, $\bar{X}$ may fall within the "continue" range even after a large drift in μ has occurred, and serious overfilling or underfilling may go uncorrected for awhile. But her rule is chosen to achieve an acceptable balance between these two erroneous actions.

APPROXIMATING THE MEAN USING GROUPED DATA

Generally, the first step in analyzing or describing a collection of raw data is to construct a frequency distribution by arranging the raw data into groups or classes according to size. It is usually possible to obtain good approximations to the mean using only these summary data. These shortcut procedures may save time and effort. And, when published data have already been grouped and the raw data are unavailable, they might be the only way to find the summary values.

The grouped procedure for approximating $\bar{X}$ is shown in Table 3-2. There the frequency distribution for fuel consumption is provided.

Every class interval is represented by its midpoint. The first of these, 15, is found by averaging the limits of the first class interval: $(14.0 + 16.0)/2 = 15$. The remaining midpoints can then be easily found by adding one class interval width (here, 2 miles per gallon) to the preceding class midpoint. A **weighted average** is then computed by multiplying each midpoint by the relative frequency for its class. The following summarizes the procedure for computing the

find summary value

MEAN USING GROUPED DATA

$$\bar{X} = \sum X(f/n)$$

TABLE 3-2 Calculation of the Mean Fuel Consumption Using Shortcut with Grouped Data

Fuel Consumption (miles per gallon)	Number of Cars f	Class Interval Midpoint X	Relative Frequency f/n	X(f/n)
14.0–under 16.0	9	15	.09	1.35
16.0–under 18.0	13	17	.13	2.21
18.0–under 20.0	24	19	.24	4.56
20.0–under 22.0	38	21	.38	7.98
22.0–under 24.0	16	23	.16	3.68
Totals	100		1.00	19.78

$$\bar{X} = \sum X(f/n) = 19.78$$

The successive class midpoints are represented by Xs and the class frequencies by fs. Each relative frequency f/n is computed by dividing the class frequency by the number of observations. The resulting approximate $\bar{X}$ gives weight to each class value in proportion to its relative frequency.

The value 19.78 found in Table 3-2 is only an *approximation* of the mean and can be expected to differ from the value calculated directly from the raw data. This is because all fuel consumptions in a particular class interval are represented by a single number. The raw fuel consumption data are provided in Table 2-3 (page 28). The arithmetic mean of these data, calculated without grouping, is 19.718 miles per gallon. This differs only slightly from the value calculated for $\bar{X}$ using the shortcut method. For practical purposes, the approximation is usually close enough.

Some statisticians prefer to use the following mathematically equivalent expression.

$$\bar{X} = \frac{\sum fX}{n}$$

Each fX term approximates the sum of all the values in the respective interval.

EXERCISES

3-1 The following numbers of new employees were hired by a sample of McBurger franchises during 1989.

14	6	12	19	2	35	5	4	3	7	5	8

Calculate the mean.

3-2 A data processing manager purchased remote terminal processing time to run special jobs at two different computer "utilities." She wishes to sign a long-term contract with the firm whose computer causes the least delay on the average. The numbers of minutes of delayed processing per week were obtained during trial periods with each firm and are provided below.

CompuQuick	210	15	47	93	104			
Dial-a-Pute	18	341	523	25	19	293	115	203

Assuming that trial experience is representative of future performance, which firm should receive the business? Substantiate your answer with appropriate calculations.

3-3 Refer to the Astronic Tonics bottle filling example (box on page 68). For each of the following sample results, (a) calculate the mean and (b) indicate whether the operations should be *continued* or *stopped* for adjustment of control valves.

(1) 8 A.M., July 5: 5.85, 5.95, 5.85, 5.75, 5.65
(2) 2 P.M., July 5: 6.05, 6.00, 6.10, 5.90, 5.95, 6.05, 6.05
(3) 1 A.M., July 6: 6.05, 5.80, 6.10, 5.90, 5.95, 6.05, 6.05
(4) 4 A.M., July 6: 6.05, 6.20, 6.15, 6.15, 6.00, 6.10

3-4 The following frequency distribution has been obtained for the lifetimes of TryHard batteries.

Lifetime (hours)	Number of Batteries
0.0–under 20.0	500
20.0–under 40.0	250
40.0–under 60.0	125
60.0–under 80.0	61
80.0–under 100.0	15
100.0–under 120.0	6

Calculate the mean.

3-5 The following frequency distribution has been obtained for the lifetimes of Whammo floppy disks.

Lifetime (hours)	Number of Disks
0.0–under 50.0	5
50.0–under 100.0	16
100.0–under 150.0	117
150.0–under 200.0	236
200.0–under 250.0	331
250.0–under 300.0	78
300.0–under 350.0	27
350.0–under 400.0	8

Calculate the mean.

3-6 The sales manager of Kleen Janitorial Supplies allows sales representatives to give special introductory prices to new customers. He wishes to weed out those salespersons who take undue advantage of specials, "milking" them of commissions and bringing in little new continuing business. Investigating the files for the past ten months, he has determined for each of the five sales representatives the following precentages of specials buyers who placed second orders.

Percentage of Specials Buyers Retained				
A	**B**	**C**	**D**	**E**
36	9	11	33	18
43	16	5	17	17
49	21	6	45	23
18	14	14	29	6
17	33	25	17	31
32	8	12	27	42
24	19	11	61	19
19	17	9	47	13
28	26	28	35	26
36	11	14	14	33

(a) Calculate the mean percentage of specials buyers retained for each salesperson.

(b) Using your answers to (a), calculate the mean percentage of such customers retained for the sales force as a whole.

(c) Assuming that the sales manager will take remedial action against those salespersons who produce lower than average retention, which salespersons should be singled out for milking specials?

3-7 Unified Airways provided the following distance data for domestic flights.

629	1076	1134	1082	704
639	956	887	901	1831
1150	1585	575	419	1209
814	869	978	928	823
730	859	745	1009	1095
746	554	757	924	1020
552	790	804	1188	974
1047	893	1653	746	1458
1087	2062	1110	625	902
1201	854	604	1390	530

Calculate the mean.

3-8 Consider the percentages of specials buyers retained by all salespersons in Exercise 3-6 as a single data set.

(a) Construct a table for the frequency distribution that has six class intervals of equal width. Use 5.0–under 15.0 as the first interval.

(b) Calculate the mean using the grouped data for the distribution in (a).

(c) Calculate the mean using the ungrouped data. By how much is this above or below your answer to (b)?

3-9 Refer to the domestic flight distances given in Exercise 3-7.

(a) Construct a table for the frequency distribution that has 17 class intervals of equal width. Use 400.0–under 500.0 miles as the first interval.

(b) Calculate the approximate level of the sample mean using your answer to (a).

(c) In Exercise 3-7 the sample mean of the ungrouped data was determined. By how much is your answer to (b) above or below the mean found in Exercise 3-7?

3-10 *Computer exercise.* Refer to the sample levels of precipitation given in Exercise 2-2. Calculate the mean.

3-11 *Computer exercise.* Refer to the sample temperatures given in Exercise 2-5. Calculate the mean.

3-2 THE MEDIAN AND THE MODE

THE MEDIAN

After the mean, the most common measure of central tendency is the **median**. Like the mean, the median provides a typical numerical value. The median, denoted by *m,* is the central observation when all the data are arranged in increasing sequence. For the heights 66, 68, 69, 73, and 74 inches, the median is *m* = 69 inches, the central value. If a person 70 inches tall were added to the initial group, then the median would be obtained by averaging the two central values from 66, 68, 69, 70, 73, 74. Thus, the median would be *m* = (69 + 70)/2 = 69.5 inches.

In general, *the median is the value above or below which lies an equal number of observations.* We find the median from the raw data by listing the observations in sequence from lowest to highest and then selecting the central value if there is an odd number of values or averaging the two central values if there is an even number of observations.

odd number
· even "

THE MEDIAN CONTRASTED WITH THE MEAN

In different senses, the arithmetic mean and the median are both averages. The mean is the arithmetic average of variates, and the median is the average of position. When we use the term **average**, we speak of the arithmetic mean.

median — the average
of position

A mean can be algebraically manipulated; the combined mean of two populations can be calculated from the individual means. Due to these convenient mathematical properties, many statistical techniques employing the mean have been developed. The median is not as well suited to mathematical operations. For example, the median of a combined population cannot be obtained from the separate component population medians. Fewer statistical techniques employ the median due to the mathematical difficulties associated with it.

mean is influenced
by extreme value

On the other hand, the mean is influenced by extreme values to a much greater degree than the median. Consider the net worth levels of your close friends. Suppose that you meet one of the world's few billionaires and include him in your circle of friends. The addition of this person would distort the mean level of wealth so greatly that "on the average" all of your friends would be multi-millionaires—hardly a meaningful summary. But the median would not be significantly influenced by the billionaire. The median is more democratic, giving each elementry unit only one "vote" in establishing the central location.

Generally, the median provides a better measure of central tendency than the mean when there are some extremely large or small observations.

THE MODE

A third measure that may be used to describe central tendency is the **mode**—the *most frequently occurring* value. Consider the simple illustration provided by the collection of five observations: 2, 3, 4, 4, and 7. The mode is 4, because 4 occurs most often.

The interpretation of the statistical mode is analogous to that of the fashion mode. A person dressing in the current style is "in the mode." But a current fashion can be a poor description of what most people are wearing, because a variety of styles is worn by the general public. In statistics, the mode only tells us which single value occurs most often; it may therefore represent a minority of the observations.

As a basis for decisions, the mode can be insidiously undemocratic. For example, most shoe stores stock only the most popular sizes, so the mode is their deciding parameter. One reason for this is that the turnover on unusual sizes is so low that they are unprofitable. When such sizes are stocked, there is ordinarily little choice of color or style (and what there is will usually be on the conservative side). A significant number of people who wear unpopular sizes find it difficult to buy shoes in stores and may have to resort to mail-order purchasing. Not being of modal size, they are forced to be hopelessly out of mode in the sense of fashion as well.

When the data are grouped into classes, the mode is represented by the midpoint of the interval having the greatest class frequency. We refer to this group as the **modal class.** When the frequency distribution is portrayed as a smoothed curve like the one in Figure 3-2, the mode corresponds to the possible observation value lying beneath the highest point on the frequency curve—the location of maximum clustering. The mode can therefore serve as a basis for comparing the typicalness of the other measures of central tendency. The modal class for the fuel consumption data in Table 3-2 is the class interval 20.0–under 22.0, and the sample mode is

modal class

$$\text{Mode} = \frac{20.0 + 22.0}{2} = 21.0$$

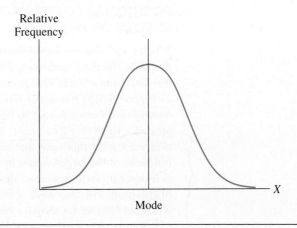

FIGURE 3-2 Illustration of the location of the mode.

FINDING THE MEDIAN AND MODE FROM A STEM-AND-LEAF PLOT

When the raw data are arranged in a stem-and-leaf plot, the median and mode can be found easily. The following stem-and-leaf plot was obtained using the temperatures given in Table 3-1.

Leaf

	3	6
	4	6 8 8
Stem	5	8 5 7 9 6 5 0 9 8 7 8 0 2 8 9 2 7 3 0 5 9 3 7 8 6 5 9 8 0 5 4 7
	6	4 3 9 0 3 1 2 4 8 2 3 5 7 4 5 5 1 8 2 2 7 8 2 3 0 7 8 6 3 5 2 2
	7	0 3 4 5 8 5 3 4 1 1 9 5 5 7 6 9 3 7

The plot must be further refined before the desired statistics can be found. By sorting the leaf digits on each stem in ascending order, an **ordered stem-and-leaf plot** is obtained. The ordered stem-and-leaf plot for the sample temperatures is constructed below.

Leaf

	3	6
	4	6 8 8
Stem	5	0 0 0 0 2 2 3 3 4 5 5 5 5 5 6 6 7 7 7 7 7 8 8 8 8 8 9 9 9 9 9
	6	0 0 1 1 2 2 2 2 2 2 2 3 3 3 3 3 4 4 4 5 5 5 5 6 7 7 7 8 8 8 8 9
	7	0 1 1 3 3 3 4 4 5 5 5 5 6 7 7 8 9 9

The median of the 86 observations is the average of the 43rd and 44th values (the boxed leaf digits).

$$m = \frac{62 + 62}{2} = 62$$

Figure 3-1, the computer printout, confirms the above value as the median.

Coincidentally, the mode is also 62, since the "6" stem has seven "2" digit leaves, the most frequently occurring of all the leaves on a single stem.

POSITIONAL COMPARISON OF MEASURES: SKEWED DISTRIBUTIONS

When a variable has a **symmetrical** frequency curve like the one in Figure 3-3(a), the mean, median, and mode coincide. When the distribution is not symmetrical, the mean and median will lie to the same side of the mode. The frequency curve in Figure 3-3(b) has a tail tapering off to the right. Such an asymmetrical frequency distribution is said to be *skewed to the right,* meaning that the data cluster around a relatively low value, although there are some extremely large observation values. In this case, the mean lies to the right of the mode, reflecting the influence of the larger values in raising the arithmetic average. The median, which is less sensitive to extremes, must lie to the left of the mean. A rightward skewed distribution will also have a mode that is smaller than the median. The median will therefore lie somewhere between the mode and the mean.

Because rightward skewed data will always have a median smaller than the mean, subtracting the median from the mean results in a positive difference. For

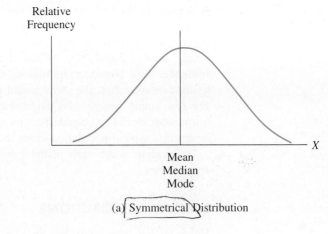

(a) Symmetrical Distribution

(b) (c)
mode & median
will lie on the
same side
Cluster

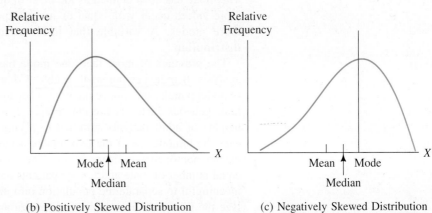

(b) Positively Skewed Distribution   (c) Negatively Skewed Distribution

FIGURE 3-3 Positional comparison of center measures for symmetrical and skewed frequency distributions.

mean > median

this reason, such a frequency distribution is said to be **positively skewed**. This expression also reflects the fact that the long tail of the distribution tapers off in a positive direction from the center of the distribution.

has lower limit →
no upper boundary

Generally, a variable having a lower limit but no theoretical upper boundary will exhibit a positively skewed distribution. This is true of the annual wages earned by construction workers in the United States. A lower limit is established by the legal minimum wage. Some blue-collar aristocrats, such as operating engineers (who drive heavy equipment), plumbers, electricians, and iron workers, earn more than many doctors when their overtime premiums are considered. In total numbers, however, the high earners are relatively sparse, creating a long, thin, rightward tail in the frequency curve. Economic data often have positively skewed frequency distributions.

Figure 3-3(c) shows a frequency curve that is *skewed to the left*—the direction toward which its long tail points. Because the extremes are relatively small values, the mean lies below the mode. Again, the median will lie somewhere in between the mean and the mode. Subtracting the median from the mean (a smaller value) results in a negative difference, so the frequency curve is said to be **negatively skewed**.

Negatively skewed distributions result when the observed values have an upper limit and no significant lower boundary. For example, the ages of viewers who watch a television program on which ''old favorites'' are played would be a negatively skewed population. Aimed at a predominantly middle-aged and elderly audience, with commercials touting denture deodorants, laxatives, and home health-care remedies, the show would not be that appealing to younger viewers. The few young people who might watch it would bring the mean viewing age below what would be considered typical, so that the *median* age would more truly represent a typical population value in this case.

 The median is the most realistic measure of location for data having skewed distributions.

BIMODAL DISTRIBUTIONS

The mode has been defined as the most frequently occurring value. But if two or more values occur with equal or nearly equal frequency, then there are two or more modes. A variable that has two modes is said to have a **bimodal distribution**.

The presence of more than one mode has a special significance in statistical analysis: It indicates potential trouble. Comparing or drawing conclusions about bimodal populations can be dangerous because they usually arise when some non-homogeneous factor is present. Figure 3-4(a) presents the frequency curve of heights of adult patients admitted to a large hospital during the past year. The curve is bimodal, with the two modes occuring at 5′3″ and 5′10″. In this case, the nonhomogeneous factor is sex: The two modes result from the fact that an equal number of male and female patients have been measured. It would be more meaningful to separate the population into male and female populations and analyze the two more homogeneous populations separately.

To illustrate the potential difficulty, suppose we wish to compare patient heights in the year before the new maternity ward opened to those in the current year. The proportion of female patients would be higher in the second year, so the overall mean height would be less. The patients would not have become shorter, as a cursory analysis might indicate. By separately comparing the two female populations, the mean heights would not noticeably change over the two-year period.

Figure 3-4(b) shows another distribution having a double-humped frequency curve. This curve represents the high school grade point average of students at a university. Humps in frequency occur at 2.8 and 3.5. Although the mode is 3.5, we would still classify this as a bimodal population, because a nonhomogeneous factor influences the grades of the high school students. A relatively small group of disadvantaged students is to be given remedial work. Although these remedial students are comparatively ill-prepared now, their *college* grade point averages are not expected to differ substantially from those of the other students.

EXERCISES

3-12 A sample audit of Gizmo Corporation records showed the following numbers of plant accidents per month.

$$0 \quad 1 \quad 3 \quad 4 \quad 5 \quad 2 \quad 2 \quad 6 \quad 7 \quad 2 \quad 0 \quad 1$$

Calculate the (a) mean, (b) median, and (c) mode.

(a)

(b)

FIGURE 3-4 Illustrations of bimodal frequency distributions.

3-13 Unified Airways provided the following distances for foreign flights.

2139	2128	2507	2350	2311
2276	2161	2750	2002	1863
2427	2011	2677	2347	2188
2227	1927	2006	1921	3192
2129	3245	2084	2096	2079
2442	2050	2230	2097	2490
2076	2061	2595	1960	2980
1988	2111	1889	2324	1750
2255	2535	2654	2121	2272
1976	1974	2035	1990	2840

Calculate the median.

3-14 Sample family installment debts are provided below.

$2,032	$ 232	$ 493	$5,555
597	4,893	4,432	4,444
203	796	978	329
97	852	1,427	972

3,333	1,712	2,121	438
1,212	1,940	5,067	705
5,769	1,843	4,337	3,976
2,347	3,525	5,213	3,034
2,137	3,414	4,896	5,035
2,049	4,327	2,172	4,222

Calculate the median.

3-15 A statistics instructor gives four exams of equal weight. From the scores on these, she will determine a single central score value for each student. Suppose that she lets each student decide *in advance of the first test* whether his or her particular grade will be determined by a mean or by a median test score.

(a) Would you request the mean or the median? Why?

(b) For each of the following hypothetical sets of test scores, indicate whether the mean or the median would provide the greatest central value.

(1)	(2)	(3)	(4)
95	80	80	60
60	50	75	80
75	75	65	90
65	70	60	90

3-16 For each of the following situations, indicate a possible source of non-homogeneity in the data, and discuss why the population should or should not be split to better serve the purposes of the statistical study.

(a) Six months ago, a new driver safety program was initiated by a state's highway patrol. For the past year, the governor's office has maintained records of the number of weekly accidents. A study is being made to evaluate highway construction standards.

(b) An appliance manufacturer wishes to make a powerful home vacuum cleaner. To be most effective, the cleaner must be heavier than the normal weight of such an appliance. A representative group of employees, including men and women, is used to obtain data on how much weight a person can carry up a flight of stairs without excessive fatigue. These data will be used to set a maximum vacuum cleaner weight.

(c) An automobile manufacturer has obtained data on the total worker-hours required to assemble each car at two identically equipped plants of the same size. Each plant produces the models of cars ordered by dealers in its geographical region. These data will be used to establish production standards for each car model.

3-17 Combine the Unified Airways data for domestic flight distances (Exercise 3-7) and foreign flight distances (Exercise 3-13).

(a) Construct a table for the frequency distribution that has successive class intervals of equal width. Use 400.0–under 500.0 miles as the first interval.

(b) Plot a histogram using your answer to (a).

(c) What common form does the shape of your histogram suggest? Do you think it is meaningful to combine the distance data for domestic and foreign flights?

3-18 *Computer exercise.* Refer to the sample levels of precipitation given in Exercise 2-2. Calculate the median.

3-19 *Computer exercise.* Refer to the sample temperatures given in Exercise 2-5. Calculate the median.

3-3 PERCENTILES, FRACTILES, AND QUARTILES

50th percentile
= .5 fractile

Another broad category of statistical measures expresses frequency information for quantitative populations. The most common is the **percentile**, which is that value below which a stated percentage of the observations lie. For example, an instructor might find that 32 out of 40 students earned less than 150 points on a final examination. The percentage of such scores is $(32/40) \times 100 = 80$, and 150 points is the 80th percentile. If 165 points is the 90th percentile, then 90% of the 40 test scores—$(.90 \times 40 = 36$ of them)—fell below 165.

Another way of conveying the same information is in terms of the **fractile**, which is that point below which a stated fraction of the values lie. Thus, 150 points is the .80-fractile, while 165 is the .90-fractile.

Earlier in this chapter you encountered one percentile in another context. *The median is the same quantity as the 50th percentile or the .50-fractile.*

There are three special percentiles. These are the **quartiles**, which divide the data into four groups of equal size. The **first quartile** is the same as the 25th percentile and the .25-fractile. The **second quartile** is the 50th percentile, while the **third quartile** equals the 75th percentile. (There is no need for a "fourth" quartile.)

EXAMPLE: YOUR CLASS STANDING

When you graduate, your school might classify your relative percentile position in terms of your grade point average (GPA). The following data apply to a particular class having exactly 800 graduates.

GPA	Percentile
2.3	25
2.5	50
3.1	75
3.5	90
3.7	95
3.9	99

We will determine the quartiles.

SOLUTION: The first quartile is 2.3; 25% of the graduates, or $.25 \times 800 = 200$ students, earned a grade point average lower than 2.3. The second quartile is 2.5, the 50th percentile; $.50 \times 800 = 400$ students earned GPAs of less than 2.5. The third quartile (also the 75th percentile) is 3.1; $.75 \times 800 = 600$ students earned GPAs below 3.1. There are 200 GPAs in each of the following groups: below the first quartile (2.3); at or above the first quartile but below the second (2.5); at or above the second quartile but below the third (3.1); and at or above the third quartile.

FINDING PERCENTILES FROM UNGROUPED DATA

When all raw data are available, the percentiles may be established by ranking the values from lowest to highest. For example, consider the ten sample completion times (seconds) for cash withdrawal transactions obtained from an automatic teller machine.

	$Q_{.10}$		$Q_{.25}$					$Q_{.75}$		
	17.2		21.25					37.25		
Value	17	19	22	28	32	33	34	37	38	39
Position	1	2	3	4	5	6	7	8	9	10
	1.1		2.75					8.25		
	$d(n+1)$		$d(n+1)$					$d(n+1)$		

The 10th percentile is any point above 17 seconds but not exceeding 19 seconds. We might use 17.5, 18.0, or 18.99 as the 10th percentile. The 20th percentile may be any point greater than 19 seconds but less than 22 seconds.

There is considerable leeway in selecting percentiles directly from raw data. To avoid ambiguity, we adopt the following procedure.

PROCEDURE FOR FINDING PERCENTILES FROM RAW DATA

1. **Sort the raw data in ascending order.** Denote X_1 as the first sorted value, X_2 as the second, and so on, up to X_n, with n being the total number of observations. The subscripts represent the *position* of the data value.

2. **Establish the decimal equivalent.** It is convenient to use the letter d to denote the decimal equivalent of the desired percentage point. This procedure is limited to $d \geq 1/n$ with the limitation that $d \leq (n-1)/n$. Using that value as a subscript, we will denote Q_d as the corresponding percentile value to be found.

3. **Find the relative position of the desired percentile.** This may be expressed as

$$d \times (n+1)$$

Then, let k be the *largest integer* such that

$$k \leq d(n+1)$$

The desired percentile will lie between X_k and X_{k+1}.

4. **Calculate the percentile value.** The following expression applies.

$$Q_d = X_k + [d(n+1) - k](X_{k+1} - X_k)$$

We will illustrate the procedure using the $n = 10$ sample ATM service completion times. The 10th percentile is calculated using $d = .10$. The relative position of $Q_{.10}$ is

$$.10 \times (10 + 1) = 1.1$$

3-3 PERCENTILES, FRACTILES, AND QUARTILES

The largest integer not exceeding 1.1 is 1, so that using $k = 1$, we have

$$X_k = X_1 = 17 \quad \text{and} \quad X_{k+1} = X_2 = 19 \text{ seconds}$$

Using these values we calculate

$$Q_{.10} = 17 + [.1(10 + 1) - 1](19 - 17)$$
$$= 17.2 \text{ seconds}$$

Now, consider the 25th percentile for the same data. Using $d = .25$, we calculate

$$.25 \times (10 + 1) = 2.75$$

so that $k = 2$, and $Q_{.25}$ will lie between positions 2 and 3. Using

$$X_k = X_2 = 19 \quad \text{and} \quad X_{k+1} = X_3 = 22 \text{ seconds}$$

we calculate

$$Q_{.25} = 19 + [.25(10 + 1) - 2](22 - 19)$$
$$= 21.25 \text{ seconds}$$

It is easy to see that the 75th percentile involves $k = 8$ and, thus, lies between positions 8 and 9. Using the respective observation values, we obtain

$$Q_{.75} = 37 + [.75(10 + 1) - 8](38 - 37)$$
$$= 37.25 \text{ seconds}$$

The median, the 50th percentile, lies between positions 5 and 6.

$$m = \text{Median} = Q_{.50} = 32 + [.50(10 + 1) - 5](33 - 32) = 32.50$$

We discovered earlier that it can be a time consuming task to sort a large set of raw data by hand. It may be easier to construct an ordered stem-and-leaf plot. Referring to the sample temperatures given in Section 3-1, we can use the following plot obtained earlier.

We can count the positions for any of the $n = 86$ observations. The 95th percentile has relative position $.95(86 + 1) = 82.65$, so that with $k = 82$, $Q_{.95}$ lies above the 82nd observation by .65 times the distance between that point and the $(k + 1)$st = 83rd observation, at

$$Q_{.95} = X_{82} + [82.65 - 82](X_{83} - X_{82})$$
$$= 77 + .65(77 - 77) = 77 \text{ degrees}$$

The 25th percentile has relative position $.25(86 + 1) = 21.75$ and lies between the 21st and 22nd observations. Both equal 57 degrees, thus the desired percentile must be the same value, and $Q_{.25} = 57$. Likewise, the 75th percentile has relative position $.75(86 + 1) = 65.25$ and lies between the 65th and 66th observations. Both positions correspond to 68 degrees, and $Q_{.75} = 68$.

FINDING PERCENTILES WITH A COMPUTER

Once data have been entered into a computer, some of the percentiles can be provided. The computer printout in Figure 3-1 reports 57 as the first quartile and 68 as the third quartile. Other percentiles can be obtained by hand computations using either a stem-and-leaf plot or a frequency distribution constructed by the computer.

FINDING PERCENTILES FROM GROUPED DATA

When the raw data are unavailable or have already been grouped into a frequency distribution, the procedure may be modified slightly to account for the missing details.

Instead of positioning individual observations, we position groups according to the *cumulative* frequencies for class intervals. We denote k as the greatest cumulative class frequency $\leq d(n + 1)$, and represent the *upper limit* of the corresponding interval as X_k. The next highest interval will have cumulative frequency h, and the upper limit will be designated as X_h. The following expression then is used to find the

PERCENTILE COMPUTED WITH GROUPED DATA

$$Q_d = X_k + [d(n + 1) - k]\left(\frac{X_h - X_k}{h - k}\right)$$

so that Q_d results from a simple linear interpolation between neighboring class limits.

(Should $d(n + 1)$ be smaller than the first cumulative class frequency, the percentile will lie within the first interval. Then $k = 0$ and for $X_k = X_0$ we use the lower limit of the first class interval. The class frequency of that same interval serves as the value for h, with X_h equal to the upper limit of the first interval. Should Q_d fall in the last class interval, h will equal the cumulative frequency for that interval and X_h will equal the upper limit.)

To illustrate, consider the following example.

EXAMPLE: FUEL CONSUMPTION DATA

The following fuel consumption data originally appeared in Table 3-2. The cumulative frequencies are listed below. We will find the 25th, 90th, and 50th percentiles.

Class Interval	Frequency	Cumulative Frequency
14.0–under 16.0	9	9
16.0–under 18.0	13	22
18.0–under 20.0	24	46
20.0–under 22.0	38	84
22.0–under 24.0	16	100
	$n = \overline{100}$	

SOLUTION: The 25th percentile has relative position $.25(100 + 1) = 25.25$. The greatest cumulative frequency not exceeding 25.25 is 22 for the second interval, so that $k = 22$, $Q_{.25}$ will fall in the subsequent (third) interval, the cumulative frequency of which is $h = 46$. This percentile is between the limits $X_{22} = 18.0$ and $X_{30} = 20.0$. We calculate

$$Q_{.25} = 18.0 + [25.25 - 22]\left(\frac{20.0 - 18.0}{46 - 22}\right)$$

$$= 18.27 \text{ mpg}$$

The 90th percentile has relative postion $.90(100 + 1) = 90.9$, so that $k = 84$, $h = 100$, and

$$Q_{.90} = X_{84} + [90.9 - 84]\left(\frac{X_{100} - X_{84}}{100 - 84}\right)$$

$$= 22.0 + 6.9\left(\frac{24.0 - 22.0}{16}\right)$$

$$= 22.86 \text{ mpg}$$

The 50th percentile or *median* $Q_{.50}$ is located at position $.50(100 + 1) = 50.5$. Using $k = 46$ and $h = 84$, we have

$$m = \text{Median} = Q_{.50} = 20.0 + [50.5 - 46]\left(\frac{22.0 - 20.0}{84 - 46}\right)$$

$$= 20.24 \text{ mpg}$$

FINDING PERCENTILES GRAPHICALLY

If the cumulative frequency distribution has already been plotted, percentiles may be read directly from the graph. This is fast and avoids the need for computation.

Figure 3-5 shows the cumulative frequency ogive for the fuel consumption data. The vertical axis now expresses cumulative *relative* frequencies. The 25th percentile is the horizontal coordinate of that point on the curve at height .25.

$$Q_{.25} = 18.3 \text{ mpg}$$

The value must agree with the computed value for $Q_{.25}$ (found earlier to be 18.27 mpg), but the graphical solution will ordinarily be less precise. Likewise, the 75th percentile is the horizontal coordinate of that point on the curve at height .75.

$$Q_{.75} = 21.6 \text{ mpg}$$

EXERCISES

3-20 The following numbers of accounting courses were taken by a sample of business students.

5	2	0	1	1	4	7	2	2	3
9	7	0	2	2	4	8	8	1	3

Determine the (a) 10th, (b) 25th, (c) 50th, (d) 75th, and (e) 90th percentiles.

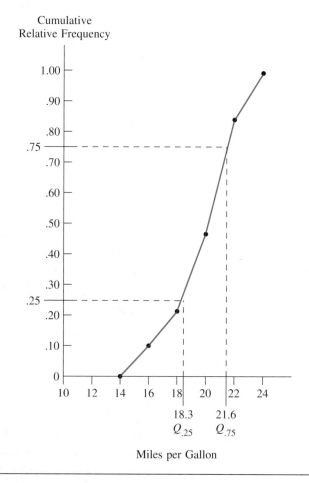

FIGURE 3-5 Fuel consumption percentiles (fractiles) read from the cumulative relative frequency ogive.

3-21 The following GMAT scores were obtained for a sample of Slippery Rock graduates.

588   462   718   725   664   395   382   455   510   584   602   644

Determine the (a) 10th, (b) 25th, (c) 50th, (d) 75th, and (e) 90th percentiles.

3-22 Refer to your answers to Exercise 2-2.
  (a) Construct an ordered stem-and-leaf plot for the sample levels of precipitation.
  (b) Determine the (1) 10th, (2) 25th, (3) 50th, (4) 75th, and (5) 90th percentiles.

3-23 Refer to your answers to Exercise 2-5.
  (a) Construct an ordered stem-and-leaf plot for the sample temperatures.
  (b) Determine the (1) 10th, (2) 25th, (3) 50th, (4) 75th, and (5) 90th percentiles.

3-24 The following cumulative frequency distribution has been obtained for the concentrations of pollutants found in air samples above Smogville.

Concentration (parts/million)	Cumulative Frequency
0–under 1	5
1–under 2	12
2–under 3	25
3–under 4	37
4–under 5	50
5–under 6	67
6–under 7	75
7–under 8	84
8–under 9	89
9–under 10	90
10–under 11	95
11–under 12	98
12–under 13	100

Determine the following values.
  (a) .90 fractile   (c) 1st quartile   (e) median
  (b) 37th percentile   (d) 3rd quartile

3-25 Use the cumulative relative frequency distribution given in Exercise 2-18 for the number of shares of stock. Determine the following values.
  (a) 36th percentile   (c) .97 fractile
  (b) .90 fractile   (d) 81st percentile

3-26 The following cumulative relative frequency distribution has been obtained for the GMAT during a base period.

Test Score	Cumulative Relative Frequency
200–below 250	.01
250–below 300	.03
300–below 350	.09
350–below 400	.19

Test Score	Cumulative Relative Frequency
400–below 450	.36
450–below 500	.55
500–below 550	.74
550–below 600	.88
600–below 650	.96
650–below 700	.99
700–below 750	1.00

(a) On graph paper, plot the ogive.
(b) Assuming that intermediate values may be read to a good approximation from your graph, determine the .25, .50, and .75 fractiles.

3-4 MEASURING VARIABILITY

We have encountered several measures of central tendency, each of which provides a valuable summary of statistical data. Means or medians will often serve as the basis for comparing two or more populations. But other summary measures can be useful for making comparisons. Next in importance to central tendency are **measures of variability**, which express the extent to which observed values differ from each other.

Statistical terminology includes **dispersion** as a synonym for variability. The concepts are illustrated by the following pairs.

Lower Variability Observations	Higher Variability Observations
.75″ .84″ .63″ .79″ .72″ (diameters of hummingbird eggs)	6.4″ 7.1″ 8.2″ 7.5″ 6.8″ (diameters of ostrich eggs)
2.3 .5 2.0 3.2 1.8 2.8 1.6 (minutes waiting, McDonald's)	15 25 34 54 2 48 (minutes before seating, Le Bistro)
11.2 13.1 8.9 10.2 10.3 7.1 (earnings per share—oils)	55 33 − 62 108 226 49 − 28 (earnings per share—high tech.)
680 650 720 700 750 690 710 670 (GMAT scores, Harvard MBAs)	350 750 460 640 530 480 510 610 (GMAT scores, seniors)

A quick comparison of the raw data values on the left with those in the same row on the right easily establishes that the second set of values are more spread out, exhibiting greater variability. When observations are represented by frequency distributions, that sample or population having higher variability will involve either more class intervals or wider class widths.

IMPORTANCE OF VARIABILITY

The role of variability is illustrated in Figure 3-6, where the frequency curves for the net earnings of dairies and ranches are compared. Although both populations have the same medians, ranch earnings exhibit *greater variability* than dairy incomes. Although both forms of agriculture involve cattle and must meet comparable feed requirements, dairy farmers are blessed with stable milk prices (often

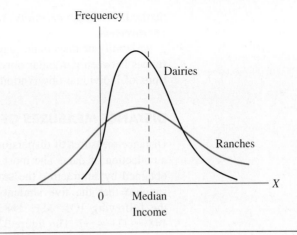

FIGURE 3-6 Frequency curves for the earnings of dairies and ranches.

due to regulation), whereas ranchers must sell their beef at the volatile market price. The greater variability in income makes ranching a riskier venture than owning a dairy, even though the earnings of both enterprises have identical central tendencies (equal medians). Here, statistical variability might help the new agricultural college graduate to choose between ranching or dairy farming.

Figure 3-7 shows the sample frequency distributions for the completion times of two chemical processes. Method B appears to be cheaper on the average. But method A would make planning easier because its completion times are less varied. If the final product is perishable or must be made to customer order, so that it can be stored in quantity for very long, then method A might be the superior

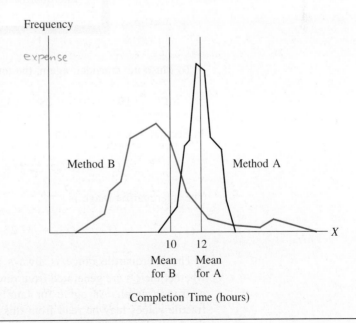

FIGURE 3-7 Frequency distributions for the completion times of two chemical processes.

method. *In a great many situations, reduction in variability is itself an improvement.*

Variability or dispersion may be measured in two basic ways: in terms of **distances** between particular observation values, or in terms of the **average deviations** of individual observations about the central value.

DISTANCE MEASURES OF DISPERSION

Distance measures of dispersion are popular when the only purpose is to describe a collection of data. The most common distance measure is the **range**, which is obtained by subtracting the smallest observation from the largest. For example, suppose that the five students in a college accounting honors program have the following IQs: 111, 118, 126, 137, 148. The range of these values is $148 - 111 = 37$. The figure 37 represents the total spread in these observations. The range provides a concise summary of the total variation in a sample or a population, but its major disadvantage as a useful measure is that it ignores all except the two most extreme observations. These two numbers may be untypical values, even among the higher and lower observations.

Other distance measures ignore the most extreme observations. These are **interfractile ranges**, which express the differences between two fractiles.

THE INTERQUARTILE RANGE

A useful measure of dispersion is the **interquartile range**. This range represents *the middle 50% of the observations.* It is computed by taking the difference between the third quartile ($Q_{.75}$) and the first quartile ($Q_{.25}$).

$$\text{Interquartile range} = Q_{.75} - Q_{.25}$$

To illustrate, consider, again, the ten sample ATM transaction times (seconds).

$$17 \quad 19 \quad 22 \quad 28 \quad 32 \quad 33 \quad 34 \quad 37 \quad 38 \quad 39$$

In Section 3-3, we obtained

$$Q_{.25} = 21.25 \qquad Q_{.50} = 32.50 \qquad Q_{.75} = 37.25$$

The interquartile range is

$$Q_{.75} - Q_{.25} = 37.25 - 21.25 = 16.00 \text{ seconds}$$

The interquartile range is always computed in the same way, regardless of whether the Qs are generated from raw data, from grouped data, with a computer, or from a graph. An ogive for family income is illustrated in Figure 3-8. The fractile values may be read from this graph. The first quartile is $7,900 and the third quartile is $18,100, so that the interquartile range is $18,100 - $7,900 = $10,200.

Fraction of Population
Having Income
below X

FIGURE 3-8 Cumulative relative frequency distribution for family income.

Other interfractile ranges, such as those representing the middle 90% or 99% of the observation values, may be used but seldom are.

STATISTICS AROUND US

Doctors' Incomes vs. Teachers' Salaries

The earnings of doctors in Kent County have a first quartile of $55,000 and a third quartile of $135,000, so that the interquartile range is

$$\$135,000 - 55,000 = \$80,000$$

The salaries of teachers in the same county have a first quartile of $13,500 and a third quartile of $22,000. The interquartile range is

$$\$22,000 - 13,500 = \$8,500$$

This means that the earnings of doctors are nearly 10 times as varied as teachers' salaries.

THE BOX PLOT AND QUARTILES

The range and interquartile range may be combined in a box plot. Figure 3-9 shows the box plot for the ATM transaction times. A line segment starts at the minimum observed level and ends at the maximum value. The box begins at the first quartile, ends at the third quartile, and is divided at the median. The overall length of the plot gives the range, while the length of the box provides the interquartile range.

Box plots can be useful when comparing data groups. Figure 3-10 shows box plots for successive samples of task completion times obtained from a worker undergoing training. Notice that as the worker gains mastery of the task, the task is completed faster and with less variability. This is demonstrated by progressively shorter plots and boxes.

MEASURES OF AVERAGE DEVIATION

The main disadvantage of the distance measures of dispersion is that they do not consider every observation. To include all observations, we can calculate how much each one deviates from the central value and then combine these deviations by averaging. The deviation most commonly considered is the difference between the observed value and the mean.

$$X - \bar{X}$$

Averaging the deviation values results in 0. For example, consider the five values 1, 2, 3, 4, and 5. Subtracting 3 (the mean) from each number, we obtain deviations of -2, -1, 0, 1, and 2. These add up to 0, so the average deviation is 0. We might avoid this difficulty by ignoring the minus signs. We could average the **absolute values** of each deviation (2, 1, 0, 1, and 2) and obtain the **mean absolute deviation** 1.2, which reflects every observation. But because it is mathematically diffcult to work with absolute values, two other measures of dispersion are more commonly used.

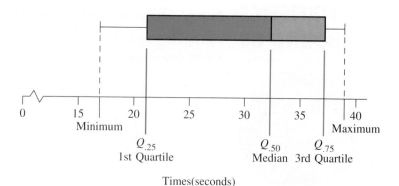

FIGURE 3-9 Box plot for sample ATM transaction times.

FIGURE 3-10 Successive sample box plots for task completion time by a trainee.

THE VARIANCE

The most important measure of variability is found by averaging the **squares** of the individual deviations; the resulting value is the **mean of the squared deviations**. Performing this calculation on the IQs for the five accounting students cited earlier, the mean value is

$$\bar{X} = \frac{111 + 118 + 126 + 137 + 148}{5} = 128$$

The deviations from the mean value are

$$111 - 128 = -17$$
$$118 - 128 = -10$$
$$126 - 128 = -2$$
$$137 - 128 = 9$$
$$148 - 128 = 20$$

and the mean of the squared deviations is

$$\frac{(-17)^2 + (-10)^2 + (-2)^2 + (9)^2 + (20)^2}{5 - 1} = \frac{289 + 100 + 4 + 81 + 400}{5 - 1}$$

$$= \frac{874}{4} = 218.5$$

The measure of variability obtained in this manner is referred to as the **variance**. In averaging the squared deviations, the divisor is reduced by one observation, so that the above calculation uses $5 - 1 = 4$ instead of 5. (This is for technical reasons to be discussed in Chapter 8.) The following expression is used to calculate the

VARIANCE

$$s^2 = \frac{\sum (X - \bar{X})^2}{n - 1}$$

THE SAMPLE AND POPULATION VARIANCE

As with the mean, a distinction is made between the computed level for s^2, which when computed from sample data is called the **sample variance**, and the **population variance** (not ordinarily computed). The population variance is represented symbolically as σ. (The symbol σ is the lowercase Greek **sigma**, and σ^2 is called "sigma squared.")

Two practical difficulties are associated with the use of the variance. First, the variance is usually a very large number compared to the number of observations themselves. Thus, if the observations are largely in the thousands, the variance is often in the millions. Second, the variance is not expressed in the same units as the observations. In the previous example, the variance is 218.5 *squared* IQ points. This is because the deviations, measured in IQ points, have all been squared. The variance for heights, originally measured in feet, will therefore be expressed in square feet. The variance for fuel consumption will be in squared miles per gallon.

In spite of these difficulties, the mathematical properties of the variance make it extremely important in statistical theory. Furthermore, the difficulties may be overcome simply by working with the square root of the variance, called the **standard deviation.**

THE STANDARD DEVIATION

The square root of the variance in IQ levels is

$$\sqrt{218.5} = 14.78$$

which yields the standard deviation in IQ level. The standard deviation is expressed in the same units as the observations themselves; the value 14.78 is a point on the same numerical scale.

The **standard deviation** is represented by the letter s without its exponent 2. The following expression may be used to calculate the

STANDARD DEVIATION

$$s = \sqrt{\frac{\sum (X - \bar{X})^2}{n - 1}}$$

Note that both sides of the equation simply contain the square root of the expression for the variance. Both the variance and the standard deviation provide the same information; one can always be obtained from the other. The standard deviation is a practical descriptive measure of dispersion, whereas the variance is generally used in developing statistical theory.

The standard deviation is computed in Table 3-3 for a sample of $n = 5$ heights.

USING A COMPUTER TO CALCULATE THE STANDARD DEVIATION

When the number of observations is large, it can be an especially tedious task to compute s. By hand or using a calculator it may easily take an hour to find s and s^2 for the temperature data in Table 3-1. As with the statistical measures encountered earlier, software packages will compute the standard deviation automatically, reporting its value with the other summary statistics. The computer-generated output in Figure 3-1 provides $s = 8.598$ degrees as the standard deviation for the temperatures. (Although the variance is not listed, the value can be computed quickly by hand by squaring s.)

TABLE 3-3 Calculation of Standard Deviation for Heights

Height (inches) X	Deviation $X - \bar{X}$	Squared Deviation $(X - \bar{X})^2$
66	$66 - 70 = -4$	16
73	$73 - 70 = 3$	9
68	$68 - 70 = -2$	4
69	$69 - 70 = -1$	1
74	$74 - 70 = 4$	16
Totals 350	0	46

$$\bar{X} = \frac{\sum X}{n} = \frac{350}{5} = 70 \text{ inches}$$

$$s = \sqrt{\frac{\sum (X - \bar{X})^2}{n - 1}} = \sqrt{\frac{46}{5 - 1}}$$

$$= \sqrt{\frac{46}{4}} = \sqrt{11.5} = 3.391 \text{ inches}$$

SHORTCUT CALCULATIONS FOR THE VARIANCE AND STANDARD DEVIATION

The standard deviation may be calculated from individual values with a mathematically equivalent equation that is usually simpler to use.

SHORTCUT CALCULATIONS

$$s^2 = \frac{\sum X^2 - n\bar{X}^2}{n-1} \qquad \text{for variance}$$

$$s = \sqrt{\frac{\sum X^2 - n\bar{X}^2}{n-1}} \qquad \text{for standard deviation}$$

The use of this formula for the standard deviation is illustrated in the following example. The shortcut procedure is recommended whenever s is computed by hand or with a calculator.

EXAMPLE: FIRST-YEAR EARNINGS OF MARKETING AND ACCOUNTING MAJORS
A university placement director collected sample data giving first-year earnings of marketing and accounting majors. The $n = 12$ marketing majors' earnings (in thousands of dollars) are:

18.5   12.0   17.0   22.5   31.4   10.2
25.6   19.2   17.6   17.3   22.2   13.3

The $n = 9$ accounting majors' earnings are:

18.5   20.1   19.4   17.3   21.0   20.5   20.2   19.0   18.6

SOLUTION: It is easiest to arrange the data in *columns*. The following apply for the marketing majors.

Earnings (thousands of dollars) X	Deviation $(X - \bar{X})$	Squared Deviation $(X - \bar{X})^2$
18.5	− .4	.16
12.0	− 6.9	47.61
17.0	− 1.9	3.61
22.5	3.6	12.96
31.4	12.5	156.25
10.2	− 8.7	75.69
25.6	6.7	44.89
19.2	.3	.09
17.6	− 1.3	1.69
17.3	− 1.6	2.56
22.2	3.3	10.89
13.3	− 5.6	31.36
226.8		387.76

The mean and standard deviation for marketing majors are

$$\bar{X} = \frac{\sum X}{n} = \frac{226.8}{12} = 18.9 \qquad s = \sqrt{\frac{\sum (X - \bar{X})^2}{n - 1}} = \sqrt{\frac{387.76}{12 - 1}} = 5.94$$

The following data and calculations apply for the accounting majors. (Here the standard deviation is computed using the shortcut expression.)

Earnings (thousands of dollars)	
X	X^2
18.5	342.25
20.1	404.01
19.4	376.36
17.3	299.29
21.0	441.00
20.5	420.25
20.2	408.04
19.0	361.00
18.6	345.96
174.6	3,398.16

The mean and standard deviation for accounting majors are

$$\bar{X} = \frac{\sum X}{n} = \frac{174.6}{9} = 19.4$$

$$s = \sqrt{\frac{\sum X^2 - n\bar{X}^2}{n - 1}} = \sqrt{\frac{3,398.16 - 9(19.4)^2}{9 - 1}} = 1.17$$

Notice that the sample earnings for the accounting majors involve the higher mean. However, the standard deviation of earnings for marketing majors is substantially greater, reflecting higher variability in that sample. (This might be explained by a substantial number of commission sales positions held by the persons in that sample group.)

Just as we calculated the mean from the frequency distribution in Section 3-1, we can use grouped data to calculate the variance and the standard deviation. We use the following procedure for the

GROUPED DATA CALCULATIONS

$$s^2 = \frac{\sum fX^2 - n\bar{X}^2}{n-1} \qquad \text{for variance}$$

$$s = \sqrt{\frac{\sum fX^2 - n\bar{X}^2}{n-1}} \qquad \text{for standard deviation}$$

The grouped data computations for the standard deviation are illustrated in Table 3-4, using the earlier fuel consumption data. We find that $s = 2.34$ miles per gallon.

As in the case of calculating the mean from grouped data, only an *approximate* value for the standard deviation can be obtained using this procedure. For most purposes, the approximate value is close enough to the true value that would be calculated directly from the raw data. In making the grouped data approximation, some statisticians prefer to use the following mathematically equivalent expressions

$$s^2 = \frac{\sum f(X - \bar{X})^2}{n-1} \qquad s = \sqrt{\frac{\sum f(X - \bar{X})^2}{n-1}}$$

A PRACTICAL USE FOR THE STANDARD DEVIATION

The standard deviation is a parameter that, when combined with statistical techniques, provides a great deal of information. When the population has a special frequency distribution called the normal curve, we can find the percentage of

TABLE 3-4 Calculation of Standard Deviation with Grouped Fuel Consumption Data

(1) Fuel Consumption (miles per gallon)	(2) Number of Cars f	(3) Class Interval Midpoint X	(4) X(f/n)	(5) X²	(6) fX²
14.0—under 16.0	9	15	1.35	225	2,025
16.0–under 18.0	13	17	2.21	289	3,757
18.0–under 20.0	24	19	4.56	361	8,664
20.0–under 22.0	38	21	7.98	441	16,758
22.0–under 24.0	16	23	3.68	529	8,464
Totals	100		19.78		39,668

$$\bar{X} = \sum X(f/n) = 19.78 \text{ miles per gallon}$$

$$s = \sqrt{\frac{\sum fX^2 - n\bar{X}^2}{n-1}} = \sqrt{\frac{39{,}668 - 100(19.78)^2}{99}}$$

$$= \sqrt{5.4865} = 2.34 \text{ miles per gallon}$$

observations falling within distances of one, two, or three standard deviations from the mean. About 68% of all observations lie within the region $\mu \pm 1\sigma$. For example, suppose a group of men have a mean height of $\mu = 5'9''$ and a standard deviation of $\sigma = 3''$. If these heights constitute a normal distribution, then 68% of all men will be between $\mu - \sigma = 5'6''$ and $\mu + \sigma = 6'0''$ tall. Furthermore, about 95.5% of the population will lie within $\mu \pm 2\sigma$, and 99.7% will fall within $\mu \pm 3\sigma$.

The normal curve is described mathematically in terms of only two parameters, μ and σ. Thus, for populations characterized by this curve, we can construct a close representation of the entire frequency distribution simply by knowing the mean and the standard deviation. We will discuss this more thoroughly in Chapter 7.

CHEBYSHEV'S THEOREM

A theoretical result called Chebyshev's theorem, named for the mathematician who proposed it, indicates that the standard deviation plays a key role in any population.

CHEBYSHEV'S THEOREM: The proportion of observations falling within z standard deviations of the mean is at least $1 - 1/z^2$.

This theorem says that regardless of the characteristics of the population, the proportions in the second column hold.

Number of Standard Deviation Units z	Chebyshev's Minimum Proportion of Observations within $\mu \pm z\sigma$	Normal Distribution Approximate Proportion of Observations within $\mu \pm z\sigma$
1	$1 - 1/1^2 = 0$	.68
2	$1 - 1/2^2 = .75$	.955
3	$1 - 1/3^2 = .89$	.997
4	$1 - 1/4^2 = .9375$	.9999

Since Chebyshev's theorem applies for any population, it is too general to be of much practical use. Usually a more precise determination of how many observations lie within z standard deviations of the mean can be found when the form of a population's frequency distribution is known, as we have shown for the normal curve. The practical significance of Chebyshev's theorem is that it tells us that a great deal of information is imparted by the population standard deviation.

FINDING THE PROPORTION OF OBSERVATIONS FALLING BETWEEN TWO VALUES

The above properties allow us to establish approximately how many observations fall between any two points, even when μ and σ are the only known population quantities. Any point X will lie at some distance above or below the mean μ. This distance may be expressed by the difference $X - \mu$ (a negative quantity when X is smaller than μ). When divided by σ, the separation distance may be converted into standard deviation units z.

$$z = \frac{X - \mu}{\sigma}$$

EXAMPLE: BANK TRANSACTION TIMES

Suppose that the time taken by a bank teller to cash a money order is on the average $\mu = 60$ seconds and that the standard deviation is $\sigma = 10$ seconds. What percentage of all money orders will take between 40 and 80 seconds to be cashed?

SOLUTION: The standard deviation distances separating the two limits are

$$z = \frac{40 - 60}{10} = -2 \text{ for } X = 40 \quad \text{and} \quad z = \frac{80 - 60}{10} = 2 \text{ for } X = 80$$

Chebyshev's theorem indicates that *at least* $1 - 1/z^2 = 1 - 1/2^2 = .75$, or 75%, of the transactions will take between $\mu \pm z\sigma$ seconds. Here the limits are $60 \pm 2\,(10)$ seconds, or from 40 to 80 seconds.

An even higher percentage would apply if the money-order transaction times were normally distributed. In that case, *approximately* 95.5% of all money orders would take somewhere between 40 and 80 seconds to cash. Chapter 7 shows how to find similar percentages for a variety of computed levels for z.

EXERCISES

3-27 The following earnings per share have been obtained for a sample of electronics stocks.

$-2.01 \quad .05 \quad .23 \quad .17 \quad 1.42 \quad -.53 \quad .12 \quad .48 \quad 1.10 \quad .24$

(a) Calculate the mean.
(b) Calculate the (1) variance and (2) standard deviation.

3-28 The following price-earnings ratios were obtained for a sample of penny stocks.

$$25 \quad 16 \quad 50 \quad 19 \quad 42 \quad 37$$

Calculate the (a) variance and (b) standard deviation.

3-29 The following hourly unit sales of Iceburgers have been obtained for a sample of McBurger restaurants.

$$35 \quad 47 \quad 57 \quad 16 \quad 12 \quad 33 \quad 38$$

(a) Calculate the range.
(b) Calculate the (1) variance and (2) standard deviation.
(c) Determine the (1) .25, (2) .50, and (3) .75 fractiles.
(d) Calculate the interquartile range.
(e) Construct the box plot.

3-30 For each of the following decision situations, discuss why a central value may not be a wholly adequate summary measure by itself.
(a) The temperatures actually achieved in each room of a building with standard temperature control settings are being used to determine whether the system should be modified.

(b) Balancing an automobile assembly line requires that sufficient personnel and equipment be positioned at each work station so that no one station will be excessively idle. The task completion times at each station are being used to help determine how this may be done.

(c) To plan for facilities expansion, a hospital administator requires data on the convalescent times of surgical patients.

3-31 Refer to the TryHard battery lifetime data given in Exercise 3-4. Calculate the standard deviation.

 3-32 *Computer exercise.* Refer to the Unified Airways domestic flight distance data given in Exercise 3-7. Calculate the (a) range, (b) variance, and (c) standard deviation.

3-33 The Unified Airways domestic flight distance data given in Exercise 3-7 provide a 75th percentile of 1,095 miles and 25th percentile of 746 miles. What is the interquartile range?

3-34 Refer to your answers to Exercise 3-26. Calculate the interquartile range.

3-35 Astronic Tonics replaces its spigots whenever the filling process becomes too erratic, based on the computed level of the standard deviation for the volume of ingredients. Whenever the computed value for s exceeds .08 oz, the spigots are replaced. For each of the samples in Exercise 3-3, (a) calculate the standard deviation, and (b) indicate whether the spigots should be replaced.

3-36 Refer to your answers to Exercise 3-22.
(a) Calculate the (1) range and (2) interquartile range.
(b) Construct a box plot.

3-37 Refer to your answers to Exercise 3-23.
(a) Calculate the (1) range and (2) interquartile range.
(b) Construct a box plot.

3-38 The following frequency distribution has been obtained for a sample of $n = 100$ student grade point averages (GPA).

GPA	Number of Students
0.0–under 1.0	1
1.0–under 2.0	7
2.0–under 3.0	58
3.0–under 4.0	34

Using grouped data calculations, calculate the (a) mean and (b) standard deviation.

3-39 Use Chebyshev's theorem to determine for each of the following non-normal populations the two points between which the percentage of values falling is (a) at least 75% of the population values, (b) at least 89%, and (c) at least 93.75%.

(1)	(2)	(3)	(4)
$\mu = 3''$	$\mu = \$100$	$\mu = 5$ min	$\mu = 75\%$
$\sigma = .15''$	$\sigma = \$5$	$\sigma = 1$ min	$\sigma = 10\%$

3-40 In describing the extent of quality control in her company, the president of

Gumby Rubber Company states that the mean weight of a particular tire is 40 pounds, with a standard deviation of 1 pound. She adds that about 68% of all tires weigh between 39 and 41 pounds, whereas almost all tires weigh between 37 and 43 pounds. State the assumptions on which these statements rest.

3-41 Dogpatch women's heights are normally distributed with $\mu = 5'5''$ and $\sigma = 2.2''$.

(a) Find the value of z such that percentages of the population falling within $\mu \pm z\sigma$ is (1) 68%, (2) 95.5%, (3) 99.7%, and (4) 99.99%.

(b) Determine in each case the two end points of the interval containing the specified percentage of the population values.

3-42 *Computer exercise.* Refer to the sample levels of precipitation given in Exercise 2-2. Calculate the (a) variance and (b) standard deviation.

3-43 *Computer exercise.* Refer to the sample temperatures given in Exercise 2-5. Calculate the (a) variance and (b) standard deviation.

3-5 THE PROPORTION

In describing a qualitative population, the key measure of interest is the **proportion** of observations that fall into a particular category. Like the measures we have already discussed, the population parameter is a separate entity from the sample statistic. The population parameter is referred to as the **population proportion** and is denoted by π (the lowercase Greek **pi**).* The analogous sample statistic is the **sample proportion**, which is represented by P. The following ratio is used to calculate the

PROPORTION

$$P = \frac{\text{Number of observations in category}}{n}$$

A proportion may assume various values between 0 and 1, according to the relative frequency with which the particular attribute occurs. Like the other population parameters, π is ordinarily unknown and may be estimated from the sample results. The statistical procedures for estimating π and P are analogous to those used to estimate a population mean from a sample. But the differences between these procedures are substantial enough to require parallel statistical development throughout this book.

The proportion is important in many kinds of statistical analysis. For example, it is often used as the basis for taking remedial action. An unusually high

*Statistics has its own special notation, and here π is not the 3.1416 used in geometry to express the ratio of the circumference to the diameter of a circle. Just as μ and σ, the Greek equivalents of *m* and *s*, are the first letters in the words *mean* and *standard deviation*, π, the Greek *p*, is the first letter in the word *proportion*.

proportion of sales returns will be singled out as a managerial problem. A machine that produces a large proportion of oversized or undersized items must be adjusted or repaired. The level of impurities in a drug might be expressed as a proportion; if this figure is too high, the drug cannot be used. In many elections for public office in the United States, the winner is the candidate who receives a plurality—that is, the person who receives the highest proportion of votes.

If a sample of $n = 500$ persons contains 200 men and 300 women, then the sample proportion of women is $P = 300/500 = .60$. If a machine has produced a sample of $n = 100$ parts, 5 of which are defective, then the sample proportion of defective parts would be $P = 5/100 = .05$. This same machine might actually produce defective items at a consistently higher rate than experienced in the sample, so that the population proportion of defective parts could be a different value, such as $\pi = .06$. The proportion may also be expressed as a percentage. Thus, 60% of the first sample are women, and 5% of the items in the second sample are defective.

<u>**The proportion is the only measure available for qualitative data.**</u> It indicates relatively how many observations fall into a particular category. (When the observations are attributes, such as male or female, central tendency or variability have no meaning.) The type of question answered by P or π is *how many* rather than *how big*.

Sometimes we may wish to express the proportion of observations having a collection of attributes. For example, the first list on page 35 presents the frequency distribution of the letters in a representative sample of 200 letters of ordinary English text. We may wish to find the proportion of vowels. We find that "a" occurs 16 times and that "e" occurs 26 times; the frequencies for "i," "o," and "u" are 13, 16, and 6, respectively. Thus, in 200 letters, vowels occur $16 + 26 + 13 + 16 + 6 = 77$ times. The proportion of vowels is therefore $P = 77/200 = .385$. These five letters, taken together, occur 38.5% of the time in the sample of ordinary English text.

The proportion is not limited to qualitative data. We may also use it to represent the relative frequency of a quantitative category. For example, the median is the .50 fractile; thus, the proportion of observations falling below the median is $P = .50$. Likewise, the proportion of items falling below the third quartile is $P = .75$.

EXERCISES

3-44 Refer to the personal debt data given in Exercise 3-14. Determine the proportion of families whose indebtedness lies below (a) $1,000, (b) $1,500, (c) $3,000, and (d) $5,000.

3-45 A Fair Employment Practices investigator wishes to identify discrimination against employees based on sex. The following data have been obtained for the number of men and women in management positions in five firms within the computer industry.

	Firm				
	A	B	C	D	E
Men	2,342	532	849	1,137	975
Women	156	115	57	145	139

Calculate the proportion of women managers in each firm. Assuming the investigator will study more thoroughly the firm with the lowest proportion of women managers, which firm would be selected?

3-46 In each of the following situations, discuss whether a mean, a proportion, or both would be an appropriate parameter on which to base decisions.

(a) A garment manufacturer wishes to ship dresses of the highest quality. Many things can cause a dress to be defective, including incorrect sizing, improper seams, creases, and missing stitches.

(b) The Federal Trade Commission requires that the weights of ingredients in packaged goods be indicated on the label. A soap manufacturer wishes to comply. Underweight production batches (populations) are reprocessed rather than shipped. For the sake of efficiency, a large number of packages (elementary units) are weighed simultaneously, and the weight of the packaging material is subtracted to obtain the weight of the ingredients.

(c) A drug maker is testing a new food supplement believed to reduce levels of anemia. The supplement is not expected to work on all patients, but when it does, the extent to which it will reduce anemia by increasing the red corpuscle count in the blood should be measurable.

3-47 MacroSoft rejects incoming shipments of floppy disks if the proportion of inspected items found to be defective exceeds .05. For each of the following four shipments, (a) determine the proportion of defectives found, and (b) state whether MacroSoft would accept or reject the shipment.

	Shipment			
	(1)	(2)	(3)	(4)
Items inspected	100	500	600	1,000
Items defective	7	25	10	39

SUMMARY

1. How are statistical data evaluated?

Statistical data are ordinarily evaluated in terms of **summary measures**. When applicable to all possible population observations, these are referred to as **population parameters**. Summary values, however, are usually computed from sample data only, and the resulting quantities are called **sample statistics**.

2. How is central tendency measured?

With quantitative data, the **computed mean** $\bar{X}$ is the common measure of **central tendency**. It can be used to estimate the value of the **population mean** μ, a parameter not usually computed. You compute the sample mean using the expression

$$\bar{X} = \frac{\sum X}{n}$$

or, for grouped data,

$$\bar{X} = \sum X(f/n)$$

There are also two other measures of central tendency. The **median** is the point dividing the data into two groups of equal size. The **mode** is the most frequently occurring value. All three measures of central tendency are helpful in describing frequency distributions, and the mode is important in explaining a **bimodal distribution**, which arises when nonhomogeneous units are observed.

3. How are percentiles and related measures obtained and used?

Quantitative data are sometimes summarized in terms of **percentiles** and **fractiles**. Such a number is the point below which a stated percentage or proportion of the observations lie. There are three special percentiles, called **quartiles**, which divide the observations into groups of successive size, each containing 25% of the data points. The **interquartile range** is the useful summary measure that encompasses the middle 50% of values; it equals the difference between the third and first quartiles.

One very useful data summary, the **box plot**, gives a visual display of the data extremes, the range and median, all the quartiles, and the interquartile range.

4. How do we measure variability?

In addition to identifying the center of a sample or a population, statisticians are concerned with measuring its <u>variability</u>, or <u>the extent to which the observed values differ from one another</u>. The simplest measure of variability is the **range**, which expresses the difference between the greatest and the smallest observation values. Since the range provides limited information, statisticians prefer to use the **variance** as the basic measure of variability. You find the variance by computing for each observation its **deviation** from the mean, then squaring those deviations and finding their average. You would not ordinarily compute the **population variance**, represented by the symbol σ^2. Instead, you will compute the variance, which is denoted by s^2, from the following.

$$s^2 = \frac{\sum (X - \bar{X})^2}{n - 1}$$

$(x - \bar{x}) \leftarrow$ *deviation*
↓
square $(x - \bar{x})^2$
↓
Average $\frac{\sum (x - \bar{X})^2}{n - 1}$

You will find it more convenient to work with the **standard deviation**, s or σ, obtained by taking the square root of the variance.

5. How do the mean and standard deviation together provide added descriptive power?

The population mean and standard deviation provide useful summaries of the underlying frequency distribution. For normally distributed populations, the values for μ and σ completely specify the characteristics of the frequency curve.

6. How do we summarize qualitative data?

Qualitative data are summarized by a single parameter, the **population proportion**, denoted by π. This quantity is estimated by the computed **proportion** P, which is equal to the number of observations having a particular characteristic divided by the number of observations.

REAL-LIFE STATISTICAL CHALLENGE

Selecting the Automobile of Your Dreams

What do you want in a car? What type of car do your classmates want to drive? What types of cars do businesses want for their fleets?   Cars can be classified in a number of ways. Crash survivability, top speed, braking distance, and passenger comfort are just a few factors. For purposes of comparing automobiles in terms of their fuel efficiency, the U.S. Environmental Protection Agency separates cars by size. These sizes include: two-seater, minicompact, subcompact, compact, midsize, and large. In 1990, there were over two hundred models sold in the

TABLE 3-5 First Set of Car Data

Manufacturer	Model	Type	Trans-mission Type	Engine Displacement (liters)	Highway Mileage/ Gallon
Alfa-Romeo	Spider	Two-seater	M5	2.0	30
Buick	Reatta	Two-seater	L4	3.8	27
Cadillac	Allante	Two-seater	L4	4.5	22
Chevrolet	Corvette	Two-seater	L4	5.7	24
Chevrolet	Corvette	Two-seater	M6	5.7	25
Chrysler	TC/Maserati	Two-seater	M5	2.2	25
Chrysler	TC/Maserati	Two-seater	L4	3.0	24
Ferarri	Testarossa	Two-seater	M5	4.9	15
Honda	Civic CRX	Two-seater	L4	1.5	35
Honda	Civic CRX	Two-seater	M5	1.5	35
Honda	Civic CRX-HF	Two-seater	M5	1.5	52
Honda	Civic CRX	Two-seater	M5	1.6	33
Lamborghini	Countach	Two-seater	M5	5.2	10
Lotus	Lotus	Two-seater	M5	2.2	27
Maserati	Karif	Two-seater	M5	2.8	20
Maserati	Karif	Two-seater	L4	2.8	18
Maserati	Spyder	Two-seater	L4	2.8	18
Maserati	Spyder	Two-seater	M5	2.8	20
Mazda	RX-7	Two-seater	M5	1.3	24
Mazda	RX-7	Two-seater	L4	1.3	23
Mazda	Miata	Two-seater	M5	1.6	30
Mazda	RX-7	Two-seater	M5	1.3	25
Mercedes-Benz	500 SL	Two-seater	M5	5.0	21
Nissan	300ZX	Two-seater	M5	3.0	24
Nissan	300ZX	Two-seater	L4	3.0	24
Maserati	222E	Minicompact	L4	2.8	18
Maserati	222E	Minicompact	M5	2.8	20
Nissan	240SX	Minicompact	M5	2.4	27
Nissan	240SX	Minicompact	L4	2.4	25
Porsche	944-S2	Minicompact	M5	3.0	26
Porsche	911-FWD	Minicompact	M5	3.6	22
Porsche	928-S4	Minicompact	M5	5.0	19
Porsche	911-4/2	Minicompact	M5	3.6	24
Porsche	928-S4	Minicompact	A4	5.0	19
Volkswagen	Cabriolet	Minicompact	M5	1.8	32
Volkswagen	Cabriolet	Minicompact	A3	1.8	28

SOURCE: U.S. Environmental Protection Agency, 1989.

United States by a wide range of domestic and foreign manufacturers.

In the next chapter, we will review the complete list. Table 3-5 gives a shorter list made up of "sportier" vehicles. It shows the highway mileage data for 25 two-seaters and 11 minicompacts. The table shows the model, manufacturer, type of car, transmission type, engine displacement in liters, and miles per gallon in the highway test. The transmission type is either manual (M) or automatic (A or L) and can have different gear-box shift configurations (3, 4, 5, or 6 forward).

TABLE 3-6 Second Set of Car Data

Manufacturer	Model	Type	Transmission Type	Engine Displacement (liters)	Highway Mileage/ Gallon
Honda	Civic CRX-HF	Two-seater	M5	1.5	52
Honda	Civic CRX	Two-seater	M5	1.5	35
Honda	Civic CRX	Two-seater	M5	1.6	33
Volkswagen	Cabriolet	Minicompact	M5	1.8	32
Mazda	Miata	Two-seater	M5	1.6	30
Alfa-Romeo	Spider	Two-seater	M5	2.0	30
Lotus	Lotus	Two-seater	M5	2.2	27
Nissan	240SX	Minicompact	M5	2.4	27
Porsche	944-S2	Minicompact	M5	3.0	26
Mazda	RX-7	Two-seater	M5	1.3	25
Chrysler	TC/Maserati	Two-seater	M5	2.2	25
Chevrolet	Corvette	Two-seater	M6	5.7	25
Mazda	RX-7	Two-seater	M5	1.3	24
Nissan	300ZX	Two-seater	M5	3.0	24
Porsche	911-4/2	Minicompact	M5	3.6	24
Porsche	911-FWD	Minicompact	M5	3.6	22
Mercedes-Benz	500 SL	Two-seater	M5	5.0	21
Maserati	Spyder	Two-seater	M5	2.8	20
Maserati	222E	Minicompact	M5	2.8	20
Maserati	Karif	Two-seater	M5	2.8	20
Porsche	928-S4	Minicompact	M5	5.0	19
Ferarri	Testarossa	Two-seater	M5	4.9	15
Lamborghini	Countach	Two-seater	M5	5.2	10
Honda	Civic CRX	Two-seater	L4	1.5	35
Volkswagen	Cabriolet	Minicompact	A3	1.8	28
Buick	Reatta	Two-seater	L4	3.8	27
Nissan	240SX	Minicompact	L4	2.4	25
Chrysler	TC/Maserati	Two-seater	L4	3.0	24
Nissan	300ZX	Two-seater	L4	3.0	24
Chevrolet	Corvette	Two-seater	L4	5.7	24
Mazda	RX-7	Two-seater	L4	1.3	23
Cadillac	Allante	Two-seater	L4	4.5	22
Porsche	928-S4	Minicompact	A4	5.0	19
Maserati	222E	Minicompact	L4	2.8	18
Maserati	Spyder	Two-seater	L4	2.8	18
Maserati	Karif	Two-seater	L4	2.8	18

SOURCE: U.S. Environmental Protection Agency, 1989.

TABLE 3-7 First Comparison by Automobile Type—Means, Variances and Standard Deviations for Engine Displacement and Highway Mileage

Type	Number	Engine Displacement (liters)			Highway Mileage (miles per gallon)		
		$\bar{X}$	s^2	s	$\bar{X}$	s^2	s
Two-seater	25	2.92	2.15	1.47	25.24	64.86	8.05
Minicompact	11	3.11	1.23	1.11	23.64	19.85	4.46
Total	36	2.98	1.83	1.35	24.75	50.71	7.12

Table 3-6 displays the same automobile data in terms of driving ease—whether cars come equipped with a manual or automatic transmission. In the Table 3-6 list, cars are separated first by transmission type and then ordered from highest to lowest gasoline mileage. This second arrangement might provide a more meaningful set of comparisons.

Two types of comparisons may be made using summary statistics. These are computed separately for the two data arrangements in Tables 3-7 and 3-8, where the respective computed values for means, variances, and standard deviations are given.

DISCUSSION QUESTIONS

1. What conclusions can you draw from the results displayed in Tables 3-7 and 3-8?

2. What other criteria would you consider before purchasing one of these automobiles?

3. Determine the mode and median values for engine displacement and mileage for each of the categories (i.e., two-seater, minicompact, automatic, manual) and the total.

4. Have the members of your class select the car of their choice (people may select the same automobiles). Compute the mean, median, mode, and standard deviation for your class's list. Compare your results with the answers in Tables 3-7 and 3-8. What conclusions can you draw?

TABLE 3-8 Second Comparison by Transmission Type—Means, Variances and Standard Deviations for Engine Displacement and Highway Mileage

Type	Number	Engine Displacement (liters)			Highway Mileage (miles per gallon)		
		$\bar{X}$	s^2	s	$\bar{X}$	s^2	s
Manual	23	2.90	1.94	1.39	25.48	66.35	8.15
Automatic	13	3.11	1.76	1.33	23.46	23.44	4.84
Total	36	2.98	1.83	1.35	24.75	50.71	7.12

REVIEW EXERCISES

3-48 The following cumulative relative frequency distribution has been obtained for the proportions of weed seed found in boxes of Sod Seeder mixtures.

Proportion of Weed Seed	Cumulative Relative Frequency
.00—under .01	.05
.01—under .02	.12
.02—under .03	.25
.03—under .04	.37
.04—under .05	.50
.05—under .06	.67
.06—under .07	.75
.07—under .08	.84
.08—under .09	.89
.09—under .10	.90
.10—under .11	.95
.11—under .12	.98
.12—under .13	1.00

Determine the following values.
(a) the .90 fractile   (d) the third quartile
(b) the 37th percentile   (e) the interquartile range
(c) the first quartile   (f) the median

3-49 Mr. Chips needs to analyze the grade point data of a random sample of ten students. The possible scores range downward from 4 points for "A" to 0 points for "F." The following data have been obtained from department records.

$$3 \quad 2 \quad 4 \quad 1 \quad 0$$
$$3 \quad 2 \quad 2 \quad 2 \quad 1$$

(a) Calculate the (1) range, (2) mean, (3) variance, and (4) standard deviation.
(b) Determine the (1) 25th, (2) 50th, and (3) 75th percentiles.
(c) Calculate the interquartile range.

3-50 The following percentiles have been obtained from a series of aptitude tests taken by all entering freshman at Old Ivy.

Score	Percentile
450	25th
573	50th
615	75th
729	90th
738	95th
752	99th

(a) Determine the (1) first, (2) second, and (3) third quartiles.
(b) Calculate the median score.
(c) Calculate the interquartile range.

3-51 The mean lifetimes for cartons of 100-watt Silk Vane long-life light bulbs have been established to be normally distributed, with mean 1,500 hours and standard deviation 100 hours. Find the upper and lower bounds for the following limits, and indicate the percentage of all cartons for which the mean lifetimes fall within these limits.

(a) $\mu \pm 1\sigma$ (b) $\mu \pm 2\sigma$ (c) $\mu \pm 3\sigma$

3-52 The following frequency distribution has been obtained for sample data related to the viable shelf life of Pumper's Nickel-a-Slice bread.

Hours to Deterioration	Number of Loaves
90.0–under 110.0	23
110.0–under 130.0	37
130.0–under 150.0	26
150.0–under 170.0	14

Calculate the (a) mean, (b) median, (c) variance, and (d) standard deviation.

3-53 The following cumulative relative frequency distribution has been obtained for sample IQ scores achieved by students at Boston Sanskrit School.

IQ Score	Cumulative Proportion of Students
70–less than 80	.02
80–less than 90	.12
90–less than 100	.24
100–less than 110	.46
110–less than 120	.65
120–less than 130	.79
130–less than 140	.88
140–less than 150	.97
150–less than 160	1.00

(a) Plot the ogive.
(b) Read the following values from your graph. (The figures obtained will be only estimates of the actual values.)
   (1) 50th percentile   (3) first quartile   (5) 90th percentile
   (2) .75 fractile   (4) median
(c) Use your answers from (b) to calculate the interquartile range.

3-54 The following ungrouped sample examination scores have been obtained for a large lecture course on human sexuality.

84	77	67	94	90
81	56	89	77	88
74	76	28	80	58
66	77	89	81	78
77	72	94	93	79
93				

(a) Calculate the (1) mean and (2) variance.
(b) The following frequency distribution for the sample data given in (a) is provided below.

Class Interval	Frequency
25.0–under 35.0	1
35.0–under 45.0	0
45.0–under 55.0	0
55.0–under 65.0	2
65.0–under 75.0	4
75.0–under 85.0	11
85.0–under 95.0	8
Total	26

Calculate the (1) mean and (2) variance.

(c) Calculating population parameters using grouped data provides only approximations of the population parameters that would be obtained directly from the ungrouped raw data. Find the amount of error in this approximation procedure for the sample mean by subtracting your answer in (b) from the value obtained in (a).

3-55 A plant superintendent fine-tuned a liquid blending operation by experimenting with control settings. The following impurity levels (parts per million) have been obtained for sample runs, with all settings unchanged during a single day.

Day 1	Day 2	Day 3	Day 4	Day 5
50	34	30	39	38
23	45	38	35	37
34	29	35	37	39
26	37	42	37	38
	27	33		
		32		

The superintendent's two objectives for the levels of impurities are (1) to minimize the variability and (2) to minimize the average.

(a) Calculate, for each day, the (1) mean, (2) standard deviation, (3) first quartile, (4) median, and (5) third quartile.

(b) Construct, on the same graph, a box plot for each day's completion times.

(c) Comment on how well the settings that the superintendent found met his goals.

3-56 Refer to the data given in Exercise 3-54.

(a) Construct a stem-and-leaf plot.

(b) Construct an ordered stem-and-leaf plot.

(c) Using the original ungrouped data, calculate the (1) mean, (2) standard deviation, and (3) mode.

(d) Using the original ungrouped data, determine the (1) 10th, (2) 25th, and (3) 75th percentiles.

(e) Calculate the median.

(f) Calculate the (1) range and (2) interquartile range.

(g) Construct the box plot.

STATISTICS IN PRACTICE

3-57 Refer to the master class data from Exercise 1-19.
  (a) Use the data for height and find the mean, mode, median, variance, and standard deviation for the ungrouped data.
  (b) Group the height data and recalculate the values.
  (c) Explain why you grouped the data in the fashion you did. What conclusions can you draw by comparing your answers from parts (a) and (b)?
  (d) Do the results demonstrate any skewing or bimodality? Explain why or why not.
  (e) Determine the quartiles for your grouped data. What value is nearest the 80th percentile?
  (f) Separate the class by sex, compare the height distributions and compare the means and standard deviations with your answers in parts (a) and (b).
  (g) Categorize the class data by state, province or country of birth. Create one category for the state or province where your school is located and one for all others. Create a cross tabulation using place of birth versus major or favorite food. Use proportions in place of frequencies.
  (h) Use the student age variable in a grouped format and compare the proportions for favorite food or place of birth.

3-58 Refer to your group's class data list developed in Exercise 1-19 and also used in Exercise 2-40. Perform the following operations for describing and displaying statistical data:
  (a) For one interval data set find the mean, mode, median, variance, and standard deviation for the ungrouped data.
  (b) Using the data from (a), group the data and recalculate the values.
  (c) Explain why you grouped the data in the fashion you did. What conclusions can you draw by comparing answers from (a) and (b)?
  (d) Do the results demonstrate any skewing or bimodality of the data? Explain the reasons for your results.
  (e) Determine the quartiles for your grouped data. Find the 85th percentile.
  (f) For one nominal variable, determine the proportion of observations in each category.
  (g) Construct a cross tabulation with two nominal variables, determining the proportions for each cell and category.

3-59 *The Last Cold War Olympics—Applied Summary Statistics.* Consider the best way to organize the medal total data in Table 2-15 from the 1988 Games of the Summer Olympics. What summary descriptive measures would be useful in analyzing these data? Demonstrate these measures.

3-60 Table 2-16 shows the twenty most populous countries for the years 1991 and 2100. What summary descriptive measures would be most meaningful in analyzing these data? Demonstrate these measures.

3-61 Table 1-2 provides data on estimates of the location of homeless people.
  (a) Determine the mean and median for the total data. Compare the mean to the median value.
  (b) Suppose New York City is deleted from the data set. What might

TABLE 3-9 Best-Selling Prerecorded Videos of All Time

Rank/Title	Distributor	Units Sold (millions)
1. E.T.–The Extraterrestrial	MCA	15.1
2. Batman	Warner	11.5
3. Bambi	Disney	10.5
4. The Little Mermaid	Disney	9.0
5. Teenage Mutant Ninja Turtles	LIVE	8.8
6. Who Framed Roger Rabbit	Touchstone	8.5
7. Cinderella	Disney	7.6
8. Peter Pan	Disney	7.0
9. Pretty Woman	Paramount	6.2
10. Honey, I Shrunk the Kids	Disney	5.8

Source: *The Universal Almanac* 1992: 252.

happen to the summary descriptive measures? Recompute the mean and median. Recompare the mean to the median.

3-62 Using the personal computer sales marketing data in Table 2-12, determine the average per capita installed base for the ten largest markets. What is the standard deviation? According to Chebyshev's theorem, what proportion of the per capita installed base should lie within the mean $\pm$ \$400?

3-63 Given the video sales data in Table 3-9, what descriptive summary measures could be used to best summarize the data? Apply the measures you selected to the data.

3-64 *NFL Individual Leaders.* Table 3-10 contains the statistics for the top 12 quarterbacks for 1992 in the National Football Conference.

TABLE 3-10 Statistics for the Top 12 Quarterbacks in the NFL for 1992

	Passes Attempted	Passes Completed	Percentage Completed	Yards Gained	Touchdowns	Interceptions
Steve Young	402	268	66.7	3465	25	7
Chris Miller	253	152	60.1	1739	15	6
Troy Aikman	473	302	63.8	3445	23	14
Randall Cunningham	384	233	60.7	2775	19	11
Brett Favre	471	302	64.1	3227	18	13
Bobby Hebert	422	249	59.0	3287	19	16
Jim Everett	475	281	59.2	3323	22	18
Chris Chandler	413	245	59.3	2832	15	15
Jim Harbaugh	358	202	56.4	2486	13	12
Vinny Testaverde	358	206	57.5	2554	14	16
Rich Gannon	279	159	57.0	1905	12	13
Mark Rypien	479	269	56.2	3282	13	17

Source: *The Universal Almanac* 1992: 252.

(a) Calculate the mean and standard deviation for yards gained.

(b) Construct a box plot for touchdowns.

(c) Calculate the median for passes attempted.

    (d) Find the mode for interceptions.

    (e) What proportion of the 12 quarterbacks completed more than 200 passes?

3-65 *Long-Running Broadway Plays.* Table 3-11 shows the top 20 running plays on Broadway through July 4, 1993.

TABLE 3-11   Long-Running Broadway Plays

Play	Performances
Chorus Line	6137
Oh, Calcutta (revival)	5959
*Cats**	4485
42nd Street	3486
Grease	3388
Fiddler on the Roof	3242
Life with Father	3224
Tobacco Road	3182
Hello Dolly	2844
My Fair Lady	2717
Les Misérables	2572
Annie	2377
Man of LaMancha	2328
Abie's Irish Rose	2327
Phantom of the Opera	2271
Oklahoma!	2212
Pippin	1944
South Pacific	1925
Magic Show	1920
Deathtrap	1792

Source: *The World Almanac and Book of Facts, 1994.*

    (a) Calculate the mean, variance, and standard deviation for the number of performances for these 20 plays.

    (b) Construct a box plot for the number of performances.

3-66 *Households with Cable TV.* Table 3-12 shows the number of U.S. households with cable TV for 1975–1992.

TABLE 3-12   Number of Households with Cable TV, 1975–1992

Year	Basic Cable Subscribers	Year	Basic Cable Subscribers
1975	9,196,690	1984	37,290,870
1976	10,787,970	1985	39,872,520
1977	12,168,450	1986	42,237,140
1978	13,391,910	1987	44,970,880
1979	14,814,380	1988	48,636,520
1980	17,671,490	1989	52,564,470

TABLE 3-12 Number of Households with Cable TV, 1975–1992

Year	Basic Cable Subscribers	Year	Basic Cable Subscribers
1981	23,219,200	1990	54,871,330
1982	29,340,570	1991	55,786,390
1983	34,113,790	1992	57,211,600

Source: *The World Almanac and Book of Facts, 1994.*

(a) Compute the mean and standard deviation for the number of households with cable TV per year.

(b) Construct a time series plot for the number of households with cable TV per year.

3-67 Table 3-13 contains final exam grades (100 points possible) for a Fall 1993 statistics class.

TABLE 3-13 Final Exam Scores for 100 Students in Business Statistics Class

Student Number	Exam Score	Student Number	Exam Score	Student Number	Exam Score	Student Number	Exam Score
00	46	25	60	50	71	75	16
01	78	26	87	51	10	76	52
02	69	27	86	52	51	77	36
03	47	28	95	53	51	78	47
04	67	29	91	54	94	79	36
05	27	30	92	55	64	80	37
06	67	31	75	56	53	81	59
07	66	32	85	57	42	82	64
08	74	33	58	58	75	83	67
09	53	34	30	59	69	84	56
10	50	35	74	60	68	85	9
11	36	36	77	61	34	86	49
12	98	37	73	62	75	87	53
13	95	38	95	63	69	88	68
14	28	39	48	64	65	89	69
15	73	40	98	65	42	90	57
16	85	41	42	66	60	91	55
17	86	42	24	67	70	92	71
18	86	43	90	68	35	93	64
19	58	44	32	69	27	94	49
20	35	45	45	70	67	95	20
21	70	46	67	71	91	96	46
22	65	47	43	72	67	97	65
23	89	48	69	73	65	98	74
24	87	49	67	74	79	99	59

Source: Janet Anaya, Fall 1993.

(a) Construct an ordered stem and leaf plot for the exam data.

(b) Construct a frequency distribution having 10 intervals of equal width.

(c) Using your answer to (b), compute the mean and standard deviation for the exam data.

(d) Using your answer to (b), compute the three quartiles.

(e) Construct a box plot for the exam data.

CASE   **Ingrid's Hallmark Shop II**

As you recall from the Case in Chapter 2, Ingrid's Hallmark Shop is a card and gift shop located in a suburban town. The owner, Ingrid, needs to make operational decisions and plan her financial strategy. Ingrid's concerns include forecasting cash flow, estimating daily sales of staple items such as birthday cards, and assessing the efficiency of her staff in performing various tasks. Ingrid's son Dan helped to resolve some of the business concerns as part of an MBA term project. To begin, Dan obtained the data for a sample of peak off-season weekdays.

Number of Transactions	Total Sales	Number of Transactions	Total Sales
68	$ 563	144	$1,220
97	729	78	464
133	826	110	601
115	633	112	598
122	912	92	653
85	552	88	532

Dan was particularly interested in Ingrid's balloon business. He decided to determine how much time an employee spent completing a balloon order, beginning at that point when the customer's choice has been made and the fresh balloons have been gathered from stock. The employee's task then is to fill the balloons, one at a time, with helium, clamp the ribbon onto the stem (which also secures the contents), and, finally, to tie on a decorative weight. Often the order will be picked up later in the day enabling the employee to handle interruptions between balloons. Over time, Ingrid's employees become more adept at completing balloon orders.

How rapid is the employee's learning process? This is what Dan set out to determine. He prepared a log for Nancy, a new hire, to fill in as she completed balloon orders. Table 3-14 is a portion of Nancy's log showing a sample of ballon orders filled during her first month of employment at Ingrid's Hallmark Shop.

Dan also selected a sample of days and asked all the employees to count carefully the number of birthday cards they sold those days. The results Dan obtained are listed below.

Date	Cards Sold	Date	Cards Sold
7/25	113	9/16	125
8/06	155	9/23	132
8/15	78	10/02	95
9/02	63	10/08	118
9/15	206	10/12	188

TABLE 3-14 Sample Balloon Order Data from Nancy's Log

Date	Order	Number of Balloons Completed	Elapsed Time (seconds)	Date	Order	Number of Balloons Completed	Elapsed Time (seconds)
8/02	1	5	335	8/28	6	5	150
	3	7	454		9	6	185
	6	2	132		14	10	290
	13	9	585		15	12	365
8/04	4	10	528		16	10	310
	5	4	206		17	8	232
	8	1	48				
	13	14	732				
	15	7	395				

QUESTIONS

1. One of Ingrid's most important forecasting measures is the individual average transaction (IAT). This is found by dividing the dollar sales by the customer count.
   (a) Use the operating data given in Table 3-14. Calculate each IAT.
   (b) Using your answers to (a), calculate the (1) mean, (2) standard deviation, and (3) median.
   (c) Determine the (1) 10th, (2) 25th, (3) 50th, (4) 75th, and (5) 90th percentiles using your answers to (a).
   (d) Construct a box plot for the sample IAT data in (a).
   (e) What do your results suggest regarding the possibility of having an IAT as small as $1.50 or as large as $20.00 on a peak weekday during the off-season?

2. Refer to Dan's sales data given on the bottom of page 116. Repeat Question 1(b)–(d) above.

3. One way to forecast a weekday's dollar sales is to multiply the mean IAT by the customer count estimated for that day. Using your answers to Question 1, forecast the dollar sales when (a) 90, (b) 110, and (c) 120 customers are projected.

4. Ingrid believes that 20% of a day's sales volume, on the average, consists of birthday cards. The average retail value of a birthday card is $1.50. Thus, on a 100-card day, the expected dollar sales would be

   $$(1/.20) \times 1.50 \times 100 = \$750$$

   (a) Assuming that your answers to Question 2 are representative, what would Ingrid's average sales be for a typical weekday?
   (b) Comment on the appropriateness of the number found in (a) for planning purposes.
   (c) Suggest another procedure Ingrid might use to predict daily sales.

5. Refer to the balloon order data given in Table 3-14.
   (a) For each sample day, construct a box plot for the average time per balloon Nancy spent while completing an order.
   (b) What do you notice about Nancy's balloon-filling skills over time?

CHAPTER 4

THE STATISTICAL
SAMPLING STUDY

BEFORE READING THIS CHAPTER, MAKE SURE YOU UNDERSTAND:

The distinction between quantitative and qualitative data (Chapter 1).

How data are displayed (Chapter 2).

The various statistical measures and how they give meaning to data (Chapter 3).

AFTER READING THIS CHAPTER, YOU WILL UNDERSTAND:

Why samples should be used.

The stages of a statistical sampling study.

How to avoid bias and control sampling error.

The main types of samples.

The various forms of random sampling.

Some important elements of a statistical experiment.

Now that we have covered the basic elements of descriptive statistics, we are ready to consider **statistical sampling**. To draw conclusions about populations from samples, we must use inferential statistics, which enables us to determine a population's characteristics by directly observing only a portion, or sample, of the population.

We obtain a sample rather than a complete enumeration (a census) of the population for many reasons. Obviously, it is cheaper to observe a part rather than the whole, but we should prepare ourselves to cope with the dangers of using samples. In this chapter, we will investigate various kinds of sampling procedures. Some are better than others, but all may yield samples that are inaccurate and unreliable. We will learn how to minimize these dangers, but some potential error is the price we must pay for the convenience and savings that samples provide.

4-1 THE NEED FOR SAMPLES

There would be no need for statistical theory if a census, rather than a sample, was always used to obtain information about populations. But a census may not be practical and is almost never economical.

Sample information must be relied on for most applications. There are six main reasons for sampling in lieu of the census: economy, timeliness, the large size of many populations, inaccessibility of some of the population, destructiveness of the observation, and accuracy.

THE ECONOMIC ADVANTAGES OF USING A SAMPLE

Obviously, taking a sample—directly observing only a portion of the population—requires fewer resources than a census. For example, consider a consumer survey to determine the reactions of all the owners of a popular automobile to several proposed colors for next year's model. A questionnaire is to be printed and mailed to all owners. Imagine the clerical chore of simply addressing the envelopes, and the cost of the postage alone could easily run into five figures. The bookkeeping problems in tabulating the replies would be overwhelming.

Perhaps the greatest difficulty would be to ensure a 100% response. A high proportion of the questionnaires will simply be ignored along with the plethora of other "junk" mail. Most persons can be reached by telephone, telegram, or personal visit. Invariably, however, an irascible few will slam their doors even in the face of the company president, and some will have to be bribed with a new car to respond. A great many car owners will have moved and will be hard to locate, necessitating the services of a detective agency. Some owners will die without responding before the survey is completed. The company could have more difficulty taking a census of its owner population than the FBI has arresting its ten most wanted men.

As unrealistic as this example is, it does illustrate the very high cost of a census. For the type of information desired, the car manufacturer would be wise to interview a small portion of the car owners. Rarely does a circumstance require a census of the population, and even more rarely is the expense justified.

THE TIME FACTOR

A sample may provide an investigator with needed information quickly. Often speed is of paramount importance, as in a political polling, where the goal is to determine from sample evidence voter preferences toward candidates for public office. The voting public as a whole is extremely fickle; polls have indicated that voters fluctuate in preference right up to the time of the election. If a poll is to be used to gauge public opinion, it must be very current; the opinions must be obtained, tabulated, and published within a very short period of time. Even if it were physically possible to use a census in such an opinion survey, its results would not be valid due to significant shifts in public opinion over the time required to conduct it.

Similarly, managerial decisions based on a population's characteristics must frequently be made very quickly. In a highly competitive environment there may not be enough time to wait for a 100% response before introducing a new product or changing service patterns. Since a census would not be feasible, sample evidence must be relied on.

THE VERY LARGE POPULATION

Many populations about which inferences must be made are quite large. For example, consider the population of high school seniors in the United States—a group numbering about 3,000,000. The plans of these soon-to-be graduates will directly affect the status of universities and colleges, the military, and prospective employers—all of whom must have specific knowledge about the students' plans in order to make compatible decisions to absorb them during the coming year. But the sheer size of the population of postgraduate plans will probably make it physically impossible to conduct a census. Sample evidence may be the only available way to obtain information from high school seniors.

PARTLY INACCESSIBLE POPULATIONS

Some populations contain elementary units so difficult to observe that they are in a sense inaccessible. One example is the population of crashed aircraft: Planes that crash and sink in the deep ocean are inaccessible and cannot be directly studied to determine the physical causes of their failure. Similar conditions hold in determining consumer attitudes. Not all of the users of a product can be queried. Some may be in prisons, nursing homes, or hospitals and have limited contact with the outside world. Others may be insulated from harassment; consider the limited accessibility to the president of the United States or the pope.

Whenever some elementary units are inaccessible, sampling must be used to provide the desired information about the population. These illustrations demonstrate physical inaccessibility, but an elementary unit's accessibility may be limited for economic reasons alone: Those observations deemed too costly to be made are, in a real sense, also inaccessible.

THE DESTRUCTIVE NATURE OF THE OBSERVATION

Sometimes the very act of observing the desired characteristic of the elementary unit destroys it for the use intended. Classical examples of this occur in quality control: To test a fuse to determine whether it is defective, it must be destroyed; to obtain a census of the quality of a shipment of fuses, all of them must be destroyed. This negates any purpose served by quality-control testing. Clearly, a *sample* of fuses must be tested to assess the quality of the shipment.

STATISTICS AROUND US

Indians and Teenage Widows

Two statisticians noticed a very unusual anomaly in the change of two categories between 1940 and 1950.* An abnormally large number of 14-year-old widows were reported in the 1950 figures—20 times as many as in 1940. Indian divorcees, who had also been extremely rare, had increased by a like magnitude. Unable to justify the changes by any sociological trends, the statisticians analyzed the data-gathering and data-processing procedures of the census. They concluded that the figures could have resulted from the erroneous reversal of the entries on a few of the punched cards used to process the data. In this instance, a census seemed to provide far from reliable or credible results.

ACCURACY AND SAMPLING

A sample may be more accurate than a census. A sloppily conducted census can provide less reliable information than a carefully obtained sample. Indeed, the U.S. census of 1950 provides us with an excellent example in the above Statistics Around Us box.

A large utility company had problems of a somewhat different nature with punched cards, described in the box at the bottom of this page.

EXERCISES

4-1 For each of the following situations, indicate whether a sample or a census would be more appropriate. Explain.

(a) AC-DC knows that due to variations in processing, a certain percentage of its spark plugs will be defective. A thorough test of a spark plug

sample

STATISTICS AROUND US

Work Sampling

The procedure for allocating a data center's data entry costs was based on a census compiled from detailed logs maintained by keypunch operators. These records were not very accurate, and record keeping reduced operator productivity. A company statistician found that operators spent 10% of their time maintaining the logs and proposed that management use **work sampling**. At random time intervals, a bell would ring and all operators would stop work and fill out a simplified form. Data entry costs were allocated to the various departments according to the percentage of forms returned, which was accurate since heavier users would accumulate more forms. Operator productivity increased, and everyone was pleased with the greater accuracy.

---

*Ansley J. Coale and Frederick F. Stephan, "The Case of the Indians and Teen-age Widows," *Journal of the American Statistical Association*, LVII (June 1962): 388–437.

destroys it, but the production output must be tested to determine whether remedial action is necessary.

(b) NASA must determine the quality of the components of a manned space vehicle. *census*

(c) A hospital administrator attempting to improve patient services wishes to determine the attitudes of persons treated. *sample*

(d) A medical researcher wants to determine the possible harmful side effects from a chemical that eases the pain of arthritis. *sample*

4-2 For each of the following reasons, give an example of a situation for which a census would be less desirable than a sample. Explain.

(a) economy   (c) size of population   (e) accuracy

(b) timeliness   (d) inaccessibility   (f) destructive observations

4-2 DESIGNING AND CONDUCTING A SAMPLING STUDY

Much of this book is concerned with how to collect samples so that meaningful conclusions can be drawn about an entire population. Figure 4-1 shows the major stages of a sampling study. The first stage—**planning**—requires careful attention so that the sampling results will achieve the best impact. In the second stage—**data collection**, where the plans are followed—a major goal is to ensure that observations are free from bias. The last phase—**data analysis and conclusions**—is the area to which a major portion of this book will be devoted.

THE IMPORTANCE OF PLANNING

Planning is the most important step in a statistical study. Inadequate planning can lead to needless expense when actual data collection begins. Poor planning may result in the eventual invalidation of the entire study. The outcome of the study may even prove strongly counterproductive. Several extreme cases of poor planning will be given in this chapter.

Planning begins with the identification of a population that will achieve the study's goals. This is followed by the selection of an observation procedure that might require a questionnaire, which would then have to be designed, or an observation-measuring instrument. The latter is a broad category that includes mechanical devices (to record physical data, such as dimensions and weight), various tests (for intelligence, aptitude, personality, or knowledge), sources of data (for example, family income could be obtained from tax records, from employers, or by directly questioning a family member), and survey techniques (written reply, telephone response, or personal interview).

Of equal importance in planning is the choice of the sample type itself. Alternative kinds of samples range from the most "scientific" random sample, like the one used in the major public opinion polls, to the convenience sample taken in campus straw votes, where practically no attention is paid to how representative the sample might be. The random sample is the most important, because statistical theory applies to it alone. As we will see, there are a variety of ways to select a sample.

If proper and valid conclusions are to be drawn from the sample data, planning must include a presampling choice of the statistical procedure to be used later in analyzing the results. Choosing an analytical technique *after* sifting through the

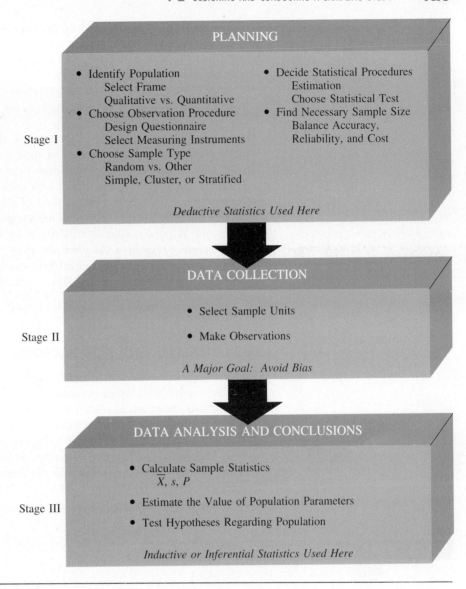

FIGURE 4-1 Major stages in a statistical sampling study.

results may lead to the most insidious kind of bias—the innocent or intentional selection of a tool that strongly supports the desired conclusion.

An important planning consideration in any sampling study is determining how many observations to make. In general, the larger its size, the more closely a random sample is expected to represent its population. But where do we draw the line? Isn't a sample ten times as large ten times as good? The first question will be answered in Chapter 8. To the second, the answer is *no*. As we will see, selection of sample size is largely an economic matter; scarce resources (funds available for gathering data) must be traded off against the accuracy and reliability of the result. A point of diminishing return is soon reached where an extra dollar buys very little in increased sample quality.

Both choosing a statistical procedure and selecting an appropriate sample size involve a great amount of deductive statistics, since both of these planning aspects require us to look at how samples are generated from "textbook" populations whose characteristics are fully known.

DATA COLLECTION

The second phase of the statistical sampling study—obtaining the raw data—usually requires the greatest amount of time and effort. Adequate controls must be provided to prevent observations from becoming biased.

Potential problem areas associated with collecting and managing the data are described in detail in subsequent sections of this chapter. Such problems include observational biases that result when the sample units are measured, queried, or investigated. A poorly asked question and an improperly operated device both lead to incorrect responses. Another source of bias arises because some parts of the population are inaccessible or difficult to observe. Additional problems may appear after the data are collected. The inevitable ambiguities and contradictions must be dealt with and the results processed so that statistical analyses can be made.

DATA ANALYSIS AND CONCLUSIONS

This last stage of a statistical sampling study is extremely important. Here, many of the descriptive tools we discussed earlier are used to communicate the results. Our emphasis, however, is placed on drawing conclusions from the necessarily incomplete information available from any sample. This is the point at which statistical inferences are made. The lion's share of statistical theory is directly related to or in support of making generalizations or **inferences** about populations from samples. Inferences generally fall into the three broad categories of estimation, hypothesis testing, and association. The goals of the study and the resources available dictate the statistical inference and technique that will be used.

4-3 BIAS AND ERROR IN SAMPLING

The manner in which the observed units are chosen significantly affects the adequacy of the sample. Here we will examine some of the pitfalls commonly encountered in sampling and learn how to avoid many of them.

A sample is expected to mirror the population from which it comes. However, there is no guarantee that any sample will be precisely representative of the population; chance may dictate that a disproportionate number of untypical observations will be made. In practice, it is rarely known when a sample is unrepresentative and should be discarded, because some population characteristics are unknown (or else no sample would be needed in the first place). Steps must be taken during the planning of the study to minimize the chance that the sample will be untypical.

SAMPLING ERROR

What can make a sample unrepresentative of its population? One of the most frequent causes is **sampling error**, for which we provide the following.

DEFINITION: *Sampling error* comprises the differences between the sample and the population that are due solely to the particular elementary units that happen to have been selected.

use large samples to correct

To illustrate sampling error, suppose that a sample of 100 American men are measured and are all found to be taller than seven feet. An obvious conclusion would be that most American males are taller than seven feet. Of course, this is absurd; most people do not know a man who is seven feet tall and might not even be sure one existed if a few basketball players were not that tall. Yet it is possible for a statistician to be unfortunate enough to obtain such a highly unrepresentative sample. However, this is highly unlikely; nature has distributed the rare seven-footers widely among the population.

More dangerous is the less obvious sampling error against which nature offers little protection. It is not difficult to envision a sample in which the average height is overstated by only an inch or two rather than a foot. It is the insidious, unobvious error that is our major concern.

There are two basic causes for sampling error. One is chance: Bad luck may result in untypical choices. Unusual elementary units do exist, and there is always a possibility that an abnormally large number will be chosen. The main protection against this type of error is to use a large enough sample. Another cause of sampling error—sampling bias—is not as easy to remedy.

SAMPLING BIAS

The size of the sample has little to do with the effects of sampling bias. In the present context, we provide the

DEFINITION: *Sampling bias* is a tendency to favor the selection of elementary units that have particular characteristics.

Sampling bias is usually the result of a poor sampling plan. Consider the following classical example from political polling.

STATISTICS AROUND US

The *Literary Digest* Said Roosevelt Would Lose

A poll was conducted by the now defunct *Literary Digest* in 1936, when Franklin D. Roosevelt was running against Republican Alfred M. Landon for the presidency. Based on several million responses obtained from a sample of the voting public, the *Digest* concluded that Landon would win by a record margin. Exactly the opposite happened: Roosevelt won one of the most one-sided victories in American history. The poll's erroneous results were later attributed to sampling bias. The *Digest* had selected its sample from magazine subscription listings and telephone directories. During the Great Depression, both sources contained a disproportionate number of prosperous persons who favored the laissez-faire Republican platform. Because a large proportion of the disgruntled majority, who strongly favored Roosevelt, had no telephones and did not subscribe to magazines, these voters were not adequately represented in the sample.

The avoidance of sampling bias is a major concern of statisticians. A means of selecting the elementary units must be designed to avoid the more obvious forms of bias. In practice, it is difficult (if not impossible) to eliminate all forms of bias. Most notable is the **bias of nonresponse**, when—for whatever reason—some elementary units have no chance of appearing in the sample. The cost considerations involved in making sample observations almost guarantee that this particular form of bias will be present to some degree in any sample.

An excellent example is provided by consumer surveys involving food products. It is relatively cheap to obtain opinions about a company's product from persons who remain at home during the day. But a large proportion of adult residents in many areas are employed and are at home only in the evenings and on weekends. If the sampling survey is conducted during normal working hours, these consumers who make food-buying decisions will not be represented. A company wishing to determine whether to expand its line of prepared frozen foods may obtain survey results indicating that there is not a great demand for such products. But working people have less leisure time and are often enthusiastic users of such items. A sample that neglected their opinions could lead to an erroneous marketing decision.

NONSAMPLING ERROR

The other main cause of unrepresentative samples is nonsampling error. This type of error can occur whether a census or a sample is being used. Like sampling error, nonsampling error may either be produced by participants in the statistical study or be an innocent byproduct of the sampling plans and procedures.

DEFINITION: A **nonsampling error** is an error that results solely from the manner in which the observations are made.

The simplest example of nonsampling error is inaccurate physical measurement due to malfunctioning instruments or poor procedures. Consider the observation of human weights. If persons are asked to state their own weights, no two answers will be of equal reliability. The people will have weighed themselves on different scales in various states of poor calibration. An individual's weight fluctuates diurnally by several pounds, so that the time of weighing will affect the answer. The scale reading will also vary with the person's state of undress. Responses will not be of comparable validity unless all persons are weighed under the same circumstances.

Biased observations due to inaccurate measurement can be innocent but devastating. A French astronomer once proposed a new theory based on spectroscopic measurements of light emitted by a particular star. When his colleagues discovered that the measuring instrument had been contaminated by cigarette smoke, they rejected his findings.

In surveys of personal characteristics, unintended errors may result from (1) the manner in which the response is elicited, (2) the idiosyncrasies of the persons surveyed, (3) the purpose of the study, or (4) the personal biases of the interviewer or survey writer.

The Interviewer's Effect

No two interviewers are alike, and the same person may provide different answers to different interviewers. The manner in which a question is formulated can also result in inaccurate responses. Individuals tend to provide false answers to particular questions. A good example of this is a person's age. Some people will lie about their age. If asked their age in years, most people will give their chronological age at their previous birthday, even if it is more than 11 months past. Both problems can be alleviated by asking the date of birth. It would require quick arithmetic to give a false date, and a date of birth is much more accurate than a person's age on his or her last birthday.

Respondents might also give incorrect answers to impress the interviewer. This is especially prevalent when survey questions are based on a knowledge of current events or on intellectual accomplishments. Many people have said that they "know" about famous people who are fictitious or that they have read books that were never written. This type of error is the most difficult to prevent, because it results from outright deceit on the part of the respondent. It is important to acknowledge that certain psychological factors induce incorrect responses, and great care must be taken to design a study that minimizes their effect.

KNOWING PURPOSE OF THE STUDY

Knowing why a study is being conducted may create incorrect responses. A classic example is the answer to the question: What is your income? If a government agency is asking, a different figure may be provided than the respondent would give on an application for a home mortgage. A teacher's union seeking to justify a wage increase may receive a different response from a member than would the brother-in-law of the member. The union would probably not be given (nor would it want to know) the member's full income, incorporating earnings from moonlighting and summer employment, whereas the brother-in-law would probably be informed about the income derived from these sources as well as any successful investments. One way to guard against such bias is to camouflage the study's goals; an independent opinion survey firm might even be employed to keep secret the objective of the investigation. Another remedy is to make the questions very specific, allowing little room for personal interpretation. For example, "Where are you employed?" could be followed by "What is your salary?" and "Do you have any extra jobs?" A sequence of such questions may produce more accurate information.

INDUCED BIAS

Finally, it should be noted that the personal prejudices of either the designer of the study or the data collector may tend to **induce bias**. A person should not design a questionnaire related to a subject he or she feels strongly about. Questions may be slanted in such a way that a particular response will be obtained even though it is inaccurate. An example of this is a preference survey sponsored by the makers of brand A, prefaced by the question "In your opinion, which of the following factors that make brand A a superior-quality product is the most important?" This could be followed by a question asking for a preference ranking of a list of products, including brand A. (Most blatantly, brand A may be the first name on the list.) The preliminary question encourages the respondent to think about the good features of brand A, creating an atmosphere that will make the later comparison unfair. Another instance of induced error may occur in an experiment in which a technical specialist selects the elementary units to be treated with a new product. For example, when doctors favoring a new drug decide which patients are going to receive it, they may select (consciously or not) those they feel have the best chance of benefiting from its administration. An agronomist may apply a new fertilizer to certain key plots, knowing that they will provide more favorable yields than others. To protect against induced bias, an individual trained in statistics should have a measure of control over the design and implementation of the entire statistical study, and someone who is aware of these pitfalls should serve in an auditing capacity.

EXERCISES

4-3 A government official must delegate the responsibility for determining employee attitudes toward a training program conducted by the personnel department. What are the dangers in asking the personnel manager to handle this matter? Suggest a procedure that would overcome these obstacles.

4-4 People who filled out the "long" form for the U.S. Census of 1970 were asked to answer questions about their employment. One question was "How many hours did you work last week?" Successive questions relating to the same work week asked about type of employer, duties, and so on. The public was instructed to provide the data by April 1, 1970. This was the Wednesday right after Easter, and most of the nation's educators had been on a holiday for the entire week in question. Comment on the possible errors that may have resulted from this set of questions. How could the questionnaire have been improved to avoid these errors?

4-5 Greenwall's Drugstore has recently experienced a significant decline in sales due to the presence of some new discount stores in the city. A questionnaire asked customers who visited the store during one week to compare its prices, convenience, and level of service with the discount stores. What do you think about the manner in which the information was obtained? What sampling procedure could you recommend?

4-6 A questionnaire prepared for a study on consumer buying habits contains the question "What is the value of your present automobile(s)?" What errors may result from this question? Suggest a better way to obtain the desired response.

4-7 Many personality profiles require that an individual provide answers to multiple-choice questions. The answers are then compiled, and various trait ratings are found. Comment on the pitfalls of this procedure. Suggest how some may be alleviated.

4-8 Testing a new drug therapy sometimes involves two patient groups. The patients in one group receive the medication under investigation. The other may receive no medication at all or may be given an innocuous substance called a **placebo** (often just a sugar pill) that looks like the drug being tested. Why is the placebo used?

4-9 A well-known television rating agency provides networks and advertisers with estimates of the audience size for all nationally televised programs. These estimates are based on detailed logs, maintained by persons in the households surveyed, that indicate which stations were watched during each period of the day. The agency has a difficult time recruiting households for its sample, because it is bothersome and inconvenient to keep the logs. Independent observers have estimated that an average of 50 families must be approached before one agrees to join the sample. Comment on the pitfalls that may be encountered when the sample results are taken as representative of the nation's television viewing habits. Can you suggest ways to minimize these pitfalls? Do you think that the sample observations obtained are in danger of being untypical? Explain.

4-4 SELECTING THE SAMPLE

In Section 4-3, we examined the most common problems associated with statistical studies. The desirability of a sampling procedure depends on both its vulnerability to error and its cost. However, economy and reliability are competing ends, because to reduce error often requires an increased expenditure of resources.

Of the two types of statistical error, only sampling error can be controlled by exercising care in determining the method for choosing the sample. We have established that sampling error may be due to either bias or chance. The chance component exists no matter how carefully the selection procedures are implemented, and the only way to minimize chance sampling errors is to select a sufficiently large sample. Sampling bias, on the other hand, may be minimized by the judicious choice of a sampling procedure.

There are three primary kinds of samples: the convenience sample, the judgment sample, and the random sample. They differ in the manner in which their elementary units are chosen. Each sample will be described in turn, and its desirable and undesirable features will be discussed.

Convenience
judgement } sample
random

THE CONVENIENCE SAMPLE *Cheapest to obtain*

A convenience sample results when the more convenient elementary units are chosen from a population for observation. Convenience samples are the cheapest to obtain. Their major drawback is the extent to which they may be permeated with sampling bias, which tends to make them highly unreliable. An important decision made on the basis of a convenience sample is in great danger of being wrong. The letters received by a member of Congress constitute a convenience sample of constituent attitudes. The legislator does not have to expend any time, money, or effort to receive mail, but the opinions voiced there will rarely be indicative of the attitudes of the entire constituency. Persons who have special interests to protect are far more likely to write than the typical voter.

The bias of nonresponse, when present, usually results in a convenience sample. This type of bias can be expected when the telephone—a very convenient device—is used to obtain responses, because the incidence of nonresponse may be relatively high. Many calls will be unanswered, and some people will have unlisted numbers or no telephones at all.

Despite the obvious disadvantages of convenience samples, they are sometimes suitable, depending on the purpose of the study. If only approximate information about a population is needed, then a convenience sample may be adequate. Or funds for a study may be so limited that only a convenience sample is feasible. But in such cases, the obvious drawbacks must be acknowledged. On the other hand, a convenience sample may result in an insignificant source of bias. For example, when there is no reason to believe that nonrespondents would provide information that would differ on the whole from the data already available, there may be little danger in using a telephone survey; but we can never be sure.

THE JUDGMENT SAMPLE

sample will be small

special skill required

A judgement sample is obtained according to the discretion of someone who is familiar with the relevant characteristics of the population. The elementary units are selected judgmentally when the population is highly heterogeneous, when the sample is to be quite small, or when special skill is required to ensure a representative collection of observations.

The judgment sample is obviously prone to bias. Its adequacy is limited by the ability of the individual who selects the sample to perceive differences. All of the dangers mentioned in Section 4-3 in connection with induced bias apply to the judgment sample. Clearly, there are instances in which this type of sample is preferred. Indeed, the consumer price index would be unworkable if it were not partly based on judgment samples.

STATISTICS AROUND US

Consumer Price Index

The Consumer Price Index of the U.S. Department of Labor is partly a judgment sample. The items to be included in establishing the index are chosen on the basis of judgment in order to measure a dollar's purchasing power. Thus, only items or commodities that are used by most people are included; for example, television sets are included, but tape recorders are not. Over time, certain items become obsolete and must be replaced by others; for instance, refrigerators have supplanted iceboxes. Judgment must be employed in deciding what will be replaced and what will be substituted. Judgment is also used in establishing weights for each item; toothpaste should only be weighted in proportion to its position in a typical family's total expenditure—and the typical expenditure is itself a matter of judgment. Finally, judgment is employed in selecting the cities to be represented in the surveys; these, too, must be assigned weights.

THE RANDOM SAMPLE

Perhaps the (most important type) of sample is the random sample. **A random sample allows a known probability that each elementary unit will be chosen.** For this reason, it is sometimes referred to as a **probability sample**.

In its simplest form, a random sample is selected in the manner of a raffle. For example, a random sample of ten symphony conductors from a population of 100 could be obtained by a lottery. The name of each symphony conductor would be written on a slip of paper and placed into a capsule. All 100 capsules would then be placed in a box and thoroughly mixed. An impartial party would select the sample by drawing ten capsules from the box.

In actual practice, a lottery can be physically cumbersome and even its randomness can be questioned, as the following example shows.

STATISTICS AROUND US

The 1970 Draft Lottery Fiasco

The 1970 U.S. draft lottery determined priorities of selection by date of birth. A physical method similar to a raffle was used, but the results appeared to have a pattern. December birth dates were assigned a disproportionate amount of early numbers, and January birth dates were assigned predominantly later numbers. Investigation showed that the undesirable outcome resulted from the fact that the capsules had not been mixed at all. Since the December capsules were the last to be placed in the hopper, many December dates were drawn first. Because persons with these birth dates were almost certain to be drafted, considerable controversy arose and lawsuits were filed to invalidate the entire lottery.

SAMPLE SELECTION USING RANDOM NUMBERS

A more acceptable way to obtain a random sample is to use **random numbers**—digits generated by a lottery process that allows for the equal probability that each possible number will appear next. For example, in a list of five-digit random numbers, each value between 00000 and 99999 has the same chance of appearing at each location. Appendix Table B is a list of five-digit random numbers that was generated by an electromechanical process at the Rand Corporation. These particular numbers have passed many tests and have been certified by the scientific community. If the Selective Service had used such a table of random numbers to select its birth dates, it would have been guiltless in the eyes of everyone except those who were chosen first.

There is no guarantee that a list of random numbers will not exhibit some sort of pattern. For example, 8 may follow 7 more frequently than any other value. But in a long list, any kind of pattern is highly unlikely (8 should follow 7 about 10% of the time).

EXAMPLE: SELECTING SYMPHONY CONDUCTORS AT RANDOM

We select a sample of ten symphony conductors. As a preliminary step, we must assign a number to each member of the population. In this case, we can use two digits; the assigned numbers will therefore range from 00 through 99. It makes no difference how these numbers are assigned, but the person making the assignments should not know which location of the random number table is being used. In Table 4-1, the 100 conductors have been arranged in alphabetical order and assigned the numbers 00 through 99 in sequence. We are now ready to use random numbers to obtain a sample of size $n = 10$.

SOLUTION: We will choose our sample of ten conductors by reading down the first column of the random number table until we obtain ten different values. Note that we only require two-digit numbers but that the table entries contain five digits, so we will use only the first two digits of each entry and ignore the extra digits. If a value is obtained more than once before all ten conductors have been chosen, then that number will be skipped and the next number on the list will be

TABLE 4-1 Alphabetical Listing for a Population of 100 Symphony Conductors

00. Abbado	25. Golschmann	50. Mehta	**74.** Santini
01. André	26. Hannikainen	51. Mitropoulos	76. Sargent
02. Anosov	27. Hollingsworth	52. Monteux	77. Scherchen
03. Ansermet	28. Horenstein	53. Morel	78. Schippers
04. Argenta	29. Horvat	54. Mravinsky	**79.** Schmidt-Isserstedt
05. Barbirolli	30. Jacquillat	**55.** Newman	80. Sejna
06. Beecham	31. Jorda	56. Ormandy	**81.** Serafin
07. Bernstein	32. Karajan	57. Ozawa	**82.** Silvestri
08. Black	33. Kempe	58. Patanè	83. Skrowaczewski
09. Bloomfield	34. Kertesz	59. Pedrotti	84. Slatkin
10. Bonynge	35. Klemperer	60. Perlea	85. Smetáčêk
11. Boult	**36.** Kletzki	61. Prêtre	86. Solti
12. Cantelli	37. Klima	62. Previn	87. Stein
13. Cluytens	38. Kondrashin	63. Previtali	88. Steinberg
14. Dorati	39. Kostelanetz	64. Prohaska	89. Stokowski
15. Dragon	40. Koussevitzky	65. Reiner	**90.** Svetlanov
16. Erede	41. Krips	66. Reinhardt	91. Swarowsky
17. Ferencsik	42. Kubelik	67. Rekai	92. Szell
18. Fiedler	43. Lane	68. Rignold	93. Toscanini
19. Fistoulari	44. Leinsdorf	69. Ristenpart	94. Van Otterloo
20. Fricsay	45. Maag	**70.** Rodzinski	95. Van Remoortel
21. Frühbeck de Burgos	46. Maazel	71. Rosenthal	96. Vogel
22. Furtwängler	47. Mackerras	72. Rowicki	97. Von Matacic
23. Gamba	48. Markevitch	73. Rozhdestvensky	98. Walter
24. Giulini	49. Martin	74. Sanderling	99. Watanabee

used instead. The values obtained by starting at the top of the first column of Appendix Table B and reading down are listed here, with the corresponding conductors who now comprise our sample.

12651	Cantelli	**74**146	Sanderling
81769	Serafin	**90**759	Svetlanov
36737	Kletzki	**55**683	Newman
82861	Silvestri	**79**686	Schmidt-Isserstedt
21325	Frühbeck de Burgos	**70**333	Rodzinski

It does not matter how the random number table is read (from left to right, right to left, top to bottom, bottom to top, or diagonally), but it is important not to read the same number location more than once and not to look ahead before deciding in which direction to proceed. If the numbers are larger than required, the beginning or ending digits can be ignored. If a number on the list has no counterpart in the population (which may happen when the population is smaller than the possible number of random numbers), it should be skipped.

Unlike judgment and convenience samples, random samples are free from sampling bias. No particular elementary units are favored. This still does not guarantee that a random sample will be extremely representative of the population from which it came, because the chance effect may cause it not to be. But it will be possible to assess the reliability of a sample in terms of probability, which can be done only with random samples. When sampling bias is present, an objective basis for measuring its effect does not exist. Therefore, *only the random sample has a theoretical basis for the quantitative evaluation of its quality.* In later chapters, we will see how probability is used for such evaluations.

TYPES OF RANDOM SAMPLES

simple
systematic
stratified
cluster

The way we chose our sample of ten conductors is only one type of a random sampling scheme. At times, it may be desirable to modify the selection procedure without altering the essential features of the random sample. The type of sampling we just discussed is a **simple random sample**, for which we provide the following

DEFINITION: A **simple random sample** is obtained by choosing elementary units in such a way that each unit in the population has an equal chance of being selected.

A simple random sample is free from sampling bias. However, using a random number table to choose the elementary units can be cumbersome. If the sample is to be collected by a person untrained in statistics, then instructions may be misinterpreted and selections may be made improperly. Instead of using a list of random numbers, data collection can be simplified by selecting, say, every 10th or 100th unit after the first unit has been chosen randomly. Such a procedure is called a **systematic random sample**, for which we have the following

DEFINITION: A **systematic random sample** is obtained by selecting one unit on a random basis and choosing additional elementary units at evenly spaced intervals until the desired number of units is obtained.

EXAMPLE: SAMPLING WITH TELEPHONE NUMBERS

A telephone company is conducting a billing study to justify a new rate structure. Data are to be collected by taking a random sample of individual telephone bills from cities and metropolitan areas classified according to population. Billing data are stored by telephone number. A company statistical analyst has designed a procedure for each regional office to employ in collecting the samples.

In one city, 10,000 telephones share the 825 prefix. The telephone numbers range from 825-0000 through 825-9999. A sample size of 200 is required.

SOLUTION: Dividing the number of telephones by 200, the interval width of 50 is obtained. Thus, the bill for every 50th telephone number will be incorporated into the sample. The analyst chooses a number between 0 and 49 at random. Suppose she chooses 37. Her instructions to the regional accounting offices specify that the billing figures for every 50th telephone number, starting with 825-0037, be forwarded to her office. It then becomes a simple manual task for a clerk to pull every 50th telephone bill from the files, and the analyst will receive the figures for 825-0037, 825-0087, 825-0137, 825-0187, and so on.

Sometimes we must ensure that various subgroups of a population are represented in the sample. (In statistics, these subgroups are referred to as **strata**.) To do this, we must collect a sample that contains the sample proportions of each

STATISTICS AROUND US

Problem in Predicting U.S. Presidential Elections

Voter preference polls have been taken prior to each presidential election. Due to the expense involved, the pollsters draw a random sample of voters from the entire United States. Sampling is not conducted independently within each state.

The electoral college determines who will be president. The membership of the college has historically voted as a block by state, and all of a state's votes have gone to the candidate winning in that state. American history shows that the popular vote leader can still lose the election in the electoral college. The winner must only achieve small margins in several large states. Thus, a candidate might win a majority of electoral votes while losing the national plurality. This has happened twice since the Civil War: In 1876, Rutherford B. Hayes beat Samuel J. Tilden, who received a greater number of popular votes; in 1888, Benjamin Harrison beat the larger popular vote getter, Grover Cleveland. The situation is further distorted by the fact that electoral votes are rationed to each state in accordance with its representation in *both* houses of Congress. Thus, Alaska, with about one hundredth the voting population of California, has about one-fourteenth as many electoral votes, making each Alaskan voter about seven times as powerful as a Californian.

A sampling scheme designed to predict the election outcome must treat each state as a separate stratum to adequately cope with the distortion of the electoral college. The sample results must be separately compiled for each state, and the winner of each state must be determined. The results must then be combined in the same proportion as the electoral votes to present a distortion-free prediction.

Stratified sample {

subgroup as the population itself does. Thus, we obtain a stratified sample, for which we provide the

DEFINITION: A **stratified sample** is obtained by independently selecting a separate simple random sample from each population stratum.

Although it depends on the purpose of the study, stratification is usually required if certain nonhomogeneities are present in the population. There are other reasons why a stratified sample may be desirable. It may be more convenient to collect samples from separate regions. Or there may be some prevailing reason to divide the population, such as to compare strata.

Another form of random sampling is used prevalently in consumer surveying, where it is more economical to interview several persons in the same neighborhood. For example, contrast the time, effort, and expense of collecting 1,000 responses in a city of 100,000 by simple random sampling with the relative ease of completely canvassing a few selected neighborhoods. In the former case, the elementary units are scattered throughout the city; in the latter, the elementary units live next door to each other. Random sampling would therefore require considerable travel between interviews, whereas the door-to-door neighborhood canvass would minimize travel time. Because the interviewer is normally paid by the hour, the simple random sample would be much more expensive.

Neighborhood groupings of people are referred to as **clusters**. Populations may be divided into clusters according to a criterion such as geographical proximity, creating groups that are easy to observe in their entirety. Most often, the clusters that are to be observed are chosen randomly, and so we can state the

DEFINITION: A **cluster sample** is obtained by selecting clusters from the population on the basis of simple random sampling. The sample comprises a census of each random cluster selected.

The only justification for using cluster sampling is that it is economical. Cluster sampling is highly susceptible to sampling bias. In neighborhood surveys, similar responses may be obtained from the entire cluster, as people of similar age, family size, income, and ethnic and educational backgrounds tend to live in the same vicinity. Thus, there is a high risk that persons with certain backgrounds or preferences will not be represented in the sample because the clusters in which they are predominant are not chosen; conversely, other groups may be unduly represented.

certain group won't be represented

At this point, it might be helpful to emphasize the similarities and differences between cluster and stratified samples. Both separate the population into groups, but the basis for distinction is usually the homogeneity within strata versus the accessibility of clusters. In stratified samples, all groups are represented, whereas the cluster sample comprises only a fraction of the groups in a population. In stratified sampling, a sample is taken from within each stratum; in cluster sampling, a census is conducted within each group. The goal of stratified sampling is to eliminate certain forms of bias; the goal of cluster sampling is to do the job cheaply, which enhances the chance of bias.

Systematic, stratified, and cluster sampling are approximations to simple random sampling. To the extent that the statistical theory applicable to simple random sampling is applied to samples obtained via these other procedures, there may be erroneous conclusions. Throughout much of the remainder of this book, techniques will be developed primarily for analyzing simple random samples. The more complex sampling schemes require more complicated methodology.

EXERCISES

4-10 What type of sample does each of the following represent?
(a) Telephone callers on a radio talk show.
(b) The 30 stocks constituting the Dow Jones Industrial Average.
(c) The record of a gambler's individual wins and losses from a day of placing bets of $1 on black in roulette.
(d) The oranges purchased by a shopper from the produce section of a market.

4-11 In the following situations, would you recommend the use of judgment, convenience, or random sampling, or some combination of these? Explain.
(a) A saleswoman for Fly Paper Company is preparing a kit of product samples to carry on her next road trip to printing concerns.
(b) A teacher asks his students for suggestions as to how he can improve curriculum. He plans to use their suggestions as a basis for a questionnaire concerning curriculum preferences.

(c) Gotham City wants to compare the wages of its clerical workers with the wages of persons holding comparable jobs in private industry.

(d) Centralia Bell plans to purchase a fleet of standard-sized cars from one of four different manufacturers. The criterion for selection will be economy of operation.

(e) A *Daily Planet* editor selects letters from the day's mail to print on the editorial page. (Answer from the editor's point of view.)

4-12 Getting Oil Company wishes to obtain a random sample of its customers to estimate the relative proportion of purchases made from other oil companies. An accountant on the operations staff has recommended that a random sample of credit card customers be selected. An independent survey firm would be retained to obtain detailed records of the following month's purchases by brand and quantity for each sample unit. Evaluate this procedure.

4-13 A medical research foundation wishes to obtain a random sample of expectant mothers to investigate postnatal developments in their newborn babies. Various metropolitan areas are to be represented. Suggest a procedure that might be used to select the sample in a particular city.

4-14 A certain U.S. senator is reputed to follow the majority opinion of his constituents on important pending legislation. Over the years, he has accumulated a panel of 20 persons whom his secretary contacts before a major Senate vote. Panel members are replaced only when they die or change their state of residence. The senator's votes usually coincide with the majority of this panel. Comment on this policy.

4-15 A random sample must be obtained in each of the following situations. Indicate whether a cluster, stratified, or combined sampling procedure should be used. Explain.

(a) A WaySafe market wishes to determine its customers' attitudes toward trading stamps. Because the funds for the survey are limited, the sample replies are to be obtained by interviewing customers on the store premises.

(b) A Fast-Gro agronomist wants to take a sample to compare the effectiveness of two fertilizers on a variety of crops under a range of climate and soil conditions.

(c) FlyMe Airlines is taking a sample of its first-class and tourist-class passengers to assess the quality of its in-flight meals. The passengers' ratings must be taken directly after they have eaten their meals.

4-5 SELECTING STATISTICAL PROCEDURES

A complete examination of statistical procedures is made in several later chapters. All of these procedures make generalizations about a population when only sample data are available. We call this process **inductive** or **inferential statistics**. There are several types of inference, and the procedures to be used depend on the goals of the study.

Statistical procedures should be determined during the planning stage. There are many ways to do this. The simplest procedure is to estimate a population's parameter, such as its mean, standard deviation, or proportion. The most complicated procedures test some hypothesis regarding the population's characteristics. Ordinarily, several testing schemes are employed. In all tests, the decision is indicated by the sample results. Many tests actually compare two or more populations and require that a separate sample be obtained from each.

In the fields of education, psychology, and medicine, the two-sample testing procedure is a popular way to decide which of two approaches is better. Often the status quo is compared to a proposed improvement. For example, a new method of teaching reading might be evaluated in terms of comprehension test scores. The population of scores achieved by students in the current reading program could be compared to the test scores achieved by another group of readers exposed to the new program. Because the new program might or might not be adopted, the associated population would not exist yet. Nevertheless, a sample of readers in the new program would represent this potentially large group, making it a target population. The actual comparison would be made between separate samples from both populations.

The readers in the sample from the current program are referred to as the **control group**, because they are not subjected to anything new. The readers in the second sample constitute the **experimental group**, because these students are exposed to a new procedure on a trial basis primarily to evaluate its merit. Control and experimental groups are common in many testing situations, such as in evaluating a new drug or medical procedure, selecting a more effective fertilizer, or checking new safety devices.

The simplest way to conduct a two-sample test is to select the two groups **independently**. Readers in the control and experimental groups would be chosen using separate lists of random numbers. (Ordinarily, both samples would be derived from a common frame of applicable students, because the experimental group represents only a target population.) One drawback to independent sampling is that any differences in the reading comprehension scores of the two groups could be attributed to causes other than the particular reading programs, such as previous level of reading or home environment. The danger that some outside influence might camouflage the actual differences between the two reading programs could be minimized by applying a stratified sampling scheme. Then two separate groups would be selected each from the same categories of student knowledge and background. If large enough, each group should provide a representative cross section of the student body.

A common method for choosing the control and experimental groups is to pair each elementary unit with one that closely matches it in terms of potential extraneous influences. One member of each pair would be assigned to the experimental group; the other member, to the control group. This is called **matched-pairs sampling**. The procedure is epitomized by studies of identical twins, who are genetically the same and who normally share the same environment as well. In our survey, one twin would be assigned to the existing reading program and the other would participate in the new program. Thus, any differences in reading scores between sample groups could be confidently attributed to differences in the reading programs and not to other causes. For practical purposes, twins are rare and are not normally used in such tests, but unrelated individuals might still be paired. For example, a new drug for heart patients could be tested with pairs matched in terms of age, sex, weight, marital status, smoking habits, medical histories, and so on, thereby producing "near twins." Identical twins who were reared apart have been extensively studied in an attempt to isolate the effects of heredity and environment on intelligence.

STATISTICS AROUND US

Evaluating a Beverage Container Law

A new law was about to become effective requiring that all soft drink and beer containers be returnable, in order to eliminate the unsightly refuse problem caused by pop-top cans. Bottles were to be used exclusively. To guarantee that the empty bottles would be returned, a deposit was required by the seller, as it had been throughout the United States 20 years earlier.

To assess the effectiveness of the beverage container law, a study was made to determine how it affected accumulations of roadside litter. A random sample of 30 one-mile stretches of highway was chosen, cleared of all beer and soda cans, and left to the vagaries of normal public neglect and mistreatment for three months before the new law became effective. The 30 miles of highway served as the control group, representing state residents' littering habits when beverage containers were not dictated by law. At the end of three months, the litter was cleared and the cans were counted. For the initial three months under the new law, the same 30 miles—now the experimental group—were again left to accumulate beverage containers (which would only be bottles this time). The accumulations of the two groups were then compared.

This study shows how the same elementary units can sometimes be used in both the control and the experimental groups. In this case, each one-mile segment after the law became effective was matched with itself in a preceding time period. In this way, traffic conditions and local idiosyncrasies were alike and could not be responsible for any differences between the two groups. However, using the same units in both groups is valid only if no bias is induced on the second set of observations by the first set—and this is the point at which the study fell apart. When the beverage litter was measured the second time, very little was found. But all other kinds of litter were practically absent, too, and adjacent stretches of highway were abnormally clean. At first blush, environmental officials were ecstatic at the apparent widespread impact of their new law. But they became embarrassed when it was determined that the pattern prevailed only near the test tracts and not throughout the state.

Who absconded with the litter and why? Perhaps environmentalists—well aware that the new law would be temporary unless it proved effective—tried to help the study along by cleaning up the test stretches. Maybe when the state cleaned the one-mile parcels, local residents were shamed into picking up their own litter.

On the advice of a statistician, officials discarded the second set of test results and matched the original 30 one-mile stretches of highway with 30 similar ones that had not been cleaned. The new areas were checked only once, and only the returnable bottles were counted (the old cans did not have to be).

The Statistics Around Us box on page 134 describes the experiences of one state during the ecology renaissance of the early 1970s. That experience illustrates the pitfalls of inadequate planning when conducting a statistical study.

SUMMARY

1. Why should samples be used?

There are several compelling reasons for sampling. The usual reason is that a sample is less expensive than a complete enumeration or **census** of the population. Samples are also more timely and more desirable when the population is large or not totally accessible. The use of samples is mandatory when the observation itself is destructive.

2. What are the stages of a statistical sampling study?

There are three stages for a statistical sampling study. First, we have the **planning stage**, where the overall study design is established and the procedures are chosen. *Deductive statistics* is used here. Next, we have the **data collection stage**, which involves the actual work of making the observations. Care must be taken to avoid procedural *errors* and *bias*. Sampling studies are completed during the **data analysis and conclusions stage**. It is here where inductive or inferential statistics comes into play.

planning,
data collection
analysis/conclusion

3. How can we avoid bias and control sampling error?

Although there are no guarantees that a sample will be typical or accurate, good statistical procedures control **sampling error**—the difference between the population and the sample that is due to the particular units selected for observation. You can control sampling error by eliminating **sampling bias**, thereby giving all units the same chance of being selected. You can avoid **nonsampling error** by eliminating inaccuracies in the observation process itself.

4. What are the main types of samples?

There are three broad categories of samples: the **convenience sample**, where the easiest observations are made; the **judgment sample**, where particular sample units are chosen to "guarantee" a representative sample; and the **random sample**, where all elementary units have an equal chance of being observed and included in the sample. Only the random sample is free from sampling bias, but it still may involve some unavoidable sampling error.

convenience
judgement
random

5. What are the various forms of random sampling?

The most common type of random sample is the **simple random sample**, which allows an equal chance that any particular unit will be observed. The sample units are often chosen using a list of **random numbers**. A **systematic random sample** uses a single random number to establish a sequential starting point. A **stratified sample** guarantees inclusion of units from various *strata*. A **cluster sample** involves the complete enumeration of a few randomly selected *clusters*.

6. What are some of the important elements of a statistical experiment?

Most statistical methodology assumes that simple random samples will be used. Although one population and sample is the usual case, some statistical investigations involve multiple populations. One common investigation compares a **control group** to an **experimental group**. Often the two samples are selected independently. An efficient alternative is the **controlled experiment**, which uses **matched-pairs sampling**.

match-pairs,
sampling

REAL-LIFE STATISTICAL CHALLENGE

Selecting the Automobile of Your Dreams

In the last chapter we calculated summary statistics for a set of sports cars. You were asked to select the "car of your dreams" from the list. From a sampling standpoint, you were then using a convenience sample. The sampling process was not random.

Consider selecting your automobile from a larger number of models. Table 4-2 lists 231 makes and models of automobiles. As in Chapter 3, we can compare automobiles in terms of their fuel efficiency. The listed cars are classified by type based primarily on size: two-seater, minicompact, subcompact, compact, midsize, and large.

Table 4-2 shows the model, manufacturer, type of car, transmission type, engine displacement (liters), and miles per gallon (highway). The transmission is either manual (M) or automatic (A or L) and may have different gear configurations (3, 4, 5, or 6 forward). The number in the first column shows a sequence number we will use for our random sampling operations. The first 36 cars are from the same list as in Chapter 3. They are followed by the remaining types of automobiles.

DISCUSSION QUESTIONS

1. Select a random sample of 15 automobiles from the list. What is the median mileage for this list?

2. Use a stratified random sample to select 30 cars from the list. Make sure each size type has equal representation. Compare the median mileage with the sample drawn for Question 1.

3. From the list in this chapter, have members of your class select the car of their choice. (People may select the same automobiles as last time.) Compare the list of cars your classmates derived from the "sporty cars" in Chapter 3 with the list derived from this chapter. Do you think the summary statistics will change? (We will compare the summary statistics for both data sets in a later chapter. It is not required that you calculate the new values at this time.)

4. Several types of vehicles are not included, such as light trucks and vans. Discuss the issues of sampling or nonsampling bias and error.

5. This list includes only 1990 model year cars. What impact would adding data from later years have on your sample?

TABLE 4-2 Mileage Data for 1990 Automobiles Showing Transmission Type, Engine Displacement (Liters) and Highway Mileage per Gallon.

Number	Type	Manufacturer	Model	Trans-mission Type	Engine Displace-ment (liters)	Highway Mileage (miles/gallon)	Number	Type	Manufacturer	Model	Trans-mission Type	Engine Displace-ment (liters)	Highway Mileage (miles/gallon)
0000	T	Alfa-Romeo	Spider	M5	2.0	30	0055	S	Chrysler	LeBaron-con	M5	2.2	28
0001	T	Buick	Reatta	L4	3.8	27	0056	S	Chrysler	LeBaron-con	A3	2.5	23
0002	T	Cadillac	Allante	L4	4.5	22	0057	S	Chrysler	LeBaron-con	L3	2.5	27
0003	T	Chevrolet	Corvette	L4	5.7	24	0058	S	Chrysler	LeBaron-con	M5	3.0	27
0004	T	Chevrolet	Corvette	M6	5.7	25	0059	S	Daihatsu	Charade	M5	1.0	42
0005	T	Chrysler	TC/Maserati	M5	2.2	25	0060	S	Daihatsu	Charade	A3	1.3	34
0006	T	Chrysler	TC/Maserati	L4	3.0	24	0061	S	Daihatsu	Charade	M5	1.3	39
0007	T	Ferrari	Testarossa	M5	4.9	15	0062	S	Dodge	Colt	L3	1.5	29
0008	T	Honda	Civic CRX	L4	1.5	35	0063	S	Dodge	Colt	M4	1.5	36
0009	T	Honda	Civic CRX	M5	1.5	35	0064	S	Dodge	Colt	M5	1.5	34
0010	T	Honda	Civic CRX	M5	1.6	33	0065	S	Dodge	Colt	L4	1.6	28
0011	T	Honda	Civic CRX-HF	M5	1.5	52	0066	S	Dodge	Colt	M5	1.6	28
0012	T	Lamborghini	Countach	M5	5.2	10	0067	S	Dodge	Daytona	M5	2.2	28
0013	T	Lotus	Lotus	M5	2.2	27	0068	S	Dodge	Daytona	A3	2.5	23
0014	T	Maserati	Karif	L4	2.8	18	0069	S	Dodge	Daytona	L3	2.5	27
0015	T	Maserati	Karif	M5	2.8	20	0070	S	Dodge	Daytona	M5	2.5	32
0016	T	Maserati	Spyder	L4	2.8	18	0071	S	Dodge	Daytona	M5	3.0	27
0017	T	Maserati	Spyder	M5	2.8	20	0072	S	Dodge	Omni	L3	2.2	30
0018	T	Mazda	RX-7	L4	1.3	23	0073	S	Dodge	Omni	M5	2.2	34
0019	T	Mazda	RX-7	M5	1.3	25	0074	S	Eagle	Talon	L4	2.0	27
0020	T	Mazda	RX-7	M5	1.3	24	0075	S	Eagle	Talon	M5	2.0	29
0021	T	Mazda	Miata	M5	1.6	30	0076	S	Eagle	Talon/4WD	M5	2.0	25
0022	T	Mercedes-Benz	500 SL	M5	5.0	21	0077	S	Ford	Festiva	A3	1.3	33
0023	T	Nissan	300ZX	L4	3.0	24	0078	S	Ford	Festiva	M5	1.3	41
0024	T	Nissan	300ZX	M5	3.0	24	0079	S	Ford	Mustang	L4	2.3	27
0025	M	Maserati	222E	L4	2.8	18	0080	S	Ford	Mustang	M5	2.3	29
0026	M	Maserati	222E	M5	2.8	20	0081	S	Ford	Mustang	L4	5.0	25
0027	M	Nissan	240SX	L4	2.4	25	0082	S	Ford	Mustang	M5	5.0	24
0028	M	Nissan	240SX	M5	2.4	27	0083	S	Geo	Metro	A3	1.0	40
0029	M	Porsche	911-4/2	M5	3.6	24	0084	S	Geo	Metro	M5	1.0	50
0030	M	Porsche	911-FWD	M5	3.6	22	0085	S	Geo	Metro LSI	A3	1.0	39
0031	M	Porsche	928-S4	A4	5.0	19	0086	S	Geo	Metro LSI	M5	1.0	50
0032	M	Porsche	928-S4	M5	5.0	19	0087	S	Geo	Metro XFI	M5	1.0	58
0033	M	Porsche	944-S2	M5	3.0	26	0088	S	Geo	Prizm	L3	1.6	29
0034	M	Volkswagen	Cabriolet	A3	1.8	28	0089	S	Geo	Prizm	L4	1.6	30
0035	M	Volkswagen	Cabriolet	M5	1.8	32	0090	S	Geo	Prizm	M5	1.6	34
0036	S	Acura	Integra	L4	1.8	27	0091	S	Geo	Storm	A3	1.6	31
0037	S	Acura	Integra	M5	1.8	28	0092	S	Geo	Storm	L4	1.6	32
0038	S	Audi	Quattro	M5	2.3	24	0093	S	Geo	Storm	M5	1.6	36
0039	S	Audi	80	A3	2.0	27	0094	S	Honda	Civic	L4	1.5	33
0040	S	Audi	80	M5	2.0	30	0095	S	Honda	Civic	M4	1.5	37
0041	S	Audi	90	A3	2.3	22	0096	S	Honda	Civic	M5	1.5	34
0042	S	Audi	90	M5	2.3	26	0097	S	Honda	Civic	L4	1.6	29
0043	S	Audi	90 Quat-20V	M5	2.3	24	0098	S	Honda	Civic	M5	1.6	32
0044	S	BMW	M3	M5	2.3	29	0099	S	Hyundai	Excel	L4	1.5	32
0045	S	BMW	325i-conv	L4	2.5	23	0100	S	Hyundai	Excel	M4	1.5	33
0046	S	BMW	325i-conv	M5	2.5	25	0101	S	Hyundai	Excel	M5	1.5	36
0047	S	BMW	325i/325s	L4	2.5	22	0102	S	Hyundai	Precis	L4	1.5	32
0048	S	BMW	325i/325s	M5	2.5	23	0103	S	Hyundai	Precis	M4	1.5	33
0049	S	BMW	325ix	L4	2.5	22	0104	S	Hyundai	Precis	M5	1.5	36
0050	S	BMW	325ix	M5	2.5	23	0105	S	Infiniti	M30	L4	3.0	25
0051	S	Chevrolet	Camaro	L4	3.1	27	0106	S	Isuzu	Impulse	L4	1.6	32
0052	S	Chevrolet	Camaro	L4	5.0	24	0107	S	Isuzu	Impulse	M5	1.6	34
0053	S	Chevrolet	Camaro	M5	5.0	26	0108	S	Maserati	430	L4	2.8	18
0054	S	Chevrolet	Camaro	L4	5.7	24	0109	S	Maserati	430	M5	2.8	20

(continued on next page)

Source: U.S. Environmental Protection Agency, 1989.
Type: T, Two-Seater; M, Minicompact; S, Subcompact; C, Compact; MS, Mid-Size; L, Large.

TABLE 4-2 (continued)

Number	Type	Manufacturer	Model	Transmission Type	Engine Displacement (liters)	Highway Mileage (miles/gallon)	Number	Type	Manufacturer	Model	Transmission Type	Engine Displacement (liters)	Highway Mileage (miles/gallon)
0110	S	Mitsubishi	Eclipse	L4	1.8	30	0171	C	Volvo	240	M5	2.0	28
0111	S	Mitsubishi	Eclipse	M5	1.8	32	0172	C	Volvo	780	A4	2.8	21
0112	S	Mitsubishi	Eclipse	L4	2.0	27	0173	MS	ASC	Grand Prix	L4	3.1	25
0113	S	Mitsubishi	Mirage	M5	1.6	28	0174	MS	Audi	V8	L4	3.6	18
0114	S	Nissan	Pulsar NX	M5	1.8	30	0175	MS	Audi	100 Quattro	M5	2.3	24
0115	S	Nissan	Sentra	M5	1.6	36	0176	MS	Audi	200 Quattro	M5	2.2	25
0116	S	Nissan	Sentra Coupe	M5	1.6	36	0177	MS	BMW	735i	L4	3.4	21
0117	S	Nissan	300ZX 22	M5	3.0	24	0178	MS	BMW	750iL	L4	5.0	18
0118	S	Plymouth	Colt	M5	1.6	28	0179	MS	Buick	Century	L4	3.3	29
0119	S	Plymouth	Horizon	M5	2.2	34	0180	MS	Buick	Regal	L4	3.1	30
0120	S	Plymouth	Laser	M5	2.0	29	0181	MS	Buick	Riviera	L4	3.8	27
0121	S	Pontiac	Firebird	M5	5.0	25	0182	MS	Cadillac	Eldorado	L4	4.5	25
0122	S	Pontiac	Sunbird Con	M5	2.0	33	0183	MS	Cadillac	Seville	L4	4.5	25
0123	S	Saab	900 Con	M5	2.0	28	0184	MS	Chevrolet	Corsica	L3	3.1	27
0124	S	Subaru	Justy	M5	1.2	37	0185	MS	Chevrolet	Lumina	L4	3.1	30
0125	S	Subaru	Justy 4WD	M5	1.2	33	0186	MS	Chrysler	New Yorker	L4	3.3	26
0126	S	Subaru	XT	M5	1.8	31	0187	MS	Dodge	Dynasty	L4	3.3	26
0127	S	Subaru	XT 4WD	M5	1.8	29	0188	MS	Dodge	Spirit	L3	2.5	27
0128	S	Suzuki	Swift	M5	1.3	44	0189	MS	Ford	Taurus	L4	3.8	28
0129	S	Suzuki	Swift GT	M5	1.3	36	0190	MS	Ford	Thunderbird	L4	3.8	23
0130	S	Toyota	Celica	M5	2.2	29	0191	MS	Hyundai	Sonata	L4	2.4	26
0131	S	Toyota	Corolla	L4	1.6	33	0192	MS	Infiniti	Q45	L4	4.5	22
0132	S	Toyota	Supra	L4	3.0	23	0193	MS	Lexus	LS400	L4	4.0	24
0133	S	Toyota	Tercel	L3	1.5	32	0194	MS	Lincoln-Mercury	Cougar	L4	3.8	23
0134	S	Volkswagen	Corrado	M5	1.8	28	0195	MS	Lincoln-Mercury	Mark VII	L4	5.0	24
0135	S	Volkswagen	Fox	M4	1.8	30	0196	MS	Lincoln-Mercury	Sable	L4	3.8	28
0136	C	Acura	Legend	L4	2.7	22	0197	MS	Maserati	228	M5	2.8	19
0137	C	BMW	525i	L4	2.5	23	0198	MS	Mazda	626	L4	2.2	25
0138	C	BMW	535i	L4	3.4	21	0199	MS	Mazda	929	L4	3.0	23
0139	C	Buick	Skylark	L3	3.3	27	0200	MS	Mercedes-Benz	300 E	L4	3.0	22
0140	C	Chevrolet	Beretta	M5	3.1	28	0201	MS	Nissan	Maxima	L4	3.0	26
0141	C	Chevrolet	Cavalier	L3	3.1	27	0202	MS	Oldsmobile	Ciera	L4	3.3	29
0142	C	Chrysler	LeBaron	L3	2.5	27	0203	MS	Oldsmobile	Supreme	L4	3.1	30
0143	C	Dodge	Shadow	L3	2.5	27	0204	MS	Oldsmobile	Trofeo	L4	3.8	27
0144	C	Eagle	Summit	M5	1.6	28	0205	MS	Plymouth	Acclaim	L3	2.5	27
0145	C	Ford	Escort	M5	1.9	30	0206	MS	Pontiac	Grand Prix	L4	3.1	30
0146	C	Ford	Probe	L4	3.0	26	0207	MS	Pontiac	6000	L4	3.1	30
0147	C	Ford	Tempo	A3	2.3	23	0208	MS	Rolls-Royce	Bentley-Cont.	A3	6.8	13
0148	C	Honda	Accord	L4	2.2	28	0209	MS	Rolls-Royce	Corniche III	A3	6.8	13
0149	C	Isuzu	Stylus	M5	1.6	33	0210	MS	Rolls-Royce	Bentley-8	A3	6.8	13
0150	C	Jaguar	Jaguar	L4	4.0	22	0211	MS	Rolls-Royce	Silver Spirit	A3	6.8	13
0151	C	Lexus	ES250	L4	2.5	25	0212	MS	Volkswagen	Passat	L4	2.0	29
0152	C	Lincoln-Mercury	Topaz	A3	2.3	23	0213	MS	Volvo	740	L4	2.3	26
0153	C	Mazda	323/Protege	L4	1.6	33	0214	MS	Volvo	740-16	L4	2.3	24
0154	C	Mitsubishi	Galant	M5	2.0	29	0215	MS	Volvo	760	A4	2.8	21
0155	C	Mitsubishi	Sigma	A4	3.0	22	0216	L	Buick	Electra	L4	3.8	27
0156	C	Nissan	Stanza	M5	2.4	29	0217	L	Buick	LeSabre	L4	3.8	27
0157	C	Oldsmobile	Calais	L3	3.3	27	0218	L	Cadillac	Brougham	L4	5.7	21
0158	C	Peugeot	405	L4	1.9	25	0219	L	Cadillac	Fleetwood	L4	4.5	25
0159	C	Plymouth	Sundance	L3	2.5	27	0220	L	Chevrolet	Caprice	L4	5.0	25
0160	C	Pontiac	Grand Am	M5	2.5	33	0221	L	Chrysler	New Yorker	L4	3.3	25
0161	C	Pontiac	LeMans	L3	2.0	30	0222	L	Dodge	Monaco	L4	3.0	26
0162	C	Pontiac	Sunbird	L3	2.0	28	0223	L	Eagle	Premier	L4	3.0	26
0163	C	Saab	900	A3	2.0	23	0224	L	Ford	LTD	L4	5.0	24
0164	C	Subaru	Legacy	M5	2.2	30	0225	L	Lincoln	Continental	L4	3.8	25
0165	C	Subaru	Loyale	L3	1.8	26	0226	L	Mercury	Grand Marquis	L4	5.0	24
0166	C	Toyota	Camry	L4	2.0	31	0227	L	Lincoln	Town Car	L4	5.0	24
0167	C	Toyota	Cressida	L4	3.0	24	0228	L	Oldsmobile	Eighty-Eight	L4	3.8	27
0168	C	Volkswagen	Golf	M5	1.8	32	0229	L	Oldsmobile	Ninety-Eight	L4	3.8	27
0169	C	Volkswagen	GTI	M5	2.0	28	0230	L	Pontiac	Bonneville	L4	3.8	27
0170	C	Volkswagen	Jetta	M5	1.8	32	0231	L	Saab	9000	L4	2.0	24

Type: T, Two-Seater; M, Minicompact; S, Subcompact; C, Compact; MS, Mid-Size; L, Large.

REVIEW EXERCISES

4-16 Starting in the fifth column of the random number table (Appendix Table B), select a simple random sample of ten symphony conductors from those listed in Table 4-1. Use only the first two digits of each random number from the table. List the names selected.

4-17 List the names for a systematic random sample of ten symphony conductors chosen from Table 4-1. Assume that the starting random number selects Sir John Barbirolli as the first name.

4-18 Suppose that each successive ten names in Table 4-1 provides a stratum. Redesignate the names in each stratum, starting with 0 and ending with 9, maintaining the original alphabetical sequence. Then select a stratified random sample that contains one conductor from each group. Assume that the following random numbers apply in the respective strata.

6   5   5   2   1   9   8   7   7   0

List the names selected.

4-19 Treat each successive five names in Table 4-1 as a cluster. A random cluster sample of two clusters from the 20 is to be selected. After assigning a number (1 through 20) to each successive cluster, use the random numbers 18 and 4 to select the sample. List the names selected.

STATISTICS IN PRACTICE

4-20 Using the master class data set that you developed in Exercise 1-19, perform the following statistical sampling study exercises.

(a) Convenience sampling: Look around your classroom and list the names of the five people sitting closest to you in your class. Referring your class data list, do you notice any unusual data patterns (people in your sample sharing a common characteristic)?

(b) Judgment sample: Select a variable from your class list and write the names of those people who share a common characteristic. List the data for these students. Do you notice any patterns in the data for the people you selected?

(c) Random sample: Using the case numbers, collect a sample of 5 people using the table of random numbers. List the data for these students.

(d) Conduct a stratified sample by classifying one variable into three categories. Randomly select 5 names from each stratum. List the data for these students.

(e) Compare the results of your samples from (a)—(d). Comment on any patterns in the data you observe. Are there detectable elements of bias and error in the sampling?

4-21 Using your group's class data from Exercise 1-21, perform the same statistical sampling study exercises listed in (a) through (e) of Exercise 4-20.

4-22 Table 4-3 shows the 20 most populous countries for the year 1991. The data list also includes gross domestic or national product. A global retailer

TABLE 4-3 Population and GNP for World's Most Populous Countries

1991 Rank	Country	Population	GNP or GDP (billions $s)
1	China	1,151,300,000	$350
2	India	859,200,000	333
3	United States	252,800,000	5,233
4	Indonesia	181,400,000	80
5	Brazil	153,300,000	377
6	Russia	147,400,000	1,330
7	Japan	123,800,000	1,914
8	Nigeria	122,500,000	30
9	Pakistan	117,500,000	43
10	Bangladesh	116,600,000	21
11	Mexico	85,700,000	137
12	Germany	79,500,000	1,105
13	Vietnam	67,600,000	14
14	Philippines	62,300,000	41
15	Thailand	58,800,000	65
16	Iran	58,600,000	94
17	Turkey	58,500,000	75
18	Italy	57,700,000	803
19	United Kingdom	57,500,000	818
20	France	56,700,000	820
	Total	3,868,700,000	$13,683

Source: *The 1992 Information Please Almanac* 136, and "Countries of the World Section": 147–286. GCP for Russia estimated by the author.

wishes to survey consumer preferences for the following items: children's toys, sports cars, condoms, and frozen foods. What would be the advantages of using a sample? Which sampling method would you suggest? Which elements of bias and error in the sampling should the market researchers watch for?

4-23 Table 1-2 (page 18) provides data on estimates of the location of homeless people discussed in Chapter 1. Discuss which sampling method would be most appropriate. Which elements of bias and sampling should the researchers watch for?

4-24 Use the exam score data in Table 3-13 to complete the following:
(a) Select a simple random sample of size 10.
(b) Select a stratified sample of size 10 by partitioning the scores into 10 groups of equal size and then randomly selecting one score from each group.
(c) Select a cluster sample of size 10 by partitioning the scores into 20 groups of equal size and then randomly selecting two groups.
(d) Select a systematic random sample of size 10 by randomly selecting the first score and then choosing every fourth score until you have 10 scores in total.

4-25 For each of the samples collected in (a)–(b) of Problem 4-24, compute the mean and standard deviation. Compare these to the mean and standard deviation obtained for the entire class in Problem 3-67. Comment on whether or not the sample parameters are close to the parameters for the class.

4-26 Refer to Problem 4-24. Suppose, for convenience, you decide to choose the first 10 scores to be your sample. Compute the mean and standard deviation of your sample and comment on the suitability of using this method of sampling.

CASE   Boomville

Peggy Jones is a marketing researcher. She has selected the city of Boomville as her marketplace barometer for testing new product concepts. The map of a Boomville test sector is provided in Figure 4-2 and will aid Peggy's evaluation of various research procedures. She has placed homes arbitrarily into "census tracts," each representing a contiguous neighborhood. Household identity, address, and family income data are given in Table 4-4.

To begin Peggy selects sample incomes from the Boomville residents. In later studies, she will observe other types of demographic data. Her present concern is to select a sampling procedure that will be representative of Boomville as a whole. She needs the expertise of a person knowledgeable in statistics.

QUESTIONS

1. To assist Peggy in determining an overall sampling procedure, you select a *simple random sample* of resident incomes from the Boomville sector.
   (a) Matching the following random numbers with the corresponding household identity codes, select a simple random sample of ten family incomes.

34	01	17	73	93	05	54	89	42	29

   List the results selected.
   (b) Calculate the mean.
   (c) Comment on the advantages and disadvantages of this procedure.

2. As an alternative procedure, Peggy may use a *systematic random sample*.
   (a) Select, from the Boomville sector, a systematic random sample of ten family incomes. To do this, use the identity codes, and pick every tenth household, starting with the randomly selected code 07. List the sample results.
   (b) Calculate the mean.
   (c) Comment on the advantages and disadvantages of this procedure.

3. A third sampling approach might be for Peggy to take a *cluster sample*.
   (a) Treat each census tract as a cluster. Use the first applicable random numbers in the following sequence to select two clusters by matching the appropriate census tract code.

1	6	8	6	3	8	7	4

   List the tracts selected.

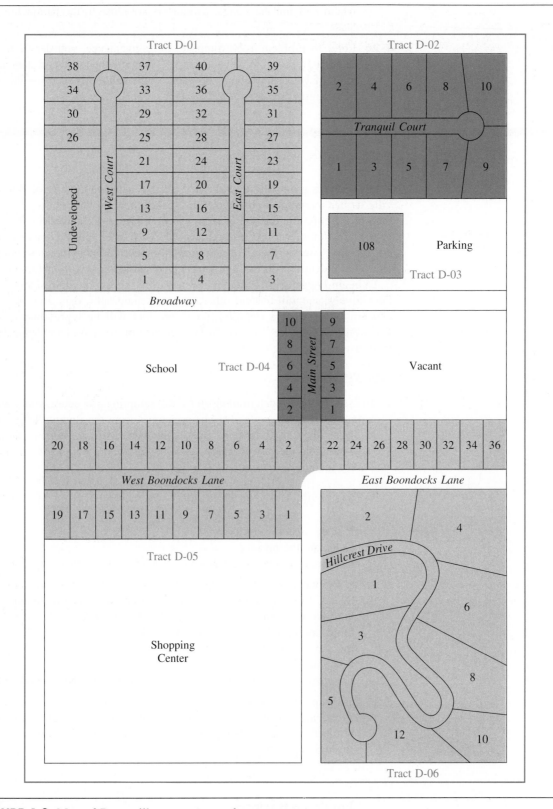

FIGURE 4-2 Map of Boomville test sector and census tracts.

TABLE 4-4 Family Income Data for the Boomville Test Sector

Household	Address	Income	Household	Address	Income	Household	Address	Income
	East Boondocks Lane			Main Street			East Court	
01	22	$15,772	29	1	$ 4,675	57	3	$18,998
02	24	14,667	30	2	6,778	58	4	13,556
03	26	21,539	31	3	5,558	59	7	17,956
04	28	11,814	32	4	8,905	60	8	14,665
05	30	7,644	33	5	5,731	61	11	19,545
06	32	12,888	34	6	7,088	62	12	16,997
07	34	11,119	35	7	6,775	63	15	15,305
08	36	10,024	36	8	9,222	64	16	15,555
	West Boondocks Lane		37	9	9,776	65	19	16,885
			38	10	5,783	66	20	17,554
09	1	$ 9,836	39	108-01	14,453	67	23	21,115
10	2	8,448	40	108-02	10,113	68	24	20,997
11	3	10,887	41	108-03	8,985	69	27	16,666
12	4	13,464	42	108-04	21,119	70	28	17,002
13	5	11,118	43	108-05	16,668	71	31	15,155
14	6	12,747	44	108-06	10,560	72	32	18,444
15	7	10,777	45	108-07	14,554	73	35	15,876
16	8	9,007	46	108-08	11,800	74	36	16,123
17	9	12,225		Tranquil Court		75	39	20,001
18	10	12,345				76	40	18,888
19	11	10,554	47	1	$24,776		Hillcrest Drive	
20	12	13,098	48	2	26,123			
21	13	10,567	49	3	30,001	77	1	$57,845
22	14	8,553	50	4	28,888	78	2	28,553
23	15	11,863	51	5	28,998	79	3	42,735
24	16	13,119	52	6	23,556	80	4	60,600
25	17	12,225	53	7	27,956	81	5	38,887
26	18	10,887	54	8	24,665	82	6	71,775
27	19	11,008	55	9	29,545	83	8	31,119
28	20	11,080	56	10	26,997	84	10	40,000
						85	12	56,337
							West Court	
						86	1	$12,223
						87	5	10,678
						88	9	14,556
						89	13	13,665
						90	17	15,997
						91	21	14,555
						92	25	16,554
						93	26	22,115
						94	29	19,997
						95	30	17,666
						96	33	16,002
						97	34	16,155
						98	37	17,444
						99	38	16,876

(b) The sample consists of household incomes for the residences in those tracts. List the sample results.

(c) Calculate the mean.

(d) Comment on the advantages and disadvantages of this procedure.

4. Instead of the cluster sample, Peggy may decide to use a *stratified random sample*. Although strata may be identified in a variety of ways, such as income, education, or occupation, Peggy limits this investigation to locational strata. To do this, treat each census tract as a separate stratum, and take a simple random sample from each.

(a) Obtain Peggy's stratified random sample using two observations per stratum. Begin with tract D-01 and proceed through the tracts with the next highest identity code. Match the following random numbers with the street or apartment number. Be sure to skip the random numbers that do not apply to an address and never go back to an earlier random number. Starting in the upper left-hand corner, proceed horizontally, line by line.

```
56  04  57  55  85  34  01  17  73  93  05  54  89  42  29  57
69  43  10  77  97  78  17  40  30  23  80  32  94  31  20  91
46  75  29  15  31  82  44  77  32  42  11  09  14  61  19  00
12  05  63  29  23  33  05  49  29  48  21  90  01  58  07  03
24  25  47  16  41  14  61  12  55  86  88  02  39  44  57  56
```

(b) List the incomes.

(b) Calculate the mean.

(c) Comment on the advantages and disadvantages of this procedure.

5. Peggy may prefer the *convenience sample*, a less sophisticated sampling approach that would enable her to choose sample residences quickly.

(a) Imagine yourself as a canvasser in Boomville, except that you forgot to take along the map. You must return with sample incomes, and you want to work quickly. Take a convenience sample by obtaining only the income data for residents of the apartment house on 108 Main Street. You find nobody home in unit 02. The tenant in unit 05 wants to preserve his privacy and does not open the door. The remaining residents provide the income information you request (listed in Table 4-4). List the sample results.

(b) Calculate the mean.

(c) Comment on the advantages and disadvantages of this procedure.

6. Peggy feels that she may be able to improve the approaches by using her judgment to pick sample incomes. There are many ways for her to take such a *judgment sample*. In order to guarantee an element of locational representation, Peggy decides that there should be one income from each census tract.

(a) Obtain her judgment sample by selecting the household with the lowest identity code in each tract. List the sample incomes.

(b) Calculate the mean.

(c) Comment on the advantages and disadvantages of this procedure.

CHAPTER 5

PROBABILITY

BEFORE READING THIS CHAPTER, MAKE SURE YOU UNDERSTAND: *→ probability*

    The distinction between deductive and inductive statistics (Chapter 1).

    The advantages of *random* samples (Chapter 4).   *p.130 — Simple*

    How to generate simple random samples (Chapter 4).

                    Choosing elementary unit
                    each has equal chance

AFTER READING THIS CHAPTER, YOU WILL UNDERSTAND:

    The basic concepts of probability and how they relate to relative frequency.

    Random experiments and the outcomes they generate.

    How to use the count-and-divide method to find probabilities for some events.

    How to express probabilities for joint events (intersections) and to display the related information.

    The advantages of the addition and multiplication laws.

    The importance of statistical independence and how that relationship may be verified.

    What conditional probabilities are and how they are distinguished from ordinary "unconditional" probabilities.

    How to construct and use probability trees.

149

Probability plays a special role in all our lives, because we use it to measure uncertainty. We are continually faced with decisions leading to uncertain outcomes, and we rely on probability to help us make our choices. Probability is a pivotal factor in most significant business decisions. A department store buyer will order heavily in a new style that is believed likely to sell well. A company will launch a new product when the chance of its success seems high enough to outweigh the possibility of losses due to failure. A new college graduate is hired when the probability for satisfactory performance is judged sufficiently high.

Modern probability theory underlies the methodology of statistics, which is less than a hundred years old. Today's probability theory has roots that were planted over 300 years ago. Since statistics uses the language of probability, some knowledge of this interesting subject is crucial before proceeding.

5-1   BASIC PROBABILITY CONCEPTS

Probability theory treats a probability as a number. Such numbers, too, are common. We are all familiar with the weather forecaster's announcement that "there is a 50 percent chance of rain tomorrow." We may extend our understanding of probability to a family of experiments. The simplest of these is the coin toss, for which there is a 50 percent chance of obtaining either outcome: head or tail.

PROBABILITY AS LONG-RUN FREQUENCY

What does a 50 percent chance of getting a head really mean? It is an expression of the **long-run relative frequency** with which a head will be obtained in a series of coin tosses. In ten tosses, we can expect to get 5 heads (50% of 10). But the exact number is uncertain, and 4 or 6 heads are likely possibilities. Fewer or more heads are possible, although most will agree extreme outcomes would be very untypical. (If everybody in your class tosses a coin ten times, how many people do you think would have 0 or 10 heads or even 1 or 9 heads? And what number do you think would be closest to the overall average number of heads per student?) If a machine were to toss a coin every second, the long-run frequency for head would be the fraction .5, and we say that the probability of getting a head on any particular toss is .5.

How do we know that .5 is the correct value? Without making some assumptions, the only way to find the long-run frequency would be to toss the coin a very long time and then see how often head occurs. But we may *logically deduce* that .5 is the correct figure by examining a coin, seeing that there are two sides—one designated the head and the other the tail. Then, we assume that weight is distributed evenly, so that we would expect any toss to be just as likely to end head-side up as tail-side up. Finally, we rely on a key property common to all situations having equally likely outcomes.

THE RANDOM EXPERIMENT AND ITS ELEMENTARY EVENTS

Probability theory focuses on uncertain events, which are generated through a **random experiment**. A coin toss is one example of a random experiment. The most basic outcomes of interest are called **elementary events**. For a coin toss, the usual elementary events are head and tail. (But we could be interested in other elementary events, such as the number of revolutions, the coin's maximum height, or the angle made by Lincoln's nose with respect to the North Pole.) In a random experiment having *N equally likely* elementary events, the long-run frequency of any one of them must be $1/N$.

$$\frac{1}{N}$$

FINDING THE PROBABILITY FOR AN EVENT

We may use the following expression to calculate the

PROBABILITY FOR ONE ELEMENTARY EVENT
(Among Equally Likely Possibilities):

$$\text{Pr[elementary event]} = \frac{1}{N}$$

For the toss of a perfect coin there are $N = 2$ equally likely sides, and

$$\text{Pr[head]} = \frac{1}{2} = .5$$

The following gives a detailed example involving an experiment having equally likely events.

EXAMPLE: ROLL OF THE DIE

A die cube has six faces, the first marked with one dot, the second with two dots, and so on, with the sixth face having six dots. Suppose that the die is rolled. One of the following possibilities applies for the up-side face:

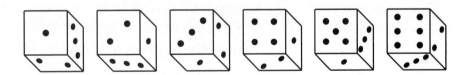

If the cube is perfectly shaped and balanced, then each of the above is an equally likely elementary event. What is the probability that the die stops two-face up?

SOLUTION: There are $N = 6$ equally likely elementary events for this random experiment, so that

$$\text{Pr[2]} = \frac{1}{6} = .1667$$

The above indicates that the long-run frequency for the two-face is 1/6, so that it occurs 16.67% of the time in repeated rolls of the die. Stated equivalently, there is a 16.67% chance of getting a two on any particular roll.

In another example illustrating how to find the probability for an elementary event, suppose that Professor Horatio Dull randomly selects a student to solve one statistics homework problem on the blackboard. If Amy Sax is among the $N = 32$ students in Professor Dull's class, her probability of being chosen is

$$\Pr[\text{AmySax}] = \frac{1}{32} = .03125$$

so that there is a 3.125% chance that she will be chosen. If Prof. Dull always selects a student randomly, then throughout the term Amy Sax would be at the blackboard 3.125% of the time.

COMPLICATING ISSUES

Although many situations involve probabilities that may be computed in the foregoing fashion, complications might arise.

ELEMENTARY EVENTS NEED NOT BE EQUALLY LIKELY

Some elementary events might be more likely than others. This would be the case if a blob of solder is attached to the head-face or if two opposing die cube faces are shaved. Furthermore, we do not know how much solder might be involved nor where it might be placed; nor do we know how deep into the die the cuts might be made. And, Amy Sax might be chosen more often than other students because she always has the right answers; also, she might get picked only for the hardest problems as the term progresses. Under those circumstances, it is impossible to logically deduce probabilities.

We emphasize that the probabilities for head with a lopsided coin, the 2-face with a shaved die, and picking Amy Sax when she is the teacher's pet are *still long-run frequencies*. But their values must be established through observation of actual outcomes. And, they cannot be known with an exactitude until the random experiment has been repeated a very long time. (Should Amy Sax be chosen with increasing frequency over time, a probability value may never become known.)

RANDOM EXPERIMENTS MAY NOT BE REPEATABLE

Consider your grade in statistics. This is strictly a one-shot phenomenon, and only one grade will ever be received. Some uncertainty about the final result undoubtedly exists. But what can we say regarding the probability of getting an "A"? It is obviously not the long-run frequency of "A"; that can happen, if at all, just once. The random experiment of receiving a grade is nonrepeatable.

OBJECTIVE AND SUBJECTIVE PROBABILITIES

Many statisticians would deny the existence of an "A" probability. Others hold that it must be a 0 or a 1, we just do not know which. But most would agree, nevertheless, that an "A" is more likely after hard study than after no studying. We just have difficulty quantifying such an event. Some might attach a value such as .10 or .20. This number is referred to as a **subjective probability**, reflecting that persons might disagree about an appropriate figure. The earlier probability values all arise from repeatable random experiments and are sometimes referred to as **objective probabilities**.

Many important uncertain business events arise from nonrepeatable circumstances. Consider next year's sales of a product, the yearly high of the Dow Jones Average, or your final grade in statistics. Any probabilities given to such events must be based solely on *judgment*. Chapter 20 describes various procedures for determining subjective probabilities.

THE LAW OF LARGE NUMBERS

Suppose a fair coin is tossed 20 times, and a head appears every time. The probability for this happening is less than one-millionth. Does this mean that 20 extra tail outcomes must occur in a long series of future tosses to balance the long-run frequency of occurrence ratio and to coincide with ''head'' having a probability of 1/2? Also, does this increase the probability for obtaining a tail on the next toss?

The answer to both questions is *no*. First, there are no guarantees that any particular sequence of results will exhibit heads even close to one-half the time. This presents no contradiction, because there is a nonzero probability that any number of heads (say, 10,000) will occur in sequence. All that can be stated is that it is not very likely that there will be many more (or fewer) heads than half the number of tosses. A law of probability, the **law of large numbers**, in essence states that the probability for the result deviating significantly from that indicated by the theoretical long-run frequency of occurrence becomes smaller as the number of repetitions (tosses) increases. Thus, if the coin were tossed several thousand more times, the effect of the 20 ''extra'' heads on the resulting frequency would be barely noticeable.

If the coin tossing process is fair (that is, if the process is not biased in favor of heads or tails), then we can infer that the probability for obtaining a head should be 1/2. Also, if the process is fair, then a head would be no more likely to follow a head than a tail would. The probability for obtaining a tail should not increase or decrease if it is accepted that fairness is present. After obtaining 20 heads in a row, human reasoning may lead to the inference that the tossing mechanism is unfair. However, this seemingly aberrant result does not constitute proof of unfairness.

EXERCISES

5-1 You buy a raffle ticket for a new convertible. A total of 20,000 tickets have been sold. The winner will be selected at random from these. What is the probability that you win? $1/20,000$

5-2 A roulette wheel has 38 slots. Two are green, numbered 0 and 00. Of the remaining pockets, 18 are red and 18 are black. Assuming that all pockets are equally likely, what is the probability that the ball for a spinning wheel lands in the 00 pocket? $1/38$

5-3 Besides head and tail, a penny toss may have other types of elementary events, such as the angle made by Lincoln's nose relative to true north. Suggest at least another set of outcomes that might serve as the elementary events.

FIGURE 5-1 Sample space for random selection of a playing card.

5-4 A history student writes 20 important names including Napoleon Bonaparte on separate slips of paper. Each name appears on just one slip. She then draws names one at a time from the box; once selected, a name is not returned to the box.

1/20   (a) What is the probability that Napoleon is the first name selected?

    (b) She has selected 10 names already, not including Napoleon. What is the

1/10   probability that Napoleon is next?

5-2 PROBABILITIES FOR COMPOSITE EVENTS

To expand our knowledge of probability concepts, let's establish additional important concepts. Consider a deck of playing cards, the contents of which are listed in Figure 5-1. Suppose that the deck is thoroughly shuffled and one card is removed. Each card is an elementary event in this random experiment.

THE SAMPLE SPACE, COMPOSITE EVENTS, AND EVENT SETS

What is the probability that the selected card is a queen? In terms of long-run frequency, the desired probability may be determined by the following calculation.

$$\Pr[\text{queen}] = \frac{4}{52} = .077$$

The above calculation reflects that 4 out of 52 cards are queens, so that in repeated experiments a queen should be obtained about 4/52 of the time. In other words, one of the four queens should be drawn in about 7.7% of all selections. Each queen card constitutes an elementary event for getting a queen. The event "queen" is a **composite event**, since it will occur if any of those elementary events occur.

The following listing of the elementary events may be helpful.

$$\text{Queen} = \{ \spadesuit Q, \heartsuit Q, \clubsuit Q, \diamondsuit Q \}$$

Every composite event may be viewed as an **event set** comprising as elements the applicable elementary events. The entire collection of elementary events is an all-inclusive event set sometimes called the **sample space**. Composite events may then be viewed as corresponding to a portion or *subset* of the sample space.

EXAMPLE: TOSSING THREE COINS

Charlie Brown has a penny, a nickel, and a dime, all of which he plans to toss at the same time. Since all three coins will land simultaneously—making one outcome—each outcome, or elementary event, is a different combination of the sides of the coins that will be showing. To impress his friends, Charlie Brown wants to list the sample space.

SOLUTION: His listing is contained in Figure 5-2. In the list, H stands for a head, T for a tail, and the subscripts p, n, and d for the respective coins. Thus, if Charlie Brown tosses his three coins and gets heads with the penny and the nickel and a tail with the dime, he would represent this event as $H_pH_nT_d$.

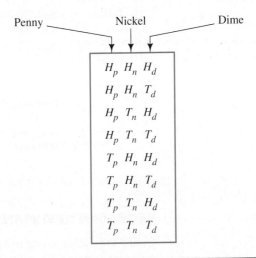

FIGURE 5-2 Sample space for tossing three coins.

THE COUNT-AND-DIVIDE METHOD
FOR COMPUTING PROBABILITIES

In the playing card illustration, all cards have the same chance of being selected. The calculation given above for Pr[queen] illustrates the **count-and-divide method** for finding composite event probabilities.

PROBABILITY—COUNT-AND-DIVIDE METHOD
(Equally Likely Elementary Events):

$$\text{Pr[event]} = \frac{\text{Number of elementary events in the event set}}{\text{Number of possible elementary events}}$$

Consider a second composite event:

$$\text{Heart} = \{ \heartsuit K, \heartsuit Q, \heartsuit J, \heartsuit 10, \heartsuit 9, \heartsuit 8, \heartsuit 7, \heartsuit 6, \heartsuit 5, \heartsuit 4, \heartsuit 3, \heartsuit 2, \heartsuit A \}$$

Counting the elementary events, we see that there are 13 heart cards, any of which yield the event "heart." The complete deck contains 52 cards, and that is the number of elementary events possible. Thus,

$$\text{Pr[heart]} = \frac{13}{52} = .25$$

Applying the count-and-divide method, you can verify the following:

$$\text{Pr[face card]} = 12/52 \qquad \text{Pr[red card]} = 26/52 \qquad \text{Pr[black jack]} = 2/52$$

To further illustrate the count-and-divide method, we will use the sample space in Figure 5-3, which shows the breakdown of the State University business students who hold scholarships. One student is selected at random from the group of 72. The following probabilities apply.

$$\text{Pr[male]} = \frac{40}{72} = .556 \qquad\qquad \text{Pr[female]} = \frac{32}{72} = .444$$

$$\text{Pr[accounting]} = \frac{16}{72} = .222 \qquad \text{Pr[graduate]} = \frac{30}{72} = .417$$

PROBABILITY ESTIMATES

Count-and-divide is one method for determining the long-run frequency at which an event occurs. When we cannot count the possibilities, the count-and-divide approach is unworkable. This is the case for events occurring over time, such as automobile accidents. The true probability for a fatal accident under a given set

FIGURE 5-3 Sample space for business scholarship students at State University.

of circumstances might be .001—the historical frequency. Such a probability value would ordinarily be an *estimate* of the underlying true probability. The count-and-divide method applies only if the elementary events are *equally likely.* What if, for example, a lopsided coin is tossed? The probability for an event in such a random experiment is still a long-run frequency, but it can only be estimated from the actual results experienced by repeating the experiment (tossing the lopsided coin) many times.

EXAMPLE: DEFECTIVE ITEMS IN A PRODUCTION PROCESS

A quality control inspector removes 100 widgets from production and finds that 14 are defective (*D*) and 86 are good (*G*). If you assume that the production process will behave identically in the future, the probability that any particular widget is defective may be *estimated.*

SOLUTION:

$$\Pr[D] = \frac{14}{100} = .14$$

But the above is an estimate, and the true probability remains unknown and could be some other value, such as .175 or .128. The sample space is *not* 100 *D*s and *G*s for the selected items, but rather the quality for every item that will be produced—possibly millions of elementary events. The total number of *D*s and *G*s may never be known, thus, the count-and-divide method will not work.

CERTAIN AND IMPOSSIBLE EVENTS

An event's probability is a fraction or decimal between 0 and 1. You can see this by looking at two extreme probabilities. Since an **impossible event** *never* occurs,

$$Pr[\text{impossible event}] = 0$$

Consider the following examples of impossible events.

$$Pr[\text{Dow Jones Average doubles yesterday's close}] = 0$$

$$Pr[\text{student is both undergraduate and graduate}] = \frac{0}{72} = 0$$

Similarly, a **certain event** (for example, "the selected card has a suit") will *always* occur.

$$Pr[\text{certain event}] = 1$$

The following examples apply.

$$Pr[\text{Dow Jones Average closes at some level}] = 1$$

$$Pr[\text{student is either undergraduate or graduate}] = \frac{72}{72} = 1$$

All other probabilities will lie between these two extremes.

ALTERNATIVE EXPRESSIONS OF PROBABILITY

In addition to ratios, probabilities can be expressed as percentages, odds, or chances. These other forms are not inconsistent with our definition, because they can be translated into the basic fraction or ratio form. For example, the probability for obtaining the head side of a coin can be expressed in the following forms:

1. 50% probability for a head. [Divide the percent by 100 to obtain the fraction 1/2.]

2. 50–50 chance for a head. [An even chance; a probability of 50/(50 + 50) = 1/2.]

3. 1 to 1 odds that a head will occur.

numerator/denominator   To express odds as a fraction, add the two numbers (in this case, 1 + 1 = 2) and place the result in the denominator; then place the first number in the numerator. For 1 to 1 odds, the result is 1/2. As another example, the odds for drawing a queen are 4 to 48 or 1 to 12, so that Pr[queen] = 4/(4 + 8) = 1/(1 + 12) = 1/13.

PROBABILITY AND SAMPLES

Probability is an essential part of statistics. This is primarily due to the uncertainties in making conclusions from samples. Probability concepts are useful in explaining how a sample is generated and what kinds of sample results might be possible when various assumptions are made regarding the parent population.

EXAMPLE: HOW MUCH DO STUDENTS PAY FOR CLOTHES?

The following yearly clothing expenditures apply to Slippery Rock's ten Iota Omega Upsilon pledges.

CT $786	WR $915	JB $125	AB $321	RT $980
MJ $553	TY $248	BB $416	HS $844	NB $377

Half of the IOU pledges spent more than $500. If one pledge is selected at random, the probability is 5/10 = .5 (5 out of 10) that the chosen person was a high-end spender (that is, over $500).

Viewing the ten IOU expenditures as a population, the figure for the randomly selected person constitutes a *sample* of size $n = 1$, and there is a .5 probability, or 50% chance, that the sample amount exceeds $500.

Suppose that a sample of size $n = 2$ is taken. We can find the probability that the mean sample expenditure lies between $450 and $550.

SOLUTION: To do this we first determine which possibilities might yield such a result:

CT&TY $517.00	CT&JB $455.50	WR&JB $520.00
MJ&BB $484.50	MJ&NB $465.00	TY &HS $546.00
JB &HS $484.50		

There are altogether 45 possible pledge pairs, 7 of which give a mean that falls in the stipulated range, so that the desired probability is

$$\Pr[\bar{X} \text{ lies between } \$450 \text{ and } \$550] = \frac{7}{45} = .16$$

Statisticians are often interested in the relation between the interval width and the probability that $\bar{X}$ will lie inside. It is easy to see that the probability is 45/45 = 1 that the sample mean will lie somewhere between $0 and $1,000 (because all 45 sample pairs will have means falling between these values). Likewise, the probability is 0/45 = 0 that the sample mean will fall between $490 and $510 (since there are no pairs with means in that range). Here we see that the looser limits result in a greater probability for getting a result, while tighter limits provide a smaller probability.

EXERCISES

5-5 You are selecting cards at random from a shuffled deck and arguing with your friends over various probabilities. For each of the following composite events, (1) list the corresponding elementary events in the event set, and (2) express the probability as a fraction.
(a) club   (c) face card   (e) black card
(b) five   (d) numbered *and* even   (f) diamond *and* nonface

5-6 In a special study, an accountant found the following information for 850 receivables: (a) 119 were paid early, (b) 340 were settled on time, (c) 221 were paid late, and (d) 170 were uncollectible. Assume that this experience is representative of the future. Estimate the probabilities that a particular receivable will fall into each of the four categories.

5-7 You are asked to toss a pair of six-sided dice, one red and one green. Each side of a die cube has a different number of dots, 1 through 6.
(a) List the possible sums of the number of dots on the two upturned faces.
(b) For each possible sum, list the corresponding elementary events and determine the sum's probability. (Identify your elementary events using a convenient code, such as 2R-5G for 2 dots showing on the red die and 5 on the green.)

5-8 Refer to the sample space in Figure 5-3 for a randomly selected business scholarship student. Determine the probabilities for the following events.
(a) finance major
(b) undergraduate in mangement
(c) graduate in finance
(d) female accounting major
(e) female undergraduate in marketing

5-9 Refer to the sample space in Figure 5-2 for three coins. Determine the following probabilities.
(a) exactly 2 heads
(b) exactly 1 tail
(c) dime and penny agree
(d) dime and penny disagree

5-3 JOINT PROBABILITY AND THE MULTIPLICATION LAW

Important issues are raised by considering two variables. Consider the relationship between SAT scores and college grades or that between college grades and career success. An employer might be interested in how a screening examination score relates to an applicant's future job performance. We now consider how to find the probability for simultaneous occurrence of two events, such as "above 700 on SAT" and "GPA of 4.00," or "pass a screening test" and "satisfactory job performance."

THE JOINT PROBABILITY TABLE

Consider the business scholarship students in Figure 5-3. Considering sex and academic level, the following cross tabulation applies.

Sex	Level Undergraduate	Graduate	Total
Male	24	16	40
Female	18	14	32
Total	42	30	72

Suppose that one student is selected at random. We are interested in the sex (M, F) and level (U, G) for that student, which are now uncertain events. Extending the count-and-divide method to the entire cross tabulation, a complete set of

TABLE 5-1 Joint Probability Table for Randomly Selected Business Scholarship Student

Sex	Level		Marginal Probability
	Undergraduate (U)	Graduate (G)	
Male (M)	24/72	16/72	40/72
Female (F)	18/72	14/72	32/72
Marginal Probability	42/72	30/72	1

probabilities applies. When arranged in an analogous table, the resulting display in Table 5-1 is called a **joint probability table**.

MUTUALLY EXCLUSIVE AND COLLECTIVELY EXHAUSTIVE EVENTS

Joint probability tables convey the essential probabilities used in a two-way classification of events. The rows represent for one category **mutually exclusive events** (only one can occur) and **collectively exhaustive events** (at least one must occur). The columns have the same feature.

JOINT EVENTS AND PROBABILITIES

Each cell in a joint probability table represents an outcome in which the respective row event and column event occur simultaneously. The cell thus signifies a **joint event**. There are four joint events in Table 5-1:

$$M \text{ and } U \qquad M \text{ and } G \qquad F \text{ and } U \qquad F \text{ and } G$$

The numerical values represent the applicable probabilities. Each cell contains the **joint probability** for the respective row and column event. The top left cell of Table 5-1 contains

$$\Pr[M \text{ and } U] = \frac{24}{72}$$

which expresses the probability that the chosen student is both a male (M) and an undergraduate (U).

MARGINAL PROBABILITIES

The margins contain the probability values for the respective row or column event. Because they are located in the *margins* of the table, these are referred to as **marginal probabilities**. The margins of the first row and first column of Table 5-1 contain

$$\Pr[M] = \frac{40}{72} \qquad \Pr[U] = \frac{42}{72}$$

Notice that the joint probabilities within each row sum to the respective marginal probability. (This feature is guaranteed by the nature of the original cross tabulation.) The same fact applies as well to the columns.

THE MULTIPLICATION LAW FOR FINDING "AND" PROBABILITIES

As we shall see, the joint probability table is a key element in many probability evaluations. But there may not be a cross tabulation available, and in those cases the count-and-divide method cannot be used in its construction. The needed probabilities must be built using some useful laws provided by probability theory.

The first probability law allows us to compute a joint probability by multiplying together the individual probabilities for the component events. This is the *multiplication law*. Before we state that law, it will be helpful to consider an illustration in which the law may be used.

Consider a quarter that has been flattened on a railroad track:

We want to establish the head and tail probabilities. But there is no reason to believe tosses of this damaged coin will be just as likely to result in a tail as a head. We cannot therefore use 1/2 as the head probability.

A student makes 100 tosses of the bad coin, each time letting it fall free to the floor. She obtained a head on only 35 tosses. The following *estimated* value for the long-run frequency may be used as the approximate head probability:

$$Pr[head] = 35/100 = .35$$

The other 65 tosses resulted in a tail, and thus a second approximate probability applies for the tail event:

$$Pr[tail] = 65/100 = .65$$

Now consider two later tosses of the bad quarter. Let's denote achieving a head on the first toss as H_1 and use T_1 to represent obtaining a tail. Similarly, for the second toss we use H_2 for a head and T_2 for a tail. We have

$$Pr[H_1] = Pr[H_2] = .35 \quad and \quad Pr[T_1] = Pr[T_2] = .65$$

What is the probability that both tosses result in heads?

To answer this question we must use the following

MULTIPLICATION LAW FOR INDEPENDENT EVENTS

$$\Pr[A \text{ and } B] = \Pr[A] \times \Pr[B]$$

The above tells us that when A and B are independent (a relation to be discussed shortly), we may find an unknown joint probability by multiplying together the known probabilities for the individual component events. The joint event's set is the **intersection** of the component events, which are logically joined by "and."

We illustrate this law with the two tosses of the damaged quarter. Multiplying together the H_1 and H_2 probabilities, we have the probability for getting two successive heads:

$$\Pr[H_1 \text{ and } H_2] = \Pr[H_1] \times \Pr[H_2]$$
$$= .35(.35) = .1225$$

The multiplication law applies even when the component events are not elementary events. To see this, let's use it to establish the probability that a randomly selected playing card is both a heart and a queen. Counting and dividing, we first get

$$\Pr[\text{heart}] = \frac{13}{52} \qquad \Pr[\text{queen}] = \frac{4}{52}$$

Then, multiplying the component event probabilities, we get

$$\Pr[\text{heart } and \text{ queen}] = \Pr[\text{heart}] \times \Pr[\text{queen}]$$
$$= \frac{13}{52} \times \frac{4}{52}$$
$$= \frac{1}{52}$$

SOME ADVICE AND WARNINGS ABOUT THE MULTIPLICATION LAW

With the card example, the multiplication law involves a lot of work. If we had first noted that "heart and queen" is the same as drawing the queen of hearts, we could have more easily just counted-and-divided to establish 1/52 as the probability of getting that card.

You should use the multiplication law when it is advantageous to do so. It is definitely *not mandatory* to use this law when you are finding a joint probability. As we have seen, joint probabilities can sometimes be more easily found by counting and dividing.

The foregoing version of the multiplication law only applies when events are *independent*, a relationship we will define in Section 5-5. When events do not have that relationship, the law will not work. Beginners find it perplexing that the multiplication law can give the *wrong answer*!

JOINT PROBABILITIES INVOLVING MORE THAN TWO EVENTS

The multiplication law for independent events extends to any number of component events.

EXAMPLE: LATE AIRLINE DEPARTURES

Each noon on weekdays, Unified Airways Flight 22 departs from Centralia. This flight experiences late departures 70% of the time, and the takeoff time on any day has no effect on a future day's experience. What is the probability that a particular week will have late departures on every day?

SOLUTION: The probability of a late departure on any particular day is .70. Denoting the respective late-departure events as LMo, LTu, LWe, LTh, and LFr, the multiplication law provides the answer:

$$Pr[LMo \ and \ LTu \ and \ LWe \ and \ LTh \ and \ LFr]$$
$$= Pr[LMo] \times Pr[LTu] \times Pr[LWe] \times Pr[LTh] \times Pr[LFr]$$
$$= .7(.7)(.7)(.7)(.7)$$
$$= (.7)^5 = .168$$

The above notation tell us that even though 70% of the daily departures are late, only 16.8% of the weeks involve late takeoffs every day.

PROBABILITIES WHEN ELEMENTARY EVENTS ARE NOT EQUALLY LIKELY

The multiplication law may be used to establish probabilities for elementary events that are *not* equally likely.

To illustrate, we return to the damaged coin. The multiplication law allows us to establish probabilities for all two-toss outcomes:

$$Pr[H_1 \ and \ H_2] = Pr[H_1] \times Pr[H_2] = .35(.35) = .1225$$
$$Pr[H_1 \ and \ T_2] = Pr[H_1] \times Pr[T_2] = .35(.65) = .2275$$
$$Pr[T_1 \ and \ H_2] = Pr[T_1] \times Pr[H_2] = .65(.35) = .2275$$
$$Pr[T_1 \ and \ T_2] = Pr[T_1] \times Pr[T_2] = .65(.65) = .4225$$

The outcomes H_1H_2, H_1T_2, and T_1T_2 (abbreviated by removing the *and*) are elementary events for the two-toss random experiment. However, they are *not* equally likely (T_1T_2 has over three times the probability of H_1H_2).

EXERCISES

5-10 The following cross tabulation applies for a consumer testing group.

Occupation	Family Income			Total
	Low	Medium	High	
Homemaker	8	26	6	40
Blue-collar Worker	16	40	14	70
White-collar Worker	6	62	12	80
Professional	0	2	8	10
Total	30	130	40	200

One person is selected at random. Construct a joint probability table for occupation versus income levels.

5-11 The statistics students at Adams College are 60% male. Exactly 20% of the men and 20% of the women are married. Use the multiplication law to determine the probability that a randomly selected student will be classified as the following.
(a) man *and* married
(b) man *and* unmarried
(c) woman *and* married
(d) woman *and* unmarried

5-12 Refer to the sample space in Figure 5-3 for a randomly selected business scholarship student. Construct a joint probability table for sex versus major.

5-13 Refer to the sample space in Figure 5-3 for a randomly selected business scholarship student. Construct a joint probability table for academic level versus major.

5-14 Professor Horatio Dull's statistics class has 3 married men and 5 married women; the rest are unmarried. There are 35 people altogether, 20 of whom are men. One student is selected at random.
(a) Construct the joint probability table for sex versus marital status.
(b) Indicate the probabilities for the following joint events:
    (1) man *and* married
    (2) woman *and* married
    (3) woman *and* unmarried
    (4) man *and* unmarried

5-15 List all the possible side-showing elementary events from three tosses of the damaged coin described on page 162. Find for each the joint probability.

5-16 A *fair* coin is tossed 5 times. Two possibilities are

(1) $H_1T_2H_3T_4H_5$
(2) $H_1H_2H_3H_4H_5$

(a) Without computing any probabilities, which outcome do you think is more likely?
(b) Use the multiplication law to determine the probability for each outcome.

5-17 Refer to the sample space for a randomly selected playing card in Figure 5-1.
(a) Use the count-and-divide method to find the following probabilities.

(1) heart   (4) black
(2) face (K,Q,J)   (5) even-numbered (2,4,6,8,10)
(3) king   (6) spade

(b) Use the count-and-divide method to find the following joint probabilities.
(1) heart *and* face   (3) black *and* face
(2) king *and* black   (4) even-numbered *and* spade

(c) Suit and denomination events are independent. Apply the multiplication law using probabilities found in (a) to compute each joint probability listed in (b).

5-18 Matchless Garments test markets its products with a consumer test panel provided by a consultant. Two panels, each made up of 100 persons, are available. Consider the characteristics of a person selected at random from each group.

(a) Panel *A* is 50% men and 50% women; 70% of the panel members are married (the rest unmarried), and just as many men as women are married. Thus, any two sex and marital status events are *independent*. Construct a joint probability table by first determining the marginal probabilities and then using the multiplication law to obtain the joint probabilities, which in this case are the products of the two respective marginal probabilities.

(b) Panel *B* is also 50% men and 50% women, and 70% of the panel members are married. However, only 60% of the men are married, whereas 80% of the women are married. Thus, any two sex and marital status events are *dependent*. This means that the product of the respective marginal probabilities does not equal the corresponding joint probability, so the multiplication law can not be used to find the joint probabilities. Instead, construct the joint probability table using the count-and-divide method.

5-4 FINDING PROBABILITIES USING THE ADDITION LAW

We have seen that the count-and-divide procedure may be used to determine the probabilities for composite events. That method, however, has limited scope. We now consider a more general approach.

To illustrate, let's return to the damaged coin of the previous section. Again, we will toss it twice. We have seen that the sample space comprises these elementary events:

$$H_1H_2 \quad H_1T_2 \quad T_1H_2 \quad T_1T_2$$

What is the probability of exactly one head?

The outcome in question is a composite event having the event set listed below.

$$\text{Exactly one head} = \{H_1T_2, T_1H_2\}$$

The desired probability is *not* equal to 2/4, which is what the count-and-divide method would provide. <u>Counting and dividing works only for equally likely elementary events.</u>

Instead we may get correct values with the following procedure, which uses the probabilities for component events as building blocks.

THE ADDITION LAW FOR FINDING *"OR"* PROBABILITIES

A second probability law allows us to find the probability of composite events whether or not the elementary events are equally likely. This is the **addition law**, which under special circumstances permits us to add together the component event probabilities. The following states the

ADDITION LAW FOR MUTUALLY EXCLUSIVE EVENTS

$$\Pr[A \ or \ B \ or \ C] = \Pr[A] + \Pr[B] + \Pr[C]$$

The above expression may be used in finding the unknown probability for a composite event whose event set is the **union** of two or more *mutually exclusive* component events, only one of which can actually occur. Those individual events are logically connected with "or" and have known probabilities.

Continuing with the example of the two damaged coin tosses, we may use the addition law to find the probability of exactly one head:

$$\Pr[\text{exactly 1 head}] = \Pr[H_1T_2 \ or \ T_1H_2] = \Pr[H_1T_2] + \Pr[T_1H_2]$$
$$= .2275 + .2275$$
$$= .4550$$

As with the multiplication law, the addition law applies even when the component events are not elementary events. To illustrate, consider again the business scholarship students in Figure 5-3. The following apply to the major of a randomly selected student:

$$\Pr[\text{accounting}] = 16/72 \qquad \Pr[\text{marketing}] = 20/72$$

$$\Pr[\text{finance}] = 24/72 \qquad \Pr[\text{management}] = 12/72$$

Using the above, we may apply the addition law to establish the probability that a nonmanagement major is selected. Note first the equivalency

$$\Pr[\text{nonmanagement}] = \Pr[\text{accounting } or \text{ finance } or \text{ marketing}]$$

Then, applying the addition law, the correct value is obtained:

$$\Pr[\text{accounting } or \text{ finance } or \text{ marketing}]$$
$$= \Pr[\text{accounting}] + \Pr[\text{finance}] + \Pr[\text{marketing}]$$
$$= 16/72 + 24/72 + 20/72$$
$$= 60/72$$

SOME ADVICE AND WARNING ABOUT THE ADDITION LAW

When the elementary events are equally likely and we can easily count possibilities, a probability for a composite event might be obtained *without* using the addition law. Directly from Figure 5-3, we determine that there are 60 nonmanagement majors (accounting, finance, or marketing) out of 72 business scholarship students, so that a single count-and-divide method more readily provides the same result:

$$\Pr[\text{nonmanagement}] = 60/72$$

Like the multiplication law, the addition law does not have to be used every time an *or* joins component events. We should use it only when advantageous to do so. It becomes essential when counting and dividing is impractical or impossible. That is the case in the following example, in which details about the sample space are not provided.

EXAMPLE: REASONS FOR DENIAL OF CREDIT

The credit manager for the Hide-Away Safe Company has several reasons for denying credit to buyers: (1) low income, (2) poor repayment history, (3) high debts, and (4) no collateral. Records of past transactions list one of these as the primary reason for denial of credit. If you assume that past frequencies will apply in the future, you have the following probabilities that the next credit application will be rejected for each primary reason.

$$\Pr[\text{low income}] = .15$$
$$\Pr[\text{poor repayment}] = .20$$
$$\Pr[\text{high debts}] = .25$$
$$\Pr[\text{no collateral}] = .40$$

Reasons (3) and (4) apply to what are called "balance sheet deficiencies." We will determine the probability that a balance sheet deficiency will be the reason for the next credit denial.

SOLUTION: We will apply the addition law.

$$\Pr[\text{balance sheet}] = \Pr[\text{high debts } or \text{ no collateral}]$$
$$= \Pr[\text{high debts}] + \Pr[\text{no collateral}]$$
$$= .25 + .40 = .65$$

The addition law can also lead to the *wrong answer*. It requires that the component events be *mutually exclusive*, and it will provide incorrect values if that is not the case.

To illustrate an improper application of the addition law, consider the following calculation for a randomly selected playing card:

$$\Pr[\text{heart}] + \Pr[\text{queen}] = 13/52 + 4/52 = 17/52$$

The above calculation gives an *incorrect* value for Pr[heart *or* queen]. (Go back to Figure 5-1. How many cards fall into the category of being either a heart or a queen?) Adding the two probabilities is fallacious because heart and queen are *not* mutually exclusive events. Both event sets have the queen of hearts in common, and the above calculation accounts for that possibility twice! (Section 5-7 describes a general version of the addition law that may be used when events are not mutually exclusive.)

MUTUALLY EXCLUSIVE AND COLLECTIVELY EXHAUSTIVE EVENTS

The relevant events from many random experiments are *mutually exclusive*—so that only one of them can occur—and also *collectively exhaustive*—making it certain that one of the events will occur. Consider the outcomes experienced by SoftWhereHaus, which takes a sample of its program diskettes every hour to determine the quality of its final product. If only 10% of the diskettes are defective, then the following probabilities apply for the number of defectives in a sample of 5 diskettes.

Number of Defectives	Probability
0	.5905
1	.3280
2	.0729
3	.0081
4	.0005
5	.0000
	1.0000

0.9^5
$5(0.9^4 \times 0.1)$
$10(0.9^3 \times 0.1^2)$

The events for "number defective" are mutually exclusive and collectively exhaustive, and their probabilities add up to 1.

APPLICATION TO COMPLEMENTARY EVENTS

When two events are complementary (opposite), their probabilities add up to 1.

$$\Pr[A \text{ } or \text{ not } A] = \Pr[A] + \Pr[\text{not } A] = \Pr[\text{certain event}] = 1$$

Thus,

$$\Pr[A] = 1 - \Pr[\text{not } A]$$

This is helpful when you want to know an event's probability, but the probability for its complementary event is easier to determine. If you want to determine the probability for "at least 1" defective diskette in the above example, you can use the addition law and add together the probabilities for "exactly 1," "exactly 2," and so on. But you can determine the answer faster if you recognize that "at least 1" is the opposite of "exactly 0." The above example gives the probability for "0 defective" as .5905, so that

$$\Pr[\text{at least 1 defective}] = 1 - \Pr[\text{exactly 0 defective}]$$
$$= 1 - .5905 = .4095$$

5-19 Refer to the randomly selected playing card sample space in Figure 5-1.

(a) Use the count-and-divide method to find the following probabilities.

    (1) club   (3) 4   (5) heart   (7) ace

    (2) king   (4) 5   (6) red   (8) jack

(b) Use the count-and-divide method to find the following composite event probabilities.

    (1) club *or* king   (3) club *or* heart   (5) ace *or* jack

    (2) 4 *or* 5 *or* 6   (4) ace *or* red

(c) Apply the addition law using your probabilities from (a) to attempt to compute each composite event probability listed in (b). Indicate for each whether the obtained result is correct or incorrect because the components are not mutually exclusive events.

5-20 An accountant randomly selects 5 trial balances out of 10. Exactly 4 of the 10 are in error. The following probabilities have been obtained for the number of selected accounts having incorrect balances.

Number of Incorrect Balances	Probability
0	1/42
1	10/42
2	20/42
3	10/42
4	1/42

Determine the probability for the following number of incorrect balances.

(a) at least 2   (c) 1 or more   (e) fewer than 4

(b) at most 3   (d) greater than 2   (f) 4 or fewer

5-21 The following joint probability table applies to marital status and job classification of a randomly selected Metropolis worker.

Marital Status	Job Classification			Marginal Probability
	Blue Collar	White Collar	Management	
Married	.15	.20	.17	.52
Divorced	.12	.02	.04	.18
Widowed	.04	.04	.02	.10
Never Married	.09	.06	.05	.20
Marginal Probability	.40	.32	.28	1.00

(a) What is the probability that the person has a nonmanagement job?

(b) What is the probability that the person is presently unmarried?

(c) What is the probability that the person is a formerly married blue-collar worker?

(d) What is the probability that he or she is a nonmanagement married person?

5-22 The following joint probability table applies to the age group and first college degree held by a randomly selected alumnus of State University.

Age	College Degree				Marginal Probability
	Science	Liberal Arts	Social Science	Professional	
Under 23	.01	.01	.01	.00	.03
23–29	.02	.02	.04	.06	.14
30–50	.07	.11	.06	.09	.33
Over 50	.10	.05	.18	.17	.50
Marginal Probability	.20	.19	.29	.32	1.00

(a) What is the probability that he is 23 or older?
(b) What is the probability that he is 30 or older?
(c) What is the probability that he is over 50 and has a science or professional degree?
(d) What is the probability that he is under 23 with a science or social science degree?

5-5 STATISTICAL INDEPENDENCE

We have been using the multiplication law to compute various probabilities. That law only works when events are *independent*. We are now ready to formally define this concept.

A DEFINITION OF STATISTICAL INDEPENDENCE

The multiplication law stated earlier applies only for independent events. The following definition applies.

DEFINITION 1: Two events A and B are **statistically independent** whenever

$$\Pr[A \text{ and } B] = \Pr[A] \times \Pr[B]$$

The above indicates that statistical independence is established only by the *probabilities* of two events—not their sequence, cause and effect, timing, or hierarchical ranking.

A BASIC TEST FOR INDEPENDENCE BETWEEN EVENTS

If the probability data are available, we can establish the independence or nonindependence between two events by comparing probabilities.

To illustrate, consider once more the business scholarship students. The following joint probability table for sex versus major applies for a randomly selected undergraduate.

Sex	Major				Marginal Probability
	Accounting	**Finance**	**Marketing**	**Management**	
Male	7/42	8/42	6/42	3/42	24/42
Female	4/42	5/42	7/42	2/42	18/42
Marginal Probability	11/42	13/42	13/42	5/42	1

Consider the events male and marketing. The joint probability for these events is

$$\Pr[\text{male } and \text{ marketing}] = \frac{6}{42} = .1429$$

Then, multiplying the respective marginal probabilities, we have

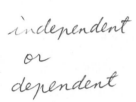

$$\Pr[\text{male}] \times \Pr[\text{marketing}] = \frac{24}{42} \times \frac{13}{42} = .1769$$

Since the above product *differs* from the joint probability, the events male and marketing are *not* statistically independent. Events that are not independent are said to be **dependent events**.

A second comparison with playing card events,

$$\Pr[\text{heart } and \text{ queen}] = \frac{1}{52} = \frac{13}{52} \times \frac{4}{52} = \Pr[\text{heart}] \times \Pr[\text{queen}]$$

establishes that heart and queen are statistically independent events.

Statistical independence may apply to any number of events. To have independence, the joint probability of any subset of those events, including the whole, must always equal the product of the individual probabilities. Although the above test is foolproof, the probability values needed to establish independence or dependence may not be readily available.

COMMONLY ENCOUNTERED INSTANCES OF STATISTICAL INDEPENDENCE

In a broad class of random experiments, independence between events may be *assumed*, due to the very nature in which they are generated. This is what we have implicitly been doing all along with coin tosses. To have independence between successive outcomes, a head should be just as likely regardless of whether the preceding toss was a head or a tail. We don't ordinarily need to test for this. (Although a person could sabotage independence by tossing the coin in special ways.)

Drawing a playing card also provides examples where independence may be assumed. Any pair of suit and denomination events involves independent events. This is because the *proportion* of cards with any denomination *is the same value*, regardless of suit. For example, the proportion of face cards (king, queen, jack) among the clubs is 3/13; the same figure applies regardless of suit.

Unequal proportions would occur only in a scrambled card deck constructed from random portions of several decks. Such scrambling is typical with groups of people. With demographic type events—such as those for sex, marital status, occupation, or income—dependence is therefore to be expected. In the case of a randomly selected individual, independence between "married person" and "male" would require that the grouping of people contain exactly the same proportion of married men as married women. Most people will agree that such an arrangement would be very uncommon—except perhaps with groups containing only married couples.

INDEPENDENT EVENTS AND THE MULTIPLICATION LAW

The multiplication law stated earlier requires independence before it can even be used. We use that law only when independence can be safely *assumed*. (And there is obviously no purpose served in comparing the joint probabilities thereby obtained to establish independence, which had to be known at the outset.)

FINDING JOINT PROBABILITIES FOR DEPENDENT EVENTS

When sufficient data are available (as with the business scholarship students), joint probabilities for dependent events may be found by counting and dividing. When no cross tabulation exists, a different procedure must be used. The alternative method works when probabilities are derived from historical frequencies rather than by counting and dividing.

Percentages are common sources of probability data. For instance, a researcher reports that the following apply to Gotham City adults.

5% drive drunk (*D*).
12% are alcoholics (*A*).
40% of all drunk drivers are alcholics.

From the above we can readily establish the following probabilities for a randomly selected Gotham City adult.

$$\Pr[D] = .05 \qquad \Pr[A] = .12$$

Multiplying the above, we obtain the product

$$\Pr[D] \times \Pr[A] = .05 \times .12 = .006$$

The above is *not* the joint probability for the two events.

To find the correct value for the joint probability, we use the fact that 40% of the 5% who are drunk drivers are also alcoholics, so that the product of the respective decimal fractions is

$$.40 \times .05 = .02$$

We see that 2% are *both* drunk drivers and alcoholics (*D and A*). This indicates that for a randomly selected adult,

$$\Pr[D \ and \ A] = .02$$

Note that *D* and *A* are *dependent* events, since

$$\Pr[D \ and \ A] = .02 \neq .006 = \Pr[D] \times \Pr[A]$$

CONSTRUCTING A JOINT PROBABILITY TABLE WITHOUT A CROSS TABULATION

We have the essential information for filling in the blanks in the 2-by-2 joint probability table for drunk driving versus alcoholism. We start by inserting the above probabilities:

Driving	Alcoholism		Marginal Probability
	Alcoholic (A)	Nonalcoholic (not A)	
Drunk Driver (D)	.02	0.03	.05
Sober (not D)	0.10	0.58 0.85	0.95
Marginal Probability	.12	0.88	1

The missing marginal probabilities are filled in next. For the right-hand margin, these must sum to 1.00, because the respective events are *complementary*. Thus, .95 applies for Pr[not *D*]. An analogous condition applies to the bottom margin, and .88 applies for Pr[not *A*]. This gives the following (new values in light face type).

Driving	Alcoholism		Marginal Probability
	Alcoholic (A)	Nonalcoholic (not A)	
Drunk Driver (D)	.02		.05
Sober (not D)			.95 ←—1 − .05
Marginal Probability	.12	.88	1.00

$$1 - .12$$

Next, the cell probabilities are obtained. First, the value .03 is found for the empty cell in the *D*-row, establishing Pr[*D and* not *A*]. That value gives cell entries in the *D*-row that sum to the marginal probability of .05 for that row. In the same way, .10 is found for the empty cell in the *A*-column, establishing the value for Pr[not *D and A*]. Then, working with the marginal probability for either the not-*D*-row or the not-*A*-column, the entry for the last empty cell has to be .85, and Pr[not *A and* not *D*] is determined. The completed joint probability table is:

Driving	Alcoholism		Marginal Probability
	Alcoholic (A)	Nonalcoholic (not A)	
Drunk Driver (D)	.02	.03 ←—	.05
Sober (not D)	.10	.85	.95
Marginal Probability	.12	.88	1.00

.05 − .02

.12 − .02

.88 − .03 or .95 − .10

Had the joint probability in the *D and A* cell been different, the other joint probabilities would differ too. In effect, there is only one *degree of freedom* in filling the inside of a 2-by-2 joint probability table. The first cell entry always dictates the joint probability values for the other cells.

5-23 Consider a randomly selected playing card.
  (a) Show that the following event pairs are independent.
    (1) club, 10   (2) red, king   (3) black, queen
  (b) Show that the following event pairs are dependent.
    (1) face, king   (2) black, club   (3) queen, ten

5-24 A cannery inspector accepts (*A*) 90% of all peach truckloads inspected and rejects (*R*) the rest. Historically, she has found that 95% of all truckloads are good (*G*), the rest bad (*B*). She rejects 90% of the bad truckloads inspected.
  (a) What percentage of all inspected truckloads are both bad and get rejected?
  (b) Construct the action versus quality joint probability table for the next truckload of peaches inspected.
  (c) What percentage of all inspected loads are (1) good and rejected, (2) good and accepted, and (3) bad and accepted?
  (d) An incorrect action is to accept a bad lot or reject a good load. What is the probability that the inspector takes an incorrect action?

5-25 Refer to the joint probability table in Problem 5-21.
  (a) Show that blue collar and widowed are statistically independent.
  (b) Show that management and never married are statistically dependent.

5-26 Refer to the joint probability table in Problem 5-22.
  (a) Show that over 50 and science are statistically independent.
  (b) Show that under 23 and science are statistically dependent.

5-27 Felina Wild is an oil wildcatter who decides that the probability for striking gas (*G*) is .40. Felina orders a seismic survey that confirms (*C*) gas with a probability of .85 in known gas fields and denies (*D*) gas with a probability of .60 when there is no gas. Construct the joint probability table for geology and survey events.

5-28 A banana inspector accepts only 10% of all bad shipments and rejects only 5% of the good shipments. Overall, 90% of the shipments inspected are good.
  (a) Construct the joint probability table for shipment quality versus inspector action.
  (b) Determine the probability that the inspector will take the wrong action on the next shipment.

5-6 CONDITIONAL PROBABILITY AND THE GENERAL MULTIPLICATION LAW

It is useful to have probability values that apply only when a special condition is met. These are called **conditional probabilities**, and they express the chance that one event will occur given that another occurs. We represent symbolically the conditional probability of *A* given *B* by

$$\text{Pr}[A \mid B] \qquad (\text{Pr}[A \text{ given } B])$$

The probability value for the above pertains to A, computed under the assumption that B will occur.

The weather provides some examples. Consider the events "rain" and "cloudy," for which the following might be true.

$$\text{Pr}[\text{rain} \mid \text{cloudy}] = .70$$

This equation is read, "The probability that there will be rain *given* that it is cloudy is .70." The event "rain" is listed first, and .70 is the probability for this event. The second event, which appears after the vertical bar, is the **given event**, "cloudy." This event establishes the condition under which .70 applies. Given some other event, "rain" could have a different probability. For example,

$$\text{Pr}[\text{rain} \mid \text{low pressure}] = .30$$

conditional

unconditional In either case, the probability for rain is conditional because it assumes that another event—"cloudy" or "low pressure"—is going to occur. Should no conditions be stipulated for the weather, we might have the value

$$\text{Pr}[\text{rain}] = .20$$

which is an **unconditional probability**.

COMPUTING CONDITIONAL PROBABILITIES

COUNT-AND-DIVIDE METHOD

The condition, or given event, eliminates extraneous possibilities that would need to be accounted for in establishing unconditional probabilities. For example, consider a randomly selected playing card. You can see that

$$\text{Pr}[\text{jack} \mid \text{face card}] = \frac{4}{12} = \frac{1}{3}$$

since there are only 12 face cards and just 4 cards are jacks. The condition of "face card" effectively reduces the sample space to just 12 cards, and the count-and-divide method can then be applied to the smaller, or restricted, sample space. Without the condition, you would have to consider the entire sample space (all 52 cards), so that

$$\text{Pr}[\text{jack}] = \frac{4}{52} = \frac{1}{13}$$

As another example, consider the student selection experiment in Figure 5-3. You can determine the probability for "finance major given undergraduate" by observing that the condition "undergraduate" eliminates all graduate students.

Therefore, the 42 students in the event set "undergraduate" are the restricted sample space. Of those 42 students, 13 are finance majors, so that

$$\Pr[\text{finance} \,|\, \text{undergraduate}] = \frac{13}{42}$$

CONDITIONAL PROBABILITY IDENTITY

If the necessary probability values are known, you may find it helpful to use the

CONDITIONAL PROBABILITY IDENTITY

$$\Pr[A \,|\, B] = \frac{\Pr[A \text{ and } B]}{\Pr[B]}$$

This equation states that the conditional probability for an event can be determined by dividing the joint probability for the two events (if known) by the unconditional probability for the given event (if that value is also known). The above calculation provides the long-run relative frequency that *A* occurs out of all those times that *B* occurs.

To illustrate, consider the values in the joint probability table found earlier for drunk driving versus alcoholism. The above identity provides the conditional probability that a randomly selected Gotham City adult is an alcoholic given that he or she is a drunk driver:

$$\Pr[A \,|\, D] = \frac{\Pr[A \text{ and } D]}{\Pr[D]} = \frac{.02}{.05} = .40$$

The above reflects that 40% of the *drunk drivers only* are alcoholics. <u>Do not confuse *A given D* with the joint event *A and D*,</u> which represents *all adults*, 2% of which are both alcoholics and drunk drivers.

Let's now reverse roles, finding the probability that this person is a drunk driver given that he or she is an alcoholic:

$$\Pr[D \,|\, A] = \frac{\Pr[D \text{ and } A]}{\Pr[A]} = \frac{.02}{.12} = .1667$$

The same value as before appears in the numerator, but a different divisor is used because now alcoholic (*A*) is the given event. The above number tells us that 17% of the alcoholics in Gotham City are drunk drivers. (Be careful when you find conditional probabilities. Reversing the events always gives a different meaning to the result, and the computed value will ordinarily differ as well.)

Although it is always a mathematically correct expression, the conditional probability identity cannot always be used to find conditional probabilities. Consider the following example.

EXAMPLE: FINDING PROBABILITIES FOR SAMPLE DEFECTIVES

The receiving department of SoftWhereHaus is sample testing a small shipment of high velocity recording heads. Suppose that out of the 10 heads in the shipment, 2 are defective (*D*) and the rest are satisfactory (*S*). (Of course, the inspector doesn't know this fact.) Two heads, represented by the subscripts 1 and 2, are randomly selected one at a time and tested just once. We want to find the various probabilities involving D_1 and D_2.

SOLUTION: You can see that

$$\Pr[D_1] = \frac{2}{10}$$

and given that the first head is defective, only 1 defective is among the 9 remaining heads, so that

$$\Pr[D_2 | D_1] = \frac{1}{9}$$

Should the first head instead be satisfactory, then 2 defectives are left in the remaining 9, and

$$\Pr[D_2 | S_1] = \frac{2}{9}$$

You can not use the conditional probability identity here since you do not know the values for $\Pr[D_1 \ and \ D_2]$ or $\Pr[S_1 \ and \ D_2]$.

———

Conditional probability is useful for decision-making purposes.

EXAMPLE: EVALUATING A CLERICAL SKILLS TEST

Probability concepts may be useful in deciding to implement an employment screening test. Consider the experience of Whirl-a-Gigs, a regional children's clothing chain. The company administered on a trial basis a clerical skills test to all employees (who were hired without reference to their test scores). Present hiring policy provides the following historical job performance percentages:

> 15% unsatisfactory
> 65% satisfactory
> 20% excellent

Matching job performance to test scores, the following percentages were obtained:

> 10% of the unsatisfactory employees received high scores
> 70% of the satisfactory employees received high scores
> 85% of the excellent employees received high scores

We want to establish a joint probability table representing job performance and test score events pertaining to a randomly selected Whirl-a-Gigs employee. We will use that table to generate probabilities which may be used to qualify the effectiveness of the test.

SOLUTION: The following table is constructed.

Performance	Test Score Low (L)	Test Score High (H)	Marginal Probability
Unsatisfactory (U)	.135	.015	**.150**
Satisfactory (S)	.195	.455	**.650**
Excellent (E)	.030	.170	**.200**
Marginal Probability	.360	.640	1.000

The historical frequencies establish the right-hand marginal probabilities (shown in boldface). The entries in Column H were found using the given percentages to establish the respective proportions of employees. For instance, just 10% of the 15% who were unsatisfactory employees scored high, and

$$Pr[U \text{ and } H] = .10 \times .15 = .015$$

The joint probabilities in column L are those values that agree with the requirement that the sum of the cell values in any row equals the respective marginal probability. The bottom marginal probabilities are the sums of the joint probabilities in the respective columns.

The following indicates how good the test would be in screening unsatisfactory employees.

$$Pr[U|L] = \frac{Pr[U \text{ and } L]}{Pr[L]} = \frac{.135}{.360} = .375$$

The above calculation tells Whirl-a-Gigs that, assuming they would be hired regardless of score, and leaving all other personnel policies the same, 37.5% of the low-scoring applicants would be unsatisfactory employees. This percentage is more than twice as high as the percentage of unsatisfactories currently experienced. This suggests that the test will effectively filter potential unsatisfactories.

The following conditional probabilities tell Whirl-a-Gigs how using the screening test should improve overall employee performance.

$$Pr[U|H] = \frac{Pr[U \text{ and } H]}{Pr[H]} = \frac{.015}{.640} = .023$$

$$Pr[S|H] = \frac{Pr[S \text{ and } H]}{Pr[H]} = \frac{.455}{.640} = .711$$

$$Pr[E|H] = \frac{Pr[E \text{ and } H]}{Pr[H]} = \frac{.170}{.640} = .266$$

Under present hiring policies, if Whirl-a-Gigs were to hire only high-scoring persons, the above equations indicate that only 2.3% of future employees would be unsatisfactory, 71.1% would be satisfactory, and 26.6% would be excellent.

The downside to using the screening test is that a lot of low-scoring people, who may otherwise be satisfactory or excellent employees, would never be hired. Consider the following probability:

Pr[may-be-satisfactory-or-excellent-but-not-hired low-scoring applicant]

$$= \text{Pr}[(S \text{ and } L) \text{ or } (E \text{ and } L)] = \text{Pr}[S \text{ and } L] + \text{Pr}[E \text{ and } L]$$

$$= .195 + .030 = .225$$

CONDITIONAL PROBABILITY AND STATISTICAL INDEPENDENCE

Two events are statistically independent if the occurrence of one has no effect on the probability of the other. In terms of conditional probability, an alternative definition of independence applies.

DEFINITION 2: Two events A and B are **statistically independent** whenever

$$\text{Pr}[A|B] = \text{Pr}[A] \quad \text{or} \quad \text{Pr}[B|A] = \text{Pr}[B]$$

Two events are independent whenever the conditional probability of one event given the second is equal to its *unconditional* probability. In effect, the occurrence, nonoccurrence, or lack of knowledge about the other event has no effect on an event's probability value.

An alternative test for independence would therefore be to compare the unconditional probability for either event to its respective conditional probability. To illustrate, queen and face are dependent, since

$$\text{Pr}[\text{queen}] = 4/52 \neq 4/12 = \text{Pr}[\text{queen} | \text{face}]$$

When the above holds, so must the reverse:

$$\text{Pr}[\text{face}] = 12/52 \neq 4/4 = \text{Pr}[\text{face} | \text{queen}]$$

Pr[face + queen]

And, queen and heart are independent, since

$$\text{Pr}[\text{queen}] = 4/52 = 1/13 = \text{Pr}[\text{queen} | \text{heart}]$$

and likewise,

$$\text{Pr}[\text{heart}] = 13/52 = 1/4 = \text{Pr}[\text{heart} | \text{queen}]$$

$$\frac{Pr[heart \text{ and } queen]}{Pr[queen]}$$

THE GENERAL MULTIPLICATION LAW

The multiplication law used so far pertains just to *independent* events. That requirement does not apply to the following

GENERAL MULTIPLICATION LAW

$$Pr[A \ and \ B] = Pr[A] \times Pr[B \,|\, A]$$

or

$$Pr[A \ and \ B] = Pr[B] \times Pr[A \,|\, B]$$

The above involves the product of one unconditional probability with a conditional probability.

To illustrate, consider the following experience of an accountant. She has established that 60% of all accounts receivable involve incorrect remittances (I), and that 10% of those involve partial payments (P). This history may be expressed in terms of the following probabilities.

$$Pr[I] = .60$$
$$Pr[P\,|\,I] = .10$$

The multiplication law provides the probability that a particular remittance will be both incorrect and a partial payment.

$$Pr[I \ and \ P] = Pr[I] \times Pr[P\,|\,I]$$
$$= .60 \times .10$$
$$= .06$$

Thus, 6% of all remittances for accounts receivable will fall into the two categories. (You can verify the result in terms of percentages: 10% of 60% is 6%.)

ILLUSTRATION: OIL WILDCATTING WITH A SEISMIC SURVEY

The owner of the Petroleum Entrepreneurship is a wildcatter who judges that there is a 30% chance of oil (O) beneath his leasehold on Fossil Ridges, with complementary chances that the site is dry (D). That is, the following unconditional probabilities apply.

$$Pr[O] = .30 \quad and \quad Pr[D] = 1 - .30 = .70$$

The wildcatter has the option of drilling now or ordering a seismic survey. Such a test is 90% reliable in predicting favorable (F) when there is actually oil, but only 70% reliable in providing an unfavorable (U) forecast when a site is dry. The given reliability percentages directly express the conditional probabilities

$$Pr[F\,|\,O] = .90 \quad and \quad Pr[U\,|\,D] = .70$$

The general multiplication law may be used to establish the joint probability that Fossil Ridges does indeed contain oil and that the seismic survey will be favorable.

$$\text{Pr}[O \text{ and } F] = \text{Pr}[O] \times \text{Pr}[F \mid O]$$
$$= .30 \times .90 = .27$$

Similarly, the joint probability for a dry site and an unfavorable seismic survey is

$$\text{Pr}[D \text{ and } U] = \text{Pr}[D] \times \text{Pr}[U \mid D]$$
$$= .70 \times .70 = .49$$

CONSTRUCTING A JOINT PROBABILITY TABLE WITH THE ASSISTANCE OF THE GENERAL MULTIPLICATION LAW

As we have seen, even when there are insufficient data to directly apply the count-and-divide method, a joint probability table may be built from percentages, as illustrated with the drunk driving example (Section 5-5) and the foregoing clerical skills test example. The general multiplication law streamlines the procedure.

To demonstrate, we continue with the oil wildcatting illustration, summarized in Table 5-2 by the joint probability table showing geology evens versus seismic results. To fill in the numbers, we applied the general multiplication law (shown earlier) to get two key joint probabilities:

$$\text{Pr}[O \text{ and } F] = .27 \quad \text{and} \quad \text{Pr}[D \text{ and } U] = .49$$

They have been placed (in boldface type) in their respective position in Table 5-2. The geology event marginal probabilities

$$\text{Pr}[O] = .30 \quad \text{and} \quad \text{Pr}[D] = .70$$

have also been positioned in boldface. Using this information, the rest of the table entries were determined. The joint probability for "oil" *and* "unfavorable," .03, is determined by subtracting the joint probability for "oil" *and* "favorable," .27, from the marginal probability for "oil," which is .30. The joint probability for "dry" *and* "favorable," .21, represents the difference between the margin probability for "dry," .70, and the joint probability for "dry" *and* "unfavorable," .49. The marginal probabililities of .48 for a favorable seismic survey and .52 for an unfavorable survey are determined by summing the joint probabilities in each column.

TABLE 5-2 Joint Probability Table for Oil Wildcatting with a Seismic Survey

	Survey Results		
Geology	**Favorable (F)**	**Unfavorable (U)**	**Marginal Probability**
Oil (O)	**.27**	.03	**.30**
Dry (D)	.21	**.49**	**.70**
Marginal Probability	.48	.52	1.00

EXERCISES

5-29 Refer to the joint probability table in Table 5-1. Determine the conditional probabilities for the following:
(a) male *given* undergraduate
(b) undergraduate *given* male
(c) female *given* graduate
(d) graduate *given* female

5-30 Refer to the joint probability table in Problem 5-21 for a randomly selected Metropolis worker. Determine the following joint probabilities.
(a) Pr[blue collar|married]
(b) Pr[management|widowed]
(c) Pr[divorced|white collar]
(d) Pr[widowed|management]

5-31 Refer to the joint probability table in Problem 5-22 for a randomly selected State University alumnus. Determine the following joint probabilities.
(a) Pr[over 50|professional]
(b) Pr[professional|over 50]
(c) Pr[social science|30—50]
(d) Pr[under 23|science]

5-32 Forty percent of Natti Nitpicker's students have done their probability homework (H). Eighty percent of all students who do homework will pass (P) the probability quiz. Ninety percent of those who do not do the homework will fail (F). Pick a student at random.
(a) Identify the following: (1) Pr[H], (2) Pr[$P|H$]. Then apply the general multiplication law to find (3) Pr[H and P].
(b) Find (1) Pr[not H], (2) Pr[$F|$not H], (3) Pr[not H and F].

5-33 One Near Miss faculty member is selected from those categorized in Figure 5-4. All instructors have the same chance of being selected. Determine the following conditional probabilities.
(a) Pr[accounting|female]
(b) Pr[finance|male]
(c) Pr[management|male *and* full-time]
(d) Pr[finance|female *and* part-time]
(e) Pr[full-time|female]
(f) Pr[full-time *and* finance|male]
(g) Pr[male|accounting *or* finance]
(h) Pr[part-time *and* accounting|male]

5-34 A card is selected at random from a deck of playing cards. Determine the following probabilities. (Count ace as a "1"—low and odd.)
(a) Pr[heart|red]
(b) Pr[odd-numbered|below 6]
(c) Pr[club|black]
(d) Pr[jack|face]
(e) Pr[below 6|nonface]
(f) Pr[above 3|below 8]

5-35 A State University business scholarship student is randomly selected. Figure 5-3 summarizes the sample space. Let U and G denote level; M and Fe, sex; A, accounting major; and Fi, finance major.
(a) Use the count-and-divide method to determine the following probabilities.

(1)	(2)	(3)	(4)	(5)	(6)
Pr[U]	Pr[Fi]	Pr[Fe]	Pr[G]	Pr[M]	Pr[Fe]
Pr[$Fe|U$]	Pr[$U|Fi$]	Pr[$A|Fe$]	Pr[$M|G$]	Pr[$Fi|M$]	Pr[$U|Fe$]

(b) Apply the multiplication law to each pair of probabilities in (a) to determine the following joint probabilities.
(1) Pr[U and Fe]
(2) Pr[Fi and U]
(3) Pr[Fe and A]
(4) Pr[G and M]
(5) Pr[M and Fi]
(6) Pr[Fe and U]

	Accounting	Finance	Marketing	Management
Full-time	♀ ♂	♀ ♂ ♂	♀ ♂ ♂	♀ ♀ ♂ ♂
	♀ ♂	♀ ♂	♀ ♂	♀ ♂ ♂
	♂	♂	♀ ♂	♀ ♂ ♂
	♂	♂	♀ ♂	♀ ♂
	♂	♂	♂	♀ ♂
Part-time	♀ ♂ ♂	♀ ♂	♀ ♂ ♂	♀ ♂ ♂
	♂	♂	♀ ♂	♀ ♂ ♂
	♂	♂	♂	♀ ♂ ♂
	♂	♂	♂	♂
	♂	♂	♂	♂

♀ Female   ♂ Male

FIGURE 5-4

5-36 Ty Ruth is a switch hitter for baseball's Gotham Flyers. He bats right-handed (R) on 40% of all trips to the plate. In that direction, Ty's batting average is .320. This means that historically he has achieved a hit (H) on 32% of "official" times at bat. He was out (O) on the remainder. Walks, bases on errors, and sacrifices are categorized separately and are not included as "official" at–bats. As a lefty (L), Ruth has hit .360. Consider Ty's next time at bat.

(a) What are the values for the unconditional probabilities (1) $\Pr[L]$ and (2) $\Pr[R]$?

(b) What are the values for the conditional probabilities (1) $\Pr[H|L]$ and (2) $\Pr[H|R]$?

(c) Using your answers to (a) and (b), determine Ty's joint probability table for "official" hitting result (H or O) versus batting direction.

(d) Given that Ty makes a hit, what is the probability that he has batted (1) right-handed? (2) left-handed?

5-37 The general manager of the Gotham City Hellcats is evaluating an employment screening test for the front office clerical staff. During this experiment, all new clerical employees are given the test. Seventy percent pass the test; the rest fail. At a later time, it is determined whether the new clerks are satisfactory or unsatisfactory. Historically, 80% of all clerical hires have been found to be satisfactory, and 75% of the satisfactory clerks in the program have passed the screening test.

(a) From the given information, determine the following values.

(1) $\Pr[\text{pass}]$ (2) $\Pr[\text{satisfactory}]$ (3) $\Pr[\text{pass}|\text{satisfactory}]$

(b) Using your answers to (a), determine Pr[pass *and* satisfactory].

(c) Construct the joint probability table for test results versus employee performance events.

(d) Using your answers in (c), determine the following conditional probabilities.

(1) Pr[fail|unsatisfactory] (5) Pr[satisfactory|pass]

(2) Pr[fail|satisfactory] (6) Pr[unsatisfactory|pass]

(3) Pr[pass|unsatisfactory] (7) Pr[satisfactory|fail]

(4) Pr[unsatisfactory|fail]

(e) Using your answers in (d), determine the following percentages.

(1) failing clerks who prove to be unsatisfactory employees

(2) passing clerks who prove to be satisfactory employees

(f) Government guidelines are that a proper screening test must provide at least 20% for (1) in (e) and at least 60% for (2). Does this test meet those guidelines?

5-38 Two playing card decks are formed from printer's rejects. Deck 1 has no black cards, twice the usual number of hearts or diamonds, equal representations among all denominations, and 52 cards. Deck 2 has 3 sets of kings, 4 sets of queens, and 6 sets of jacks, and no other denominations. Each set has exactly one heart, one diamond, one club, and one spade, so that altogether deck 2 also has 52 cards. One of the decks is selected at random, thoroughly shuffled, and a card drawn and turned over.

(a) Find the joint probabilities for (1) ace of hearts *and* deck 1, (2) ace of hearts *and* deck 2.

(b) Given that an ace of hearts shows, what is the probability that it comes from (1) deck 1? (2) deck 2?

5-7 PROBABILITY TREES AND FURTHER LAWS

We have seen how the joint probability table arranges probability information in a convenient display. We are now ready to discuss a second display that is especially useful for decision making purposes. We then complete our probability introduction by extending the probability laws presented so far and giving some warnings on their misuse.

THE PROBABILITY TREE DIAGRAM

Business decision makers find the joint probability table cumbersome at times. They prefer to organize their probability calculations using a **probability tree**. The probability tree diagram for the preceding oil wildcatting illustration is shown in Figure 5-5. There, each event is represented as a **branch** in one or more **event forks**. This representation is especially convenient when events occur at different times or stages.

In probability trees, time moves from left to right. Since the geology events precede the seismic events, the branches for oil (*O*) and dry (*D*) appear in the event fork on the left. Each is followed by a separate event fork representing the seismic events, with a branch for favorable (*F*) and another for unfavorable (*U*). Two seismic event forks are required, since the seismic results can occur under two distinct geological conditions. The complete tree exhibits each outcome as a

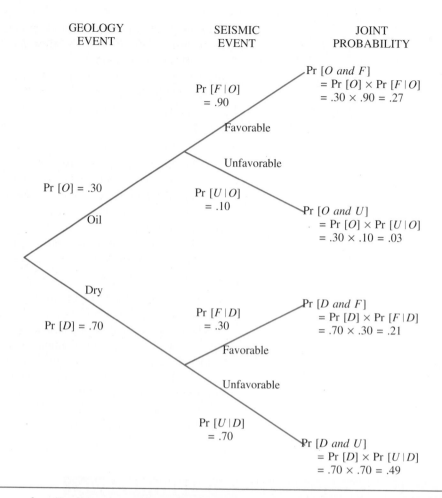

GEOLOGY
EVENT

SEISMIC
EVENT

JOINT
PROBABILITY

Pr [O] = .30

Oil

Pr [F|O]
= .90

Favorable

Unfavorable

Pr [U|O]
= .10

Pr [O and F]
= Pr [O] × Pr [F|O]
= .30 × .90 = .27

Pr [O and U]
= Pr [O] × Pr [U|O]
= .30 × .10 = .03

Dry

Pr [D] = .70

Pr [F|D]
= .30

Favorable

Unfavorable

Pr [U|D]
= .70

Pr [D and F]
= Pr [D] × Pr [F|D]
= .70 × .30 = .21

Pr [D and U]
= Pr [D] × Pr [U|D]
= .70 × .70 = .49

FIGURE 5-5 Probability tree diagram for oil wildcatting with a seismic survey.

single **path** from beginning to end. The probability tree in Figure 5-5 has four paths: oil-favorable, oil-unfavorable, dry-favorable, dry-unfavorable. Each path corresponds to a distinct joint event.

The probabilities for each event are placed alongside its branch. The values listed in the left fork, $Pr[O] = .30$ and $Pr[D] = .70$, are unconditional since that event fork has no predecessor. Probabilities for later stage events will all be *conditional* probabilities, with the branch or subpath leading to the branching point signifying the given events. The top seismic event fork lists the probabilities $Pr[F|O] = .90$ for favorable and $Pr[U|O] = .10$ for unfavorable. Since that fork is preceded by the oil (O) branch, both conditional probabilities involve O as the given event. A *completely different* set of conditional probabilities, $Pr[F|D] = .30$ and $Pr[U|D] = .70$, apply in the bottom event fork; that branching point is preceded by the dry (D) branch, so that D is the given event.

The events emanating from a single branching point are mutually exclusive and collectively exhaustive, so that exactly one must occur. All the probabilities on branches within the same fork must therefore sum to 1.

The probability tree is very convenient for determining joint probabilities. A joint event is represented by a path through the tree, and its probability is determined by multiplying together all the individual branch probabilities for its path. For instance, the topmost path represents the outcome sequence oil-favorable. The corresponding joint probability is

$$\Pr[O \text{ and } F] = \Pr[O] \times \Pr[F|O]$$
$$= .30(.90)$$
$$= .27$$

All of the joint probabilities for the oil wildcatter are listed in Figure 5-5 at the terminus of the respective event path. Notice that these sum to 1. That is because the joint events themselves are mutually exclusive and collectively exhaustive.

MULTIPLICATION LAW FOR SEVERAL EVENTS

The general multiplication law can be expanded to apply to situations involving more than two component events. For three events,

$$\Pr[A \text{ and } B \text{ and } C] = \Pr[A] \times \Pr[B|A] \times \Pr[C|A \text{ and } B]$$

All terms except the first are conditional probabilities, with the preceding events assumed as given events. There may be any number of component events.

To illustrate, in a particular industry it has been found that 80% of all new firms survive (S) past one year. Of those, 40% close (C) within the second year, half due to bankruptcy (B) and the rest for a number of other reasons. This experience provides the following probabilities for a start-up.

$$\Pr[S] = .80$$
$$\Pr[C|S] = .40$$
$$\Pr[B|S \text{ and } C] = .50$$

The multiplication law provides the joint probability that a particular new firm will survive the first year, close during the second, and then go bankrupt.

$$\Pr[S \text{ and } C \text{ and } B] = \Pr[S] \times \Pr[C|S] \times \Pr[B|S \text{ and } C]$$
$$= .80 \times .40 \times .50$$
$$= .16$$

EXAMPLE: THE MATCHING BIRTHDAY PROBLEM

Consider the probability that there is at least one matching birthday (day and month) among a group of persons.

SOLUTION: It will be simplest to determine the probability of the complementary event—no matches—by using the general multiplication law. Envision each member of a group of size n being asked in succession to state his or her birthday. We conveniently define our events as follows:

A_i = the ith person queried does not share a birthday
with the previous $i - 1$ persons.

TABLE 5-3 Probabilities for at Least One Matching Birthday

Group Size	Pr[no matches]	Pr[at least one match]
3	.992	.008
7	.943	.057
10	.883	.117
15	.748	.252
23	.493	.507
40	.109	.891
50	.030	.970
60	.006	.994

Then Pr[no match] = Pr[A_1 *and* A_2 *and . . . and* A_{n-1} *and* A_n], which is the probability of the event that no person shares a birthday with the preceding persons. For simplicity, assume all dates to be equally likely and ignore leap year. Thus,

$$\text{Pr}[A_1] = \frac{365}{365} \qquad \text{Pr}[A_2|A_1] = \frac{364}{365} \qquad \text{Pr}[A_3|A_1 \text{ and } A_2] = \frac{363}{365}$$

so that the nth person cannot have a birthday on the previously cited $n - 1$ dates, $365 - (n - 1) = 365 - n + 1$ days are allowable for his or her birthday. Therefore, we may apply the multiplication law to obtain

$$\text{Pr}[\text{no matches}] = \frac{365}{365} \times \frac{364}{365} \times \frac{363}{365} \times \ldots \times \frac{365 - n + 1}{365}$$

The probability for at least one match may be determined from this:

$$\text{Pr}[\text{at least one match}] = 1 - \text{Pr}[\text{no matches}]$$

One interesting issue is finding the size of the group for which the probability exceeds 1/2 that there is at least one match. Knowing this number, you can amaze your less knowledgeable friends and perhaps win a few bets. The "magical" group size turns out to be 23.

Why such a low group size? If it were physically possible to list all the ways (triples, sextuples, septuples, and so forth) in which 23 birthdays can match (there are several million, and for each a tremendous number of date possibilities), an intuitive appreciation as to why could be attained. Table 5-3 shows the matching probabilities for several group sizes. Note that for groups above 60 there is almost certain to be at least one match.

THE GENERAL ADDITION LAW

The addition law encountered earlier requires that the component events be *mutually exclusive*. That condition is not required by the following

GENERAL ADDITION LAW

$$\Pr[A \; or \; B] = \Pr[A] + \Pr[B] - \Pr[A \; and \; B]$$

The above acknowledges that when A and B are not mutually exclusive, they have elementary events in common, and the joint probability must be subtracted from the sum of the individual probabilities in order to avoid double accounting of possibilities.

To illustrate, consider a randomly selected playing card. The addition law gives the probability that the card is either heart or queen:

$$\Pr[heart \; or \; queen] = \Pr[heart] + \Pr[queen] - \Pr[heart \; and \; queen]$$

$$= \frac{13}{52} + \frac{4}{52} - \frac{1}{52}$$

$$= \frac{16}{52}$$

The general addition law may always be employed. Should A and B happen to be mutually exclusive, then $\Pr[A \; and \; B]$ must be zero. (The original addition law is just the general law applied when $\Pr[A \; and \; B] = 0$, so that in those cases the joint probability may be ignored without creating erroneous results.)

COMMON ERRORS IN APPLYING THE LAWS OF PROBABILITY

Some of the most prevalent errors in determining probability values result from the improper use of the laws of probability. Four common mistakes are listed on page 190.

STATISTICS AROUND US

Natural Disasters

Casualty insurance underwriters have determined the probabilities for a city experiencing one of the following natural disasters over the next decade.

Disaster	Probability
Tornado	.5
Flood	.3
Earthquake	.4

We cannot say that the probability for one disaster occurring is .5 + .3 + .4 = 1.2. Two or more of these disasters may occur over a ten-year period, and some may occur more than once.

1. Using the addition law to find the probability for the union of several events when they are *not* mutually exclusive. (See box on page 189.)

2. Using the addition law when the multiplication law should be used, and vice versa. Remember that *or* signifies addition and that *and* signifies multiplication.

   For example, the probability for drawing a red face card is the same as the probability for the event "red *and* face card." Recall that

$$Pr[red] = \frac{26}{52} \quad and \quad Pr[face\ card] = \frac{12}{52}$$

If we add these values to determine the joint probability, we obtain a meaningless result.

$$\frac{26}{52} + \frac{12}{52} = \frac{38}{52}$$

Since "red" and "face card" are independent events,

$$Pr[red\ and\ face\ card] = \frac{26}{52} \times \frac{12}{52} = \frac{6}{52}$$

3. Using the multiplication law for independent component events when the events are dependent.

4. Improperly identifying the complement of an event. For example, the complement of "none" is "some," which may be expressed as "one or more" or "at least one."

The incident described in the following Statistics Around Us box, which actually happened, dramatically illustrates how ludicrous results may be obtained by applying the probability laws incorrectly.*

EXERCISES

5-39 Refer to Exercise 5-27. Construct a probability tree diagram. Determine the joint probability for each geology and seismic outcome.

5-40 Refer to Exercise 5-28. Construct a probability tree diagram using shipment quality events in the first stage and inspector actions in the second. Determine the joint probabilities for each path outcome.

5-41 For simplicity, suppose that all months of the year are equally likely to be a person's birth month. Several people are comparing their birth months. Determine the probability for at least one matching birth month when this group consists of (a) two people (b) three people, and (c) five people.

5-42 A playing card is randomly selected from a standard deck. Establish for the following (1) the component event and joint probabilities. Then (2) apply the addition law to get the indicated composite event probability.
(a) Pr[diamond *or* face]   (c) Pr[face *or* king]
(b) Pr[9 *or* red]   (d) Pr[spade *or* odd-numbered]

*For a detailed discussion, see "Trial by Mathematics," *Time* (April 26, 1968), p. 41.

STATISTICS AROUND US

Wrongly Convicted by Probability

An elderly woman was mugged in the suburb of a large city. A couple was convicted of the crime, although the evidence was largely circumstantial. The multiplication law was used to demonstrate the extremely low probability that a couple fitting the description of the muggers could have committed the crime. The events (the characteristics that witnesses ascribed to the couple) are listed below, along with their assumed probabilities.

Characteristic Event	Assumed Probability
Drives yellow car	1/10
Interracial couple	1/1,000
Blond woman	1/4
Woman wears hair in ponytail	1/10
Man bearded	1/10
Man black	1/3

These values were multiplied to obtain the probability that any specific couple, selected at random from the city's population, would have all six characteristics.

$$\frac{1}{10} \times \frac{1}{1,000} \times \frac{1}{4} \times \frac{1}{10} \times \frac{1}{10} \times \frac{1}{3} = \frac{1}{12,000,000}$$

Since the defendants exhibited all six characteristics and the jury was mystified by the overwhelming strength of the probability argument, they were convicted.

The Supreme Court of the state heard the appeal of one of the defendants. The defense attorneys, after obtaining some good advice on probability theory, attacked the prosecution's analysis on two points: (1) the rather dubiously assumed probability values for the events, and (2) the invalid assumption of independence implicit in using the multiplication law in this manner (examples: the proportion of black men having beards may be greater than the proportion of the population as a whole having beards; "interracial couple" and "man black" are not independent events). The judge accepted the arguments of the defense and noted that trial evidence was misleading on another score: A high probability that the defendants were the *only* such couple should have been determined to demonstrate a strong case. Using the prosecution's original figures and its assumptions of independence, it can be demonstrated that the probability was large that at least one other couple in the area had the same characteristics.

5-43 Consider the joint probability table in Exercise 5-22 for a randomly selected State University alumnus. Find the probability for the following.
(a) professional *or* under 23
(b) older than 29 *or* social science
(c) over 22 *or* non-professional
(d) liberal arts *or* under 23

5-44 Consider the joint probability table in Exercise 5-21 for a randomly selected Metropolis worker. Find the probability for the following.
(a) white collar *or* divorced
(b) blue collar *or* never married
(c) management *or* widowed
(d) previously married *or* management

SUMMARY

1. **What are the basic concepts of probability and how do they relate to relative frequency?**
Probability in this book represents the **long-run frequency** with which an uncertain event occurs after repeated random experiments of identical nature. Probability theory is crucial to statistics since it explains how likely various sample results might be.

2. **What are random experiments and the outcomes they generate?**
The term **random experiment** refers to the situation giving rise to the uncertain event, such as a coin toss, a lottery, or a random selection. Random experiments involve **elementary events**, the most detailed outcomes of interest, which may or may not be **equally likely**.

3. **How is the count-and-divide method used to find probabilities for some events?**
When the elementary events are equally likely, the probability for any one of them is one divided by the number of possibilities. And, in that case the **count-and-divide method** provides the probability for any **composite event**; this procedure divides the number of applicable elementary events (size of the **event set**) by the total number possible. But, it works only when the elementary events are equally likely.

4. **How do we express probabilities for joint events (intersections), and how is the related information displayed?**
One special composite event is the **joint event**, which happens when two or more component events occur simultaneously, and they are logically connected by "and" (so that the joint event is the **intersection**). For some random experiments the probability for such a result, called **joint probability**, may sometimes be computed by counting and dividing or established by finding the percentage of the time both occur.
    Joint probabilities may be represented in a two-way **joint probability table** as entries in the cells. The row and column totals are then referred to as **marginal probabilities**. Like a cross tabulation, the sum of the entries in any row or column must equal the respective marginal value.

5. **What are the advantages of the multiplication law?**
Should the count-and-divide method not be suitable (either because the elementary events are not equally likely or because counts are not available), joint probabilities might be found using the **multiplication law**, which states that the desired result equals the product of the individual component event probabilities. One stipulation must be met: The component events have to be **statistically independent**.

6. **What is the importance of statistical independence, and how may that relationship be verified?**
Two events are **statistically independent** if the probability of any one of

them is unaffected by the occurrence of the other. One test for this is to check whether the product of the component events does indeed equal the joint probability (found earlier, either by counting and dividing or from an established percentage). Events found not to be independent are **dependent events**.

7. **How do we use the addition law for components joined by "or"?**
A second type of composite event involves components connected by "or" (so that the composite event is their **union**). In some cases, the count-and-divide method can often be used to find the probability for the composite event. When that is not possible, the **addition law** should give the desired value as the sum of the individual probabilities for the components. This law requires that the components be mutually exclusive. It gives rise to the useful **complementary event property**, which allows us to find a probability by taking one minus the probability of the opposite event.

8. **What are conditional probabilities and how are they distinguished from ordinary "unconditional" probabilities?**
Useful values are **conditional probabilities**, which are probabilities that apply for one event under the condition that a given event occur as well. For statistically independent events, the **unconditional** probability of any event will always be equal to its conditional probability given the other event. Conditional probabilities can sometimes be computed by applying the count-and-divide method, counting only those possibilities permissible by the stated condition. When that is not possible, a conditional probability may sometimes be available as given information (perhaps as a historical percentage). Finally, if sufficient probability values are already known, the **conditional probability identity** may be used. That identity works well when the data have been arranged in a joint probability table.

9. **What are the general forms for the multiplication and addition laws?**
General forms exist for the multiplication and addition laws. The **general multiplication law** does not require statistical independence, and the joint probability for two events is found by multiplying the *unconditional* probability for the first event times the *conditional* probability of the second given the first. (The general law still works if the events are independent, since the conditional probability for the second event must then equal its unconditional probability.) The **general addition law** does not require that the component events be mutually exclusive. For two events it corrects for double accounting of possibilities by subtracting their joint probability.

10. **How do we construct and use probability trees?**
Analogous to the joint probability table is the graphical **probability tree diagram**. Trees are especially useful when events occur at different points in time. Each branching point, or fork, in a probability tree represents a collectively exhaustive and mutually exclusive set of events as branches, the probabilities for which sum to 1. The probability values for events preceded by other branches are *conditional* probabilities, given those branches on the path leading to that branch. Each path represents a distinct outcome, or joint event, of the random experiment. The general multiplication law coincides naturally with the probability tree, since any joint event's probability is equal to the product of the branch probabilities for its path.

REAL-LIFE STATISTICAL CHALLENGE

Convicted by Your Genes?

The idea of applying probability theory to the successful arrest and conviction of individuals accused of criminal behavior is not new. Unfortunately neither is the misuse of probability theory. (See the box on page 191.) Now questions are being raised concerning one of the most recent scientific applications to crime-stopping—the use of DNA analysis.

USING DNA FOR HEALTH AND THE LAW

In exploring patterns in human DNA (deoxyribonucleic acid), researchers discovered there are parts of the DNA that can serve to match an individual's sequences of genetic code to samples. This matching procedure has been applied in major areas:

- DNA diagnosis of inheritable diseases passed on from a child's mother or father.
- DNA analysis or "fingerprinting" for comparing samples of unknown origins.

HOW DNA IS TESTED

The procedure for testing either for analysis or diagnosis involves subjecting the DNA to enzymes that break the strands into fragments at "restriction points." The lengths of the fragments will vary from person to person because of mutations that occur to the DNA code as it is transmitted from generation to generation. Through a series of steps the DNA fragments are sorted and tagged with radioactive markers. (The process of sorting is called electrophoresis, where the smallest DNA fragments are drawn furthest across an electrically charged gel.) An X-ray photograph is then taken. The photographic results can then be compared to other X-rays. A sample comparison is displayed in Figure 5-6.

By comparing the pattern for one individual with genetic material gathered from a large sample of people, some scientists argue it is possible to compare how closely individuals may be related. The probability for a close match between a person and a sample is considered to be extremely small. The unlikelihood of a match occurring by chance underlies the idea of genetic "fingerprint" matching. Indeed, genetic markers were first applied to establish probabilities that a particular male was the father of a child. Physical evidence gathered from a crime scene is often used in determining whether an alleged suspect was at the location. Even small pieces of DNA material have been used to aid in the successful conviction of accused individuals. In one multiple murder/rape case, over 3,000 people were sampled in villages and hamlets before the culprit was identified.

THE CONTROVERSY CONCERNING DNA "FINGERPRINTING"

Not everyone is convinced DNA "fingerprinting" will always lead to the conviction of the right man or woman. The heated debate involves a number of respected scholars. Two points are at issue:

- The procedures used to carry out the testing.
- The samples from which the isotopic markers are based.

Source: Figure A Cellmark Diagnostics found in Leslie Roberts, "Fight Erupts Over DNA Fingerprinting," *Science* 29 December 1991 Vol. 254, pp. 1721–1723.

FIGURE 5-6 Compelling Evidence. Bands indicate that blood on the defendant's shirt came from the victim (V), not from the defendant (D).

Representing the pro-genetic fingerprinting side is the argument defended by Ranajit Charkraborty (University of Texas at Houston) and Kenneth Kidd (Yale University), "it is the general frequency in the total population that is desired." They further indicate if *proper* procedures are followed in testing samples the results should be accurate enough for use as forensic evidence. (In one case, the odds are as extreme as 738,000,000,000,000 to 1 against a match being based on chance.)

Dissenting views are held by such scholars as Richard C. Lewontin (Harvard University), Daniel L. Hartl (Washington University) and Eric S. Lander (Massachusetts Institute of Technology). They believe that the total population data hide significant *similarities* found within various subgroups, especially among African-Americans and Hispanics. Additional samples of these subgroups are needed. They argue, furthermore, that some of the probability values (such as the above) entered as court testimony are based on faulty statistical methods. Additional issues are raised about the level of regulation needed to ensure proper procedures are followed.

The experts are lined up on both sides. In the realm of DNA "fingerprinting" the courts and the legal system may be faced with a hung jury.

QUESTIONS

1. Put yourself in the position of the defendant's attorney. How would you attack the credibility of the evidence gathered by the prosecution?

2. Reverse your position and develop arguments for the prosecution.

3. Imagine you are on a jury. What type of questions would the discussion in this box raise for you?

4. Should everyone be genetically tested and the results kept on file by law enforcement agencies?

Sources: Tim Beardsley, "Pointing Fingers: DNA Identification Is Called into Question," *Scientific American*, March 1992, Vol. 266, No. 3, pp. 26–27. R. Charkraborty and Kenneth. K. Kidd, "The Utility of DNA Typing in Forensic Work," *Science* 29 December Vol. 254, pp. 1735–1739. Cassandra Franklin-Barbajosa "DNA Profiling The New Science of Identity," *National Geographic*, May 1992, Vol. 181, No. 5, pp. 112–124. R. C. Lewontin and Daniel L. Hartl "Population Genetics in Forensic DNA Typing," *Science* 29 December Vol. 254, pp. 1745–1750. Leslie Roberts, "Fight Erupts Over DNA Fingerprinting," *Science* 29 December 1991, Vol. 254, pp. 1721–1723.

REVIEW EXERCISES

5-45 The faculty at Transylvania University are represented in Figure 5-7. One is chosen at random.
  (a) Construct a joint probability table for sex versus highest degree.
  (b) Are male and doctorate statistically independent or dependent events?
  (c) Given that the selected professor is female, find the conditional probability that she (1) holds a doctorate, (2) has a master's, as the highest degree.
  (d) Given that the selected professor has a doctorate, find the conditional probability that he or she is (1) male, (2) female.

FIGURE 5-7 Sample space for randomly selected Transylvania University faculty member.

5-46 Suppose that the professors in Figure 5-7 are selected at random for various committee assignments. Each person has the same chance of being selected for each successive assignment. Determine the following probabilities.

(a) The next two assignments go to (1) males, (2) females, (3) holders of doctorates.

(b) At least one female professor is selected out of the next (1) 2 assignments, (2) 3 assignments, (3) 4 assignments.

5-47 The faculty at Transylvania University are represented in Figure 5-7. One is chosen at random.

(a) Construct a joint probability table for sex versus academic assignment.

(b) Are female and researcher statistically independent or dependent events?

(c) Given that the selected professor is female, find the conditional probability that she is (1) a researcher, (2) an administrator, (3) teaching.

(d) Given that the selected professor is an administrator, find the conditional probability that he or she is (1) male, (2) female.

5-48 The faculty at Transylvania University are represented in Figure 5-7. One is chosen at random.

(a) Construct a joint probability table for highest degree versus academic assignment.

(b) Are doctorate and researcher statistically independent or dependent events?

(c) Given that the selected professor has a master's degree as the highest degree, find the conditional probability that he or she is (1) a teacher, (2) a researcher, (3) an administrator.

(d) Given that the selected professor is a researcher, find the conditional probability that he or she (1) holds a doctorate, (2) has a master's degree.

5-49 The probability is .95 that a GizMo Corporation traveling sales representative will have no automobile accidents in a year. Assuming that accident frequencies in successive years are independent events, determine the probability that a selected driver (a) goes 5 straight years with no accident; (b) has at least 1 accident in 5 years.

5-50 The Centralia plant of DanDee Assemblers experiences power failures with a probability of .10 during any given month. Assume that power events in successive months are independent. Determine the probability that there will be (a) no power failures during a 3-month span; (b) exactly 1 month involving a power failure during the next 4 months; (c) at least 1 power failure during the next 5 months.

5-51 A new family with two children of different ages has moved into the neighborhood. Suppose that it is equally likely that either child will be a boy or girl. Hence, the following situations are equally likely.

Youngest	Oldest	
boy	boy	(B, B)
boy	girl	(B, G)
girl	boy	(G, B)
girl	girl	(G, G)

(a) Determine Pr[at least one girl].

(b) If you know there is at least one girl, what is the conditional probability that the family has exactly one boy?

(c) Given that at least one child is a girl, what is the conditional probability that there are two girls?

5-52 The Ourman-Friday Employment Agency specializing in clerical and secretarial help classifies candidates in terms of primary skills and years of experience. The skills are bookkeeping, reception, and word processing. (We will assume that no candidate is proficient in more than one.) Experience categories are less than one year, one to three years, and more than three years. There are 100 persons currently on file, and their skills and experience are summarized in the following table.

Experience	Skill			Total
	Bookkeeping	Reception	Word Processing	
Less than One Year	15	5	30	50
One to Three Years	5	10	5	20
More than Three Years	5	15	10	30
Total	25	30	45	100

One person's file is selected at random. Determine the probability that the selected person will fall into the following categories.

(a) bookkeeping

(b) less than one year of experience

(c) reception

(d) one to three years of experience

(e) word processing

(f) more than three years of experience

5-53 Refer to Exercise 5-52.

(a) Assume the selected person has less than one year of experience. What is the probability that his or her skill is bookkeeping?

(b) Does the bookkeeping probability in (a) differ from the one you determined in Exercise 5-52? Are bookkeeping and less than one year of experience statistically independent events?

(c) Determine Pr[bookkeeping *and* less than one year of experience]. Can the multiplication law be used to determine this probability?

5-54 Refer to Exercise 5-52.

(a) Use the addition law to determine the probabilities for the following composite events.

(1) bookkeeping *or* reception

(2) word processing *or* reception

(3) less than one year of experience *or* more than three years of experience

(b) Use the count-and-divide procedure to determine the probabilities for the following composite events.

(1) bookkeeping *or* less than one year of experience

(2) reception *or* more than three years of experience

(3) word processing *or* one to three years of experience

5-55 The business faculty at Near Miss University are categorized in Figure 5-4. One instructor is selected at random. Construct a joint probability table for sex versus employment status events.

5-56 Repeat Exercise 5-55 for discipline versus employment status events.

5-57 The following data have been obtained for the employees of the Metropolis branch office of Kryptonite Corporation.

Name	Age	Sex	Salary	Marital Status	Years of Education	Years of Service
Emily Brown	26	female	$150/week	single	12	2
Thomas Duncan	54	male	3/hour	single	8	1
David Eckhart	34	male	400/week	married	18	10
Thelda Hunt	48	female	3/hour	widowed	10	21
James Mohair	33	male	200/week	single	12	7
Irvin Odle	31	male	175/week	married	14	2
Stacy Parker	35	female	190/week	divorced	12	4
Norman Raab	27	male	4/hour	divorced	12	2
Tammy Salazar	28	female	200/week	married	15	1
Ted VanDorn	42	male	500/week	married	16	15

For one person selected at random determine the following probabilities.
(a) Pr[older than 35] (c) Pr[more than 12 years of education]
(b) Pr[paid hourly] (d) Pr[more than 5 years of service]

5-58 An Admiral Motors quality control inspector accepts only 5% of all bad items and rejects only 1% of all good items. Overall production quality of items is such that only 90% are good.
(a) Using the percentages as probabilities for the next item inspected, determine the following probabilities.
   (1) Pr[accept | bad] (2) Pr[reject | good] (3) Pr[good]
(b) In the following joint probability table, determine the missing values.

Quality	Inspector Action Accept	Reject	Marginal Probability
Good			
Bad			
Marginal Probability			

(c) What is the probability that the inspector will accept or reject the next item incorrectly?

5-59 Applicants to a business school are 70% male. Regardless of their sex, 40% are married. Use the multiplication law to determine the probability for each of the following characteristics for a selected applicant.
(a) man *and* married (c) man *and* unmarried
(b) woman *and* married (d) woman *and* unmarried

5-60 Refer to Exercise 5-57. Consider the characteristics for one employee of Kryptonite Corporation selected at random from those listed.
(a) Construct a joint probability table for sex versus marital status events.

(b) Determine the following probabilities.
  (1) Pr[widowed *or* divorced]   (3) Pr[male *or* single]
  (2) Pr[single *or* divorced]   (4) Pr[female *or* married]

5-61 Consider again the random selection of one employee from those listed in Exercise 5-57. In each of the following cases, determine the unconditional probability of event (1). Then determine the conditional probability of event (1) given event (2). Comparing each pair of values, indicate whether the two events are statistically independent or dependent.
  (a) (1) age over 35   (2) more than 10 years of service
  (b) (1) female   (2) hourly worker
  (c) (1) married female   (2) age under 30
  (d) (1) more than 12 years   (2) single
        of education

5-62 Refer to Exercise 5-57. Two employees are selected by pulling names out of a hat. The first name picked is not placed back into the hat.
  (a) Construct a probability tree diagram for this experiment, with the sex of the selected employees as the events at each stage. Then, identify the elementary events in the sample space, and determine the joint probability for each.
  (b) Determine the probability that the two selections will involve employees of the same sex.

5-63 Suppose that Giant Enterprises increases its computer facilities, so that a busy signal is encountered only 10% of the time. Let B_1 denote that the first message gets a busy signal, D_1 that it goes through directly, and similarly for remaining messages. List all the joint events possible for the first three messages, and determine the probabilities for these events.

5-64 Refer to your answers to Exercise 5-63.
  (a) Determine the following probabilities for the number of busy signals encountered in the three messages.
    (1) Pr[exactly 0]   (3) Pr[exactly 2]
    (2) Pr[exactly 1]   (4) Pr[exactly 3]
  (b) Using your answers to (a), determine the following probabilities for the number of busy signals encountered in the three messages.
    (1) Pr[exactly 2 *or* exactly 3]   (3) Pr[at least 1]
    (2) Pr[at most 2]   (4) Pr[at most 1]

5-65 BriDent toothpaste has a 20% market share. Thus, there is a 20% chance that a randomly selected user of toothpaste will be a buyer (*B*) of BriDent. Suppose that 60% of BriDent buyers remember (*R*) a funny commercial about the product, while only 10% of nonbuyers do.
  (a) Determine the following probabilities.
    (1) Pr[*B*]   (2) Pr[not *B*]   (3) Pr[*R*|*B*]   (4) Pr[*R*|not *B*]
  (b) Construct the joint probability table for a person's buying category and memory regarding the commercial.
  (c) What percentage of all toothpaste users remember the commercial?

5-66 Consider the first three telecommunications queries by Giant Enterprises. Suppose that the system is busy (*B*) 20% of the time and that a direct connection (*D*) is achieved the rest of the time. Assume that the status of the system at each query is independent of that for preceding messages.
  (a) Construct a probability tree diagram for the system status encountered by those three queries.

(b) Identify all elementary events.

(c) Determine the joint probability for each event.

5-67 Callers to the Midget Motors switchboard encounter busy signals (*B*) 20% of the time. The remainder of the time calls are connected directly (*D*). Because of the slow rate at which calls are placed, the connection status of successive calls is dependent. Records show that half of all calls placed after a preceding call encountered a busy signal will also find the switchboard busy. But 90% of calls placed after the preceding call was directly connected will also be directly connected.

(a) Construct a probability tree diagram for the system status encountered by the first three calls to the Midget Motors switchboard.

(b) Identify all elementary events.

(c) Determine the joint probability for each event.

STATISTICS IN PRACTICE

5-68 Using the master class data from Exercise 1-19, one student will be selected at random. Perform the following probability operations.

(a) Construct a joint probability table using two data sets. Use either your nominal data or create categories for the ordinal or interval data. Possible comparisons include favorite food versus major or sex; place of birth versus age.

(b) Using the joint probability table, create some examples to demonstrate your understanding of the multiplication and addition laws.

(c) Using the joint probability table, create some examples to demonstrate your understanding of mutually exclusive events and conditional probability.

5-69 Using your group's class data list, developed in Exercise 1-21, repeat (a) through (c) of Exercise 5-68.

5-70 The First Post-Cold War Olympics: The following table shows the medal results for the top six countries and the total medals won by participants from other countries in the Albertville, France Winter Olympics of 1992.

Country	Gold	Silver	Bronze	Total
Germany	10	10	6	26
Unified Team	9	6	8	23
Austria	6	7	8	21
Norway	9	6	5	20
Italy	4	6	4	14
United States	5	4	2	11
Others	14	19	23	56
Total	57	58*	56*	171

*Two silver medals were awarded in Woman's Giant Slalom. No bronze medal was awarded.

Source: *San Jose Mercury News* February 24, 1992 p. 6C

One medalist will be chosen at random.

(a) Construct a joint probability table using the data.

(b) What is the probability that the selected medalist came from one of two listed countries bordering on the Swiss Alps?

(c) Assuming an American is chosen what is the probability that he or she won a gold medal.

5-71 Back at the 1988 Summer Olympics. Consider the best way to organize the medal total data presented from the 1988 Summer Olympics (Exercise 2-41). Construct a joint probability table and demonstrate applications of the addition law, multiplication law and conditional probability.

5-72 Use the data in the gas mileage data displayed in Table 3-5 to carry out the following probability operations.

(a) Construct a joint probability table and demonstrate applications of the addition law, multiplication law and conditional probability.

(b) What is the probability of selecting a car at random with a mileage value of less than 20; greater than 26; between 27 and 18 mpg inclusively? Greater than 25 mpg given the vehicle is a two-seater? Create two other examples showing your understanding of conditional probability.

5-73 Refer to the exam score data given in Table 3-13 (page 115). Grades are assigned as follows:

90–99: A   75–89: B   65–74: C   50–64: D   49 and below: F

Assume that students with even student numbers are male and odd student numbers are female.

(a) Construct a joint probability table for exam grade versus gender.

(b) What percent of the males received a grade of B?

(c) What percent of the C grades did females receive?

(d) Compute the probability of a randomly selected student's receiving a D or being male.

(e) If it is known that a randomly chosen score is below 75, what is the probability that the grade was a C?

5-74 Refer to the NFL quarterback information in Table 3-11 (page 114). One quarterback will be selected at random.

(a) Construct a joint probability table for touchdowns (*TD*)/(*Int*) versus interceptions.

(b) Compute $\Pr[TD \geq 17 \mid Int \geq 11]$.

(c) Compute $\Pr[TD > 21 \text{ or } Int < 11]$.

5-75 *The 103rd Congress.* Table 5-4 provides information on the 100 United States senators of the 103rd Congress. One senator will be selected at random.

(a) Construct a joint probability table for the year the term ends versus the political party.

(b) What percentage of the Democrats' terms end in 1997?

(c) What percentage of the Republicans' terms end in 1995?

(d) Of the senators whose terms end in 1999, what percentage are Democrats?

5-76 *World Series Results.* Table 5-5 contains the World Series winners for thirty years. One year will be chosen at random.

TABLE 5-4 Senators of the 103rd Congress

Term Ends	Senator	Party	Term Ends	Senator	Party
1999	R. Shelby	D	1997	H. Heflin	D
1999	F. Murkowski	R	1997	T. Stevens	R
1999	J. McCain	R	1995	D. DeConcini	D
1999	D. Bumpers	D	1997	D. Pryor	D
1999	B. Boxer	D	1995	D. Feinstein	D
1999	B. N. Campbell	D	1997	H. Brown	R
1999	C. Dodd	D	1995	J. Lieberman	D
1995	W. Roth, Jr.	R	1997	J. Biden, Jr.	D
1999	B. Graham	D	1995	C. Mack	R
1999	P. Coverdell	R	1997	S. Nunn	D
1999	D. Inouye	D	1995	D. Akaka	D
1999	K. Kempthorne	R	1997	L. Craig	R
1999	C. M. Braun	D	1997	P. Simon	D
1999	D. Coats	R	1995	R. Lugar	R
1999	C. Grassley	R	1997	T. Harkin	D
1999	B. Dole	R	1997	N. Kassebaum	R
1999	W. Ford	D	1997	M. McConnell	R
1999	J. Breaux	D	1997	J. B. Johnston	D
1995	G. Mitchell	D	1997	W. Cohen	R
1999	B. Mikulski	D	1995	P. Sarbanes	D
1995	E. Kennedy	D	1997	J. Kerry	D
1995	D. Riegle, Jr.	D	1997	C. Levin	D
1995	D. Durenberger	R	1997	P. Wellstone	D
1995	T. Lott	R	1997	T. Cochrane	R
1999	C. Bond	R	1995	J. Danforth	R
1995	C. Burns	R	1997	M. Baucus	D
1995	J. R. Kerrey	D	1997	J. Exon	D
1999	H. Reid	D	1995	R. Bryan	D
1999	J. Gregg	R	1997	R. Smith	R
1995	F. Lautenberg	D	1997	B. Bradley	D
1995	J. Bingaman	D	1997	P. Domenici	R
1999	A. D'Amato	R	1995	D. Moynihan	D
1999	L. Faircloth	R	1997	J. Helms	R
1999	B. Dorgan	D	1995	K. Conrad	D
1999	J. Glenn	D	1995	H. Metzenbaum	D
1999	D. Nickles	R	1997	D. Boren	D
1999	B. Packwood	R	1997	M. Hatfield	R
1999	A. Specter	R	1995	H. Wofford	D
1995	J. Chafee	R	1997	C. Pell	D
1999	E. Hollings	D	1997	S. Thurmond	R
1999	T. Daschle	D	1997	L. Pressler	R
1995	J. Sasser	D	1997	H. Matthews	D
1995	K. B. Hutchison	R	1997	P. Gramm	R
1999	R. Bennett	R	1995	O. Hatch	R
1999	P. Leahy	D	1995	J. Jeffords	R
1995	C. Robb	D	1997	J. Warner	R
1999	P. Murray	D	1995	S. Gorton	R
1995	R. Byrd	D	1997	J. Rockefeller	D
1999	R. Feingold	D	1995	H. Kohl	D
1995	M. Wallop	R	1997	A. Simpson	R

Source: *The World Almanac and Book of Facts, 1994.*

TABLE 5-5 World Series Results for Thirty Years

Year	Team	League	Games	Year	Team	League	Games
1964	St. Louis	NL	4–3	1979	Pittsburgh	NL	4–3
1965	Los Angeles	NL	4–3	1980	Philadelphia	NL	4–2
1966	Baltimore	AL	4–0	1981	Los Angeles	NL	4–2
1967	St. Louis	NL	4–3	1982	St. Louis	NL	4–3
1968	Detroit	AL	4–3	1983	Baltimore	AL	4–1
1969	New York	NL	4–1	1984	Detroit	AL	4–1
1970	Baltimore	AL	4–1	1985	Kansas City	AL	4–3
1971	Pittsburgh	NL	4–3	1986	New York	NL	4–3
1972	Oakland	AL	4–3	1987	Minnesota	AL	4–3
1973	Oakland	AL	4–3	1988	Los Angeles	NL	4–1
1974	Oakland	AL	4–1	1989	Oakland	AL	4–0
1975	Cincinnati	NL	4–3	1990	Cincinnati	NL	4–0
1976	Cincinnati	NL	4–0	1991	Minnesota	AL	4–3
1977	New York	AL	4–2	1992	Toronto	AL	4–2
1978	New York	AL	4–2	1993	Toronto	AL	4–2

Source: *The World Almanac and Book of Facts,* 1994.

(a) Construct a joint probability table for winning league versus the number of games played in the series.
(b) Of the National League winners, what percentage won the series in exactly 7 games?
(c) Of the series that lasted exactly 6 games, what percentage was won by the American League?

CASE **The Three Marketeers**

Dar Tan Yun, president of the Three Marketeers, has formed a consumer test panel to help devise a marketing strategy for a line of microwavable gourmet meals. The panel would be responsible for choosing promotions, formulating advertising copy, and selecting advertising media.

Table 5-6 shows a partial breakdown of the 25 panel members. Dar believes that they are microcosm of the target market. If true, the probability that a potential customer has various characteristics should coincide with the probability that a randomly selected panel member has them also.

QUESTIONS

1. Various two-way joint probability tables might be constructed for the characteristics of a randomly selected panel member.
   (a) Including a person's sex as a main feature, how many different joint probability tables may be constructed using the demographic groupings in Table 5-6?

(b) Construct the following joint probability tables.
  (1) marital status versus education
  (2) education versus home
  (3) home versus sibling status
  (4) sex versus marital status
  (5) marital status versus children at home
  (6) sibling status versus education
(c) Using your answers to (b), identify any event pairs that are statistically independent.
(d) What might you conclude regarding the incidence of independence among demographic characteristics in target markets?

2. Determine the following conditional probabilities for a randomly selected panel member.
  (a) Pr[bachelor's|married]
  (b) Pr[married|bachelor's]
  (c) Pr[renter|master's]
  (d) Pr[master's|renter]
  (e) Pr[firstborn|owner]
  (f) Pr[owner|firstborn]
  (g) Pr[unmarried|no children at home]
  (h) Pr[no children at home|unmarried]

3. A recent survey showed that 20% of the subscribers to the *Rising Loafer* are college graduates. Another 10% of the subscribers have master's

TABLE 5-6 Demographic Breakdown of Three Marketeers Consumer Test Panel

Name	Marital Status	Level of Education	Home	Sibling Status	Children at Home
Ruth Baird	married	high school	renter	firstborn	yes
Ann Schultz	unmarried	some college	renter	youngest	no
Mark Maris	unmarried	bachelor's	renter	firstborn	no
Tom Steel	married	some college	owner	youngest	yes
Bill Adamson	unmarried	master's	renter	only child	yes
Pete Gonzales	unmarried	bachelor's	renter	middle	no
Morris Chin	married	high school	owner	middle	yes
Heidi Gravitz	married	bachelor's	owner	middle	no
Todd Fullmer	unmarried	bachelor's	renter	firstborn	yes
Scott Meadows	unmarried	master's	owner	youngest	no
Harvey Abramovitz	married	bachelor's	owner	firstborn	yes
Andy Pilsner	unmarried	some college	renter	youngest	no
Ann Goldberg	unmarried	some college	renter	only child	yes
Mike O'Hara	married	bachelor's	renter	youngest	yes
Larry Ellington	married	high school	owner	only child	no
Dick Senn	unmarried	bachelor's	renter	firstborn	no
Tom Sellers	married	bachelor's	renter	middle	no
Jack Beringer	unmarried	high school	owner	middle	no
Don McKinsey	unmarried	bachelor's	renter	only child	no
Sally Deerwalker	married	some college	owner	firstborn	yes
Ingrid Folsom	married	bachelor's	owner	only child	yes
Gloria Gravenstein	married	high school	owner	middle	yes
Marsha Markovich	unmarried	some college	renter	middle	yes
Ursula Hernandes	unmarried	bachelor's	renter	only child	no
Tom Fujimoto	unmarried	bachelor's	renter	youngest	no

degrees, and only 5% never went beyond high school. Determine the probability that a randomly selected panel member who reads this magazine (a) owns his or her home; (b) is married.

4. Half of the subscribers to *Foodaholics NewScooper* have siblings. Of these, 10% are the firstborn, and 30% are the youngest child. Determine the probability that a panel member who subscribes to this newsletter (a) is a homeowner; (b) has a master's degree.

5. Half of all the people in the target market eat oatmeal. Of these, 30% of the females prefer that dried fruit be added to the premix, whereas only 20% of the men do. Assuming that the same percentages apply to the panel members, determine the probability that a panel member will (a) eat oatmeal; (b) prefer dried fruit in their oatmeal.

6. Crunchy-Munchy is a new snack food. Of the children living with a married parent, only 20% will eat the snack. And of the children living with a single parent, 40% will eat it. Crunchy-Munchy will be marketed if at least 5% of all potential buyers have a child at home who would eat it. Assuming that the panel matches the market, should Crunchy-Munchy be marketed?

PART II

DRAWING CONCLUSIONS FROM SAMPLES: INFERENTIAL STATISTICS

PROBABILITY DISTRIBUTIONS, EXPECTED VALUE, AND SAMPLING

BEFORE READING THIS CHAPTER, MAKE SURE YOU UNDERSTAND:

The distinction between the sample and the population (Chapter 1).

The difference between a sample statistic and a population parameter (Chapter 3).

The advantages of *random* samples (Chapter 4).

The basic concepts of probability (Chapter 5).

How to construct a probability tree (Chapter 5).

The addition and multiplication laws of probability (Chapter 5).

AFTER READING THIS CHAPTER, YOU WILL UNDERSTAND:

About random variables and their probability distributions.

About the two basic types of random variables.

How probability distributions are obtained.

About sampling with and without replacement and the effect on probabilities.

About expected value and variance and their uses.

How to represent sample results as random variables.

About the sampling distributions of the mean and proportion.

About the binomial distribution and how to compute binomial probabilities.

This chapter focuses on **deductive statistics**: determining probabilities for obtaining particular sample results when the population values are known. As an illustration, we will determine the possible sample outcomes for a population of Graduate Management Admissions Test scores. Studying how random samples are generated and learning what to expect when working with *known* populations will lay the essential groundwork for evaluating *unknown* populations.

The average test score, or sample mean, is an important value to use in establishing admissions policies. When its value is uncertain (the case *before* the sample is taken), the sample mean is referred to as a **random variable**. The values of a random variable are treated as uncertain events that occur with a set of probabilities called a **probability distribution**.

We can summarize the information in a probability distribution in terms of central tendency and variability. The "average" figure for a random variable is referred to as its **expected value**. We use expected values to compare probability distributions. In sampling, they enable us to analyze the kinds of results that we might obtain.

6-1 RANDOM VARIABLES AND PROBABILITY DISTRIBUTIONS

We have seen (in Chapter 2) that frequency of occurrence plays an important role in statistics. We also have become familiar with probability (in Chapter 5). We are now ready to combine these concepts, laying the foundation for statistical analysis of samples and for evaluating decisions made under uncertain conditions.

THE RANDOM VARIABLE

A numerical value that may result from a future random experiment is unknown and should be considered a *variable*. The value actually achieved is subject to chance and is therefore determined *randomly*. Such a quantity is given the following

DEFINITION: A **random variable** is a numerical quantity whose value is determined by chance.

All of the following are random variables.

your income next year	your score on the next exam
tomorrow's high temperature	the number of errors in a phone book
how long you wait for a soda	IBM's next quarterly dividend
length of a movie line	the height of the next person you see
amount of money you will lose	your GPA for the present term

A random variable must be a numerical quantity. There can be no random variable for a random experiment involving qualitative outcomes unless points, a cost, or some other number can be associated with the elementary events.

THE PROBABILITY DISTRIBUTION

Random variables are fundamental to statistical theory. The relationship between a random variable's values and their probabilities is summarized by the probability distribution.

DEFINITION: The **probability distribution** provides a probability for each possible value of a random variable.

A probability distribution can be analogous to a relative frequency distribution. To illustrate, a data set was formed by keeping track of the number of customers arriving at the checkout counter at a WaySafe market. The frequency distribution in Table 6-1 applies for each six-minute time interval over a period of five hours on the first day of December.

The relative frequency for each number of customer arrivals is shown in column (3). Recall that the relative frequency indicates the *proportion* of observations falling into a particular category. (Here, the elementary units are six-minute *time spans*, not customers, and the categories are the *number of arrivals*.) Thus, .36, or 36% of the intervals involve exactly 1 arriving customer, while .04, or 4% of the intervals have exactly 4 arrivals.

Now consider a random experiment where one of the 50 time intervals is selected at random and the corresponding number of arrivals determined. The outcome might be the number of customers who arrived during 10:36–10:42, during 12:06–12:12, or within any of the time spans. The number of arrivals during the selected time is the random variable. The probability that the selected segment has exactly 1 arrival is

$$\text{Pr[exactly 1 arrival]} = \frac{18}{50} = .36$$

Similarly, the probability that it will be one having 4 arrivals is

$$\text{Pr[exactly 4 arrivals]} = \frac{2}{50} = .04$$

Notice that the probability for any particular number of arrivals matches the relative frequency. The individual probabilities for all possibilities are listed in Table 6-2, which constitutes the probability distribution for the random variable.

The possible values of a random variable are mutually exclusive and collectively exhaustive events. The probabilities in a complete listing must therefore

TABLE 6-1 Frequency Distribution for Customer Arrivals at Checkout Counter

(1) Number of Arrivals	(2) Number of Six-Minute Intervals	(3) Relative Frequency
0	18	.36
1	18	.36
2	8	.16
3	3	.06
4	2	.04
5	1	.02
6	0	.00
7 or more	0	.00
	50	1.00

sum to 1. For mathematical convenience we use symbols. A capital letter represents the random variable itself. Here, X denotes the yet-to-be-determined number of arrivals in the sample time segment. A lower case letter, here x, is the stand-in or **dummy variable** for all possible levels of the random variable. This makes it easier to communicate and permits use of algebraic expressions that summarize statistical procedures. The following example should be helpful.

EXAMPLE: A RAFFLE

A raffle is to be conducted with 10,000 tickets, numbered consecutively from 1 through 10,000. One ticket is to be selected from a barrel after thorough mixing. Because each ticket is equally likely to be selected, the probability that a particular ticket will be selected is 1/10,000. If we define a random variable for the raffle as the number of the selected ticket, to be denoted by X, we can shorten the statement "The number of the selected ticket will be 7,777" to read

$$X = 7{,}777$$

We wish to find the probability distribution for this random variable.

SOLUTION: We express the probability for this event as

$$\Pr[X = 7{,}777] = \frac{1}{10{,}000}$$

Because there are 10,000 possible outcomes, all having the same probability, we can express the probability distribution more concisely by using a statement of the form

$$\Pr[X = x] = \frac{1}{10{,}000} \quad \text{for values of } x = 1, 2, \ldots, 10{,}000$$

which is equivalent to duplicating the previous probability expression 10,000 times, once for each ticket number.

TABLE 6-2 Probability Distribution for Customer Arrivals during Randomly Selected Six-Minute Intervals

Number of Arrivals x	Probability $\Pr[X = x]$
0	.36
1	.36
2	.16
3	.06
4	.04
5	.02
6	.00
7 or more	.00
	1.00

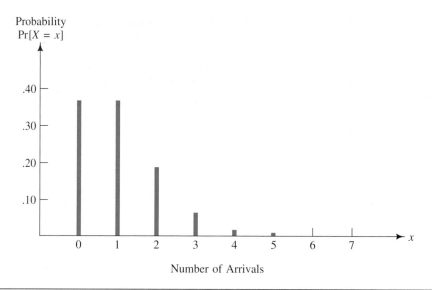

FIGURE 6-1 Graph of the probability distribution for the number of arrivals.

It is important to keep in mind that the capital letter X represents the number of the ticket that *will be* selected and has no determined value until the raffle is completed. The lowercase letter x is a stand-in for *each* ticket number to avoid 10,000 repetitious statements.

Figure 6-1 shows how the WaySafe arrival probability distribution appears on a graph. The values for each possible variable level are on the horizontal axis. The vertical axis provides the probability. For each variable level, a spike is drawn on the graph with a height equal to the appropriate probability.

Many random variables have probability distributions for which individual probabilities can be calculated from a mathematical expression. Later you'll encounter illustrations of those expressions that are applicable to some common probability distributions. Such expressions are called **probability mass functions**.

In a random sampling experiment, the population observations are also the elementary events of the sample space, as in Figure 6-2. Each element of the sample space corresponds to a level $x = 0$, $x = 1$, ... Mathematicians think of X as a function that maps each elementary event onto the x-line.

FINDING THE PROBABILITY DISTRIBUTION

A probability distribution can be established by applying the probability concepts and procedures found in Chapter 5. The following example shows how to create a probability distribution using the multiplication and addition laws.

EXAMPLE: AMOUNT PAID FOR A PERSONAL COMPUTER
Quant Jacques wishes to buy a personal computer made by VBM (Very Big Machines). From past purchases, VBM has established the following breakdown for the percentage of times that a particular component is selected for a system.

Sample Space

FIGURE 6-2 Illustration of the random variable for a randomly selected time interval.

Computer and Memory	Printer	Monitor
30%–250K ($1500)	50%–Matrix ($500)	60%–Monochrome ($200)
70%–500K ($2000)	50%–Laser ($1000)	40%–Color ($400)

Assuming that Quant selects the three components independently and that the probability for each choice agrees with the percentages given in the table, what is the probability distribution for his total system cost?

SOLUTION: Begin by listing all the possible combinations. You can determine the probability for each by using the multiplication law.

Computer and Memory	Printer	Monitor	Cost	Probability
250K	Matrix	Monochrome	1,500 + 500 + 200 = $2,200	.3(.5)(.6) = .09
250K	Matrix	Color	1,500 + 500 + 400 = 2,400	.3(.5)(.4) = .06
250K	Laser	Monochrome	1,500 + 1,000 + 200 = 2,700	.3(.5)(.6) = .09
250K	Laser	Color	1,500 + 1,000 + 400 = 2,900	.3(.5)(.4) = .06
500K	Matrix	Monochrome	2,000 + 500 + 200 = 2,700	.7(.5)(.6) = .21
500K	Matrix	Color	2,000 + 500 + 400 = 2,900	.7(.5)(.4) = .14
500K	Laser	Monochrome	2,000 + 1,000 + 200 = 3,200	.7(.5)(.6) = .21
500K	Laser	Color	2,000 + 1,000 + 400 = 3,400	.7(.5)(.4) = .14

List the possible costs, applying the addition law as needed, to construct the probability distribution table.

Cost		Probability
$2,200		.09
2,400		.06
2,700	.09 + .21 =	.30
2,900	.06 + .14 =	.20
3,200		.21
3,400		.14
		1.00

PROBABILITY TREES AND SAMPLING

Especially important to statistical investigations are probability distributions that summarize the potential results from sampling. Sampling ordinarily involves multiple observations, and, therefore, the probability calculations can be complicated. Probability trees are helpful in organizing those computations.

To illustrate, consider a shipment of 100 printed circuit (PC) boards received by a computer manufacturer. Each board is either defective (D) or good (G). The decision to accept or reject the shipment will be based on a sample of three boards selected at random. The inspector has no way of knowing ahead of time how many defective boards there are. Let's assume that there are exactly 5 defective boards and 95 good boards.

The probability tree in Figure 6-3 summarizes the essential information. The first observation is represented by the two branches in the event fork farthest to the left. We use the abbreviation D_1 to denote the event "the first board is defective" and G_1 to denote the event "the first board is good." The subscripts help

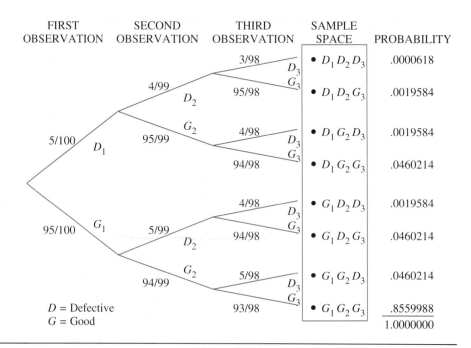

FIGURE 6-3 Probability tree diagram for selecting a sample of three PC Boards without replacement.

to distinguish the results from different observations. Each branch for the first observation leads to a separate event fork for the second. Both forks for the second observation have a D_2 and a G_2 branch. Together, the initial observations create four distinct circumstances under which the third observation might occur, and each of these is represented by a separate fork that has a D_3 and G_3 branch.

The probabilities for each branch are determined using the count-and-divide method, according to the number of defective and good boards remaining up to that point in the tree. The initial fork has probabilities

$$\Pr[D_1] = \frac{5}{100} \quad \text{and} \quad \Pr[G_1] = \frac{95}{100}$$

Because the quality mix of the remaining items varies at the second stage, the probabilities for D_2 and G_2 differ in the two event forks for that observation. The values shown are *conditional probabilities*. The top set applies when D_1 has occurred, when there are only 4 defective boards and 95 good boards remaining. With 99 boards available for testing, the count-and-divide procedure provides

$$\Pr[D_2|D_1] = \frac{4}{99} \quad \text{and} \quad \Pr[G_2|D_1] = \frac{95}{99}$$

Likewise, the lower second stage fork involves

$$\Pr[D_2|G_1] = \frac{5}{99} \quad \text{and} \quad \Pr[G_2|G_1] = \frac{94}{99}$$

since, at that point—with 1 good board removed—the tree indicates that 5 defective and 94 good boards remain.

The forks for the third stage involve probabilities reflecting the respective histories of defective and good for the previously tested items. The fork at the top right is preceded by D_1 and D_2 branches, so that the following conditional probabilities appear.

$$\Pr[D_3|D_1 \text{ and } D_2] = \frac{3}{98} \quad \text{and} \quad \Pr[G_3|D_1 \text{ and } D_2] = \frac{95}{98}$$

It is easy to verify the remaining third stage probabilities.

Each path through the tree in Figure 6-3 corresponds to a distinct outcome, and is summarized in the sample space listed in the box beside the tree. The probability for these elementary events is determined by multiplying together the branch probabilities on its respective path. For instance, to determine the second elementary event probability we have

$$\Pr[D_1 D_2 G_3] = \frac{5}{100} \times \frac{4}{99} \times \frac{95}{98} = .0019584$$

We are actually applying the multiplication law for several joint events.

$$\Pr[D_1 \text{ and } D_2 \text{ and } G_3] = \Pr[D_1] \times \Pr[D_2|D_1] \times \Pr[G_3|D_1 \text{ and } D_2]$$

TABLE 6-3 Probability Distribution for the Number of Defective PC Boards when Three Sample Items are Inspected without Replacement

Number of Defectives r	Corresponding Elementary Events	Elementary Event Probability	Probability $\Pr[R = r]$
0	$G_1G_2G_3$	.8559988	.8559988
1	$D_1G_2G_3$	.0460214	.1380642
	$G_1D_2G_3$	.0460214	
	$G_1G_2D_3$	<u>.0460214</u>	
		.1380642	
2	$D_1D_2G_3$	.0019584	.0058752
	$D_1G_2D_3$	.0019584	
	$G_1D_2D_3$	<u>.0019584</u>	
		.0058752	
3	$D_1D_2D_3$	.0000618	<u>.0000618</u>
			1.0000000

By itself, the probability tree is too detailed to help the inspector decide how to dispose of a particular shipment. However, she would find useful the probability distribution for the number of defectives R provided in Table 6-3. The table probabilities were determined using the information in the last two columns of Figure 6-3 and then applying the addition law for mutually exclusive events.

Using the values in Table 6-3, the inspector can determine the probability that the shipment would contain more than 1 defective.

(sampling without replacement)

$$\Pr[R > 1] = \Pr[R = 2] + \Pr[R = 3]$$
$$= .0058752 + .0000618$$
$$= .0059370$$

If she rejects shipments having more than 1 defective item, less than 1% of similar shipments would be unacceptable.

INDEPENDENT SAMPLE OBSERVATIONS

The preceding illustration involves **sampling without replacement**, since the inspected sample units are set aside. Although it seems inherently wasteful (and even impossible when testing destroys the items), some inspection schemes *put back* replace the items in the original population, allowing them the same chance of being selected for each subsequent observation as the other items. Such a procedure is called **sampling with replacement**. As we shall see, sampling with replacement simplifies the probability calculations.

Figure 6-4 shows the probability tree diagram that would apply if the inspector sampled with replacement. Notice that all the D branches have identical probabilities of .05, and, similarly, the probabilities for the G branches are all .95. Since sampled items are replaced, the probabilities for later quality events must be unaffected by what happens earlier. In effect, successive quality events are *statistically independent*. Independence between successive sample observations arises naturally when sampling from a continuing production line, when replacement or

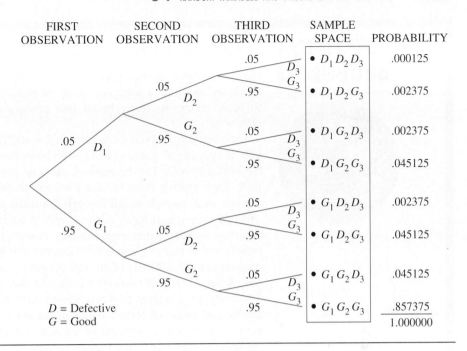

FIGURE 6-4 Probability tree for selecting a sample of three PC Boards with replacement.

statistically
independent

nonreplacement would yield identical probabilities due to the theoretically infinite population size.

The probability distribution for the number of defectives found using sampling with replacement is given in Table 6-4. The probabilities are obtained in the same manner as before. To help compare the two procedures, the two sets of probabilities are given side by side.

The two sets of values are very close. As noted earlier, the probabilities computed for sampling without replacement involve cumbersome calculations, and they are often *approximated* using the cleanly computed values that strictly apply for sampling with replacement. The computations for both types of similar distributions can be streamlined. When there is replacement—or, more generally, when successive observations are independent—the *binomial distribution*

TABLE 6-4 Probability Distributions for the Number of Defective PC Boards

Number of Defectives r	Pr[R = r] for Sampling	
	without Replacement	with Replacement
0	.8559988	.857375
1	.1380642	.135375
2	.0058752	.007125
3	.0000618	.000125
	1.0000000	1.000000

STATISTICS AROUND US

No Ball Bearing Is Exact

For use in large motors, precision 1-inch-diameter ball bearings must be machined to within a tolerance of .01 of an inch. Each bearing is assumed to be so nearly perfectly round that no measuring device can perceive otherwise.

Each bearing sold has been inspected at uniform temperature by using a pair of "go-no go" gauges (stands with holes through which a bearing being tested is dropped). The diameter of one hole is 1.01 inches, the other is .99 inch. Each bearing must be small enough to fall through the large gauge but not small enough to fall through the small gauge.

To determine how many of the 1 million bearings produced annually are precisely 1 inch in diameter, a more accurate measuring system must be established. A pair of gauges could determine if bearings were within a hundred-thousandth (.00001) of an inch of being exactly 1 inch in diameter, but only about 1,000 ball bearings would pass this test (assuming nearly equal frequency for all values between .99 and 1.01 inches). Bearings that passed this second stage of testing could be measured again with gauge blocks accurate to within a millionth of an inch. About 100 bearings would pass the test. Optical tests would filter out the majority of these bearings, leaving a handful to be measured even more accurately in a fourth stage. But how many would pass the fourth test? Would greater precision of measurement eliminate all of the bearings?

We cannot be certain whether one or more of the bearings would be precisely 1 inch in diameter, as the standard inch is presently defined and within our capability to measure it. But we can conclude that such ball bearings would be extremely rare. Consider the random selection of one bearing. Taking the diameter of the ball bearing as our random variable, we can conclude that the probability that it will be exactly 1 inch is so small as to be considered zero for all practical purposes.

(described in Section 6-5) applies. Using sampling without replacement in finite populations, the *hypergeometric distribution* would be applied.

DISCRETE AND CONTINUOUS RANDOM VARIABLES

Any random variable that can assume only integer (whole number) values is classified as **discrete**. An example is the variable for the number of arrivals. But some variables, such as those involving physical measurements or time, might assume any value over a continuous range of possibilities. Those random variables are classified as **continuous**.

Special difficulties arise when random variables do not assume a discrete number of possible values.

The dichotomy of discrete versus continuous random variables is important in probability theory because different mathematical procedures are used to describe the probability distributions of each. However, continuous and discrete random variables share many properties, and the more significant ones attributable to both can be explored using discrete examples.

EXERCISES

6-1 Shirley Smart has assigned the following probabilities for her final grades.

	A	B	C
Statistics	.2	.8	0
Finance	0	.4	.6
Accounting	.5	.5	0
Marketing	0	.2	.8

(a) List all possible elementary events for Shirley's grades.
(b) Assuming independence between courses, apply the multiplication law to determine the probability for each elementary event.
(c) The following grade points have been assigned.

$$A = 4 \qquad B = 3 \qquad C = 2$$

    (1) Determine Shirley's total grade points for each elementary event in (a).
    (2) Calculate the grade point average (GPA) for each event.
    (3) Construct the probability distribution table for GPA X.

6-2 Refer to the personal computer example (pages 212–214). Suppose that the cost of the laser printer is reduced to $700. Construct the new probability distribution table for total system cost.

6-3 For each of the following, describe a circumstance that would create a random variable.
(a) tomorrow's weather
(b) the sex of an unborn child
(c) the winner of the World Series

6-4 A GizMo Corporation inspector randomly selects three widgets from a production line assumed to yield 90% satisfactory (S) and 10% unsatisfactory (U) output. Assume successive quality events to be independent.
(a) Construct a probability tree diagram, identify all the elementary events in the sample space, and calculate the joint probability for each event.
(b) Determine the probabilities for the following number of unsatisfactory items.

    (1) none   (3) exactly 2   (5) at least 1
    (2) exactly 1   (4) exactly 3   (6) at most 2

6-5 The point spread for tossing two fair dice is the difference between the number of dots showing on the upturned faces. Determine the probability distribution for this random variable. (You may refer to your answer to Exercise 5-7 to obtain the probabilities for the possible dice sums.)

6-6 DanDee Assemblers receives shipments of 50 widgets each from GizMo Corporation. Suppose that a particular shipment contains exactly 90%

satisfactory and 10% unsatisfactory widgets. A sample of three widgets is selected without replacement and the quality of each is determined.

(a) Construct a probability tree diagram, identify all the elementary events in the sample space, and calculate the joint probability for each event.

(b) Determine the probabilities for the following number of unsatisfactory items.

(1) none	(3) exactly 2	(5) at least 1
(2) exactly 1	(4) exactly 3	(6) at most 2

6-7 Refer to the faculty data in Figure 5-4 (page 184). A lottery is held to select the membership of a university grievance panel. Three persons will be selected. Determine the following probabilities.

(a) exactly 2 males will be selected

(b) at least 1 female will be selected

(c) all will be from the finance department

(d) at least 1 part-time instructor will be selected

6-8 "Craps" is a favorite gambling game in which a pair of six-sided dice are tossed. One way to place a bet is to "play the field," where the bettor places a bet with a complicated payoff, depending on which faces of the dice show. If a "field" number (defined by a sum value of 2 through 4 or 9 through 12) occurs, the player wins. If the roll of dice yields any other total, the player loses. A field gamble is further complicated by varying payoffs: 1 to 1 on all field numbers except 2 or 12; 2 to 1 on a 2; and 3 to 1 on a 12. A winning bettor keeps the original bet and is also paid winnings. A losing bettor forfeits the original bet.

(a) For a bet of $1, determine the probability distribution for W, the gambler's net winnings from one field bet in craps. (Refer to your answer to Exercise 5-7 to obtain the probabilities for the possible dice sums.)

(b) Solve (a) for a bet of $2.

6-2 EXPECTED VALUE AND VARIANCE

THE EXPECTED VALUE OF A RANDOM VARIABLE

A probability distribution is similar to the frequency distribution of a quantitative population because both provide a long-run frequency for each possible outcome. In Chapter 3, we saw that the population mean is a desirable summary for comparing populations or for making decisions about a population. It is also useful to find the average of the random variable values to be achieved from repeated circumstances. Because the outcomes are in the future, the average result is called an expected value.

In Chapter 3, we learned that an average can be calculated in several different ways. The computation that we will use to determine the expected value is analogous to the computation used to find the mean of grouped data.

DEFINITION: The **expected value** of a discrete random variable X, denoted by $E(X)$, is the weighted average of that variable's possible values, where the respective probabilities are used as weights.

$$E(X) = \sum x\Pr[X = x]$$

TABLE 6-5 Probability Distribution for the Number of Dots Showing on a Tossed Die

Possible Value x	Probability Pr[X = x]
1	1/6
2	1/6
3	1/6
4	1/6
5	1/6
6	1/6
	6/6 = 1

To illustrate how to calculate the expected value of a random variable, let X represent the number of dots on the upturned face after a six-sided die is tossed. The probability distribution for X is provided in Table 6-5. Multiplying each possible result by its corresponding probability produces a weighted value. Summing these results gives the expected value.

$$E(X) = 1\left(\frac{1}{6}\right) + 2\left(\frac{1}{6}\right) + 3\left(\frac{1}{6}\right) + 4\left(\frac{1}{6}\right) + 5\left(\frac{1}{6}\right) + 6\left(\frac{1}{6}\right) = \frac{21}{6} = 3.5$$

On the average, the number of dots obtained for a large number of tosses will be 3.5. Because it is the average value achieved by the random variable X, we sometimes refer to $E(X)$ as the *mean of X.*

The expected value has many uses. In a gambling game, it tells us what our long-run average losses per play will be. Sophisticated gamblers know that slot machines pay poorly in relation to the actual odds and that the average loss per play is less in roulette or dice games. A mathematician, Edward Thorp, caused quite a stir in the early 1960s when he demonstrated that various betting strategies in playing the card game of blackjack result in positive expected winnings.*

THE VARIANCE OF A RANDOM VARIABLE

Just as the expected value of a random variable is analogous to the weighted mean, the variability of random variables may be measured in much the same way as the variability in a population or a sample. The measure we will consider is the variance. Like the mean, the variance of a random variable represents the same thing that it does for the population: the average of the squared deviations from the mean or expected value.

DEFINITION: The **variance** of a discrete random variable X, denoted by Var(X), is the average of the squared deviations from the expected value calculated using probability weights.

$$\text{Var}(X) = \sum [x - E(X)]^2 \Pr[X = x]$$

*See Edward Thorp, *Beat the Dealer*, Revised Edition (New York: Random House, 1966). Unlike other gambling games, blackjack allows bets to be placed when the odds are in a player's favor. This is because the card deck may not be reshuffled after each stage of play. By significantly raising bets at these times, a player will make a profit on the average.

As an example, again consider the roll of a six-sided die. Table 6-6 shows how the variance $\text{Var}(X) = 2.924$ is calculated for the number of dots on the upturned face.

The **standard deviation** of a random variable X, which we will abbreviate $\text{SD}(X)$, will have the same meaning as that of the population. It is found by taking the square root of the variance.

$$\text{SD}(X) = \sqrt{2.924} = 1.71$$

EXPECTED VALUE AND VARIANCE IN DECISION MAKING

Expected value often serves as the basis for decision making under uncertainty. A chief executive officer might use rates of return to evaluate various projects, selecting the one providing the greatest expected value. Investors must make evaluations similar to those of CEOs. To illustrate, consider two stocks having the following probability distributions for prices at the year's end.

ChipMont		Gotham Electric	
Price x	Pr[X = x]	Price y	Pr[Y = y]
$10	.10	$28	.20
20	.25	29	.20
30	.30	30	.20
40	.25	31	.20
50	.10	32	.20
	1.00		1.00

Although historical data are important in reaching the probability distributions used to make such evaluations, the greatest role is played by *judgment*. In business decision making, probability distributions typically involve *subjective* probabilities.

If the choice is made solely on the basis of expected value, the two stocks are equally attractive, each having an expected price of $30.00. However, many investors would actually prefer Gotham Electric, concurring that it is less risky.

TABLE 6-6 Variance Calculation for Die Toss

(1) Possible Values of X x	(2) Probability Pr[X = x]	(3) Deviation x − E(X)	(4) Squared Deviation [x − E(X)]²	(5) Weighted Value [(2) × (4)] [x − E(X)]²Pr[X = x]
1	1/6 = .167	− 2.5	6.25	1.044
2	.167	− 1.5	2.25	.376
3	.167	− .5	.25	.042
4	.167	.5	.25	.042
5	.167	1.5	2.25	.376
6	.167	2.5	6.25	1.044
				Var(X) = 2.924

TABLE 6-7 Expected Value and Variance Calculations for Future Stock Prices

	ChipMont Price			Gotham Electric Price	
x	xPr[X = x]	[x − E(X)]²Pr[X = x]	y	yPr[Y = y]	[y − E(Y)]²Pr[Y = y]
$10	1.00	40.00	$28	5.60	0.80
20	5.00	25.00	29	5.80	0.20
30	9.00	0.00	30	6.00	0.00
40	10.00	25.00	31	6.20	0.20
50	5.00	40.00	32	6.40	0.80
	30.00 = E(X)	130.00 = Var(X)		30.00 = E(Y)	2.00 = Var(Y)

Assuming that each stock were bought for the same price, the loss potential for ChipMont is greater, as shown in Table 6-7.

The comparative risks of the two investments may be summarized by the respective *variances* (or standard deviations). We have the following.

ChipMont: Gotham Electric:

$Var(X) = 130.00$ $Var(Y) = 2.00$

$SD(X) = 11.40$ $SD(Y) = 1.41$

Notice that the variance for Gotham Electric is $Var(Y) = 2.00$, while the variance for ChipMont is a much higher $Var(X) = 130.00$. The same conclusions may be reached by comparing standard deviations.

The variance is a common measure of risk. It is fundamental in some models of portfolio theory, which can be used in prescribing an investment strategy.

EXERCISES

6-9 Using Quant Jacques' probability distribution for personal computer cost (pages 212–214), calculate his expected system cost.

6-10 The following probability distribution table has been obtained for the number of telephone calls arriving at a Centralia Bell switching device during any given millisecond.

x	Pr[X = x]
0	.37
1	.37
2	.18
3	.06
4	.02

Calculate the (a) expected value, (b) variance, and (c) standard deviation of X.

6-11 The following probability distribution table has been obtained for the number of requests Million Bank receives daily for credit verifications.

Number of Requests	Probability
0	.1
1	.2
2	.3
3	.2
4	.1
5	.1

Calculate the expected number of daily verification requests.

6-12 The following probability distribution table has been obtained for the number of customer arrivals during any given minute at a Beta Alpha supermarket.

Number of Arrivals	Probability
0	.1
1	.2
2	.3
3	.3
4	.1

Calculate the (a) expected value, (b) variance, and (c) standard deviation of the number of arrivals.

6-13 Consider the *sum* of the dots on the upturned sides after tossing a pair of fair dice. (Refer to the answer to Exercise 5-7.) Calculate the (a) expected value, (b) variance, and (c) standard deviation of the random variable.

6-14 Willy B. Rich wishes to buy a stock and hold it for one year in anticipation of capital gain. He has narrowed his choice to High-Volatility Engineering or Stability Power. Both stocks currently sell for $100 per share and yield $5 dividends. The following probability distributions for next year's price have been judgmentally assessed for each stock, where S_1 = selling price of High-Volatility Engineering and S_2 = selling price of Stability Power.

High-Volatility Engineering		Stability Power	
s	$Pr[S_1 = s]$	s	$Pr[S_2 = s]$
$ 25	.05	$ 95	.10
50	.07	100	.25
75	.10	105	.50
100	.05	110	.15
125	.10		1.00
150	.15		
175	.12		
200	.10		
225	.12		
250	.14		
	1.00		

(a) Calculate the expected prices for a share of each stock.
(b) Should Willy select the stock with the highest expected value? Discuss.

TABLE 6-8 Population Data and Calculations for Customer Arrivals at Checkout Counter

Number of Arrivals X	Frequency f	Relative Frequency f/n	Weighted Value $X(f/n)$	X^2	fX^2
0	18	.36	.00	0	0
1	18	.36	.36	1	18
2	8	.16	.32	4	32
3	3	.06	.18	9	27
4	2	.04	.16	16	32
5	1	.02	.10	25	25
6	0	.00	.00	36	0
	50	1.00	1.12		134

6-3 POPULATION PARAMETERS AND SAMPLING

Deductive statistics applies probability concepts to the process of sampling. It is appropriate when the sample elementary units are selected *randomly* from the population. In this section, we consider the probability distribution for the level of a quantitative variable pertaining to the selected unit.

POPULATION PARAMETERS

For quantitative populations, the most important parameters are the population mean μ and the population variance σ^2 (and its square root, the population standard deviation σ). The exact values for these parameters are not usually known, since for a variety of reasons discussed in Chapter 4, a census of the population data will not be made. Indeed, a major thrust of inferential statistics is drawing conclusions about the unknown population parameters based largely on the computed values of the sample counterparts.

To lay the foundation for drawing conclusions from the sample, we will now examine the sample results that *might* be obtained when the population is *known*. We illustrate this using an experimental population made by taking the 50 WaySafe market time intervals used earlier.

The first two columns of Table 6-8 provide the frequency distribution for the number of arrivals for this experimental population. With those data, the shortcut expressions are used to obtain the mean number of arrivals, using $n = 50$ as the number of observations.

$$\bar{X} = \sum X(f/n) = 1.12$$

Since all of the population data are represented, the above provides the true value for the population mean, and we have

$$\mu = 1.12$$

Similarly, the variance is computed,

$$s^2 = \frac{\sum fX^2 - n\bar{X}^2}{n-1} = \frac{134 - 50(1.12)^2}{49} = 1.4547$$

TABLE 6-9 Probability Distribution for Customer Arrivals during a Randomly Selected Time Interval

Possible Number of Arrivals x	Pr[X = x]	xPr[X = x]	x − E(X)	[x − E(X)]²	[x − E(X)]²Pr[X = x]
0	.36	.00	− 1.12	1.2544	.451584
1	.36	.36	− .12	.0144	.005184
2	.16	.32	.88	.7744	.123904
3	.06	.18	1.88	3.5344	.212064
4	.04	.16	2.88	8.2944	.331776
5	.02	.10	3.88	15.0544	.301088
6	.00	.00	4.88	23.8144	.000000
	1.00	E(X) = 1.12			Var(X) = 1.425600

$$\frac{\sum \mu}{(n-1)} \qquad \frac{\sum x_i^2 - N\mu^2}{N}$$

Adjusting the above number, we obtain the true value of the population variance.*

population variance
$$\sigma^2 = \left(\frac{50 - 1}{50}\right) \times 1.4547 = 1.4256$$

The population standard deviation is

$$\sigma = \sqrt{1.4256} = 1.194$$

PROBABILITY DISTRIBUTION FOR A RANDOMLY SELECTED OBSERVATION

A randomly selected elementary unit should mirror the population from which it comes. Suppose that one of the original five-minute intervals is so chosen. The number of arrivals X for the interval is a random variable. The present example illustrates the following

RELATION: The value of an elementary unit randomly selected from a quantitative population is a random variable. Its expected value equals the population mean and its variance equals the population variance.

The probability distribution for the number of arrivals during a randomly selected time interval is provided in Table 6-9, where calculations are made for finding $E(X)$ and $Var(X)$. Probabilities are used in the same manner as class frequencies, and the values correspond. We find that $E(X) = 1.12$, $Var(X) = 1.4256$, and $SD(X) = 1.194$. These are the same values as the corresponding population parameters, so that

$$E(X) = \mu \qquad Var(X) = \sigma^2 \qquad SD(X) = \sigma$$

If the actual values for μ and σ were known, there would be little purpose in collecting a sample, since most of the essential population information would already be known! But whatever μ and σ are—even unknown quantities—it is always true that $E(X) = \mu$ and $SD(X) = \sigma$.

*Ordinarily, σ^2 is not computed at all, since the complete population is rarely observed 100% (as was the case here). Under the usual circumstances, s^2, computed from sample data only, is used unadjusted as an *estimate* of σ^2.

STATISTICS AROUND US

Auditing Accounts Receivable

Compu-Quik's accounts receivable balances constitute a population. One amount is selected *at random;* you can denote this uncertain quantity as X. Historically, it has been established that the mean balance is $\mu = \$137.50$ and the standard deviation is $\sigma = \$15.20$. If these values apply presently, then the expected balance for the selected account is $E(X) = \$137.50$, and the standard deviation is $\text{SD}(X) = \$15.20$.

Of course, there may be no reason to assume that prior levels for μ and σ still apply.

EXERCISES

6-15 The following frequency distribution applies for a population formed by the number of defective floppy disks found in each of 100 batches.

Number of Defectives	Frequency
0	44
1	21
2	13
3	7
4	6
5	3
6	4
7	2

(a) Find the (1) population mean, (2) variance, and (3) standard deviation. (Multiply s^2 by .99 to get the properly adjusted value for σ^2.)

(b) One of the batches is selected at random. Specify the probability distribution for the number of defectives X in that batch.

(c) Using your probability distribution in (b), determine (1) $E(X)$, (2) $\text{Var}(X)$, (3) $\text{SD}(X)$.

6-16 The following frequency distribution applies for the number of absent employees found per day at a branch office of Big-M Corporation during a recent sales campaign.

Number Absent	Frequency
0	2
1	4
2	8
3	5
4	3
5	2
6	1

(a) Find the (1) population mean, (2) variance, and (3) standard deviation. (Multiply s^2 by .96 to get the properly adjusted value for σ^2.)

(b) One of the days is selected at random. Specify the probability distribution for the number of absent employees X during that day.

(c) Using your probability distribution in (b), determine (1) $E(X)$, (2) $Var(X)$, (3) $SD(X)$.

6-17 Refer to the probability distribution in Exercise 6-15. Determine the probabilities for the following numbers of defective floppy disks in the randomly selected batch.

(a) at most 7
(b) at least 2
(c) between 2 and 3, inclusively
(d) 4 or more

6-4 THE SAMPLING DISTRIBUTION OF THE MEAN

We are now ready to make the transition from probability theory to statistical planning and analysis. For now, we will assume that many details regarding the population are known, and we will study the kinds of *possible* results that may be obtained for samples taken from the population. Such a deductive viewpoint is not usually encountered in a real sampling situation, because the sample results are known and the population details are unknown. But if we know how sample results are generated and what values are likely, we can easily learn how to generalize about an unknown population from a known sample.

Estimating the population mean μ is an important inference. Usually, we would employ the corresponding sample mean $\bar{X}$ to make this estimate.

In the planning stage of a sampling study, before the data are collected, we can speak of $\bar{X}$ only in terms of probability. Its value is not determined and will depend on which particular elementary units happen to be randomly selected. Thus, before the sample results are obtained, $\bar{X}$ is a random variable. We emphasize that at one stage $\bar{X}$ is viewed as a random variable and later as a statistic whose value can be calculated from observed data. The probability distribution of $\bar{X}$ is of key importance. It is called a **sampling distribution**.

The basic concepts underlying the sampling distribution of $\bar{X}$ are illustrated in Figure 6-5. This distribution may be viewed as roughly analogous to the results that would be obtained if many different samples were taken and the sample mean $\bar{X}$ were calculated each time. In practice only one sample will ever be taken. Prob-

TABLE 6-10 Hypothetical Population of GMAT Scores

Name	GMAT Score
Chen	600
Jones	500
O'Hara	700
Sandor	600

$$\mu = 600$$
$$\sigma^2 = 5,000$$
$$\sigma = \sqrt{5,000} = 70.71$$

IMAGINARY EXPERIMENT

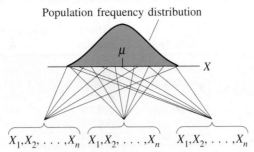

Population frequency distribution

THEORETICAL COUNTERPART

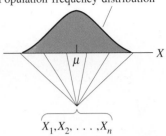

Population frequency distribution

Many samples of size n are taken from the same population. Means are calculated from each sample and grouped into a frequency distribution.

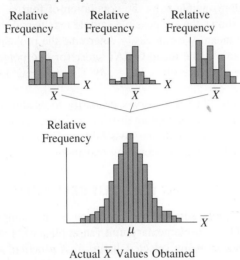

A single sample of size n is to be taken from the population and the $\bar{X}$ is to be calculated.

The sampling distribution of possible $\bar{X}$ values is determined, using only the principles of probability theory.

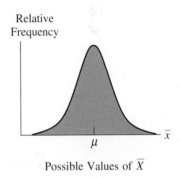

Actual $\bar{X}$ Values Obtained

Possible Values of $\bar{X}$

Note: The procedure outlined at the left is never necessary but shows the concepts underlying the theory. The histogram at the bottom left is an experimental representation of the sampling distribution at bottom right.

FIGURE 6-5 Interpretation of a theoretically derived sampling distribution.

ability concepts are used to establish the sampling distribution of $\bar{X}$, represented in the lower right-hand corner of Figure 6-5.

Next, we illustrate how probability concepts can be extended to finding the sampling distribution of the mean. As a matter of convenience, a tiny population is considered.

Table 6-10 shows the population of Graduate Management Admissions Test (GMAT) scores for four hypothetical Slippery Rock University seniors applying to the Harvard Business School. The population mean is $\mu = 600$ and the population variance is $\sigma^2 = 5,000.$* Suppose that Harvard will admit exactly two of

*When all the data are available from a population of size N, these are computed from

$$\mu = \frac{\sum X}{N} \qquad \sigma^2 = \frac{\sum (X - \mu)^2}{N}$$

TABLE 6-11   Possible Sample Results for Two GMAT Scores Selected without Replacement

Applicants Selected	GMAT Scores	Sample Mean $\bar{x}$
Chen, Jones	600,500	550
Chen, O'Hara	600,700	650
Chen, Sandor	600,600	600
Jones, O'Hara	500,700	600
Jones, Sandor	500,600	550
O'Hara, Sandor	700,600	650

these applicants by drawing their names from a hat. The scores of the two selected will be a random sample from the population of four.

Table 6-11 shows the six possible sample results and the corresponding values of the sample mean. We can easily determine the probabilities for each possible value. For example, the mean GMAT score for two potential samples is 600, so the probability of this result is 2/6 = 1/3. The sampling distribution of $\bar{X}$ is shown in Table 6-12.

The procedure illustrated serves primarily to establish the conceptual framework for understanding sampling distributions. Populations ordinarily involve too many units for us to catalogue possibilities. Chapter 7 provides a more direct method for establishing the sampling distribution of $\bar{X}$.

SAMPLING WITH AND WITHOUT REPLACEMENT

Our business school admissions illustration is an example of *sampling without replacement*: Once an elementary unit (an applicant) is selected for the sample, it has no chance of being selected again. *As a practical matter, statistics almost always involves sampling without replacement.* However, to help us understand some essential concepts, we will also consider *sampling with replacement,* in which every elementary unit has an equal chance of being selected for each successive observation. In this case, some population units may be represented more than once in the sample. Table 6-13 shows the possible sample results for randomly selecting two of the four GMAT scores when sampling with replacement. There are $4 \times 4 = 16$ equally likely outcomes.

A somewhat different sampling distribution applies depending on whether or not replacement is made. The sampling distribution for mean GMAT scores is given in Table 6-14 for the replacement case.

TABLE 6-12   Sampling Distribution of $\bar{X}$ for GMAT Scores Selected without Replacement

Possible Value $\bar{x}$	Probability $Pr[\bar{X} = \bar{x}]$
550	1/3
600	1/3
650	1/3
	1

TABLE 6-13 Posssible Sample Results for Two GMAT Scores Selected with Replacement

Applicants Selected	GMAT Scores	Sample Mean $\bar{x}$	Applicants Selected	GMAT Scores	Sample Mean $\bar{x}$
Chen, Chen	600,600	600	O'Hara, Chen	700,600	650
Chen, Jones	600,500	550	O'Hara, Jones	700,500	600
Chen, O'Hara	600,700	650	O'Hara, O'Hara	700,700	700
Chen, Sandor	600,600	600	O'Hara, Sandor	700,600	650
Jones, Chen	500,600	550	Sandor, Chen	600,600	600
Jones, Jones	500,500	500	Sandor, Jones	600,500	550
Jones, O'Hara	500,700	600	Sandor, O'Hara	600,700	650
Jones, Sandor	500,600	550	Sandor, Sandor	600,600	600

Sample outcomes are statistically independent when sampling with replacement and statistically dependent when sampling without replacement. Whether or not sample outcomes are independent influences many statistical procedures that we will encounter later. For example, consider the population of the heights of all adult American males. If the height of the first man randomly selected for the sample is 7′, independence does not permit this height to influence the probability distribution for the height of any other man selected. But if the selection is made without replacement, selecting a man 7′ tall first will influence any probability for the second man's height.

(w/o replacement will affect small population but not big population)

No practical difficulty exists unless the population is small. For instance, if our population contains 1,000 men, exactly one of whom is over 7′ tall, then independence is violated when sampling without replacement. For a very large population, the degree of dependence will be so slight that it can be ignored. For the United States as a whole, the removal of one seven-footer from the population would not appreciably change the remaining proportion of persons who are 7′ tall, but in a small population it could seriously affect the sampling outcome.

AN EMPIRICAL APPROXIMATION OF THE SAMPLING DISTRIBUTION OF THE MEAN

The nature of the sampling distribution of the mean may be illustrated through an approximation involving a series of sampling experiments.

TABLE 6-14 Sampling Distribution of $\bar{X}$ for GMAT Scores Selected with Replacement

$\bar{x}$	$Pr[\bar{X} = \bar{x}]$
500	1/16
550	4/16
600	6/16
650	4/16
700	1/16
	1

ILLUSTRATION: BASEBALL SUPERSTAR SALARIES

In recent years, salaries of baseball players have increased substantially. For the 1991 season, 127 players listed in Table 6-15 were paid salaries of at least $2 million. From this population, separate random samples were selected, each having size $n = 10$.

The histograms in Figure 6-6 describe the experimental results. The top histogram portrays the complete population, which is bimodal. Beneath this histogram are those constructed from the data of the first three samples. Included are the respective values of $\bar{X}$ and s. Notice that the value of $\bar{X}$ varies from one sample to the next.

Altogether, 100 random samples were taken without replacement. All players had the same chance of being selected for the successive sample groups. The 100 separate sample means are collectively described by the histogram at the bottom of Figure 6-6. That histogram is the experimental counterpart to the sampling distribution of the mean.

Repeated samples, like those illustrated here, are not really necessary to establish the key features of the sampling distribution of $\bar{X}$. Certain properties of that distribution have already been established theoretically. The bottom histogram in Figure 6-6 illustrates those properties.

Notice that the $\bar{X}$s tend to *cluster tightly* about the value for μ and that their computed mean of 2,634.6 thousand dollars lies very *close* to the population mean of $\mu = 2,643.2$. Our intuition should suggest that:

TABLE 6-15 Salaries (thousands of dollars) of Baseball Superstars Earning at Least Two Million Dollars in 1991

1 Larry Anderson	2000	27 Chili Davis	2000	53 Mike Greenwell	2650	79 Fred McGriff	2750	105 Mike Scott	2337
2 Kevin Bass	2000	28 Eric Davis	3600	54 Kevin Gross	2217	80 Mark McGwire	2875	106 Ruben Sierra	2650
3 George Bell	2150	29 Glenn Davis	3275	55 Kelly Gruber	3033	81 Kevin McReynolds	2267	107 Bryn Smith	2133
4 Bert Blyleven	2000	30 Mark Davis	3625	56 Mark Gubicza	2667	82 Kevin Mitchell	3750	108 Lee Smith	2792
5 Mike Boddicker	3167	31 Storm Davis	2367	57 Pedro Guerrero	2283	83 Paul Molitor	3253	109 Lonnie Smith	2042
6 Wade Boggs	2750	32 Andre Dawson	3325	58 Tony Gwynn	2388	84 Jack Morris	3700	110 Ozzie Smith	2225
7 Barry Bonds	2300	33 Jose DeLeon	2367	59 Von Hayes	2200	85 Dale Murphy	2500	111 Zane Smith	2225
8 Bobby Bonilla	2400	34 Jim Deshaies	2100	60 Dave Henderson	2625	86 Eddie Murray	2562	112 Dave Stewart	3500
9 George Brett	3675	35 Bill Doran	2833	61 Rickey Henderson	3250	87 Randy Myers	2000	113 Dave Stieb	3000
10 Hubie Brooks	2317	36 Doug Drabek	3350	62 Tom Henke	2967	88 Pete O'Brien	2038	114 Darryl Strawberry	3800
11 Tom Browning	2650	37 Shawon Dunston	2100	63 Orel Hershiser	3167	89 Lance Parrish	2417	115 Rick Sutcliffe	2275
12 Tom Brunansky	2650	38 Len Dykstra	2217	64 Ted Higuera	2750	90 Tony Pena	2350	116 Greg Swindell	2025
13 Tim Burke	2328	39 Dennis Eckersly	3100	65 Danny Jackson	2625	91 Pascual Perez	2100	117 Danny Tartabull	2250
14 Brett Butler	2833	40 Chuck Finley	2500	66 Howard Johnson	2242	92 Dan Plesac	2267	118 Bobby Thigpen	2417
15 Ivan Calderon	2215	41 Nick Esasky	2100	67 Wally Joyner	2100	93 Kirby Puckett	3192	119 Alan Trammell	2200
16 Tom Candiotti	2500	42 Steve Farr	2400	68 Jimmie Key	2217	94 Tim Raines	3500	120 Andy Van Slyke	2160
17 Jose Canseco	3500	43 Sid Fernandez	2167	69 Mark Langston	3550	95 Jeff Reardon	2608	121 Frank Viola	3167
18 Joe Carter	3792	44 Tony Fernandez	2100	70 Barry Larkin	2100	96 Dave Righetti	2500	122 Bob Welch	3450
19 Jack Clark	3400	45 Carlton Fisk	2455	71 Charlie Leibrandt	2183	97 Jose Rijo	2613	123 Lou Whittaker	2000
20 Will Clark	3775	46 John Franco	2633	72 Craig Lefferts	2042	98 Cal Ripkin Jr.	2433	124 Dave Winfield	3750
21 Roger Clemens	2700	47 Julio Franco	2313	73 Greg Maddux	2425	99 Jeff Russell	2450	125 Mike Witt	2417
22 Vince Coleman	3113	48 Gary Gaetti	2700	74 Dennis Martinez	3348	100 Nolan Ryan	3300	126 Matt Young	2267
23 David Cone	2350	49 Kent Hrbek	2600	75 Don Mattingly	3420	101 Bret Saberhagen	2950	127 Robin Yount	3200
24 Kal Daniels	2025	50 Andres Galarraga	2485	76 Kirk McCaskill	2100	102 Ryne Sandberg	2725		
25 Ron Darling	2067	51 Scott Garrelts	2400	77 Roger McDowell	2200	103 Scott Sanderson	2175		
26 Danny Darwin	3250	52 Dwight Gooden	2467	78 Willie McGee	3563	104 Mike Scioscia	2183		

Source: *New York Times*

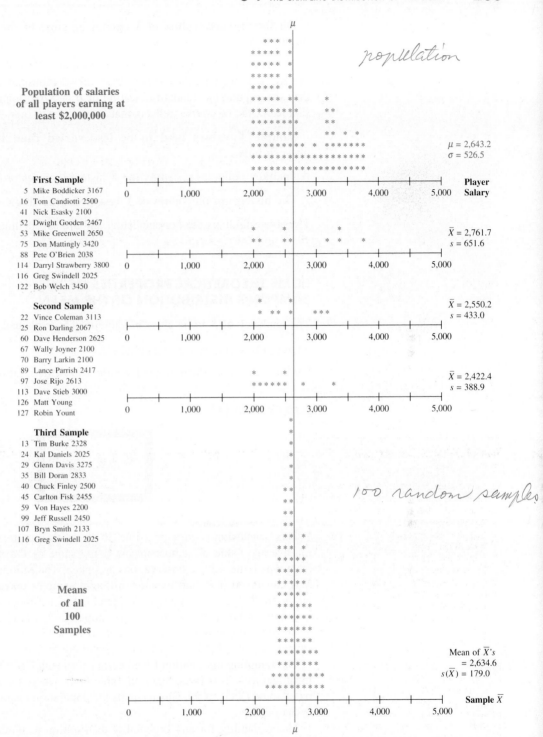

FIGURE 6-6 Histograms for salaries of high-income baseball players.

On the average, values of $\bar{X}$ should be close to the mean of their parent population.

Notice also that the standard deviation computed from the 100 $\bar{X}$s (each an average of 10 superstar salaries) is $S(\bar{X}) = 179.0$ thousand dollars, a *smaller* value than the population standard deviation of $\sigma = 526.5$ applicable to the individual salaries. This, of course, reflects that:

Sample $\bar{X}$ values tend to be less varied than individual population observations.

A final key point suggested by the $\bar{X}$ histogram is its profile:

The histogram for values of $\bar{X}$ resembles the shape of a bell curve.

The above findings are not accidental and are substantiated by statistical theory.

SOME THEORETICAL PROPERTIES OF THE SAMPLING DISTRIBUTION OF THE MEAN

The tendency of $\bar{X}$ to be close in value to μ is explained by *expected value*.

EXPECTED VALUE OF SAMPLE MEAN

For any sampling situation, we have the following relation for the

EXPECTED VALUE OF $\bar{X}$

$$E(\bar{X}) = \mu$$

This conclusion is quite plausible. In effect, this expression says that the long-run average value of sample means is the same as the mean of the population from which the sample observations are taken. The rationale for this is simple. If $\bar{X}$ is calculated over and over for different samples taken from the same population, the successive sample means tend to cluster about the population mean. If a sample of 100 men is taken from a population where the mean height is $\mu = 5'10''$, the sample mean $\bar{X}$ is expected to be $5'10''$. This does not imply that $\bar{X}$ cannot be $5'9\frac{1}{2}''$, but *on the average $\bar{X}$ will equal* $5'10''$.

The sampling distribution found earlier for mean GMAT scores (using replacement and $n = 2$) is listed again in Table 6-15, where the expected value is computed to be $E(\bar{X}) = 600$, which equals the population mean of $\mu = 600$ established at the outset.

The variability for any probability distribution is summarized by its variance and standard deviation.

STANDARD ERROR OF THE SAMPLE MEAN

When a random variable is the yet-to-be computed value of a sample statistic, its standard deviation is usually referred to as its **standard error**. Because we use

TABLE 6-16 Expected Value and Standard Deviation of $\bar{X}$ for GMAT Scores Selected with Replacement

$\bar{x}$	$Pr[\bar{X} = \bar{x}]$	$\bar{x}Pr[\bar{X} = \bar{x}]$	$\bar{x} - E(\bar{X})$	$[\bar{x} - E(\bar{X})]^2$	$[\bar{x} - E(\bar{X})]^2 Pr[\bar{X} = \bar{x}]$
500	1/16	500/16	-100	10,000	10,000/16
550	4/16	2,200/16	-50	2,500	10,000/16
600	6/16	3,600/16	0	0	0
650	4/16	2,600/16	50	2,500	10,000/16
700	1/16	700/16	100	10,000	10,000/16
		$E(\bar{X}) = 600$			$Var(\bar{X}) = 2,500$

$$\sigma_{\bar{X}} = SD(\bar{X}) = \sqrt{2,500} = 50$$

it often, the standard error of $\bar{X}$ is represented by the special symbol $\sigma_{\bar{X}}$. The standard error of $\bar{X}$ is computed in Table 6-16 for the mean GMAT score to be

$$\sigma_{\bar{X}} = SD(\bar{X}) = 50$$

We have found that $E(\bar{X}) = \mu$. Similarly, $\sigma_{\bar{X}}$ relates to the population standard deviation. *When sampling with replacement or from large population,* we can use the following expression to calculate the

STANDARD ERROR OF $\bar{X}$

$$\sigma_{\bar{X}} = \frac{\sigma}{\sqrt{n}}$$

Both the population standard deviation σ and sample size n influence the level of $\sigma_{\bar{X}}$. In Table 6-9 we found that the population of GMAT scores had a standard deviation of $\sigma = 70.71$. In this illustration, $n = 2$, so that

$$\sigma_{\bar{X}} = \frac{70.71}{\sqrt{2}} = \frac{70.71}{1.414} = 50$$

which is the same value of $\sigma_{\bar{X}}$ calculated in Table 6-16 directly from the sampling distribution.

When samples are taken without replacement from small populations, $\sigma_{\bar{X}}$ does not equal $\sigma/\sqrt{n}$. In such cases, a canceling effect arises from the potential early selection of extremely large or small population values. In Chapter 7, we will learn how to correct for this.

6-18 The following monthly incomes have been obtained from five residents of Dogpatch.

Identity	Income
Mr. A	$1,000
Mrs. D	1,200
Mr. J	1,200
Ms. P	1,000
Miss R	900

A sample of two residents is randomly selected *without replacement*. Determine the sampling distribution of the sample mean.

6-19 The number of children in each of the five families who have won the California State Lottery is provided below.

Family	Number of Children
Chavez	2
Luke	5
Markowitz	3
Rogers	4
Williams	1

A sample of two families is randomly selected *without replacement*. Determine the sampling distribution of the sample mean.

6-20 Assume that the sample in Exercise 6-18 is selected *with replacement*.
(a) Determine the sampling distribution of the sample mean.
(b) Calculate the (1) expected value, (2) variance, and (3) standard deviation of the sample mean.

6-21 Refer to the data given in Exercise 6-19, repeat Exercise 6-20.

6-5 BINOMIAL PROBABILITIES: THE SAMPLING DISTRIBUTION OF THE PROPORTION

Until now, we have been considering the sampling distribution of the mean, which involves quantitative data. For qualitative populations, the *sample proportion P* is of primary interest, and at this point we will consider the sampling distribution of *P*. We will begin by describing the **binomial distribution**—one of the most important concepts in statistics. This distribution is concerned with the *number of outcomes* in a particular category.

To illustrate, consider an evenly balanced coin that is tossed fairly five times. The corresponding probability tree diagram appears in Figure 6-7, where the sample space is also listed. Our initial problem is to determine the probability for obtaining exactly two heads. As each of the 32 outcomes is equally likely, the basic definition of probability allows us to find the answer by counting the number of elementary events involving two heads and dividing this result by the total

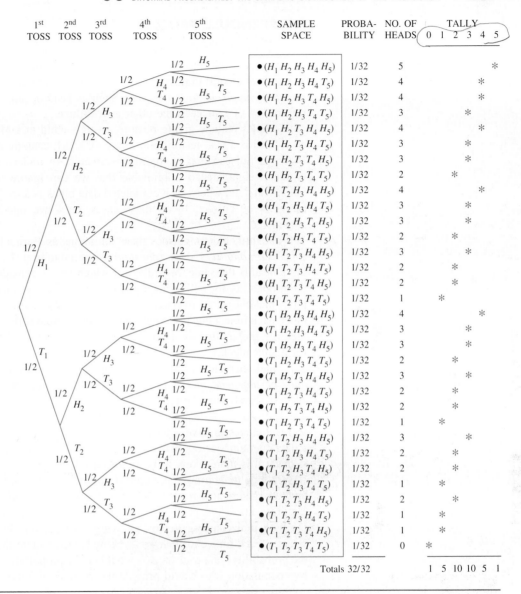

FIGURE 6-7 Probability tree diagram for five coin tosses.

number of equally likely elementary events. The sample space contains 32 elementary events, and Figure 6-7 shows that 10 of these are two-head outcomes. Thus, we can determine that

$$\Pr[\text{exactly two heads}] = \frac{10}{32}$$

It is impractical to list all possible outcomes unless there are only a few. For instance, if 10 tosses were to be considered, the list would contain 1,024 (2^{10}) entries. Before discussing a procedure to simplify finding such probabilities, it will be helpful to relate coin tossing to a similar class of situations.

THE BERNOULLI PROCESS

only two outcomes

A sequence of coin tosses is one example of a **Bernoulli process**. A great many circumstances fall into the same category: All involve a series of situations (such as tosses of a coin) that are referred to as **trials**. For each trial, *there are only two possible complementary outcomes*, such as head or tail. Usually one outcome is referred to as a **success**; the other as a **failure**.

Examples include giving birth to a single child in a maternity hospital, where each birth is a trial resulting in a boy or a girl; canning a vegetable, where each trial is a full can that is slightly overweight or underweight (cans of precisely correct weight are so improbable that we can ignore them); and transcribing numerical data, where each completed data block is a trial that will either contain errors or be correct. In all these cases, only two opposite trial outcomes are considered.

success probability remain constant

What further distinguishes these situations as Bernoulli processes is that *the success probability remains constant* from trial to trial. The probability for obtaining a head is the same, regardless of which toss is considered; this is also true of the probability for delivering a girl for any successive birth in the maternity hospital, picking up an overweight can of vegetables, and receiving a correct data block each time. (The last condition would not hold if the operator tires over time; then the probability would be larger for an earlier block being correct than that for a later block.)

independent outcome

A final characteristic of a Bernoulli process is that *successive trial outcomes must be independent events*. Like a tossed coin, the probability for obtaining a success (head) must be independent of what occurred in previous trials (tosses). The births in a *single family* may violate this requirement if the parents use medical techniques to have a second child of the opposite sex of their first child. Or, a data operator's errors may occur in batches due to fatigue, so that once an error is made it is more likely to be followed by another.

Sampling to determine the impact of advertising, voter preference, or response to drug treatment can all be classified as Bernoulli processes. To preserve the requirements of independence and constant probability for success, we must sample with replacement, thereby allowing each person the same chance of being selected each time and perhaps of being selected more than once.* In each case, the probability for a trial success would be the proportion of persons in the respective population who would provide the desired response.

THE NUMBER OF COMBINATIONS

Now we will derive an algebraic expression for computing binomial probabilities. Looking at Figure 6-7 again, we see that 10 elementary events involve exactly two heads.

$$
\begin{array}{lll}
H_1 H_2 T_3 T_4 T_5 & T_1 H_2 H_3 T_4 T_5 & T_1 T_2 H_3 H_4 T_5 \\
H_1 T_2 H_3 T_4 T_5 & T_1 H_2 T_3 H_4 T_5 & T_1 T_2 H_3 T_4 H_5 \\
H_1 T_2 T_3 H_4 T_5 & T_1 H_2 T_3 T_4 H_5 & T_1 T_2 T_3 H_4 H_5 \\
H_1 T_2 T_3 T_4 H_5
\end{array}
$$

---

*When sampling without replacement, a different probability distribution, the *hypergeometric distribution* should be used. In practice, when the population is large, the conditions of a Bernoulli process are very neatly met and the binomial distribution is acceptable.

Each of these outcomes represents one path of branches in the probability tree. They differ only in terms of which particular two tosses are heads.

If we want to find out the number of two-head outcomes without constructing an entire probability tree we can determine how many different ways there are to pick the two tosses to be heads from the total of five. It will help if each toss is represented by a fork.

| FIRST TOSS | SECOND TOSS | THIRD TOSS | FOURTH TOSS | FIFTH TOSS |

We want to save one branch from each fork. Two of the branches saved will be Hs; three will be Ts. Our problem is to determine how many ways there are to pick two H branches to save from the five.

If we pick the H branches one at a time, we have 5 possibilities for the first choice. No matter which H branch is chosen first, 4 H branch possibilities remain for the second choice. Multiplying the possibilities gives

$$5 \times 4 = 20$$

This answer is twice as large as it should be because the order of selection is considered. But we don't care whether an H_3H_5 resulted from H_3 being the first or the second choice, so we divide by 2 to avoid accounting for order of selection.

$$\frac{5 \times 4}{2} = 10$$

This calculation can be used to find the **number of combinations** of items for a variety of situations. It will be helpful if we re-express this fraction in the equivalent form

$$\frac{5 \times 4}{2} = \frac{5 \times 4}{2 \times 1} = \frac{5 \times 4 \times 3 \times 2 \times 1}{2 \times 1 \times 3 \times 2 \times 1} = 10$$

Multiplying both the numerator and the denominator of the middle fraction by 3, then by 2, and finally by 1 leaves the result unchanged. The final fraction contains factorial terms. A **factorial** is the product of successive integer values ending with 1. Such a product is denoted by placing an exclamation point after the highest number.

$$2! = 2 \times 1 \quad (= 2)$$

$$3! = 3 \times 2 \times 1 \quad (= 6)$$

$$5! = 5 \times 4 \times 3 \times 2 \times 1 \quad (= 120)$$

We define

$$1! = 1$$

$$0! = 1$$

In factorial notation, the number of two-head sequences in five coin tosses is

$$\frac{5 \times 4 \times 3 \times 2 \times 1}{2 \times 1 \times 3 \times 2 \times 1} = \frac{5!}{2!3!} = 10$$

This result suggests the general procedure for finding the

NUMBER OF COMBINATIONS: The number of combinations of *r* objects taken from *n* objects may be determined from

$$\frac{n!}{r!(n-r)!}$$

In our illustration, there are $n = 5$ tosses and we are considering exactly $r = 2$ heads occurring in those tosses. Thus, the number of two-head sequence combinations is

$$\frac{5!}{2!(5-2)!} = \frac{5!}{2!3!} = 10$$

THE BINOMIAL FORMULA

When the trial outcomes are the results of a Bernoulli process, the number of successes is a random variable having a binomial distribution. The following expression may then be used to determine the probability values. It is referred to as the

BINOMIAL FORMULA

$$\Pr[R = r] = \frac{n!}{r!(n-r)!} \pi^r (1 - \pi)^{n-r}$$

where R = number of successes achieved
n = number of trials
π = trial success probability
$r = 0, 1, \ldots, n$

The binomial formula can be used to determine the probability we found earlier for obtaining $r = 2$ heads in $n = 5$ tosses of a fair coin. In this case, $\pi = \Pr[H] = \frac{1}{2}$ and $1 - \pi = \Pr[T] = \frac{1}{2}$, so that

$$\Pr[R = 2] = \frac{5!}{2!(5-2)!}\left(\frac{1}{2}\right)^2\left(1 - \frac{1}{2}\right)^{5-2}$$

$$= \frac{5!}{2!3!}\left(\frac{1}{2}\right)^2\left(\frac{1}{2}\right)^3$$

$$= 10\left(\frac{1}{2}\right)^5 = \frac{10}{32}$$

The product involving 1/2 represents the probability for obtaining any one of the 10 two-head sequences shown in the probability tree in Figure 6-7. Each of these positions is reached by traversing a particular path of 2 head and $5 - 2 = 3$ tail branches. The probability for doing this may be obtained by applying the multiplication law. Since a two-head result can occur in any one of 10 equally likely ways, the addition law of probability tells us to add 10 of the identical product terms together or more simply to multiply by 10. The entire binomial distribution for the number of heads is given in Table 6-17.

Labeling one attribute the "success" is a completely arbitrary designation, but we must be sure to use the appropriate value of π. An interesting feature of the binomial formula is that it can also be used to obtain the probability that some number of failures will occur. For instance, the probability for obtaining exactly three tails in five tosses of the coin has the same value as the probability for obtaining two heads, because whenever there are two heads there must be three tails. In general, *when there are r successes, there must be n − r failures.*

TABLE 6-17 Binomial Distribution for the Number of Heads Obtained in Five Coin Tosses

Possible Number of Heads r	$\Pr[R = r]$	
0	$\dfrac{5!}{0!5!}\left(\dfrac{1}{2}\right)^0\left(\dfrac{1}{2}\right)^5 = \dfrac{1}{32} =$	.03125
1	$\dfrac{5!}{1!4!}\left(\dfrac{1}{2}\right)^1\left(\dfrac{1}{2}\right)^4 = \dfrac{5}{32} =$	.15625
2	$\dfrac{5!}{2!3!}\left(\dfrac{1}{2}\right)^2\left(\dfrac{1}{2}\right)^3 = \dfrac{10}{32} =$	.31250
3	$\dfrac{5!}{3!2!}\left(\dfrac{1}{2}\right)^3\left(\dfrac{1}{2}\right)^2 = \dfrac{10}{32} =$	.31250
4	$\dfrac{5!}{4!1!}\left(\dfrac{1}{2}\right)^4\left(\dfrac{1}{2}\right)^1 = \dfrac{5}{32} =$	.15625
5	$\dfrac{5!}{5!0!}\left(\dfrac{1}{2}\right)^5\left(\dfrac{1}{2}\right)^0 = \dfrac{1}{32} =$	.03125
		1.00000

Different Bernoulli processes will have different binomial probability values. Note that the probabilities for all possible values of R depend on the value of π. Different sizes for n will result in a larger or smaller number of possible values for R and will also affect each probability value. *For purposes of calculating probabilities, one Bernoulli process differs from another only by the values of π and the sizes of n.*

IMPORTANT PROPERTIES OF THE BINOMIAL DISTRIBUTION

You should be aware of several important properties of the binomial distribution.

Binomial distributions apply to a family of random variables. Two parameters, n and π, determine which specific binomial distribution applies. It is convenient to view all possible distributions as a *family*, members of which are distinguished by the levels of n and π. An infinite number of members exist. Consider varying one parameter while the other is held fixed.

ROLE PLAYED BY THE TRIAL SUCCESS PROBABILITY π

Figure 6-8 shows the probability distributions for several levels of π when the number of trials is held fixed at $n = 5$. Notice that there is a skewed spike pattern

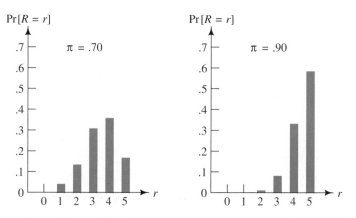

FIGURE 6-8 Binomial probability distributions for several levels of π, when $n = 5$.

except when $\pi = .50$. That symmetrical case applies to the series of coin tosses considered earlier. Notice also that complementary trial success probabilities, $\pi = .10$ and $\pi = .90$ or $\pi = .30$ and $\pi = .70$, have distributions that are mirror images.   *mirror image*

EFFECT OF THE NUMBER OF TRIALS n

Figure 6-9 shows the binomial distributions for three levels of n when the trial success probability is fixed at $\pi = .20$. Notice how the spikes grow more numerous and become shorter as n increases. Notice also that the spike clusters take on progressively symmetrical patterns, becoming almost bell-shaped as n gets larger. This is an important feature that you'll learn more about in Chapter 7.

EXAMPLE: AIRCRAFT DELAY PROBABILITY

The Gotham City airport administrator wishes to determine the number of aircraft departure delays that are attributable to inadequate control facilities. A random sample of 10 aircraft takeoffs is to be investigated. If the true proportion of such delays in all departures is .40, what is the probability that 4 of the sample departures will be delayed due to control inadequacies? $R = 4$

SOLUTION: Letting a control-caused delay be a success, the trial success probability is equal to the proportion of such outcomes, so that $\pi = .40$. The probability

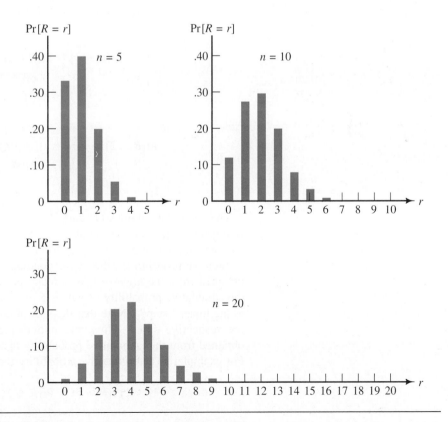

FIGURE 6-9 Binomial probability distributions for three levels of n, when $\pi = .20$.

for $R = 4$ control caused delays (successes), using the binomial formula when $\pi = .40$, $n = 10$, and $r = 4$, is

$$\Pr[R = 4] = \frac{10!}{4!(10 - 4)!}(.40)^4(1 - .40)^{10 - 4}$$
$$= 210(.40)^4(.60)^6$$
$$= 210(.0256)(.046656)$$
$$= .2508$$

The complete probability distribution is given in Table 6-18.

THE CUMULATIVE PROBABILITY DISTRIBUTION

Just as it can be convenient to deal with cumulative frequencies, which are readily determined from the population frequency distribution, we may wish to use **cumulative probabilities** for random variables. These can be simply obtained from the probability distribution for the number R of aircraft delays in the above example by creating column (3) for $\Pr[R \leq r]$, as shown in Table 6-18. The values in this column are obtained by adding all the preceding entries for the values of $\Pr[R = r]$. Thus,

$$\Pr[R \leq 0] = \Pr[R = 0] = .0060$$

and

$$\Pr[R \leq 1] = \Pr[R = 0] + \Pr[R = 1]$$
$$= .0060 + .0404$$
$$= .0464$$

and

$$\Pr[R \leq 2] = \Pr[R = 0] + \Pr[R = 1] + \Pr[R = 2]$$
$$= .0060 + .0404 + .1209$$
$$= .1673$$

The values in columns (1) and (3) constitute the **cumulative probability distribution** of the random variable R. The binomial probability distribution of R and the cumulative probability distribution of R are graphed in Figure 6-10. The cumulative probability value corresponding to any particular proportion value is obtained from the *highest point* directly above on the "stairway." For instance, the cumulative probability of values 5 or less is .8338 (not .6331, which belongs to the lower "step"). Note that the size of each step is the same as the height of the respective spike. Thus, the underlying probability distribution may be obtained from the cumulative probability distribution by finding these step sizes. For example, to determine the probability that $R = 5$, we find the difference

$$\Pr[R = 5] = \Pr[R \leq 5] - \Pr[R \leq 4]$$
$$= .8338 - .6331 = .2007$$

TABLE 6-18 Probability Distribution for the Number of Aircraft Delays ($n = 10$ and $\pi = .40$)

(1) r	(2) Pr[R = r]	(3) Pr[R ≤ r]
0	.0060	.0060
1	.0404	.0464
2	.1209	.1673
3	.2150	.3823
4	.2508	.6331
5	.2007	.8338
6	.1114	.9452
7	.0425	.9877
8	.0106	.9983
9	.0016	.9999
10	.0001	1.0000
	1.0000	

FIGURE 6-10 (a) Binomial probability distribution and (b) cumulative probability distribution ($n = 10$ and $\pi = .40$).

STATISTICS AROUND US

Brand Preference—Skinny Sip vs. Tummy Trim

A TipsiCola Bottling Company marketing researcher wishes to determine whether to recommend introduction of Skinny Sip, a new diet soda that will compete with HokeyCola's Tummy Trim. His final action depends on how high a proportion of the millions of potential customers will prefer Skinny Sip over the other brand.

Some information is provided by the number of sample test subjects R who have been found to prefer Skinny Sip. The researcher is satisfied that the binomial distribution closely approximates the true probabilities for R. The probability that a randomly selected person will prefer the brand equals the true population proportion π. Although that quantity is unknown, the following value might apply.

$$\pi = \Pr[\text{a subject prefers Skinny Sip}] = .40$$

The researcher administered a taste test to $n = 20$ subjects. Although the numbers are large, the binomial formula can be used to establish the probability that 12 of those subjects prefer Skinny Sip.

$$\Pr[R = 12] = \frac{20!}{12!8!}(.40)^{12}(1 - .40)^8 = .0355$$

Of course the true value of π remains unknown. The actual sample resulted in 8 subjects preferring Skinny Sip. Consider how different levels of π affect the probability for getting that many or fewer positive responses. Using a probability table published by a statistician who originally applied the binomial formula with computer assistance, the researcher determined the following values.

Assumed value:	$\pi = .20$	$\pi = .30$	$\pi = .40$	$\pi = .50$	$\pi = .60$	$\pi = .70$
$\Pr[R \le 8]$:	.9900	.8867	.5956	.2517	.0565	.0051

For $\pi = .50$ or higher, the probability is small that 8 or fewer positive responses would have been achieved. The researcher's sample evidence is consistent with a low level for π. Therefore, he doesn't recommend introducing Skinny Sip.

USING BINOMIAL PROBABILITY TABLES

Because determining binomial probabilities involves working with large factorial values and small numbers raised to large powers, it is convenient to have them already calculated. Appendix Table C provides cumulative binomial probability values computed for various sizes of n (with separate tabulations for several πs).

We use this table to compute probabilities for the number of successes in the variety of situations described in the following list. Suppose we wish to determine probabilities regarding the number of $n = 100$ patients who will respond favorably (success) to treatment with a new drug. We assume the drug will be successful 30% of the time, so that $\pi = .30$. To simplify our discussion, only a portion of Appendix Table C is reproduced below.

1. **Obtaining a result less than or equal to a particular value.** The probability that 20 or fewer patients will respond favorably is a cumulative probability value that may be read directly from the table when $r = 20$ successes.

$$\Pr[R \leq 20] = .0165$$

2. **Obtaining a result exactly equal to a single value.** Recall that cumulative probabilities represent the sum of individual probability values and are portrayed graphically as a stairway (see Figure 6-10). A single value

		n = 100		
$\pi \cdots$		.20	.30	.40 $\cdots$
r	r/n			
$\vdots$	$\vdots$	$\vdots$	$\vdots$	$\vdots$
19	.19	.4602	.0089	.0000
20	.20	.5595	.0165	.0000
21	.21	.6540	.0288	.0000
22	.22	.7389	.0479	.0001
23	.23	.8109	.0755	.0003
24	.24	.8686	.1136	.0006
25	.25	.9125	.1631	.0012
26	.26	.9442	.2244	.0024 $\cdots$
27	.27	.9658	.2964	.0046
28	.28	.9800	.3768	.0084
29	.29	.9888	.4623	.0148
30	.30	.9939	.5491	.0248
31	.31	.9969	.6331	.0398
32	.32	.9984	.7107	.0615
33	.33	.9993	.7793	.0913
$\vdots$	$\vdots$	$\vdots$	$\vdots$	$\vdots$

probability may be obtained by determining the size of the step between two neighboring cumulative probabilities. For example, the probability that exactly 32 of the patients will respond favorably would be

$$\Pr[R = 32] = \Pr[R \leq 32] - \Pr[R \leq 31]$$
$$= .7107 - .6331$$
$$= .0776$$

3. **Obtaining a result strictly less than some value.** The probability that fewer than 30 successes are achieved is the same as the probability that exactly 29 or fewer successes are obtained, or

$$\Pr[R < 30] = \Pr[R \leq 29] = .4623$$

4. **Obtaining a result greater than or equal to some value.** To determine the probability that at least 20 patients will respond favorably, we look up the cumulative probability that 19 or fewer will respond and subtract this value from 1.

$$\Pr[R \geq 20] = 1 - \Pr[R \leq 19]$$
$$= 1 - .0089 = .9911$$

Note that the situation is similar when the result must be *strictly greater than* some value. Then, we determine the cumulative probability for r itself and subtract this from 1. For example, the probability that more than 20 patients will respond to treatment is 1 minus its complementary probability that 20 or fewer patients will respond, or

$$\Pr[R > 20] = 1 - \Pr[R \leq 20]$$
$$= 1 - .0165 = .9835$$

5. **Obtaining a result that lies between two values.** Suppose we want to determine the probability that the number of successes will lie somewhere between 25 and 35, inclusively. Thus, we want to determine

$$\Pr[25 \leq R \leq 35]$$

In this case, we obtain the difference between two cumulative probabilities.

$$\Pr[R \leq 35] - \Pr[R \leq 24] = .8839 - .1136 = .7703$$

The first term on the left represents all outcomes of 35 or fewer successes. But we do not want to include outcomes of 24 or fewer successes, so we subtract the second cumulative probability from the first, thereby accounting for only outcomes of between 25 and 35 successes.

6. **Finding probabilities when the trial success probability exceeds .50.** For brevity, our binomial table stops at $\pi = .50$. If we wish to determine probabilities for the number of successes when the trial success probability is larger (say, .70), we can still use Appendix Table C by letting R represent the number of failures and π represent the trial failure probability.

Consider a data operator who receives correct data blocks 99% of the time. Suppose we want to determine the probability that at least 95 of $n = 100$ blocks are correct. Here, a success represents a correct block and $\pi = .99$. At least 95 correct blocks is the same as 5 or fewer incorrect blocks (failures). Using $\pi = 1 - .99 = .01$ as the trial failure probability, from Appendix Table C we determine

$$\Pr[R \leq 5] = .9995$$

This makes use of the fact that for every success event there is a corresponding failure event with the same probability.

EXPECTED VALUE AND VARIANCE OF A BINOMIAL RANDOM VARIABLE

It's not necessary for you to use individual probabilities and take weighted averages to calculate $E(R)$ or $Var(R)$. It has been mathematically established that the following apply

$$E(R) = n\pi \quad \text{and} \quad Var(R) = n\pi(1 - \pi)$$

Returning to the coin toss illustration when $n = 5$ and $\pi = 1/2$, you have

$$E(R) = 5\left(\frac{1}{2}\right) = 2.5$$

so that you expect 2.5 heads whenever tossing a fair coin 5 times. That is, if you perform 5 tosses, repeating the experiment many times, you should come close to getting 2.5 heads for every 5 tosses.

Likewise,

$$Var(R) = 5\left(\frac{1}{2}\right)\left(1 - \frac{1}{2}\right) = 1.25$$

By taking the square root of this answer, you find that the standard deviation for the number of heads is

$$SD(R) = \sqrt{1.25} = 1.12$$

THE SAMPLING DISTRIBUTION OF THE PROPORTION

Often random samples are taken from qualitative populations. The sample proportion P of observations falling in a particular category may be used to estimate the population proportion π.

You can find the proportion of successes by dividing the number of successes by the number of trials.

$$\text{sample proportion} \rightarrow P = \frac{R}{n} \begin{array}{l} \leftarrow \text{number of success} \\ \leftarrow \text{number of trial} \end{array}$$

The probability that P assumes any level can be determined by using the probability for the corresponding value for R. Consider the following table, which partially lists the binomial probability distribution for the number of defectives and the proportion of defectives found in a batch of $n = 100$ items arriving from a production line yielding 10% defective, so that $\pi = .10$.

Number of Defectives r	Proportion Defective r/n	Probability $\Pr[R = r] = \Pr[P = r/n]$
0	0	.0000
1	.01	.0003
2	.02	.0016
3	.03	.0059
4	.04	.0159
5	.05	.0339
6	.06	.0596
7	.07	.0889
8	.08	.1148
9	.09	.1304
10	.10	.1319
⋮	⋮	⋮

When sampling with replacement or when dealing with a large population, *the successive observations are trials in a Bernoulli process.* The probability that a particular observation is a "success" is equal to π. For example, if one-half the population is men, so that the overall proportion of men is $\pi = .50$, there is a .50 chance that any particular person selected at random will be a man. The binomial distribution provides probabilities for various possible levels for the sample proportion P of men observed.

On the average, P will equal π, even though it may differ for a particular sample. The following property applies for the

EXPECTED VALUE OF P

$$E(P) = \pi$$

P may turn out to be many possible values. As we did with $\bar{X}$, we may summarize the variability in the sample proportion by its standard deviation or standard error. The following expression, applicable whenever sampling with replacement or from large populations, provides the

STANDARD ERROR OF P

$$\sigma_P = \sqrt{\frac{\pi(1 - \pi)}{n}}$$

This expression tells us that the variability in P depends on both the level of the population proportion π and the sample size n.

As an illustration, suppose that a large population of voters is 80% Democrat ($\pi = .80$). A sample of size $n = 100$ is taken. If P represents the sample proportion of Democrats,

$$E(P) = .80$$

$$\sigma_P = \sqrt{\frac{.80(1 - .80)}{100}}$$

$$= \sqrt{\frac{.16}{100}} = .04$$

Knowing how to determine the values of $E(P)$ and σ_P will be quite helpful later when we consider a variety of statistical procedures.

The major obstacle to using the binomial distribution is that in sampling, the assumption of independence between trial outcomes is usually violated. Consider a random sample taken from a population of fixed size N. Unless sampling is done *with* replacement (rarely the case), the proportion of the remaining population having a particular attribute will change as each successive unit is removed and observed. This makes every observation or trial outcome statistically dependent on the earlier findings. The Bernoulli process doesn't strictly apply, and the binomial formula doesn't provide exactly proper probability values.

Another probability distribution, called the *hypergeometric* (which is related to the binomial), can provide exact probabilities when sampling *without replacement*. Unfortunately, that distribution is very cumbersome to use. However, as long as the population size N is large in relation to the sample size n, the binomial distribution provides a reasonably good approximation of the true probabilities.

EXERCISES

6-22 Calculate the following factorial products.

    (a) 4!   (b) 6!   (c) 7!   (d) 8!

6-23 Calculate the following quantities.

    (a) $\dfrac{4!}{2!2!}$ (b) $\dfrac{6!}{3!3!}$ (c) $\dfrac{7!}{5!2!}$ (d) $\dfrac{6!}{2!4!}$

6-24 An evenly balanced coin is tossed fairly seven times.

    (a) Determine the probability for obtaining (1) exactly two heads, (2) exactly four heads, (3) no tails, and (4) exactly three tails.

    (b) What do you notice about your answers to (2) and (4)? Why is this so?

6-25 Can each of the following situations be classified as a Bernoulli process? If not, state why.

    (a) The outcomes of successive rolls of a die, considering only the events "odd" and "even."

    (b) A crooked gambler has rigged a roulette wheel, so that whenever the player loses, a mechanism is released that gives the player better odds;

whenever a player wins, the chance of winning on the next spin is somewhat smaller than before. Consider the outcomes of successive spins.

(c) The measuring mechanism that determines how much dye to squirt into paint being mixed occasionally violates the required tolerances. The mechanism is highly reliable when it is new, but, with use it continually wears, becoming less accurate. Consider the outcomes (within or not within tolerance) of successive mixings.

(d) A machine produces items that are sometimes too heavy or too wide to be used. The events of interest express the quality of each successive item in terms of both weight and width.

6-26 The proportion of consumers favoring a new product is $\pi = .70$. A sample of $n = 5$ persons is randomly selected. Use the binomial formula to determine the probabilities for the following number of consumers favoring a new product.

(a) exactly 5   (b) none   (c) exactly 3

6-27 The following binomial probabilities have been obtained for the number of successes in $n = 10$ Bernoulli trials when the probability for success is $\pi = .49$.

r	Pr[R = r]
0	.0012
1	.0114
2	.0495
3	.1267
4	.2130
5	.2456
6	.1966
7	.1080
8	.0389
9	.0083
10	.0008
	1.0000

Construct the cumulative probability table.

6-28 From a production process that yields 5% defectives, n parts are randomly selected. What is the expected proportion of defectives?

6-29 A consumer testing agency has contacted a random sample of $n = 50$ persons. The true proportion of all persons favoring a new package is $\pi = .30$. Assuming that the binomial distribution applies, use Appendix Table C to determine the probabilities for the following outcomes relating to the number of favorable responses R.

(a) $R \leq 11$ (c) $R < 18$ (e) $R > 25$
(b) $R = 15$ (d) $R \geq 20$ (f) $17 \leq R \leq 23$

6-30 A fair coin is tossed 20 times. Using Appendix Table C, determine the probabilities for the following number of heads obtained.

(a) less than or equal to 8   (d) greater than or equal to 12
(b) equal to 10   (e) greater than 13
(c) less than 15   (f) between 8 and 14, inclusively

6-31 The following probability distribution table has been obtained for P.

p	Pr[P = p]
.0	.59049
.2	.32805
.4	.07290
.6	.00810
.8	.00045
1.0	.00001

Calculate $E(P)$ as a weighted average. (Your answer should equal π, which is .10.)

6-32 The following probability distribution table has been obtained for values when $n = 5$ and $\pi = .70$.

p	Pr[P = p]
.0	.00243
.2	.02835
.4	.13230
.6	.30870
.8	.36015
1.0	.16807

Construct the cumulative probability distribution table for P.

6-33 The BugOff Chemical Company chief engineer has established a testing procedure using five sample vials drawn from the final stage of a chemical process at random times over a four-hour period. If one or more vials contain impurities, all the settling tanks are cleaned. Determine the probability that the tanks must be cleaned when the following probabilities of a dirty vial apply.
(a) $\pi = .01$ (b) $\pi = .05$ (c) $\pi = .20$ (d) $\pi = .50$
(*Hint:* Use the fact that Pr[at least one dirty vial] $= 1 - $ Pr[no dirty vials].)

6-34 A process produces defective parts at a rate of .05. If a sample of five items is randomly selected, what is the probability that at least four of the sample will be defective?

6-35 A batch of 100 items in which 5% are defective is sampled *without replacement*. Five items are selected. Does the binomial distribution apply here? Explain.

6-36 A lopsided coin provides a 60% chance of a head on each toss. If the coin is tossed 20 times, determine the probabilities for obtaining the following number of heads.
(a) less than or equal to 8   (d) greater than or equal to 12
(b) equal to 9   (e) greater than 13
(c) less than 15   (f) between 8 and 14, inclusively

6-37 A DanDee Assemblers inspector accepts shipments of parts whenever two or fewer defectives are found in a sample of ten items tested. The following proportion of defectives apply.
(1) $\pi = .01$ (2) $\pi = .05$ (3) $\pi = .10$ (4) $\pi = .20$
(a) Calculate, for each case, the expected number of defectives.
(b) Determine, for each case, the approximate binomial probability for accepting a shipment.

6-38 The proportion π of defective spindles wound on automatic fiber-processing systems is unknown. An inspector requests equipment adjustments whenever one or more spindles are found to be defective in a sample of $n = 100$. Determine the probability for adjustment when the following assumptions apply.

(a) $\pi = .01$ (b) $\pi = .05$ (c) $\pi = .10$ (d) $\pi = .20$

6-6 CONTINUOUS PROBABILITY DISTRIBUTIONS

We will begin our discussion of continuous probability distributions by considering an uncertain situation involving the selection of a sample from a population. The frequency distribution obtained from grouping the years of company service of each of the 22,000 employees of the Wheeling Wire Works is given in Figure 6-11. The height of each bar of this histogram represents the relative frequency for duration of employment in the interval covered by the bar. The random variable of interest, denoted by X, is the length of service of one person randomly selected from the population. The time an employee has worked for the company can be measured on a continuous scale and therefore can be expressed to any desired fraction of the year. This makes X in our example a *continuous random variable*.

The probability that X lies within a particular class interval will be the same as the relative frequency of persons employed for that duration. Recall that the bars of the histogram for a relative frequency distribution have areas proportional to the relative frequency of the variate values in the corresponding interval. Since the relative frequencies must sum to 1, we can consider the total area under the histogram to be equal to 1. There, each class interval is one 5-year unit wide.

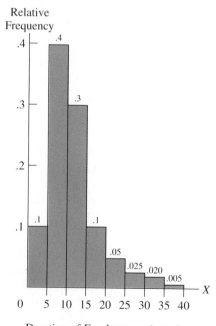

FIGURE 6-11 Frequency distribution for years of employment.

Thus, the probability that X lies inside a particular class interval is equal to the area of the bar covering that interval. Therefore, the probability that our employee served between 10 and 15 years must be .3 (the area under the bar or rectangle of the histogram that covers these values, or width $\times$ height $= 1 \times .3 = .3$).

But what if we want to consider an event that is more specific? For example, we may wish to determine the probability that our selected person was employed between 10.95 and 11.05 years—a range of values lying totally within a single class interval. In this case, the frequency distribution does not provide sufficiently detailed information for us to determine the probability directly.

SMOOTHED CURVE APPROXIMATION

Our problem arises from the fact that the histogram artificially forces us to treat population variates in discrete lumps. Each value is arbitrarily placed into one of very few class intervals. To accurately consider intervals of any width, we may construct a smoothed, continuous approximation to the histogram, like the one in Figure 6-12, where the curve is superimposed on the histogram from Figure 6-11. This approximation may then be used to generate any probability value we desire.

If the smoothed curve is drawn properly, the area under portions of the curve will correspond closely to the area of the histogram bars for that part of the horizontal axis, and the total area under the curve can also be taken as unity. Thus, in Figure 6-12, the shaded area under the portion of the curve covering the points between A and B is nearly the same as the corresponding area under the bar covering the values from A to B. Here, the curve has been drawn so that the wedge-

FIGURE 6-12 Frequency distribution from Figure 6-10 approximated by a continuous curve.

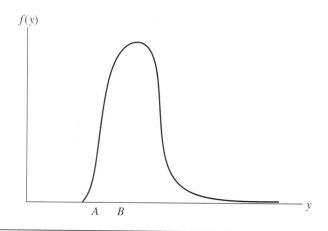

FIGURE 6-13 Two probability density function curves.

shaped area described by the points *a, b, c* is nearly the same as the area described by *c, d, e*. The sum of the areas for portions that are cut off the histogram by the curve should equal the sum of those areas that the curve adds by smoothing the corners.

The relative frequency of the population values lying between *A* and *B* in Figure 6-12 can be approximated by the area under the portion of the curve covering these values. We may therefore conclude the following

PROPERTY: The probability that a continuous random variable assumes some value in an interval is represented by the area under the portion of the continuous curve covering that interval.

PROBABILITY DENSITY FUNCTION

In Chapter 2, we learned that population frequency distribution graphs can be categorized according to their general shapes. We can construct smoothed curve approximations for any of these distributions. Essentially, we select a curve by choosing the appropriate shape.

Curves that have a particular shape can be defined by an equation or function. This allows us to group population frequency distributions according to the mathematical function that defines the curve corresponding most closely to the shape of the population histogram. If we know the function that defines the curve, we can mathematically calculate the area over an interval to obtain the required probability.

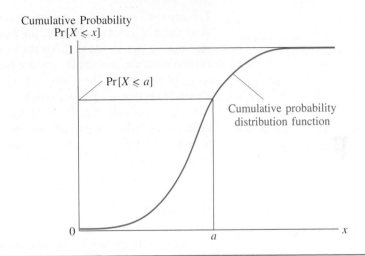

FIGURE 6-14 Graphical expressions of the probability distribution for a continuous random variable.

A unique set of probabilities is obtained from a particular curve. For example, consider the two curves in Figure 6-13 for two random variables, X and Y, whose values range over the same scale. The areas covering the values between points A and B are different for the two curves, because the shapes of the two curves are different. Thus,

$$\Pr[A \leq X \leq B] \neq \Pr[A \leq Y \leq B]$$

so that X and Y have different probability distributions. Note that the thickness or density of the two curves is distributed differently. For this reason, the mathematical expression describing such a curve is sometimes called a **probability density function**. In general, this function is denoted by $f(x)$, where x represents the possible values of the random variable X. The probability density function therefore describes the probability distribution for a continuous random variable, so that a random variable may be categorized by the form of its function.

CUMULATIVE PROBABILITY DISTRIBUTION

The graphic expressions of the probability distribution for a continuous random variable are presented in Figure 6-14. Although the cumulative probability distributions for discrete and continuous random variables are defined identically, the cumulative probability distribution for a continuous random variable resembles a smoothed curve (Figure 6-14) instead of a stairway (Figure 6-10). Both distributions may be expressed algebraically, graphically, or as a table of values.

It follows that for a continuous random variable,

$$\Pr[X \leq x] = \Pr[X < x]$$

because $\Pr[X = x] = 0$. (There is zero area under the portion of the density curve that covers a single *point*, since there is no width.)

THE EXPECTED VALUE AND THE VARIANCE

The expected value of a continuous random variable, like that of a discrete random variable, can be viewed as the long-run average of many repetitions. This is also true of the variance. Both the expected value and the variance can be calculated from the probability density function, but the calculations are beyond the scope of this book. These values have already been determined for the common distributions that we will encounter.

Random variables that have the same basic density function and differ only in terms of the values of the parameters specifying that particular function are said to belong to the same *distribution family*. In Chapter 7, we will discuss one of these families—the normal distribution. Other continuous probability distributions will be introduced in later chapters.

SUMMARY

1. **What is a random variable and its probability distribution?**
   An uncertain quantity whose value is subject to chance is a **random variable**. The set of possible variable values and their probabilities constitutes the **probability distribution** for the random variable. A probability distribution is sometimes graphed.

2. **What are the two basic types of random variables?**
   Discrete random variables are those that assume integer values. A second type is the **continuous** random variable, which may assume any value over a continuous range of possibilities.

3. **How do we obtain a probability distribution?**
   Probability distributions are founded on the basic concepts and laws of probability, and these may be used directly to determine individual probability values. A useful tool for constructing a group of probability distributions is the *probability tree diagram*. Probability trees can help determine the distribution for the number of *sample* units having a particular characteristic.

4. **How do result probabilities for sampling with replacement differ from those applicable to sampling without replacement?**
   An important statistical dichotomy is the way sample units are selected. Different probability values apply when **sampling with replacement** than when **sampling without replacement**. When the sample units are replaced prior to each successive selection, the characteristics of successive items are *statistically independent* events. When sampling without replacement, those events are dependent, unless the population size N is infinite.

5. **What are the expected value and variance of a random variable and how do we find and use them?**

Each random variable has a measure of central tendency, called its **expected value** $E(X)$. This quantity is found by taking a weighted average of the possible variable values, with their associated probabilities serving as weights.

$$E(X) = \sum x \Pr[X = x]$$

Two measures of dispersion, the **variance** $\text{Var}(X)$ and the **standard deviation** $\text{SD}(X)$, apply to any random variable.

$$\text{Var}(X) = \sum [x - E(X)]^2 \Pr[X = x]$$

$$\text{SD}(X) = \sqrt{\text{Var}(X)}$$

The standard deviation is the more useful of the two, because it does not distort the amount of variability.

6. **When sample results are represented as random variables, how do the expected value and variance relate to the parameters of the parent population?**

   Expected value concepts apply to sampling, where each quantitative sample observation may be considered a random variable. The expected value and standard deviation for such an observation are equal to their population parameter counterparts.

7. **What are the characteristics of the sampling distribution of the mean?**

   Before sample data are collected, the values of the sample statistics are random variables. The probability distributions for these variables are called **sampling distributions**. The sample mean $\bar{X}$ is a very important statistic. Its sampling distribution may be derived from the known characteristics of the population. Even if the population details are sketchy, the expected value of $\bar{X}$ must always be equal to the population mean μ. The standard deviation of $\bar{X}$ may be derived using the values for n (sample size) and σ (population standard deviation).

   $$\sigma_{\bar{X}} = \frac{\sigma}{\sqrt{n}}$$

   The quantity σ is usually referred to as the **standard error** of $\bar{X}$. The equation above is theoretically correct when sampling with replacement or when sample observations are statistically independent. Otherwise, it is approximately correct, as long as the population size N is large in relation to the sample size n.

8. **What is the binomial distribution?**

   The **binomial distribution** provides probabilities for the number of "successes" (R) in a series of repeated random experiments or trials with only two possible outcomes. Those experiments where the binomial distribution applies are referred to as **Bernoulli processes**, and one example is a series of coin tosses. The requirements of a Bernoulli process are (1) there are just two complementary trial outcomes; (2) the probability of success must remain constant from trial to trial; and (3) successive trial outcomes must be statistically independent events.

9. How are binomial probabilities computed?

Binomial probabilities are computed using an algebraic expression called the **binomial formula**. It is easy to see from a probability tree why the formula works. However, it is so computationally cumbersome that in actual practice, tables of binomial probabilities are used instead. These are usually provided for composite groupings of events in terms of **cumulative probabilities** (of the form $R \leq r$).

There are two parameters that determine which particular member of the binomial distribution family applies. These are the **trial success probability** π and the **number of trials** n. Binomial distributions become progressively more skewed as π falls further above or below .5, the only level for that parameter for which the binomial distributions are symmetrical. As n gets larger, the graph of the mass functions has more numerous spikes that tend progressively toward a bell-shaped pattern. The expected value and variance of R, the number of successes, may be computed directly from expressions involving n and π.

$$E(R) = n\pi \quad \text{and} \quad \text{Var}(R) = n\pi(1 - \pi)$$

10. What are the characteristics of the sampling distribution for the proportion?

Perhaps the greatest importance of the binomial distribution is that it ordinarily represents the **sampling distribution of the sample proportion** P. That statistic is useful for investigations involving samples from qualitative populations. The binomial distribution usually only serves as an *approximation,* however, since random sampling typically violates the Bernoulli process assumptions of independence and constant trial success probability. That approximation is a good one if the population size N is large in relation to the sample size n.

The proportion of successes is the number of successes divided by the number of trials, $P = R/n$. The probability for any value r/n of P is equal to the probability for the counterpart value of R. The expected value of P is π, and the **standard error** of P is calculated

$$\sigma_P = \sqrt{\frac{\pi(1 - \pi)}{n}}$$

REAL-LIFE STATISTICAL CHALLENGE

Sampling from the Automobile Dream List

In Chapters 3 and 4 we calculated summary statistics and practiced taking random samples from a list of automobile models. Using the concepts of probability distributions we will explore other uses for this data set.

Table 4-2 lists 232 makes and models of automobiles, classified by type based primarily on size. These types include: two-seater, minicompact, subcompact, compact, midsize, and large. The table also gives model, manufacturer, type of car, transmission type, engine displacement in liters and miles per gallon (high-way). The transmissions were either manual (M) or automatic (A or L) and may have had different gear configurations (3, 4, 5 or 6 forward). The numbers in the first column are sequence numbers we use for our random sampling operations.

Using Appendix Table B, three samples of five automobiles each were drawn from the list of 232 autos. The results are listed in Table 6-19. A combined list for the 15 random sampled cars is shown in Table 6-20. The population parameters for engine displacement for all 232 are $\mu = 2.69$ liters and $\sigma = 1.23$ liters. The mileage parameters are $\mu = 27.48$ mpg and $\sigma = 6.23$ mpg.

DISCUSSION QUESTIONS

1. Consider the set of sample data in Table 6-19. Suppose 3 cars are picked at random from this list of 15. Determine the probability that at least two of the automobiles will have a manual transmission.

2. Use the second data list from Table 6-19 and determine the sampling distribution of the sample mean for mileage when sampling *two* automobiles from

TABLE 6-19 Three Random Samples of $n = 5$ for Mileage Data for 1990 Automobiles Showing Transmission Type, Engine Displacement (liters) and Highway Mileage per Gallon

Number	Type	Manufacturer	Model	Transmission Type	Engine Displacement in Liters	Highway Mileage Miles/gallon
0126	Subcompact	Subaru	XT	M5	1.8	31
0140	Compact	Chevrolet	Beretta	M5	3.1	28
0154	Compact	Mitsubishi	Galant	M5	2.0	29
0186	Mid-Size	Chrysler	New Yorker	L4	3.3	26
0213	Mid-size	Volvo	740	L4	2.3	26
					$\bar{X} = 2.50$	$\bar{X} = 28.00$
					$s = 0.67$	$s = 2.12$
0053	Subcompact	Chevrolet	Camaro	M5	5.0	26
0111	Subcompact	Mitsubishi	Eclipse	M5	1.8	32
0149	Compact	Isuzu	Stylus	M5	1.6	33
0151	Compact	Lexus	ES250	L4	2.5	25
0218	Large	Cadillac	Brougham	L4	5.7	21
					$\bar{X} = 3.32$	$\bar{X} = 27.40$
					$s = 1.90$	$s = 5.03$
0026	Minicompact	Maserati	222E	M5	2.8	20
0088	Subcompact	Geo	Prizm	L3	1.6	29
0178	Mid-Size	BMW	750i	L4	5.0	18
0185	Mid-Size	Chevrolet	Lumina	L4	3.1	30
0199	Mid-Size	Mazda	929	L4	3.0	23
					$\bar{X} = 3.10$	$\bar{X} = 24.00$
					$s = 1.22$	$s = 5.34$

Source: United States Environmental Protection Agency, 1989.

**REAL-LIFE
STATISTICAL
CHALLENGE**

this list of five cars. First assume you are sampling *without replacement*, then repeat the process by sampling *with replacement*.

3. Develop two examples based on all fifteen cars in Table 6-20 that apply binomial probability concepts. Determine the expected value and variance of R. Determine the expected value and standard error of P.

4. Determine the standard error of the mean, $\sigma_{\bar{X}}$, for the separate and the combined samples (Tables 6-19 and 6-20).

TABLE 6-20 Combined Random Sample of $n = 15$ for 1990 Automobiles.

Number	Type	Manufacturer	Model	Transmission Type	Engine Displacement in Liters	Highway Mileage Miles/gallon
0026	Minicompact	Maserati	222E	M5	2.8	20
0053	Subcompact	Chevrolet	Camaro	M5	5.0	26
0088	Subcompact	Geo	Prizm	L3	1.6	29
0111	Subcompact	Mitsubishi	Eclipse	M5	1.8	32
0126	Subcompact	Subaru	XT	M5	1.8	31
0140	Compact	Chevrolet	Beretta	M5	3.1	28
0149	Compact	Isuzu	Stylus	M5	1.6	33
0151	Compact	Lexus	ES250	L4	2.5	25
0154	Compact	Mitsubishi	Galant	M5	2.0	29
0178	Mid-size	BMW	750i	L4	5.0	18
0185	Mid-Size	Chevrolet	Lumina	L4	3.1	30
0186	Mid-size	Chrysler	New Yorker	L4	3.3	26
0199	Mid-Size	Mazda	929	L4	3.0	23
0213	Mid-Size	Volvo	740	L4	2.3	26
0218	Large	Cadillac	Brougham	L4	5.7	21
					$\bar{X} = 2.97$	$\bar{X} = 26.47$
					$s = 1.31$	$s = 4.47$

Source: United States Environmental Protection Agency, 1989.

REVIEW EXERCISES

6-39 The following probability distribution table has been obtained for the number of persons arriving at Shangrila Theater during any specified minute between 8 and 9 P.M.

Persons	Probability
0	.4
1	.3
2	.2
3	.1
	1.0

Calculate the (a) expected value and (b) variance of the number of persons arriving between 8:30 and 8:31 P.M.

6-40 Refer, once more, to the personal computer example (pages 212–214. Suppose that a third choice for a printer is allowed: the hybrid, at a cost of $1,200. The new probabilities are .3 (matrix), .5 (laser), and .2 (hybrid). Suppose, also, that only the color monitor may be selected. Construct the probability distribution table for the total system cost.

6-41 The following probability distribution table has been obtained for the number of unsatisfactory widgets in a random sample.

x	Pr[X = x]
0	.35
1	.39
2	.19
3	.06
4	.01

Calculate the (a) expected value, (b) variance, and (c) standard deviation of X.

6-42 The proportion of adult U.S. citizens who approve of presidential policy is $\pi = .50$. A sample of $n = 5$ persons is randomly selected. Use the binomial formula to determine the probabilities for the following number of citizens who approve.
(a) exactly 5   (b) none   (c) exactly 3

6-43 An inspector for Yellow Giant Corn will remove a random sample of 100 cans. He is interested in the number R of overweight cans. The inspector assumes that 5% are overweight, so that $\pi = .05$ is the probability that any particular can is overweight. Determine the probabilities for the following outcomes.
(a) $\Pr[4 \le R \le 10]$ (c) $\Pr[2 \le R \le 11]$
(b) $\Pr[7 \le R \le 9]$ (d) $\Pr[9 \le R \le 11]$

6-44 Twenty percent of the cars leaving a Midget Motors automobile assembly line have defective brakes. A sample of $n = 4$ cars is randomly selected. Determine the probabilities for the following number of defective brake systems.
(a) 1   (b) 2   (c) 0

6-45 A chemical flow control device underfills 10% of all barrels. A sample of five barrels is randomly selected. Determine the probabilities for the following number of underfilled barrels.
(a) exactly 3   (b) exactly 2   (c) zero   (d) at least 1

6-46 The ages of the straight-A students in Bill Bernoulli's statistics class are provided below.

Student	Age
Mr. C	24
Miss H	19
Mr. J	21
Mr. M	20
Mrs. T	23

A sample of two students is randomly selected *without replacement.*
(a) Determine the sampling distribution of the mean age $\bar{X}$.
(b) Using your answer to (a), calculate the (1) expected value, (2) variance, and (3) standard deviation of $\bar{X}$.
(c) Calculate the standard deviation of the age *population* of students. Multiply s^2 by .80 to get σ^2.
(d) Using your answers to (c), determine the standard error of $\bar{X}$ if the sample of two students is randomly selected *with replacement.*

6-47 A statistics class provided the following examination grades for five MBA students.

Name	Grade	Grade Points
Ann	B	3
Bob	C	2
Cal	B	3
Don	A	4
Eve	C	2

A sample of two students is randomly selected *without replacement.*
(a) Determine the sampling distribution for the mean number of grade points $\bar{X}$.
(b) Using your answer to (a), calculate, for $\bar{X}$, the (1) expected value, (2) variance, and (3) standard deviation.

6-48 Refer to the student grade point population in Exercise 6-47. A sample of $n = 2$ students is randomly selected without replacement. Construct a table for sampling distributions for the following random variables.
(a) the sample proportion of B's
(b) the sample range (largest value minus smallest value)

6-49 Refer to the student grade point population in Exercise 6-47. Construct a table of probabilities for the sampling distribution of the mean for *three* randomly selected values without replacement.

6-50 Dumpty-Humpty Disposal serves 100 industrial customers. Of these, 15 are delinquent (D) in paying their bills, and the rest are on time (O). An auditor randomly selects 3 accounts, one at a time without replacement. The subscripts 1, 2, and 3 denote the sequence in which the audited bills are selected.
(a) Determine the following probabilities.

(1) $\Pr[D_1]$ (3) $\Pr[D_2|D_1]$ (5) $\Pr[O_2|D_1]$
(2) $\Pr[O_1]$ (4) $\Pr[D_2|O_1]$ (6) $\Pr[O_2|O_1]$

(b) Determine the following probabilities.
(1) $\Pr[D_3|D_1 \text{ and } D_2]$ (5) $\Pr[O_3|D_1 \text{ and } D_2]$
(2) $\Pr[D_3|D_1 \text{ and } O_2]$ (6) $\Pr[O_3|D_1 \text{ and } O_2]$
(3) $\Pr[D_3|O_1 \text{ and } D_2]$ (7) $\Pr[O_3|O_1 \text{ and } D_2]$
(4) $\Pr[D_3|O_1 \text{ and } O_2]$ (8) $\Pr[O_3|O_1 \text{ and } O_2]$

STATISTICS IN PRACTICE

6-51 Use the master class data from Exercise 1-19.
  (a) For one of your variables, determine the following probabilities for the results of three random selections *without replacement.*
    (1) That at least 2 people will be selected that share the same characteristic (such as, liking Italian or Chinese food, gender, or age 21 or older).
    (2) That exactly 3 people will be selected who do not have that characteristic.
  (b) Using the first five people on your data list, select a quantitative characteristic (such as height or age). Determine the sampling distribution of the sample mean when sampling *two* individuals from this list of five people, assuming (1) sampling *without replacement* and (2) sampling *with replacement.*
  (c) Develop two examples based on your data set that apply binomial probability concepts. Determine the expected value and variance of *R*. Determine the expected value and standard error of *P*.

6-52 Using your group's class data list developed in Exercise 1-21, repeat (a) through (c) of Exercise 6-51.

6-53 Using Exercise 6-1 as a guide, assign probabilities for *your* final grades in each of *your* classes. (Feel free to be optimistic about your grades. If you are taking only one or two classes add two or three more you expect to take in the next term or two.)
  (a) List all possible events for your grades.
  (b) Assuming independence between courses, apply the multiplication law to determine the probability for each elementary event.
  (c) The following grade points have been assigned:

$$A = 4 \qquad B = 3 \qquad C = 2 \qquad D = 1 \qquad F = 0$$

    (1) Determine total grade points for each elementary event in (a).
    (2) Calculate the grade point average (GPA) for each event.
    (3) Construct the probability table for GPA X.

6-54 Refer to the personal computer example on pages 212–214. (Note: The original problem uses simplified data for ease of computation.) Research the costs of two types of computer systems (computer and memory, printer, monitor). Typically these costs can be found in newspaper advertisements. In small groups of 3–5 students, assess the probabilities of purchasing each type (high/low memory, laser/nonlaser printer, color/monochrome monitor).
  (a) List all the possible combinations.
  (b) Construct the probability distribution table for total system cost.
  (c) Determine the expected cost.
  (d) Compare your results with those in the example.

6-55 Go to a local store or other retail outlet and determine a frequency distribution for the number of arrivals during each of several one-minute intervals. Be sure to ask permission of the store manager before you engage in this experiment. Assuming that your frequencies are representative, use them to construct a probability distribution for the number of arrivals during any minute. From your distribution, calculate the expected value, variance, and standard deviation. Comment on your results. Be sure to note the *time of day* and the *day of the week*.

6-56 Toss a coin 4 times and record your results. Repeat this process 39 more times and construct a relative frequency distribution for X = number of heads you obtained in 4 tosses of the coin.

(a) Suppose you take one of your 40 results at random. You can then use your frequency distribution to represent the probability distribution for X. Compute $E(X)$, $\text{Var}(X)$, and $\text{SD}(X)$.

(b) Assuming that the coin you are tossing is fair, the binomial distribution applies for R = number of heads in four tosses. Compute $E(R)$, $\text{Var}(R)$, and $\text{SD}(R)$.

(c) Compare your results for (a) and (b) and comment. What do you think would happen if you repeated this 400 times instead of 40 times? Can you conclude whether or not the coin you used is fair?

6-57 Roll a die cube 100 times. Record your results and construct a relative frequency distribution for X = number of dots on the top showing face of the die.

(a) Suppose you take one of your 100 results at random. You can then use your frequency distribution to represent the probability distribution for X. Compute $E(X)$, $\text{Var}(X)$, and $\text{SD}(X)$.

(b) Compare these values to those computed in Section 6-2 for a fair die. Can you conclude whether or not the die you used is fair?

6-58 Refer to Table 3-10 (page 113) which contains the data for the top twelve NFL quarterbacks for 1992. Consider as a population only the first four quarterbacks on the list.

(a) Using touchdowns (TD), compute μ, σ^2, and σ.
  [Note: $\sigma^2 = (n - 1)\, s^2/n$.]

(b) Construct the sampling distribution of $\overline{X}$ by selecting all possible samples of size 2 chosen with replacement.

(c) Compute $E(\overline{X})$, $\text{Var}(\overline{X})$, and $\text{SD}(\overline{X})$.

(d) Compare the values of σ^2 and $\text{Var}(\overline{X})$. How are they related?

CASE AlphaComp

AlphaComp is a specialized microcomputer manufacturer. Mark Wun, the head of procurement and quality assurance, needs to refine company policy regarding the disposal of shipments. To begin, Mark investigates two micro-circuit chips: the customized-logic Z-1020 and the A-19, for harddrive controllers. The Z-1020 chips are shipped from a sole supplier in lots of 1,000 chips each. The A-19 chips are sent from a different source in lots of 50.

Mark contemplates two actions for all the microcircuit chip shipments: (1) accept the shipment and install all the chips untested or (2) reject the shipment, test all the chips, and eliminate the defective ones before installation. Accepting a shipment can be very costly, since defective chips will be identified in later system testing and will have to be removed from assembled computers. The late replacement cost is estimated to be $25 for defective Z-1020s and $100 for defective A-19s. Individual testing costs for a Z-1020 chip and an A-19 chip are $2.00 and $4.00, respectively. But, all of the chips in a rejected lot must be tested, so that the decision to reject a shipment is not necessarily cheaper. The suppliers will replace, for free, all the defective chips, whether or not they have first been installed.

Mark's current acceptance sampling plan for Z-1020 shipments is based on a sample of $n = 5$ chips randomly selected *without replacement*. If the number of sample defectives is 0, the Z-1020 shipment is accepted; otherwise, the shipment is rejected. A similar plan is used for shipments of A-19 chips, but a smaller sample of size $n = 3$ is selected. As for the Z-1020 chips, an A-19 shipment is accepted only when 0 defectives are found.

1. Two levels are possible for the proportion of defective chips found in a Z-1020 shipment: (1) $\pi = .05$ and (2) $\pi = .10$.
   (a) For each assumed level of π above, use the binomial distribution to determine the approximate probabilities for the number of defective chips found in a sample of Z-1020s.
   (b) For each level of π, determine the probability that a Z-1020 shipment will be accepted.
   (c) For each level of π, determine the probability that a Z-1020 shipment will be rejected.

2. Two levels are possible for the proportion of defective chips found in an A-19 shipment: (1) $\pi = .10$ and (2) $\pi = .20$.
   (a) For each assumed level of π above, determine the probability distribution for the number of defective chips found in a sample of A-19s. (*Hint:* The binomial distribution cannot be used. To start, construct for each case a probability tree diagram similar to Figure 6-3.)
   (b) For each level of π, determine the probability that an A-19 shipment will be accepted.
   (c) For each level of π, determine the probability that an A-19 shipment will be rejected.

3. Find the breakeven level for the proportion of defectives π found in a shipment of (a) Z-1020s and (b) A-19s. This will be the level for π at which the net cost for accepting a shipment is equal to that for rejecting. (For simplicity, ignore the cost of the sample.)

4. There is a 50% chance that the Z-1020 supplier will send shipments containing either exactly 5% or exactly 10% defectives. Mark has no way of knowing how many defectives a particular shipment contains. Cal-

culate the expected cost for (a) accepting and (b) rejecting every shipment without the benefit of any sample evidence.

5. For a Z-1020 shipment, Mark wants to determine the expected cost of, first, conducting the sampling study and then using the sample results to determine a final action.

   (a) Refer to the probability results from Question 1 and assume that the two levels for π are equally likely. Find the missing values in the following table.

Proportion Defective	Sample Result	Joint Probability
$\Pr[\pi = .05] = \underline{\quad}$	$\Pr[\text{Accept } (R = 0)\|\pi = .05] = \underline{\quad}$	$\Pr[\pi = .05 \text{ and Accept}] = \underline{\quad}$
$\Pr[\pi = .05] = \underline{\quad}$	$\Pr[\text{Reject } (R > 0)\|\pi = .05] = \underline{\quad}$	$\Pr[\pi = .05 \text{ and Reject}] = \underline{\quad}$
$\Pr[\pi = .10] = \underline{\quad}$	$\Pr[\text{Accept } (R = 0)\|\pi = .10] = \underline{\quad}$	$\Pr[\pi = .10 \text{ and Accept}] = \underline{\quad}$
$\Pr[\pi = .10] = \underline{\quad}$	$\Pr[\text{Reject } (R > 0)\|\pi = .10] = \underline{\quad}$	$\Pr[\pi = .10 \text{ and Reject}] = \underline{\quad}$

   (b) Determine the expected cost of, first, conducting a sampling study and then using the results to determine whether to accept or reject a Z-1020 shipment. Find the missing values in the following table. Include the cost of the sample.

Proportion Defective	Sample Result	Total Cost	Joint Probability	Cost × Probability
$\pi = .05$	Accept $(R = 0)$	____	____	____
$\pi = .05$	Reject $(R > 0)$	____	____	____
$\pi = .10$	Accept $(R = 0)$	____	____	____
$\pi = .10$	Reject $(R > 0)$	____	____	____
			Expected sampling cost =	____

   (c) Does sampling provide a lower expected cost than either of the two actions in Question 4?

6. Suppose that Mark raises the acceptance number from 0 to 1 sample defective for shipments of Z-1020 chips. Repeat Questions 5(a) and 5(b). Determine, separately, the joint probabilities and costs for $R = 0$ and $R = 1$ sample defectives. In the cases where sample defectives are found, the total cost must reflect the amount saved as a result of not having to remove the defective chips found before installation.

7. Suppose that Mark increases the sample size of Z-1020s to $n = 10$. Repeat Question 1(a).

8. Suppose that when $n = 10$ Mark would modify further his sampling scheme by raising the acceptance number to 2 sample defectives. Using the analogous ground rules given in Question 6, repeat Questions 5(a) and 5(b).

9. Refer to your answers to Questions 4–8. What might you conclude Mark should do before finalizing his choices of acceptance sampling plans?

6-7 OPTIONAL TOPIC: THE POISSON DISTRIBUTION

Many practical statistical problems involve events occurring over time. One of the most notable of these problems is how to design a facility to service customers arriving at unpredictable times. Knowledge of the probability distribution for the number of arrivals may help the designer to achieve an optimal balance between the amount of time the facility is idle and the time spent by customers waiting in line. For example, the number of tellers hired for a bank's new branch office will be affected by the pattern of customer arrivals over a period of time. During 5 minutes, the number of newly arrived customers may be expected to vary from 0, 1, 2, or perhaps 20 or more up to the limit of space available in the bank. There will be times when all tellers are busy, so that lines will form. Because customers do not enjoy waiting and may switch their business to a competing bank if they feel unduly delayed, the bank may decide to have ten tellers when five would be sufficient to handle any day's transactions. Many familiar events, such as airplanes landing at an airport with limited capacity, persons arriving at a bank of elevators in a busy office building, or telephone calls arriving at a switchboard, require similar decisions.

Such decisions, which balance idle time against waiting time, are called waiting-line or **queuing** problems. In analyzing arrival patterns, we are concerned not with the nature of the event (an arrival) but rather with the number of event occurrences. Questions involving occurrences over time are also common in establishing inventory policies and in setting criteria for the reliability of a system. In some businesses, the distribution for customer orders over a period of time may be critical to finding the best inventory level. Enough stock must be available to fill orders, but too large an inventory could be quite costly. In designing systems to achieve a desired level of reliability, the pattern of failures over time is also an important consideration. For example, the probability distribution for the number of component malfunctions during the life of a communications satellite may be helpful in determining how much redundant capability ought to be provided. Likewise, a hospital would want a heart-lung machine to have a very small probability for malfunctioning during open-heart surgery.

THE POISSON PROCESS

There are many different patterns of unpredictable occurrences of events over time. A large class of situations in which events occur randomly may be characterized as a **Poisson process**, named after the eighteenth-century mathematician and physicist Siméon Poisson.

There are two very important probability distributions associated with a Poisson process. One, to be described here, provides probabilities for the *number* of events that occur in a time interval. This is the *discrete* Poisson distribution.

The Poisson and Bernoulli processes are similar; however, it is important to note the differences between them. Recall that the binomial distribution provides probabilities for the number of events of a *particular kind* (successes) occurring in *n* independent trials of a random experiment. With a Poisson process, there is no fixed number of trials; the events occur randomly over time—which is continuous. There is only one kind of event, such as arrival of a customer or an equipment breakdown, instead of two complementary ones, success and failure, as in a Bernoulli process.

EXPRESSING THE POISSON DISTRIBUTION

The probabilities for the number of events X that occur in a Poisson process in a period of duration t may be obtained from the following expression for the

POISSON DISTRIBUTION

$$\Pr[X = x] = \frac{e^{-\lambda t}(\lambda t)^x}{x!}$$

where $x = 0, 1, 2, \ldots$. The constant e is the base of natural logarithms and is equal to 2.7183. The parameter λ (the lowercase Greek *lambda*) *represents the mean rate at which events occur during the process.* That is, on the average, λ events per unit time will occur. Multiplying λ, a rate, by t, a duration of time, results in λt,* *the mean number of events occurring in a period of length t.* Note that we place no upper limit on the number of events that may occur; that is, X may assume any integral value from zero to infinity.

The Poisson distribution is completely defined by the process rate λ and the duration t. Its mean and variance are identical and are expressed as

$$E(X) = \lambda t \quad \text{and} \quad \text{Var}(X) = \lambda t$$

EXAMPLE: ARRIVALS AT A BARBERSHOP

Sammy Lee owns a one-man barbershop. A customer informs Sammy that during the lunchtime rush his customers arrive in a pattern that is approximately a Poisson process having a mean rate of 6 persons per hour. If Sammy spends 15 minutes (.25 hour) cutting one man's hair, what is the probability that exactly 2 new customers will arrive before he is finished?

SOLUTION: We have $\lambda = 6$ customers per hour and $t = .25$ hour. Therefore,

$$\lambda t = 6(.25) = 1.50 \text{ customers}$$

We obtain

$$\Pr[X = 2] = \frac{e^{-1.50}(1.50)^2}{2!}$$

From Appendix Table I, we find that $e^{-1.50} = .223130$, so that

$$\Pr[X = 2] = \frac{.223130(1.50)^2}{2!} = .2510$$

---

*In many books, $t = 1$, a standard unit of time, and λ represents the mean number of occurrences over a standard time period. There, $\lambda t = \lambda \times 1 = \lambda$.

If the duration t is increased, the probabilities for large numbers of arrivals will become greater. This seems logical, since there is more time for events to occur. For example, if $t = .4$ hour, then $\lambda t = 6(.4) = 2.4$, so that

$$\Pr[X = 2] = \frac{e^{-2.4}(2.4)^2}{2!} = \frac{.090718(2.4)^2}{2!} = .2613$$

Analogously, the probabilties for few arrivals will be reduced when t is increased.

ASSUMPTIONS OF A POISSON PROCESS

As we have indicated, the events of a Poisson process occur randomly over time. Three additional assumptions are required to distinguish it from other types of occurrence patterns.

1. A Poisson process has *no memory*. That is, the number of events occurring in one interval of time is *independent* of what happened in previous time periods.

2. The process rate λ *must remain constant* for the entire duration considered.

3. It is extremely *rare* for more than one event to occur during a short interval of time; the shorter the duration, the rarer the occurrence of two or more events becomes. The probability for exactly one event occurring in such an interval is approximately λ times its duration.

If we divide a duration into small time segments, letting each represent a trial with just two possible outcomes—(a) exactly one event occurring or (b) a nonoccurrence—then the Poisson probabilities may be roughly represented by the binomial distribution. This is only approximately so, since more than one event may occur in each time segment (so that each "trial" actually has more than two possible outcomes, violating assumptions of the Bernoulli process). But our third assumption makes the probability of the occurrence of more than one event close to zero. When the time segments are very tiny, the approximation becomes quite close, and the Poisson distribution is obtained mathematically from the binomial formula.

PRACTICAL LIMITATIONS OF THE POISSON DISTRIBUTION

A very serious mistake to make when applying the Poisson distribution is to assume that the mean event occurrence rate λ holds over an extended duration when it does not. Many queuing situations, for example, involve random arrivals whose rate changes with the time of day, day of week, season, or other circumstances. The mean rate of vehicle arrivals at a metropolitan toll plaza will be different at 9 A.M. than at 3 A.M.; it will be different on Fridays than on Mondays; and it will be greater in the fall than in the summer, when many drivers are on vacation. It is still proper to treat such situations as a Poisson process, but care must be taken to keep short the durations considered and to apply the appropriate value of λ. Thus, a bank may keep only a third of its teller windows open at 10:30 A.M. on Tuesday, when λ is small, but it will probably keep them all open around

TABLE 6-21 Poisson Probabilities, When $\lambda t = 1.50$

x	Pr[X = x]
0	.2231
1	.3347
2	.2510
3	.1256
4	.0470
5	.0141
6	.0036
7	.0007
8	.0002
9	.0000

5 P.M. on a Friday that is also the first of the month, when transaction traffic proves heaviest.

A second difficulty is that the Poisson distribution sets no limit on the number of customers who may arrive. In Table 6-21, the probabilities for several possible values of X have been calculated for $\lambda t = 1.50$. Although Pr[9] = .0000, this is a nonzero value that has been rounded off. There is a nonzero probability that 9 or 20 or even 100 customers may arrive at the barbershop in any 15-minute interval, but the probability is quite tiny. As discussed in connection with the normal distribution, even absurd outcomes have nonzero probabilities. For instance, there is a nonzero probability that 10,000 men would try to crowd into Sammy's barbershop during a 15-minute period.

Finally, a random variable is only approximated by a Poisson distribution. However, the approximation is often empirically well justified. For example, a statistician has shown that the number of U.S. Supreme Court seats vacated in a given year very closely fits a Poisson distribution. Some studies have shown that the deaths of Prussian army recruits kicked by horses and the very rare Lake Zurich freezes are closely approximated by the Poisson process. Of far more practical significance is the fact that a vast number of waiting-line, reliability, and inventory situations are adequately characterized by the Poisson process.

USING POISSON PROBABILITY TABLES

Computing Poisson probabilities by hand may be an onerous chore. The cumulative values of the Poisson probabilities are computed in Appendix Table J for levels of λt ranging from 1 to 20.

The table provides values of $Pr[X \leq x]$. For example, to find the cumulative probability values for the number of cars arriving at a toll booth during an interval of $t = 10$ minutes when the arrival rate is $\lambda = 2$ per minute, we consult Appendix Table J where $\lambda t = 2(10) = 20$. The probability that the number of arriving cars is ≤ 15 is

$$Pr[X \leq 15] = .1565$$

whereas the probability that ≤ 20 cars will arrive during the 10-minute interval is

$$Pr[X \leq 20] = .5591$$

Like the cumulative binomial tables discussed in Chapter 6, it is possible to obtain from Appendix Table J Poisson probability values for other cases (= , >, <, or ≥ some number, or the interval between two numbers). For example, the probability that exactly 15 cars will arrive in 10 minutes is

$$\Pr[X = 15] = \Pr[X \leq 15] - \Pr[X \leq 14] = .1565 - .1049 = .0516$$

Similarly, we may obtain the probability that the number of cars arriving lies between two values. Thus, the probability that between 16 and 20 cars will arrive in 10 minutes is

$$\Pr[16 \leq X \leq 20] = \Pr[X \leq 20] - \Pr[X \leq 15] = .5591 - .1565 = .4026$$

The probability that >20 cars will arrive is

$$\Pr[X > 20] = 1 - \Pr[X \leq 20] = 1 - .5591 = .4409$$

APPLICATIONS NOT INVOLVING TIME

Events occurring in space, as well as events occurring over time, may be characterized as Poisson processes. For instance, if finding objects spread randomly over a space (such as misspelled names in a telephone directory) is viewed as an event, then encountering objects while the space (in this case, pages of the directory) is searched may be viewed as a Poisson process. Application of the Poisson process to events occurring in space has proven fruitful in quality control and in such esoteric areas as developing search techniques for radar, establishing tactics for ships sailing through mine fields, and hunting for submarines. Here λ would represent the mean number of events per unit distance (such as an inch), area (a square mile), or space (a cubic centimeter). More generally, λ may be the mean number of particular events per observation made of the phenomena in question. Thus, λ may be 3 errors per page, or it may be 5 bad debts per 1,000 installment contracts. The "durations" would be analogous: the space searched, the number of pages scanned, the number of contracts written, and so on.

OPTIONAL EXERCISES

6-59 Between 9 and 10 A.M. on Saturday, the peak business period, customers arrive at Sammy Lee's barbershop at a mean rate of $\lambda = 5$ per hour. During the Thursday slump, between 2 and 3 P.M., customers arrive at a rate of $\lambda = 1$ per hour. In either case, the arrivals may be represented as a Poisson process.
(a) Does this mean that there will always be more customers arriving during the peak than during the slump? Explain.
(b) Compare the probability of exactly two customers arriving during Sammy's slump to that of the same number arriving during his peak.
(c) If the mean rate of arrivals for the week as a whole is three customers per hour, can Sammy use the Poisson distribution with $\lambda = 3$ to determine the probability that next week's arrivals will be between 100 and 150? Explain.

6-60 Com Piler is a typesetter who makes on the average $\lambda = .5$ error per page. What is the probability that she will make no errors in the first $t = 10$ pages? What is the probability that she will make exactly 5 errors in the first 10 pages?

6-61 During the late Friday rush at Million Bank, an average of $\lambda = 5$ customers per minute arrive. What is the probability that no customers arrive during a specified 1-minute interval?

6-62 The Jekyl family receives an average of $\lambda = 2$ pieces of regular mail each delivery day. Assume that the Poisson distribution applies.
   (a) What is the probability that they will get no mail on the next two consecutive days?
   (b) What is the probability that, given two days without mail, they will get no mail for another two days?

6-63 Use Appendix Table J to determine the probabilities that the stated number of events occur in a Poisson process at a rate of $\lambda = 8$/hour when the following durations are considered.
   (a) $t = 2$ hours; 10 or fewer events
   (b) $t = 1.5$ hours; 6 or more events
   (c) $t = 1$ hour; exactly 3 events
   (d) $t = .5$ hour; between 1 and 5 events

6-64 A typist commits errors at the rate of .01 per word. Assuming that a Poisson process applies, use Appendix Table J to determine the probabilities for each of the following numbers of errors committed in a 500-word letter.
   (a) exactly 5   (b) zero   (c) more than 10   (d) between 3 and 7

6-65 A California Central Valley tomato grower wishes to protect his crop against destruction by aphids. Two alternatives are open to him: Spray with a powerful insecticide that may harm the local ecology or wait for ladybugs to eat the aphids. Each spring, massive flights of ladybugs are wafted by wind currents across the California valleys from their Sierra Nevada hibernating points. Unfortunately, where and when a flight of ladybugs lands is purely a matter of chance. Wherever there are plenty of aphids, they lay eggs that rapidly hatch. If at least one flight of ladybugs lands on part of the grower's crop within five days, they and their larvae will devour all the aphids. Otherwise he will spray, killing all aphids and the unfortunate late-coming aphid-eaters as well, for by that time irreparable crop damage will have been suffered. On any given day, 10% of the Central Valley is covered by ladybugs. Assume that the arrivals of ladybugs may be considered a Poisson process. (The size of the farm may be ignored.)
   (a) Assuming that the mean arrival rate is $\lambda = .1$ flight of ladybugs per day, what is the probability that no flights arrive during $t = 5$ days?
   (b) What is the probability that the farmer won't have to spray?

6-66 Two tourists are enjoying the view from San Francisco's Golden Gate Bridge. They have decided to spend a half hour waiting for ships to pass under the bridge. Suppose that ship arrivals at the Golden Gate (leaving or entering San Francisco Bay) are a Poisson process at the mean rate of $\lambda = .2$ per hour. Determine the probability that the tourists will see passing beneath them (a) no ships; (b) 1 ship; (c) 2 ships.

CHAPTER 7

THE NORMAL DISTRIBUTION

BEFORE READING THIS CHAPTER, MAKE SURE YOU UNDERSTAND:

The difference between a sample statistic and a population parameter
(Chapter 3).

The basic concepts of probability (Chapter 5).

About sampling distributions (Chapter 6).

AFTER READING THIS CHAPTER, YOU WILL UNDERSTAND:

About the properties of the normal distribution and why it is so important.

About the role played by *areas* under the normal curve and how these relate
to *probabilities*.

How the *central limit theorem* enables us to use the normal curve to find
probabilities for future levels of the sample mean.

How we may use the normal distribution to approximate probabities for future
levels of the sample proportion.

The **normal distribution** may be the most important distribution used in statistical applications. The observed frequency distributions for many physical measurements and natural phenomena closely resemble the normal distribution. These include distributions for physical measurement, such as height and weight, as well as other human characteristics, such as IQ. The frequency distributions for these and many more populations closely resemble the **normal curve** in Figure 7-1. But there is a more fundamental reason why the normal distribution is so important in statistics. A theoretical property of the sample mean allows us to use the normal distribution to determine probabilities for various sample results. Thus, the normal curve plays a basic role when inferences are made regarding the population mean and only the sample mean can be calculated directly.

7-1 CHARACTERISTICS OF THE NORMAL DISTRIBUTION

Several features of the normal curve in Figure 7-1 are interesting. Note that the curve is shaped like a bell with a single peak, making it **unimodal**, and that it is **symmetrical** about its center. The mean of a normally distributed population lies at the center of its frequency curve. Due to symmetry, the median and the mode of the distribution also occur at the normal curve's center, so that the mean, median, and mode all have the same value. Although it is impractical to show this on the graph, the tails of a normal curve extend indefinitely in both directions, never quite touching the horizontal axis.

We say that a population with a frequency distribution approximating the shape of the normal curve is *normally distributed*. If the random variable X is the value of an elementary unit selected at random from a normally distributed population, then we say that X is normally distributed. The normal curve also represents the probability density function for X.* The normal curve depends on only two parameters: the mean μ and the standard deviation σ. Whatever the values of μ and σ are, the total area under the normal curve is always 1.

We know that the mean is a measure of central tendency or location. When normal curves for populations having different means are graphed together, they are located at different positions along the horizontal axis. This is illustrated in Figure 7-2 for three different populations with means of 30, 80, and 120, respectively.

Figure 7-2 also illustrates that the shape of a normal curve is determined by the population's standard deviation σ. Distributions with small standard deviations have narrow, peaked "bells," and those with large σs have flatter curves with less pronounced peaks. The three populations in Figure 7-2 have standard deviations of 5, 10, and 2, respectively. A large class of populations belong to the normal family, and each member differs only by its mean and its standard deviation.

The probability that a normally distributed random variable will assume values within a particular interval is equal to the area of the portion of the curve covering that interval. Before we learn to use a table to find the areas under the

*The function denoting the height of the curve is

$$f(x) = \frac{1}{\sqrt{2\pi\sigma^2}} e^{-[(x-\mu)^2/2\sigma^2]}$$

where π is the ratio of the circumference to the diameter of a circle (3.1416), and e is the base of natural logarithms (2.7183).

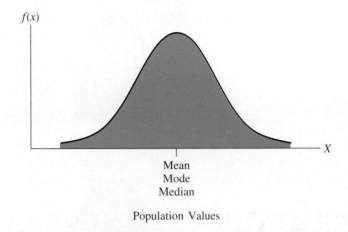

FIGURE 7-1 Frequency curve for the normal distribution.

normal curve, we should note a useful property of any normal distribution (see Figure 7-3).

PROPERTY: The area under the normal curve covering an interval that is symmetrical about the mean is determined solely by the distance that separates the end points from the mean, measured in standard deviations.

For instance, the values of about 68% of the population lie within one standard deviation in either direction from the mean, that is, the area under the curve over the interval $\mu - \sigma$ through $\mu + \sigma$ is .68. This is true no matter what the values of μ and σ are. The values of about 95.5% of the population lie within two standard deviations of the mean, and approximately 99.7% fall within three standard deviations.

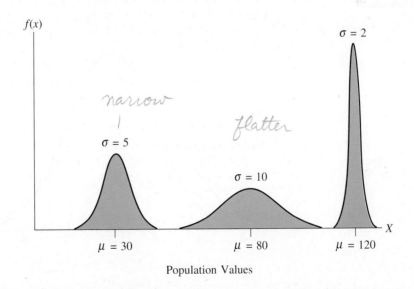

FIGURE 7-2 Three normal distributions graphed on a common axis.

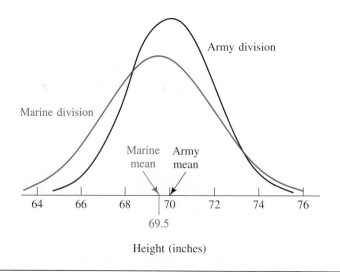

FIGURE 7-3 Relationship between the area under the normal curve and the distance from the mean, expressed in units of standard deviation.

FIGURE 7-4 Normal curves for the heights of the marine and army divisions.

STATISTICS AROUND US

Are Marines Taller than Soldiers?

The commander of an army division has wagered with the commander of a marine division that his army troops are taller. To verify this, the army commander's aide compiles the heights of the army soldiers from their medical records and calculates that the mean height is 70 inches and the standard deviation is 2 inches. The aide also constructs a histogram, which exhibits an almost perfect bell shape, indicating that the heights of the soldiers may be described in terms of the normal distribution.

The marine commander arrives at similar conclusions. The mean height of his men is 69.5 inches, with a standard deviation of 2.5 inches. The two populations are compared in the following table. Figure 7-4 shows the frequency curves for these two populations.

	Army Heights	Marine Heights
Mean (μ)	70 inches	69.5 inches
Standard deviation (σ)	2	2.5
68% from $\mu - \sigma$ to $\mu + \sigma$	68 to 72	67 to 72
95.5% from $\mu - 2\sigma$ to $\mu + 2\sigma$	66 to 74	64.5 to 74.5
99.7% from $\mu - 3\sigma$ to $\mu + 3\sigma$	64 to 76	62 to 77

The army commander claims to have won the bet, because the mean height of the army soldiers is .5 inch greater than the mean marine height. The marine commander objects, noting that his division contains a greater percentage of overly tall men. (Note that the upper tail of the marines' frequency curve lies above the army division's curve.) The army commander agrees but retorts that there is also a higher percentage of shorter marines. (Observe the lower tails of the two frequency curves.)

This example illustrates how difficult it is to compare populations by using a measure of location, such as the mean. The fact that some marines are taller than the tallest army soldiers is due to the difference in population variabilities. The marine division is a more diverse group with a larger standard deviation (2.5 inches compared with 2.0 inches for the army division).

7-2 FINDING AREAS UNDER THE NORMAL CURVE

Before we can obtain probability values for normally distributed random variables, we must find the appropriate area lying under the normal curve by using Appendix Table D. To illustrate, we will determine the desired areas for the time a particular typesetter takes to compose 500 lines of standard type. We will assume that the population of times is normally distributed, with a mean of $\mu = 150$ minutes and a standard deviation of $\sigma = 30$ minutes. The time it takes to set any given 500 lines, such as the next 500 to be composed, represents a randomly selected time from this population.

The probability that it takes between 150 and 175 minutes to set 500 lines is represented by the shaded area under the normal curve in Figure 7-5. We know

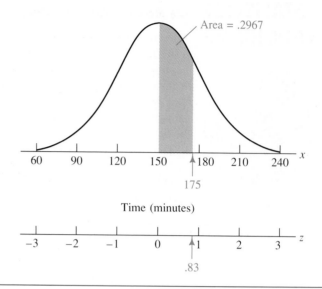

FIGURE 7-5 Determining the area under a normal curve.

that the area beneath the normal curve between the mean and a certain point depends only on the number of standard deviations separating the two points. We see that 175 minutes is equivalent to a distance above the mean of .83 standard deviation. This figure is determined by observing that 175 minutes minus the mean of 150 minutes is equal to 25 minutes. Since the standard deviation is 30 minutes, 25 minutes is only a fraction, $25/30 = .83$, of the standard deviation.

Appendix Table D has been constructed for a special curve, called the **standard normal curve**, which provides the area between the mean and a point above it at a specified distance measured in standard deviations. Because this distance will vary, as a convenience it is represented by the letter z. Sometimes the value of z is referred to as a **normal deviate**. The distance z that separates a possible normal random variable value x from its mean, expressed in terms of standard deviations, is given by the following expression for the

NORMAL DEVIATE

$$z = \frac{x - \mu}{\sigma}$$

A negative value will be obtained for z when x is smaller than μ.

To ease our discussion, a portion of Appendix Table D is reproduced here.

Normal Deviate z	.00	.01	.02	.03	.04	.05	.06	.07	· · ·
⋮				⋮					
0.6	.2257	.2291	.2324	.2357	.2389	.2422	.2454	.2486	
0.7	.2580	.2612	.2642	.2673	.2704	.2734	.2764	.2794	
0.8	.2881	.2910	.2939	**.2967**	.2995	.3023	.3051	.3078	
0.9	.3159	.3186	.3212	.3238	.3264	.3289	.3315	.3340	· · ·
1.0	.3413	.3438	.3461	.3485	.3508	.3531	.3554	.3577	
1.1	.3643	.3665	.3686	.3708	.3729	.3749	.3770	**.3790**	
1.2	.3849	.3869	.3888	.3907	.3925	.3944	.3962	.3980	
⋮				⋮					

The first column of the table lists values of z to the first decimal place. The second decimal place value is located at the head of one of the remaining ten columns. The area under the curve between the mean and z standard deviations is found at the intersection of the correct row and column. For example, when $z = .83$, we find the area of .2967 by reading the entry in the .8 row and the .03 column. The area under the normal curve for a completion time between 150 and 175 minutes is thus .2967, which represents the probability that it will take this long to set the next 500 lines of print.

USING THE NORMAL CURVE TABLE

Appendix Table D provides areas only between the mean and some point above it, but we can also use this table to find areas encountered in other common probability situations. Each of these areas is described in this section.

(a) Area between the mean and some point below the mean.

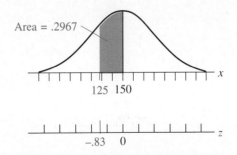

To determine the probability that the completion time lies between 125 and 150 minutes, first we must calculate the normal deviate.

$$z = \frac{x - \mu}{\sigma} = \frac{125 - 150}{30} = -.83$$

Here, z is negative because 125 is a point lying below the mean. Since the normal curve is symmetrical about the mean, this area must be the same as it would be for a positive value of z of the same magnitude (in this case .2967, as before). It is therefore unnecessary to tabulate areas for negative values of z. The area between the mean and a point lying below it will be equal to the area between the mean and a point lying the same distance above it.

(b) Area to the left of a value above the mean.

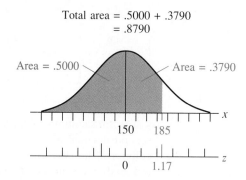

To determine the probability that 500 lines can be set in 185 minutes or less, we must find the entire shaded area below 185. Here, we must consider the lower half of the normal curve separately. Since the entire area of the normal curve is 1, the area under the half to the left of 150 must be .5. The area between 150 and 185 is found from Table D, with $z = (185 - 150)/30 = 1.17$, to be .3790. The entire shaded area below 185 is the sum of the two areas, or .5000 + .3790 = .8790.

(c) Area in upper tail.

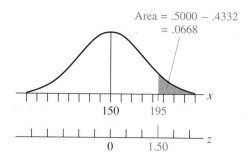

To determine the probability that the number of minutes required exceeds 195, we must first determine the area between the mean and 195. The normal deviate is $z = (195 - 150)/30 = 1.50$; the area from Table D is .4332. Since the area under the upper half of the normal curve is .5, we find the area above 195 by subtracting the unwanted portion: .5000 − .4332 = .0668.

Because the total area under the normal curve is 1, we may use the value of the upper tail area to calculate the area to the left of 195. Subtracting the upper tail area of .0668 from 1 gives us 1.0000 − .0668 = .9332 for the area to the left of 195 (or the probability that the time will be less than 195 minutes). Similarly, when the area to the left of a point is known, the area to its right can be found by subtracting this value from 1. For example, in **(b)** we found that the area to the left of 185 is .8790; thus, the area in the upper tail to the right of 185 must be $1 - .8790 = .1210$.

(d) Area in lower tail.

(d) Area in lower tail.

To determine the probability that it will take 90 minutes or less to set the type, we follow two steps similar to those in **(c)**. First, we find the area between 90 and 150. Using $z = (90 - 150)/30 = -2.00$, we obtain .4772 from Table D. Subtracting this value from .5 yields $.5000 - .4772 = .0228$.

(e) Area to the right of a value below the mean.

To determine the probability that the completion time will be equal to or greater than 85 minutes, the area between 85 and the mean is added to the area to the right of the mean, which is .5. Here, we calculate $z = (85 - 150)/30 = -2.17$. Adding the area from Table D (.4850) to .5, the combined area is $.5000 + .4850 = .9850$.

We can find the area in the lower tail below 85 by subtracting .9850 from 1, or $1 - .9850 = .0150$. We can also find the area to the right of 90 by subtracting the lower tail area found in **(d)** from 1, or $1 - .0228 = .9772$.

To determine the probability that it will take between 140 and 170 minutes to set the 500 lines, we simply add the portion of the shaded area below the mean to the portion above it. The respective normal deviate values are $z = (140 - 150)/30 = -.33$ and $z = (170 - 150)/30 = .67$. From Table D, the lower area is .1293 and the upper area is .2486, so that the combined area is $.1293 + .2486 = .3779$.

(f) Area under portion overlapping the mean.

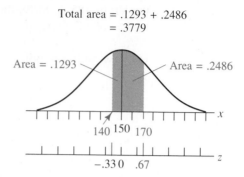

Total area = .1293 + .2486
= .3779

Area = .1293

Area = .2486

140 150 170

−.33 0 .67

If we wish to determine the probability that it will take between 120 and 180 minutes to set the type, the normal deviates are $z = (120 − 150)/30 = −1$ and $z = (180 − 150)/30 = 1$. From Table D, .3413 is the same area for both sides, so that the combined area is .3413 + .3413 = .6826. Because z expresses the number of standard deviation units from the mean, we see that .6826 is a more precise value for the area between $\mu \pm \sigma$ than the value used in the top graph of Figure 7-3.

(g) Area between two values lying above or below the mean.

Area of shaded portion = .4082 − .1915
= .2167

Area = .1915

Area = .4082

150 165 190

0 .50 1.33

To determine the probability that the composition time is between 165 and 190 minutes, we must first find the areas between the mean and each of these values. The respective normal deviates are $z = (165 − 150)/30 = .50$ and $z = (190 − 150)/30 = 1.33$. From Table D, the area between the mean and 190 is .4082, and the area between the mean and 165 is .1915. Thus, the shaded area is found by subtracting the smaller area from the larger one, or .4082 − .1915 = .2167.

A similar procedure can be applied to an area lying below the mean. It is also possible to find the value for a complementary situation—that the time will be either below 165 minutes or greater than 190 minutes—by subtracting the shaded area from 1, or 1 − .2167 = .7833.

The normal curve represents values that lie on a continuous scale, such as height, weight, and time. There is zero probability that a specific value, such as 129.40 minutes, will occur (there is zero area under the normal curve covering a single point). Thus, in determining probabilities, it does not matter whether we

$\leq$ or $<$

use "strict" inequalities, such as the composition time is "less than" ($<$) 129.40 minutes, or an ordinary inequality, such as the time is "less than or equal to" ($\leq$) 129.40 minutes. Using $z = (129.40 - 150)/30 = -.69$, the area is the same in either case: $.5000 - .2549 = .2451$.

CUMULATIVE PROBABILITIES AND PERCENTILES

Cases **(b)** and **(d)** in our discussion of normal curve areas show us how all the values for a normal cumulative probability distribution can be determined. We have seen that the probability of a time of 185 minutes or less is .8790 and that the probability of 90 minutes or less is .0228. For values above the mean, when z is positive, we obtain the cumulative probabilities from Appendix Table D simply by adding .5 to the tabulated areas. For values below the mean, when z is negative, we subtract the area given in the table from .5 to obtain the cumulative probability.

It is frequently necessary to determine the percentile values of a normally distributed population. Recall from Chapter 3 that a percentile is the population value below which a certain percentage of the population lies and that a percentile or fractile value can be obtained directly from the cumulative relative frequency distribution.

use in reverse   To determine a population percentile, we must read Appendix Table D in _reverse_, since the specified percentage represents an area under the normal curve. For instance, in our example, the 90th percentile is a particular number of minutes, and the area under the normal curve to the left of this value will be .90. Thus, the area between the mean and the number of minutes to be determined will be $.90 - .50 = .40$.

Searching through the body of the table, we select the area that lies closest to this figure—in this case, .3997. Since .3997 is in the $z = 1.2$ row and the .08 column, the corresponding normal deviate is $z = 1.28$. This means that the desired time is 1.28 standard deviations, or $30 \times 1.28 = 38.4$ minutes, above the mean. Adding this to the mean, we determine that the 90th percentile is $150 + 38.4 = 188.4$ minutes.

In general, to determine a percentile, we begin by reading Appendix Table D in reverse to find z. We can then calculate the corresponding population value x from the following expression, which provides the

PERCENTILE FOR A NORMAL POPULATION

$$x = \mu + z\sigma$$

Note that below the 50th percentile, the lower tail area is used to find z, which will be negative in these cases.

EXAMPLE: DESIGNING WITHIN HUMAN LIMITATIONS

Engineers who are designing an aircraft cockpit want to arrange the controls so that 95% of all pilots can reach them while seated. This involves finding the maximum reach radius exceeded by 95% (but not by 5%) of all pilots. Thus, the engineers must find the reach that corresponds to the 5th percentile.

SOLUTION: The maximum reach radii of airline pilots are assumed to be approximately normally distributed, with a mean of $\mu = 48$ inches and a standard deviation of $\sigma = 2$ inches. The engineers seek the point below which the area under the normal curve is equal to .05. This means that Appendix Table D must be searched to find the area closest to $.50 - .05 = .45$. Two areas, .4495 and .4505, are equally close. Therefore, the desired figure lies somewhere between the corresponding normal deviates 1.64 and 1.65. For simplicity, the engineers select 1.64, preferring to err on the side of a larger rather than a smaller tail area. Since the 5th percentile is below the 50th, they are dealing with a lower tail area and their normal deviate is negative, so that $z = -1.64$. (The 5th percentile lies *below* the mean and is smaller, so that a distance of 1.64 standard deviations must be *subtracted* from the mean.) The 5th percentile is therefore

$$x = \mu + z\sigma = 48 - 1.64(2) = 44.72 \text{ inches}$$

THE STANDARD NORMAL RANDOM VARIABLE

The area under any normal curve can be found by using the standard normal curve. This curve provides the probability distribution for the **standard normal random variable**.

In our typesetting illustration, we essentially transformed the original random variable X, the time to complete 500 lines, into the standard normal random variable whenever we used Appendix Table D to find areas under the normal curve.

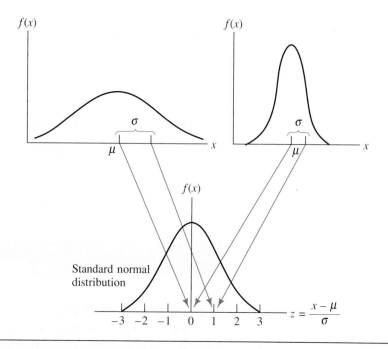

FIGURE 7-6 Illustration of the linear transformation of normal random variables into the standard normal distribution.

This transformation can be accomplished physically by shifting the center of the curve and then stretching or contracting it. To shift the original curve so that its center lies above the point $x = 0$, we subtract μ from each point on the x axis. Then the repositioned curve can be stretched or squeezed until the scale on the horizontal axis matches the scale for the standard normal distribution. <u>If all values of the random variable are divided by its standard deviation, the transformed curve will have the same shape as the standard normal curve in Figure 7-6.</u> The net effect will always be the same, no matter what the values of μ and σ are. The horizontal scale may be either expanded or contracted.

Fortunately, we do not need to physically transform the original random variable X into the standard normal random variable because we can manipulate the possible values of x algebraically.

ILLUSTRATION: TWO IQ TESTS

IQ tests illustrate this concept. These tests are designed so that the scores achieved by a cross section of persons are normally distributed for all practical purposes. One of the most popular, the Stanford-Binet test, has a mean of $\mu = 100$ points and a standard deviation of $\sigma = 16$. Letting X represent the IQ score achieved by a randomly selected person, it is possible to determine various probabilities for the value achieved.

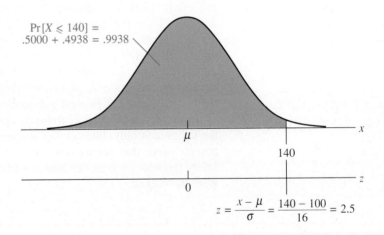

$$\Pr[X \le 140] = .5000 + .4938 = .9938$$

$$z = \frac{x - \mu}{\sigma} = \frac{140 - 100}{16} = 2.5$$

For example, we find the probability that this person's IQ is at most 140. Here, we see that there is better than a 99% chance that this person's IQ falls below 140 on the Stanford-Binet scale.

Other IQ tests have different standard deviations than the Stanford-Binet, although the mean of most IQ tests is 100 points. If we ask the same question using another test with a standard deviation of $\sigma = 10$ points, we have

$$z = \frac{x - \mu}{\sigma} = \frac{140 - 100}{10} = 4.0$$

$$\Pr[X \le 140] = .50000 + .49997 = .99997$$

Note that IQs above 140 are considerably rarer using this test.

Because various types of IQ tests are scaled differently, it is hard to compare IQ scores. For this reason, intelligence test results are often transformed into **standard scores**, or normal deviate values. In our example, 140 points on the

Stanford-Binet scale provides a standard score of 2.50. Thus, a person scoring 140 points on the second test would exhibit a much higher level of intelligence. (To obtain a standard score equal to 4.0 on the Standford-Binet test, a person would have to be 4 standard deviations above the mean and have an IQ of $100 + 4(16) = 164$ on that scale.)

If σ is smaller than the 10 applicable to the second IQ test, the absolute value of z will be too large to obtain the area from Appendix Table D. Our table has to stop somewhere, but the tails of the normal curve extend indefinitely. In general, whenever z exceeds 4.00, the area between the mean and z is so close to .5 that for practical purposes .5 is used. In such cases, the upper and lower tail areas are so close to 0 that they are *negligible*. For example, the area below $z = 5$ is approximately 1, as is the area above $z = -5$; the areas above $z = 5$ and below $z = -5$ are each approximately 0.

ADDITIONAL REMARKS

The fact that the tails of the normal curve never touch the horizontal axis implies a probability (although tiny) that the random variable can exceed any value. Consider the distribution for heights of men, for instance. The normal curve literally assigns a probability to the event that a man will grow to be more than one mile tall. This seems impossible, but according to the normal curve the probability for this event is not zero, although it is quite remote. The normal curve also assigns a probability to the fact that a man will be negatively tall. Although these implications are absurd, they should not detract from the utility of the normal distribution. They are by-products of the use of a convenient mathematical expression to describe a particular curve that fits some empirical frequency distributions quite accurately. According to Appendix Table D, only about .13% of the area under the normal curve lies beyond a distance of 3σ above the mean. Areas in the tails of the theoretical normal distribution are miniscule for greater distances. (At 4σ, the tail area is only .003%.) Any discrepancy between reality and the theoretical normal curve that occurs beyond 4 standard deviations from the mean can be safely ignored. (A mile-tall man would be more than 40,000 standard deviations from the mean.)

EXERCISES

7-1 Cash balance errors at Do-Nut Dunker Cafés are approximately normally distributed with a mean of $0 and a standard deviation of $1.00. Determine the relative frequency for the following balance errors.

(a) less than $1.25
(b) greater than − $.75
(c) less than − $2.50
(d) greater than $3.50
(e) between $1.50 and $1.75
(f) between − $.50 and − $.25
(g) less than − $2.80 or greater than $.65
(h) less than $.65 or greater than $.75

7-2 The lifetime of a disk drive head is normally distributed, with a mean of $\mu = 1,000$ hours and a standard deviation of $\sigma = 100$ hours. Determine the probability for each of the following lifetime outcomes for one drive unit. (*Hint:* It will help if you first sketch the normal curve and identify the corresponding area for each outcome.)

(a) between 1,000 and 1,150 hours
(b) between 950 and 1,000 hours
(c) 930 hours or less
(d) longer than 1,250 hours
(e) 870 hours or less
(f) longer than 780 hours
(g) between 700 and 1,200 hours
(h) between 750 and 850 hours

7-3 Determine the following percentiles for the cash balance errors given in Exercise 7-1.
(a) 10th   (b) 25th   (c) 85th   (d) 95th   (e) 99th

7-4 The heights of men attending Near Miss University form a normally distributed population with a mean of 69" and a standard deviation of 2". One man is selected at random. Determine the probability that his height falls in the following ranges.
(a) between 69" and 70.5"   (e) 68" or shorter
(b) between 65" and 69"   (f) taller than 65"
(c) 72" or taller   (g) between 69.5" and 70"
(d) taller than 72"   (h) between 67.6" and 68.2"

7-5 The wrist circumference of adult males is normally distributed with a mean of $\mu = 6.85"$ and a standard deviation of $\sigma = .40"$. One man is selected at random.
(a) Determine the probabilities for the following possible wrist sizes.
   (1) less than 8.00"   (3) between 5.75" and 6.75"
   (2) between 6.50" and 7.50"   (4) greater than 7.00"
(b) Determine the following percentiles.
   (1) 5th   (2) 10th   (3) 75th   (4) 95th

7-6 An architect designing the men's gymnasium at Slippery Rock University wants to make the interior doors high enough, so that 95% of the men will have at least a 1-foot clearance. Assuming that the heights will be normally distributed, with a mean of 70 inches and a standard deviation of 3 inches, how high must the architect make the doors?

7-7 The Precision Die Company quality control manager shuts down an automatic lathe for corrective maintenance whenever a sample of the parts it produces has an average diameter greater than 2.01 inches or smaller than 1.99 inches. The lathe is designed to produce parts with a mean diameter of 2.00 inches, and the sample averages have a standard deviation of .005 inches. Assume that the normal distribution applies.
(a) What is the probability that the quality control manager will stop the process when the lathe is operating as designed, with $\mu = 2.00$ inches? (The manager does not know that the lathe is operating correctly.)
(b) If the lathe begins to produce parts that on the average are too wide, with $\mu = 2.02$ inches, what is the probability that the lathe will continue to operate?
(c) If an adjustment error causes the lathe to produce parts that on the average are too narrow, with $\mu = 1.99$ inches, what is the probability that the lathe will be stopped?

7-3 SAMPLING DISTRIBUTION OF THE SAMPLE MEAN
FOR A NORMAL POPULATION

The normal curve describes the frequency distributions for a great many populations, notably measurements of persons and things. Some important questions can be answered by applying the normal curve.

It has been established mathematically that under certain circumstances **when the population frequencies are described by the normal curve, the sampling distribution of $\bar{X}$ itself is also normally distributed.**

SAMPLING DISTRIBUTION OF $\bar{X}$:

If $\bar{X}$ is the mean of a random sample taken from a normally distributed population having a mean of μ and a standard deviation of σ, then the sampling distribution for $\bar{X}$ is also normal, its mean is also μ, and its standard deviation is $\sigma_{\bar{X}} = \sigma/\sqrt{n}$. This is true no matter what the size of the sample happens to be.*

The area under the normal curve between μ and a possible level of the sample mean is found by transforming $\bar{X}$ into the corresponding

NORMAL DEVIATE FOR THE SAMPLE MEAN

$$z = \frac{\bar{x} - \mu}{\sigma_{\bar{X}}}$$

Recall that many physical dimensions are closely represented by the normal distribution. In these cases, knowing μ and σ establishes the sampling distribution for the mean of any sample.

ILLUSTRATION: NORMAL DISTRIBUTION FOR INSEAMS

To illustrate this concept consider a trousers manufacturer. The president must determine how many pairs of pants to make of various sizes. He is concerned with inseam lengths of its adult male customers. Although μ and σ are not known, suppose that this population is normally distributed and that the following parameters are assumed to apply.

$$\mu = 34.52'' \qquad \sigma = 1.75''$$

The top normal curve in Figure 7-7 represents the frequency distribution of this population.

Suppose the manufacturer hires a statistician as a consultant. The statistician is going to collect a random sample of $n = 100$ men and measure the inseams for each. Many different sample results are possible. Therefore, before any men are selected, $\bar{X}$ is a random variable that is normally distributed with mean $\mu = 34.52''$ (identical to that of the population), and standard deviation

$$\sigma_{\bar{X}} = \frac{\sigma}{\sqrt{n}} = \frac{1.75''}{\sqrt{100}} = .175''$$

The above standard deviation is only one-tenth as large as its population counterpart. This is because possible values for $\bar{X}$ (representing the average of 100 men's inseams) will tend to be more alike than individual population values (inseams of single men). The normal curve for $\bar{X}$ is shown at the bottom of Figure 7-7. Notice that the bottom curve is shaped like a taller, thinner bell. That curve's

*As we will see in Chapter 8, when σ is *also* of unknown value and n is small, it is necessary to use the Student t statistic instead of $\bar{X}$. This statistic has a different sampling distribution.

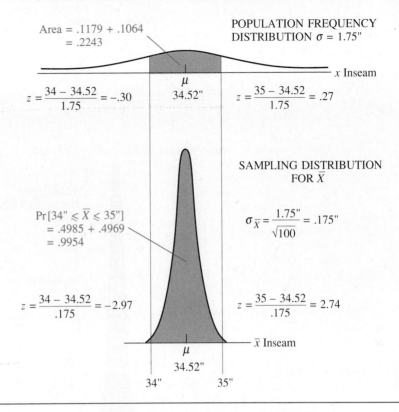

FIGURE 7-7 Population frequency curve and sampling distribution for sample mean inseam of adult males.

mass is concentrated more tightly about the center, reflecting the smaller variability in possible values of $\bar{X}$.

The effect of the smaller variability in $\bar{X}$ is reflected in the shaded areas under each curve. Each area provides the frequency of inseam dimensions falling between 34″ and 35″. The proportion of the inseam population (top curve) falling between these limits is .2243. A much higher probability of .9954 applies for $\bar{X}$ (bottom curve) falling inside the same limits.

To help appreciate the above result, imagine what would happen if the company statistician collected a series of different samples, each involving 100 inseams taken from the same population. For every sample group a different $\bar{X}$ value would be computed. These means would be close to each other in value, and their average should be very near to μ. The several sample means would cluster more tightly about μ than the inseams of individual mean. (This is reflected in a level for $\sigma_{\bar{X}}$ that is smaller than σ.)

THE ROLE OF THE STANDARD ERROR

The standard error of $\bar{X}$ gauges how closely to μ the computed sample mean tends to be. A sampling situation when $\sigma_{\bar{X}}$ is small can be expected to result in a computed $\bar{X}$ falling more closely to the population center than when $\sigma_{\bar{X}}$ is large. The amount of sampling error becomes smaller as $\sigma_{\bar{X}}$ does.

When populations are normally distributed, two factors affect the level for $\sigma_{\bar{X}}$. These are the population standard deviation σ and the sample size n.

$$\sigma_{\bar{X}} = \frac{\sigma}{\sqrt{n}}$$

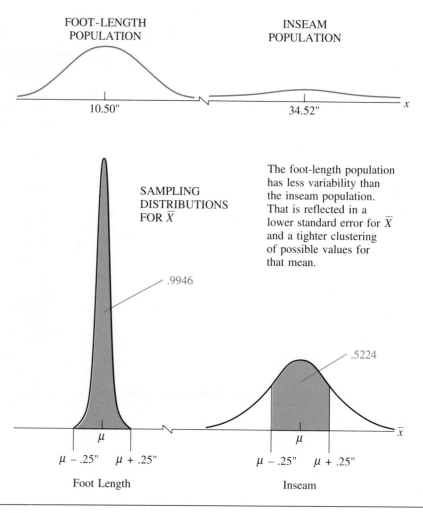

FIGURE 7-8 Normal curves for adult male anthropometric data.

⟨ INFLUENCE OF THE STANDARD DEVIATION ⟩

The standard error of $\bar{X}$ is directly proportional to the population standard deviation σ. This means that the amount of error in using the computed $\bar{X}$ to estimate μ is expected to be greater when sampling from a population having a large σ than it would be if a sample of the same size were taken from a population having a smaller σ.

ILLUSTRATION: NORMAL DISTRIBUTION FOR FOOT LENGTH

For example, a men's shoe manufacturer would be interested in the population of foot lengths of adult males. Suppose that the mean is $\mu = 10.50''$ with a standard deviation of $\sigma = .45''$. The standard deviation for this population is smaller than the earlier one for inseam, where $\sigma = 1.75''$. The respective values of $\sigma_{\bar{X}}$ will reflect this difference in σ size. When separate random samples of $n = 25$ measurements are obtained for foot length and for inseam, the respective standard errors are

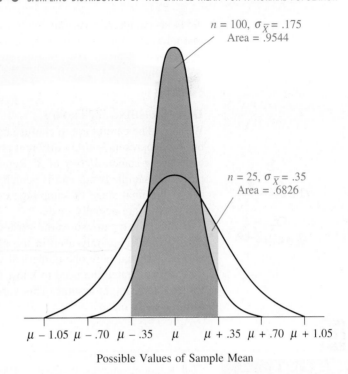

FIGURE 7-9 The effect of increased sample size on the sampling distribution of $\bar{X}$.

$$\sigma_{\bar{X}} = \frac{.45''}{\sqrt{25}} = .09'' \qquad \text{(foot length)}$$

$$\sigma_{\bar{X}} = \frac{1.75''}{\sqrt{25}} = .35'' \qquad \text{(inseam)}$$

The respective pairs of normal curves are shown in Figure 7-8. The probability is quite high, .9946, that $\bar{X}$ (foot length) will fall within $\mu \pm .25''$. The analogous chance is only .5224 that $\bar{X}$ (inseam) will fall within .25'' of the mean of the inseam population. The smaller σ for foot length will lead to less sampling error.

INFLUENCE OF THE SAMPLE SIZE

The sample size n is a second influence on $\sigma_{\bar{X}}$. The standard error of $\bar{X}$ is inversely proportional to the square root of n. Greater sample reliability in using $\bar{X}$ can be expected as n becomes larger (making $\sigma_{\bar{X}}$ smaller).

The company statistician for the trousers manufacturer described earlier may want to achieve the lower sampling error that results from increased sample size. Suppose that for a particular market segment the mean inseam μ is unknown, but the same standard deviation as before, $\sigma = 1.75''$, is believed to apply.

Figure 7-9 shows the sampling distibutions for mean inseam $\bar{X}$ when $n = 25$ and $n = 100$. Notice that the normal curve for the larger sample size (and smaller standard error) exhibits less dispersion, with possible levels of $\bar{X}$ clustering more tightly about μ. When $n = 100$, the probability that $\bar{X}$ falls within $\mu \pm .35''$ is

.9544, as compared with only .6826 for the like event when $n = 25$. This indicates that a larger sample size provides a more reliable estimate of μ for the same level of precision. Since a larger sample size is reflected by a smaller value of $\sigma_{\bar{X}}$, we can conclude that the smaller the value of $\sigma_{\bar{X}}$, the more accurate the sample result will be.

DISTINGUISHING $\sigma_{\bar{X}}$ FROM s.

We should be careful not to confuse $\sigma_{\bar{X}}$ with s. They are both standard deviations, but they represent entirely different phenomena—another reason why we usually call $\sigma_{\bar{X}}$ the standard error of $\bar{X}$. Remember that s is the standard deviation of a particular sample result and is actually calculated from the observed sample values at the final stage of sampling; s measures the variability among the observations that are actually made.

In contrast, $\sigma_{\bar{X}}$ measures the variability of the *possible* $\bar{X}$ values that *might be* obtained and is mainly used in the planning stage of sampling. Even though $\bar{X}$ will be assigned only one numerical value, depending on the sample results, we have demonstrated the need to know the pattern of variation among the possible values that $\bar{X}$ might assume. This variation is summarized by the standard error of the sample mean.

[handwritten margin notes: s actual; $\sigma_{\bar{X}}$ possible]

EXERCISES

7-8 Random samples of size $n = 100$ are selected from five normally distributed populations with the following standard deviations σ.

(a) .1   (b) 1.0   (c) 5.0   (d) 20   (e) 100

Calculate the value of $\sigma_{\bar{X}}$ for each sample.

7-9 A random sample of 100 Old Ivy men is chosen, and their heights are determined. Assume that the population mean in 69.5″ and the standard deviation is 3″.

(a) Calculate the standard error of $\bar{X}$.

(b) Determine the probability that the mean height for the sample falls in the following ranges.

  (1) between 70″ and 70.3″   (4) less than 68″
  (2) less than 69.5″   (5) between 69.4″ and 70.3″
  (3) greater than 72″

7-10 Consider operator reaction time to a warning signal that BugOff Chemical Company is experiencing significant drops in pressure. This variable is normally distributed with a mean of $\mu = 45$ seconds and a standard deviation of $\sigma = 8$ seconds. Calculate (1) the standard error of $\bar{X}$ and (2) the probability that $\bar{X}$ falls within $\mu \pm 1$ second when random samples of the following sizes are selected.

(a) $n = 25$ (b) $n = 100$ (c) $n = 200$ (d) $n = 500$

7-11 The times taken to install bumpers on cars passing along a Midget Motors assembly line are normally distributed with mean time $\mu = 1.50$ minutes and standard deviation $\sigma = .25$ minute. A sample of $n = 25$ cars is selected and the mean bumper installation time $\bar{X}$ is to be calculated.

(a) Calculate $\sigma_{\bar{X}}$.

(b) Determine the probability that $\bar{X}$ will fall in the following ranges.

  (1) between 1.40 and 1.50 minutes
  (2) exceed 1.35 minutes

      (3) at or below 1.45 minutes
      (4) between 1.52 and 1.58 minutes
      (5) exceed 1.65 minutes

7-12 The hand length of adult males is normally distributed with a mean of $\mu = 7.49''$ and a standard deviation of $\sigma = .34''$. One man is selected at random.

  (a) Determine the probabilities for the following possible hand sizes.

      (1) less than 7.00''   (3) between 7.80'' and 8.20''
      (2) between 6.75'' and 7.25''   (4) greater than 8.00''

  (b) Determine the following percentiles.

      (1) lst   (2) 10th   (3) 90th   (4) 99th

7-4 SAMPLING DISTRIBUTION OF $\bar{X}$ WHEN THE POPULATION IS NOT NORMAL

The preceding section describes how the normal curve determines the sampling distribution of $\bar{X}$ when samples are taken from a parent population that is normally distributed. In this section we see that, under proper conditions, *the same conclusions may be reached even when the parent population is not normally distributed*. This feature is a theoretical property, the **central limit theorem**.

A MULTIPLE-SAMPLE EXPERIMENT

Before we discuss that theorem in detail, it should be helpful to consider once more the results achieved from a multiple-sample experiment.

ILLUSTRATION: BASEBALL SUPERSTAR SALARIES

In Chapter 6, we investigated properties of samples generated from the population of 1991 salaries of baseball superstars, listed in Table 6-15 on page 232.

    The histograms in Figure 7-10 describe the experimental results. The top histogram portrays the complete population, which is positively skewed and bimodal. The population frequency distribution is not even close to the shape of a normal curve.

    A series of 100 random samples were taken with replacement from the population for each of three sample sizes. The second histogram in Figure 7-10 summarizes the results with $n = 10$ salaries in each sample. The next two histograms resulted when $n = 25$ and $n = 100$.

    Notice that regardless of sample size, the $\bar{X}$ values cluster about the mean of the parent population. This further illustrates the property already established that the expected value of the sample mean is the population mean μ. Notice also that as the sample size increases, the $\bar{X}$ values cluster more tightly about the respective centers. This is consistent with our earlier finding that $\bar{X}$ has a sampling distribution with standard deviation equal to $\sigma/\sqrt{n}$. (Notice how closely the computed standard deviations come to the theoretical counterpart.) Finally, notice that the $\bar{X}$ histograms tend to have the bell shape associated with the normal curve. Although the bell form is only hinted at by the histogram for $n = 10$, the bell shape is very pronounced for the two larger sample sizes.

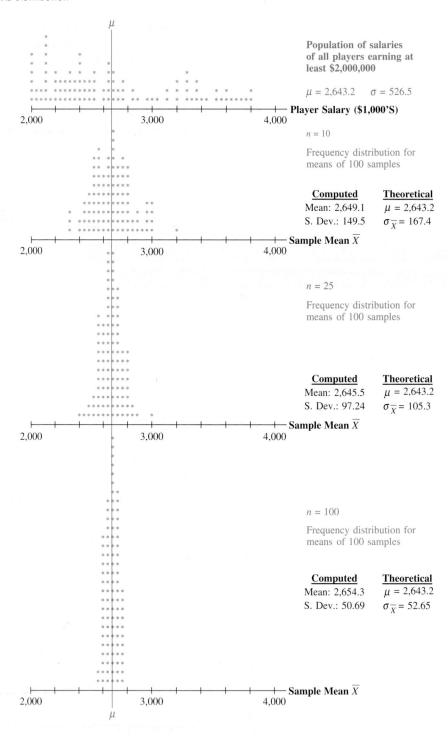

FIGURE 7-10 Frequency distributions for means computed from repeated samples from population of baseball superstar salaries.

The theoretical sampling distribution of $\overline{X}$ for baseball superstar salaries is closely approximated by the normal distribution.

THE CENTRAL LIMIT THEOREM

As the foregoing illustration suggests, it has been established mathematically that the normal distribution may be used as a basis for approximating the sampling distribution of $\overline{X}$. This fact alone makes the normal distribution so fundamentally important in statistics.

We now state the

CENTRAL LIMIT THEOREM: As sample size n becomes large, when each observation is independently selected from a population with a mean of μ and a standard deviation of σ, the sampling distribution of $\overline{X}$ tends to assume a normal distribution with a mean of μ and a standard deviation of $\sigma_{\overline{X}}$.

Note that the central limit theorem can be applied regardless of the shape of the population frequency distribution. It may be used whether the observation random variable is discrete or continuous.* Figure 7-11 shows the sampling distribution of $\overline{X}$ obtained mathematically for samples taken from populations having frequency distributions of various shapes. Note that the sampling distribution of $\overline{X}$ becomes more bell shaped as sample size increases.

The central limit theorem is useful because it permits us to make an inference about a population without knowing anything about its frequency distribution except what we can determine from a sample, although we must still presume a specific value for σ.

EXAMPLE: ESTIMATING MEAN INCOMES FOR SURGEONS AND TEACHERS

Suppose that you are asked to estimate the mean income of persons in various professions. You are to determine this by taking a random sample of persons from each group and calculating the mean income $\overline{X}$.

Consider surgeons and teachers. You are interested in the population mean income μ for each group. These are unknowns, but the following "ballpark" guesses apply for the respective standard deviations.

Teachers	Surgeons
$\sigma = \$2,000$	$\sigma = \$25,000$

Income data ordinarily provide population frequency curves that are positively skewed, as shown in Figure 7-12. Even though the particular shapes are not known, the central limit theorem allows you to use normal distributions in determining probabilities for $\overline{X}$.

Suppose that you take samples of size $n = 100$ from each population. You want to determine the probability that $\overline{X}$ lies within $\pm$ \$500 of the population mean of each group.

---

*One restriction is that the population must have a finite variance. This is a theoretical limitation of no practical significance to populations ordinarily encountered in statistical study.

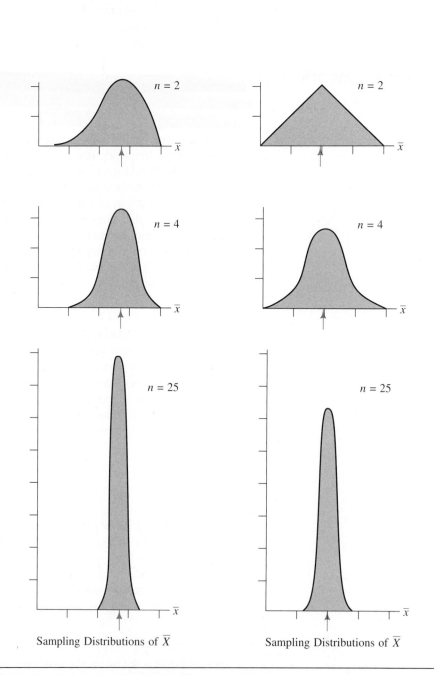

FIGURE 7-11 Illustration of the central limit theorem, showing the tendency toward normality in the sampling distribution of $\overline{X}$ as n increases for various populations.

FIGURE 7-11 *(continued)*

SOLUTION: The following standard errors apply for $\bar{X}$.

	Teachers	Surgeons

$$\sigma_{\bar{X}} = \frac{\$2,000}{\sqrt{100}} \qquad \sigma_{\bar{X}} = \frac{\$25,000}{\sqrt{100}}$$

$$= \$200 \qquad\qquad = \$2,500$$

Find the normal deviates, substituting $500 for $(\bar{x} - \mu)$ in the equation $z = (\bar{x} - \mu)/\sigma_{\bar{X}}$. Then read the areas from Appendix Table D. Since you wish to obtain a value that is both above and below the means ($\pm\$500$), you must multiply each tabled area by 2.

Teachers

$$= \frac{\$500}{\$200} = 2.50$$

$$\Pr[-\$500 \le \bar{X} - \mu \le +\$500]$$
$$= 2(.4938) = .9876$$

Surgeons

$$z = \frac{\$500}{\$2,500} = .20$$

$$\Pr[-\$500 \le \bar{X} - \mu \le +\$500]$$
$$= 2(.0793) = .1586$$

As reflected by the shaded areas under the bottom curves in Figure 7-12, there is a higher probability that $\bar{X}$ will be close to its target with teachers than with surgeons. This is because the smaller standard deviation for that more homogeneous income group provides a smaller standard error of $\bar{X}$.

The above example again shows that lower population variability will increase the probability that the computed $\bar{X}$ will be close to μ. And, as the following example shows, greater reliability can be achieved by increasing the sample size.

EXAMPLE: PROBABILITY OF NOT MEETING THE MINIMUM LIFETIME
Idea Lightbulb Company replaces a seam control mechanism whenever a sample of test bulbs has a mean lifetime less than or equal to 450 hours. When the process is exactly on target, the mean lifetime of all bulbs μ is 500 hours. The lifetimes of individual bulbs have a standard deviation σ that is also 500 hours.

Even though individual lifetimes have a frequency distribution that fits the pattern of an exponential curve (reverse J-shaped), the central limit theorem allows Idea's statistician to use the normal curve in determining probabilities for $\bar{X}$.

Present company policy calls for a test sample of $n = 25$ test bulbs, and a manager wants to determine the probability of unnecessarily replacing the control mechanism under this policy.

SOLUTION: The standard error of $\bar{X}$ is $\sigma_{\bar{X}} = 500/\sqrt{25} = 100$. The normal deviate for a possible level of 450 hours is $z = (450 - 500)/100 = -.50$. The tabled normal curve area between the mean and $z = .50$ is .1915. The probability for unnecessary replacement is thus

$$\Pr[\bar{X} \le 450] = .5000 - .1915 = .3085 \qquad (\text{when } n = 25)$$

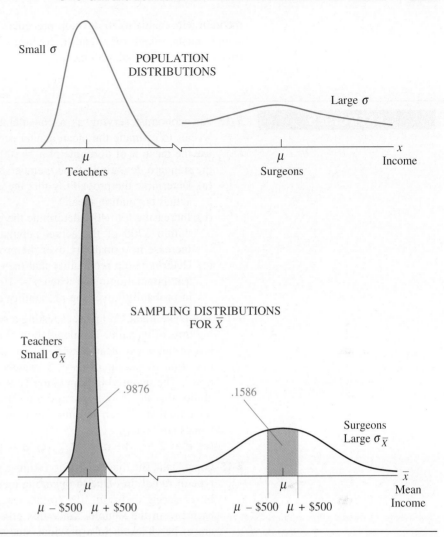

FIGURE 7-12 How the size of σ affects $\sigma_{\overline{X}}$ and thus reliability of $\overline{X}$. (Scales are approximate.)

This probability indicates a substantial chance of unnecessary repairs. The manager wants to see what effect increasing the sample size to $n = 400$ will have. The standard error of $\overline{X}$ now becomes $\sigma_{\overline{X}} = 500/\sqrt{400} = 25$, so that the normal deviate is $z = (450 - 500)/25 = -2.00$, giving a tabled area of .4772. If the company adopts this new policy, the probability for replacing the mechanism when it is functioning correctly will be

$$\Pr[\overline{X} \leq 450] = .5000 - .4772 = .0228 \qquad \text{(when } n = 400\text{)}$$

Because the central limit theorem can be applied universally, the normal curve plays a fundamental role in a great portion of statistical theory. In Chapter 8, we will make use of this result in estimating population means. In Chapter 9, the theorem will enable us to develop procedures for making decisions based on the sample mean, which may tend to confirm or deny an assumption regarding the true value of the population mean.

7-13 An economist serving as a consultant to a large teamsters' local union wishes to estimate the mean annual earnings μ of the membership. He will use the mean $\bar{X}$ of a sample of $n = 100$ drivers as an estimate. Assume that the standard deviation of the membership's annual earnings is $\sigma = \$1,500$.
(a) Determine the probability that the estimate will fall within $200 of the actual population mean.
(b) Increasing n to 400, determine the probability that the estimate will fall within $200 of the actual population mean. What is the percentage increase in probability over the probability determined in (a)?
(c) Determine the probability that the estimate will fall within $100 of the true population mean when $n = 100$. What is the percentage reduction in probability over the probability determined in (a)?

7-14 Van Dyke Paint Company is testing a solvent to determine the average drying time of its paint. The population of drying times for individual swatches has an unknown mean μ, and some value must be assumed for the standard deviation. A sample of $n = 25$ swatches will be tested to determine drying times. The underlying population is of unlimited size. Determine the probability that the sample mean drying time deviates from the unknown μ by no more than 1 hour, assuming that the standard deviation has the following values (in hours).
(a) $\sigma = 2$ (b) $\sigma = 4$ (c) $\sigma = 8$ (d) $\sigma = 16$

7-15 Great Dane Buslines wishes to estimate the mean mileage obtained by a new type of radial tire. Due to operating methods, a tire may be used on several buses during its useful life, so that a separate mileage log must be kept for each tire in the sample. Since this procedure is costly, only $n = 100$ tires are to be checked. In a previous study on another type of tire, a standard deviation of $\sigma = 2,000$ miles was determined. It is assumed that the same figure will apply to the new tires.
(a) What is the probability that the sample mean will fall within 500 miles of the population mean?
(b) The maintenance superintendent states that the new tires may exhibit greater mileage variability than the tires in current use. Assuming that the standard deviation is increased to $\sigma = 4,000$ miles, determine the probability that the sample mean will differ from the population mean by no more than 500 miles.
(c) Compare your answers to (a) and (b). What can you conclude about the effect of increased population variability on the reliability of the sample mean as an estimator?
(d) Suppose that a sample of $n = 200$ tires is used instead. If a standard deviation of $\sigma = 2,000$ miles is determined, find the probability that the sample mean will differ from the population mean by no more than 500 miles.
(e) Compare your answers to (a) and (d). What can you conclude about the effect of increased sample size on the reliability of the sample mean as an estimator?

7-16 Hops Brewery has automated filling equipment. To monitor the quantity of ingredients placed in cans, a random production sample is selected each hour, and the average weight $\bar{X}$ is determined. As long as the sample mean falls between 11.9 and 12.1 ounces, the operation continues; otherwise, the equipment is shut down and adjusted. Assuming that the true process mean μ is unknown and that the standard error of $\bar{X}$ is $\sigma_{\bar{X}} = .05$ ounce, determine the following probabilities.

(a) The equipment is operating properly ($\mu = 12$ ounces), but it is adjusted anyway.

(b) The equipment is overfilling ($\mu = 12.05$ ounces), but it is not adjusted.

(c) The equipment is underfilling ($\mu = 11.95$ ounces), and it is adjusted.

7-17 The operations manager of a port authority ordered an extensive study to determine the optimal number of toll booths to open during various times of the week. One unanticipated finding is that the mean time to collect a toll decreases as traffic becomes heavier. For example, on late Friday afternoons, collection times were found to have a mean of $\mu = 10$ seconds, with a standard deviation of $\sigma = 2$ seconds. On less busy Wednesday mornings, the mean was $\mu = 12$ seconds and the standard deviation was $\sigma = 3$ seconds. A consistency check is now being made to determine whether the season of the year affects efficiency. Random samples of $n = 25$ cars are taken on Wednesday mornings and Friday afternoons. Assume that these results are true population parameters.

(a) What is the probability that the Wednesday sample mean will differ by no more than 1 second from the assumed mean?

(b) What is the same probability for Friday?

(c) Why do the probabilities you determined in (a) and (b) differ?

7-5 SAMPLING DISTRIBUTION OF *P* AND THE NORMAL APPROXIMATION

In Chapter 6, we established that the proportion of successes obtained from a Bernoulli process is a random variable having the binomial distribution. A random sample selected from a population of two complementary attributes may be construed to be a Bernoulli process when the population is very large or when sampling with replacement.

ADVANTAGES OF APPROXIMATING THE BINOMIAL DISTRIBUTION

Calculating probabilities from the binomial formula can be a tedious chore that may seem insurmountable in many cases. For example, consider calculating the probability that $R = 324$ convictions are obtained in the next $n = 2,032$ criminal cases brought to trial in a state, when the average rate of convictions is $\pi = .537$. This would involve evaluating

$$\frac{2,032!}{324!(2,032 - 324)!}(.537)^{324}(1 - .537)^{2,032 - 324}$$

Such computations would require working with both extremely large and small numbers, making the use of logarithms or other approximations almost mandatory.

Of course, using a high-speed digital computer might make the task manageable. Binomial probabilities can be calculated and tabulated, but then a new problem arises: For what values of π and n should tables be constructed? Obviously, not all π values can be accommodated, because they are infinite in number (all possible values between 0 and 1), and the probability table for a particular π would be quite long for even a moderately large n. Clearly, no table can be constructed that would contain all the binomial probabilities.

THE NORMAL DISTRIBUTION AS AN APPROXIMATION

The difficulties just discussed can be avoided if a satisfactory approximation to the binomial distribution can be used. Remember that a graph of the binomial distribution tends to become bell shaped as n increases (see Figure 6-9). This suggests that for large sample sizes, the binomial distribution approaches the shape of the normal curve.

In fact, the central limit theorem indicates that P tends to have a normal curve as its sampling distribution. To see why this must be so, suppose you assign points to the trial outcomes, with each success getting a 1 and each failure a 0. The outcome of any given trial, then, is a random variable having either of these two values. Let X_1 denote the first trial value, X_2 the second, and so on. Consider the mean of these,

$$\bar{X} = \frac{X_1 + X_2 + \cdots + X_n}{n}$$

This value $\bar{X}$ is the same as the proportion of successes P (because the sum of all the Xs must equal the total number of successes, and P is that value divided by the number of trials n). When n is large, the *central limit theorem* states that $\bar{X}$, and hence P, has a sampling distribution closely approximated by the normal curve.

The commonly accepted guidelines for using the normal approximation are given in Table 7-1. These guidelines have been constructed according to the

TABLE 7-1 Guidelines for Using the Normal Approximation to the Binomial Distribution

Whenever π Equals			Use the Normal Approximation Only if n Is No Smaller than
	.5		10
.40	or	.60	13
.30	or	.70	17
.20	or	.80	25
.10	or	.90	50
.05	or	.95	100
.01	or	.99	500
.005	or	.995	1,000
.001	or	.999	5,000

popular rule that the normal approximation to the binomial distribution is adequate whenever both of the following hold.

$$n\pi \geq 5$$

$$n(1 - \pi) \geq 5$$

Some statisticians insist that even larger sample sizes than those listed in Table 7-1 must be used before the approximation is acceptable. In some cases, a very large sample size should be used, because the skew of the binomial distribution is so pronounced for large or small π that the bell shape is assumed by the binomial distribution only for very large n.

In Chapter 6, we established expressions for the mean and the standard deviation of *P*. The expected value of *P* is π and the standard error of *P* is

$$\sigma_P = \sqrt{\frac{\pi(1 - \pi)}{n}}$$

Using a normal curve centered at π with a standard deviation of σ_P, we can determine for any possible level p of the sample proportion the corresponding

NORMAL DEVIATE FOR THE SAMPLE PROPORTION

$$z = \frac{p - \pi}{\sigma_P}$$

To illustrate the suitability of the normal approximation, we will consider the two distributions when $n = 10$ and $\pi = .5$. The actual sampling distribution is plotted in Figure 7-13. (The probability values were obtained from Appendix Table C.) To compare this discrete distribution to the continuous normal distribution, the probabilities are presented as bars rather than spikes. The height of each bar represents the probability that *P* assumes the value at the midpoint of the bar's base. Since the base of each bar may be considered to be of unit width (letting each unit represent a .10 increment on the scale of p), the area of a bar also represents the probability of the *P* value at the midpoint. The area .3770 of all the bars at or above the point $P = .6$ therefore represents the probability that *P* will be greater than or equal to .6 (the gray area in Figure 7-13).

We can obtain the normal approximation to the sampling distribution of *P*. Here, the mean and the standard error are

$$E(P) = \pi = .5$$

$$\sigma_P = \sqrt{\frac{.5(1 - .5)}{10}} = .158$$

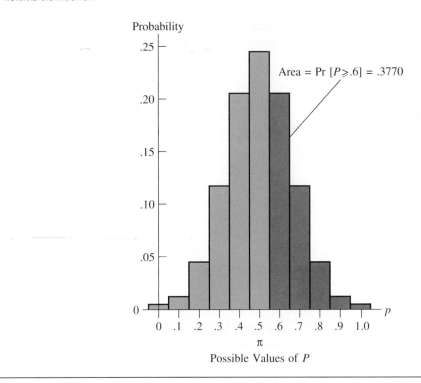

Area = Pr [$P \geq .6$] = .3770

FIGURE 7-13 Binomial sampling distribution of P.

The corresponding normal curve is graphed in Figure 7-14. Treating P as an approximately normal random variable, the probability that P lies at or above .6 is .2643 (the gray area under the approximating normal curve in Figure 7-14).

Note that the area under the normal curve above .6 only approximates the true probability indicated by the gray area under the bars in Figure 7-13. The true probability is .3770, but the normal curve provides a probability of .2643. The discrepancy between the binomial probabilities and the probabilities determined by using the normal curve are negligible for large sample sizes. It is easier to assess the nature of the approximation in Figure 7-15, where the graph for the binomial distribution of P is superimposed on the normal curve. Here, a continuity correction has been applied to obtain a better approximation.*

*In Figure 7-14, we could have obtained a value from the normal curve area above .55 rather than above .60.

$$z = \frac{.55 - .50}{.158} = .32$$

$$\Pr[P \geq .55] = .5000 - .1255 = .3745$$

The value .3745 is much closer to the true binomial probability of .3770. Using .55 instead of .60 applies a continuity correction of $.5/n = .5/10 = .05$. A continuity correction is needed because the *discrete* binomial distribution is being approximated by *continuous* normal distribution. Thus, we may improve our normal curve approximation by subtracting $.5/n$ from the lower limit for P and adding $.5/n$ to the upper limit. The continuity correction will be ignored in this book to make discussion conceptually simpler. For most sample sizes where the normal approximation will be made, n is large enough so that $.5/n$ is relatively small, and the continuity correction only slightly improves the approximation.

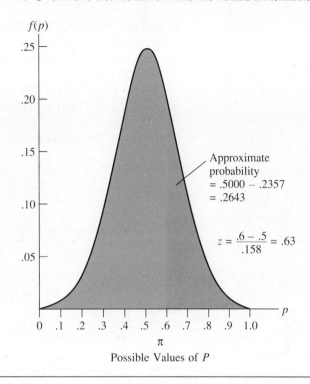

FIGURE 7-14 Normal approximation to the sampling distribution of *P* when $n = 10$ and $\pi = .5$.

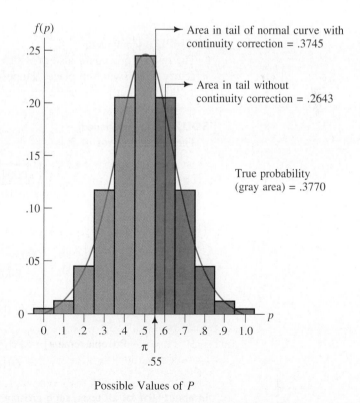

FIGURE 7-15 A comparison of the binomial sampling distribution of *P* to its normal approximation.

EXAMPLE: WHEN TO REPLACE A RELAY SWITCH

Centralia Bell replaces its relay switches whenever the proportion of erroneous characters in a test transmission is greater than .0003. Each test involves $n = 10,000$ characters.

An error rate of $\pi = .0002$ is considered satisfactory. What is the probability that a satisfactory relay is replaced?

SOLUTION: The standard error of P is

$$\sigma_P = \sqrt{\frac{.0002(.9998)}{10,000}} = .00014$$

The normal deviate for a sample proportion of level .0003 is

$$z = \frac{.0003 - .0002}{.00014} = .71$$

Thus,

$$\Pr[\text{replacement}] = \Pr[P > .0003] = .5000 - .2612 = .2388$$

About 24% of all tests involving satisfactory relays will involve unnecessary replacement.

EXAMPLE: (continued)

The testing procedure also provides good protection against leaving an unsatisfactory relay switch in place. Suppose that the error rate π is instead a too high $\pi = .0004$. What is the probability that the unsatisfactory switch gets replaced?

SOLUTION: (continued)

The standard error of P is

$$\sigma_P = \sqrt{\frac{.0004(.9996)}{10,000}} = .00020$$

The normal deviate is

$$z = \frac{.0003 - .0004}{.00020} = -.50$$

which is negative and so lies below the center of the normal curve. Thus,

$$\Pr[\text{replacement}] = \Pr[P > .0003] = .5000 + .1915$$
$$= .6915$$

In about 69% of all tests, such grossly malfunctioning switches will get replaced.

AN APPLICATION OF THE NORMAL APPROXIMATION TO ACCEPTANCE SAMPLING

We can illustrate the usefulness of the normal approximation to the binomial distribution with an example of **acceptance sampling**. A manufacturer who depends on outside suppliers for raw materials or components for production will accept only shipments of some set minimum quality. Due to the expense involved, the decision to accept or reject an incoming shipment is based on a sample of the items received. The procedure for accomplishing this is an acceptance sampling plan—a common approach in quality control.

ILLUSTRATION: INSPECTING CAR HEADLAMPS

Consider an automobile assembly plant that procures headlamps. The supplier has designed its production operation in such a way that, for various reasons, about 5% of its output is defective. The assembly plant quality control manager inspects a sample of $n = 100$ from each shipment. If 7 or fewer (that is, 7% or fewer) items in the sample are defective, the manufacturer will accept the shipment; otherwise, the batch will be rejected and returned to the supplier.

The number 7 is referred to as the **acceptance number**. It forms the basis for a **decision rule**, which specifies the action to be taken regarding a particular batch. We can determine the implications for both the consumer and the producer by using such a rule to calculate various probabilities.

Suppose a large batch of headlamps contains $\pi = .10$ defectives. If the quality control manager knew the value of π, she would reject the shipment. But because only a sample will be taken, she may accept the poor batch. What is the probability that the manager will accept the shipment?

The shipment will be accepted if the sample proportion of defectives P is $\leq .07$. Employing the normal approximation, we first calculate the standard error of P.

$$\sigma_P = \sqrt{\frac{\pi(1 - \pi)}{n}} = \sqrt{\frac{.10(1 - .10)}{100}} = .03$$

The probability for accepting the bad batch is then calculated.

$$z = \frac{p - \pi}{\sigma_P} = \frac{.07 - .10}{.03} = -1.00$$

$$\Pr[P \leq .07] = .5000 - .3413 = .1587$$

Thus, there is a .1587 probability that this poor batch of headlamps will be accepted. Because accepting an inferior shipment is an incorrect decision that will hurt some product users, such a probability value is referred to as the **consumer's risk**.

The supplier can be hurt by another kind of erroneous decision. Suppose that an acceptable lot having $\pi = .05$ defectives is shipped. If, by chance, more than 7 defectives are sampled, the good shipment will be rejected. To determine the probability that this will occur, we again use the normal approximation. The standard error of P is

$$\sigma_P = \sqrt{\frac{.05(1 - .05)}{100}} = .0218$$

The probability for rejecting the good batch is therefore

$$z = \frac{.07 - .05}{.0218} = .92$$

$$\Pr[P > .07] = .5000 - .3212 = .1788$$

A probability that an acceptable shipment will be erroneously rejected is referred to as the **producer's risk**.

The producer's risk and the consumer's risk are illustrations of the more general Type I and Type II errors of hypothesis testing that we will discuss in Chapter 9. There, we will describe how a decision rule may be constructed to balance both risks and to keep the probabilities for making erroneous decisions at desired levels.

EXERCISES

7-18 A Speak E-Z quality control inspector tests a random sample of 100 video display terminals from each outgoing shipment. In one large shipment, 5% of the units are defective, though the inspector does not know this. If 7% or more of the tested units are defective, she will hold the entire shipment for further testing. Determine the probability that the inspector will hold the shipment.

7-19 A Bernoulli process has a trial success probability of $\pi = .5$. Determine the approximate probability that the proportion P of successes will fall between .4 and .6 when the following number n of trials apply.
(a) 64   (b) 100   (c) 400
(d) What relationship do you notice between the probability values you obtained and the trial size n? How do you explain this relationship?

7-20 A marketing researcher for Big Sky Enterprises believes that the proportion of persons favoring a new package design is $\pi = .6$. Suppose that a sample of $n = 100$ persons is selected at random from the entire market, which numbers in the millions. The sample proportion favoring the new design may be approximated by the normal distribution.
(a) Calculate the standard error of P.
(b) Assuming that the given parameter applies, determine the probability that 70% or more of the persons queried will favor the new package.
(c) Suppose that the parameter value is only $\pi = .57$.
    (1) Recalculate the standard error of P.
    (2) Determine the probability that 70% or more of the sample persons will favor the new design.

7-21 A robot that shapes metal needs overhauling if it is out of tolerance on 4.5% of the items processed, and it is operating satisfactorily if it is off on only .8% of its output. A test is performed involving 50 sample items. If the sample proportion of out-of-tolerance items is greater than .02, the robot will be overhauled. Otherwise, it will be allowed to continue to operate.
(a) What is the probability that a satisfactory robot will be overhauled unnecessarily?
(b) What is the probability that a robot in need of overhauling will be left in operation?

7-22 The manufacturer of WeeTees is considering reformulating the product. The cereal currently has 30% of the total market. The value .30 is assumed to apply to the proportion of all persons in the market who will favor the reformulated product. The final decision for reformulating will be based on the results of a sample taste test involving 100 randomly selected persons representing the entire market. If more than 25% of the sample likes the new formulation, it will be marketed.

(a) Suppose that the new product tastes so horrible that only 15% of the population likes it. Determine the probability that the new formulation will be adopted.

(b) Suppose that the new WeeTees is so luscious that its market share would immediately jump to 40% if it is reformulated. Determine the probability that it does not get adopted in spite of that.

7-23 A Red Giant cannery accepts a shipment of tomatoes whenever P (the proportion that is ripe in a sample of $n = 100$) is $\geq .90$. Assume that the shipments are sufficiently large that the sampling process can be represented (with only minor error) as a Bernoulli process.

(a) What is the approximate probability for accepting a poor shipment in which the proportion of ripe tomatoes is $\pi = .8$?

(b) What is the approximate probability for rejecting a good shipment in which the proportion of ripe tomatoes is $\pi = .95$?

(c) How do you account for the fact that these probabilities indicate some shipments of poor quality will be accepted and some shipments of good quality will be rejected?

SUMMARY

1. **What are the properties of the normal distribution and why is it so important?**

   The **normal distribution** is used to represent the frequency distributions of many populations that are often encountered—especially those resulting from physical measurements. The frequency curve of such a population is called a **normal curve**. Normal curves have a bell shape, are symmetrical, and have tails extending indefinitely above and below the center. Three measures of central tendency coincide at that point: the mean, the median, and the mode.

2. **How are the various normal distributions distinguished?**

   All normal curves belong to a common family, the members of which are distinguished by their *location* and *scale* parameters, the mean μ and standard deviation σ.

3. **What role is played by areas under the normal curve and how do these relate to probabilities?**

   The *area* under the normal curve between any two points provides the relative frequency for the population values in that range. That area is specified by the **normal deviate**, which is the distance (in units of standard deviations) separating each endpoint from the mean.

   When a sample unit from a normally distributed population is observed at random, the possible value achieved is a random variable whose **probability density function** graphs as a normal curve. The probability that such a variable assumes a value in any particular range is equal to the matching area.

4. **How does the *central limit theorem* enable us to use the normal curve to find probabilities for future levels of the sample mean?**

   The key role played by the normal distribution in statistics is that it allows us to draw conclusions regarding the *sample mean* $\bar{X}$. According to the **central limit theorem**, $\bar{X}$ is a random variable whose sampling distribution can usually be represented by a normal curve. The mean of that normal distribution is the population mean itself, and its standard deviation is $\sigma_{\bar{X}} = \sigma/\sqrt{n}$ for large populations. The central limit theorem applies even when the population frequency curve isn't normal, although then the normal curve is only an *approximation* that improves as n increases. Before the sample data are available, the normal distribution provides probability values for any possible level of $\bar{X}$.

5. **How may we use the normal distribution to approximate probabilities for future levels of the sample proportion?**

   The normal distribution may also approximate the sampling distribution of the *sample proportion P*. This is advantageous primarily from a computational point of view; the normal distribution is easier to work with than the binomial. Care must be taken that n is large enough, and a **continuity correction** can be made to improve the accuracy of the approximation.

REAL-LIFE STATISTICAL CHALLENGE

Applying the Normal Distribution to the Automobile Dream List

We will observe whether the normal distribution would be a good measurement tool for analyzing the automobile data for 232 cars originally listed in Table 4-2. Table 7-2 shows the distributions of both the mileage and engine displacements for the automobiles. The population parameters for engine displacement for all 232 automobiles are $\mu = 2.69$ liters and $\sigma = 1.23$ liters. The mileage parameters are $\mu = 27.48$ mpg and $\sigma = 6.23$ mpg. The percentage of cases that are within one standard deviation of the mean are 79.3% for engine displacement and 79.7% for mileage respectively.

DISCUSSION QUESTIONS

1. Determine how many automobiles would have engine displacements exceeding 4.3 liters assuming that the normal distribution applies. Compare this to the actual number exceeding that displacement.

2. Construct histograms for the two distributions. Are the shapes similar to those of normal curves?

3. Mark the first two standard deviations from the mean for both mileage and displacement. What proportion of the population values should lie between these if the normal distributions apply?

4. Refer to Tables 6-19 and 6-20. Incorporate into your histograms the location of the respective sample means. Comment on your results.

TABLE 7-2 Mileage Data for 1990 Automobiles Showing Engine Displacement (liters) and Highway Mileage per Gallon

Engine Displacement in Liters	Frequency	Highway Mileage Miles/gallon	Frequency
1.0	6	10	1
1.1	0	11	0
1.2	2	12	0
1.3	9	13	4
1.4	0	14	0
1.5	16	15	1
1.6	22	16	0
1.7	0	17	0
1.8	14	18	6
1.9	2	19	3
2.0	19	20	4
2.1	0	21	6
2.2	12	22	10
2.3	12	23	14
2.4	4	24	21
2.5	19	25	20
2.6	0	26	12
2.7	1	27	29
2.8	11	28	18
2.9	0	29	14
3.0	17	30	16
3.1	10	31	3
3.2	0	32	11
3.3	7	33	11
3.4	2	34	7
3.5	0	35	2
3.6	3	36	7
3.7	0	37	2
3.8	13	38	0
3.9	0	39	2
4.0	2	40	1
4.1	0	41	1
4.2	0	42	1
4.3	0	43	0
4.4	0	44	1
4.5	5	45	0
4.6	0	46	0
4.7	0	47	0
4.8	0	48	0
4.9	1	49	0
5.0	14	50	2
5.1	0	51	0
5.2	1	52	1
5.3	0	53	0
5.4	0	54	0
5.5	0	55	0
5.6	0	56	0
5.7	4	57	0
5.8	0	58	1
5.9	0		
6.0	4		
$\mu = 2.69$	$N = 232$	$\mu = 27.48$	$N = 232$
$\sigma = 1.23$		$\sigma = 6.23$	

Source: United States Environmental Protection Agency, 1989.

REVIEW EXERCISES

7-24 The mean μ and standard deviation σ for accountants' salaries is unknown. A sample of $n = 25$ is taken at random from a population of accountants, and the sample mean is calculated. Assume that the population is of large size. Determine the probability that $\bar{X}$ falls within $\mu \pm \$500$ when the following standard deviations apply.

(a) $\sigma = \$1,500$ (b) $\sigma = \$2,000$ (c) $\sigma = \$2,500$

7-25 The height of women is normally distributed with a mean of $\mu = 66$ inches and a standard deviation of $\sigma = 1.5$ inches. Determine the (a) 50th, (b) 15th, (c) 95th, (d) 75th, and (e) 33rd percentiles.

7-26 The annual incomes of consultants constitute a highly positively skewed population. Nevertheless, according to the central limit theorem, it is still possible to find the sampling distribution of the mean for a random sample of these incomes by using the normal distribution. Suppose the population has an unknown mean of μ and a standard deviation of $\sigma = \$10,000$. An estimate of μ is to be made using the value of the sample mean $\bar{X}$. This estimate must fall within $\pm\$1,000$ of the true mean.

(a) If $n = 100$ incomes, determine the probability that the estimate will meet the desired accuracy.

(b) If a sample $n = 625$ incomes is used instead, determine the probability that the estimate will meet the desired accuracy.

7-27 The time that each payroll waits to be processed at Comp-U-Quik's data service bureau is assumed to have a positively skewed distribution. A sample of 25 waiting times is collected. Both the mean and the standard deviation for individual waiting times are equal to .5 day. A large population size is assumed. Determine the probabilities for the following possible sample mean waiting times.

(a) doesn't exceed .6 day   (c) equals $.5 \pm .1$ day
(b) is greater than .7 day   (d) is between .3 and .7 day

7-28 The weights of "1-ounce" gold ingots cast by Midas Metals are normally distributed, with a mean of $\mu = 28$ grams and a standard deviation of $\sigma = 1$ gram. Consider a shipment of 25 ingots.

(a) What is the probability that the mean ingot weight will be less than 27.5 grams?

(b) Determine the probability that the entire shipment will weigh more than 705 grams.

7-29 The Water Wheelies production process is designed to produce only 10% defective items. Once each day, a sample of 100 items is selected and the proportion of defectives P is determined. If this value lies below .15, production is continued. Otherwise, production is stopped for maintenance.

(a) Assuming that the process is operating as designed, determine the probability that operations will be continued.

(b) Suppose that the process is producing too many defectives, at the rate of 20%, but management does not know this. Determine the probability that the process will be stopped for maintenance.

7-30 A parapsychologist is testing the extrasensory perception of a purported clairvoyant. Using a deck of cards, half of which are red and half of which are black, she selects the top card and asks her subject (who is in another room) to identify its color. The procedure is repeated 100 times. Each successive card is replaced in the deck, and the deck is shuffled before the next card is drawn. A subject with no powers of ESP should identify the correct color 50% of the time, so that $\pi = .5$. Under this assumption, what is the probability that a correct response will be obtained for 65 or more of the 100 cards? Use the normal approximation.

7-31 For each of the following sampling situations, indicate (by *yes* or *no*) whether the sampling distribution of the sample proportion can be approximated by the normal curve.
(a) $\pi = .50; n = 9$ (c) $\pi = .83; n = 100$ (e) $\pi = .01; n = 1,000$
(b) $\pi = .10; n = 36$ (d) $\pi = .45; n = 20$

7-32 Assume the population of members of the U.S. Army has a mean height of 70 inches and a standard deviation of 3 inches. A random sample of 100 soldiers is selected. Determine the probabilities for the following mean heights.
(a) between 70 and 70.5 inches   (d) less than 68 inches
(b) less than 69.5 inches   (e) between 69.4 and 70.8 inches
(c) greater than 72 inches

7-33 Procrastinator Pete marks an examination consisting of 36 true-or-false questions by tossing a coin. For each question, he answers "true" for a head or "false" for a tail. Assuming that half the correct answers should be marked "true," what is the probability that the student will pass the examination by marking at least 75% of the answers correctly? Use the normal approximation.

7-34 A clerk at the Fox Box Company measures the quantities in all bulk products purchased. On the average, 1,000-foot rolls of transparent tape should be close to the specified length. In evaluating a shipment, a random sample of 100 rolls of tape is selected, and the mean length is determined. If the mean is greater than or equal to 990 feet, the entire shipment is accepted; otherwise, the shipment is rejected and returned to the manufacturer.
(a) If a shipment has a mean roll length of only 980 feet, with a standard deviation of 50 feet, determine the consumer's risk (probability of accepting these inferior tapes).
(b) If a shipment has a mean roll length of 1,005 feet, with a standard deviation of 60 feet, determine the producer's risk (probability of rejecting these good tapes).

STATISTICS IN PRACTICE

7-35 Using the master class data found for Exercise 1-19, answer the following for one of your quantitative variables (e.g., age or height).
(a) Using all data points, compute the mean and standard deviation. Those values will serve as the μ and σ.
(b) You will select a sample of 5 observations randomly from the list. Find the standard error of the sample mean. After selecting your sample, compute the mean and standard deviation.
(c) Compare the means from (a) and (b). What is the probability of getting

a sample mean as far or farther (in the same direction) from the population mean as the one actually found?

(d) Develop an example based on your data set that demonstrates how the binomial distribution may be approximated by the normal curve in finding probabilities for the sample proportion. Find the probability that the sample proportion falls between .60 and .70.

7-36 Using your group's class data list developed in Exercise 1-21, repeat (a) through (d) of Exercise 7-35. Use $n = 7$ as the sample size and change the limits in (d) to .25 and .75.

7-37 Refer to the data you created in Exercise 6-54 for the personal computer system cost. Assume that the probability distribution found actually represents the relative frequency distribution for the *population* relative frequency distribution.

(a) Compute the mean and standard deviation. Those values will serve as the μ and σ.

(b) Assume a sample size of $n = 100$ is selected. Compute three meaningful probability values for the sample mean system cost.

7-38 In Exercise 6-55 you were asked to go to a local store or other retail outlet and find the number of customer arrivals during each of several one-minute intervals.

(a) For those data, compute the mean and standard deviation for the number of arrivals in any given minute. Assume that these values will serve as the μ and σ.

(b) A sample will be taken of $n = 9$ one-minute intervals. Find the probability that the mean number of arrivals will be (1) less than .5, (2) above 2, (3) between 1 and 3.

7-39 Using the final exam grade data in Table 3-13, answer the following questions.

(a) Using all of the data, compute the mean and standard deviation. These values will be used for μ and σ.

(b) You will be selecting a random sample of size 9 from the list. Find the standard error of the sample mean. Then select the sample and compute its mean and standard deviation.

(c) Compare the means from (a) and (b). What is the probability of getting a sample mean as far as or farther (in the same direction) from μ as the one actually found?

7-40 Per capita spending in the United States for public libraries in 1991 is given on the top of page 317. Suppose we consider a group consisting of one person from each state.

(a) Using all of the data, compute the mean and standard deviation. These values will be used for μ and σ.

(b) You will be selecting a random sample of size 4 from the list. Find the standard error of the sample mean. Now, select the sample and compute its mean and standard deviation.

(c) Compare the means from (a) and (b). What is the probability of getting a sample mean equal to or less than the one actually found?

State	Spending	State	Spending	State	Spending
AL	9.88	KY	9.16	ND	8.70
AK	28.64	LA	12.62	OH	28.34
AZ	16.16	ME	15.40	OK	12.37
AR	6.75	MD	25.52	OR	17.86
CA	17.54	MA	21.36	PA	12.92
CO	20.51	MI	15.51	RI	18.63
CT	27.20	MN	20.58	SC	9.67
DE	9.48	MS	7.62	SD	13.59
DC	35.62	MO	15.50	TN	7.44
FL	15.09	MT	9.02	TX	9.53
GA	11.62	NE	15.38	UT	15.71
HI	19.39	NV	16.41	VT	13.24
ID	13.62	NH	17.40	VA	18.79
IL	22.72	NJ	27.40	WA	23.79
IN	22.80	NM	10.71	WV	8.38
IA	14.67	NY	30.36	WI	19.10
KS	17.41	NC	12.01	WY	22.40

7-41 High school graduation rates for the United States for 1991 are given below.

State	Graduation %	State	Graduation %	State	Graduation %
AL	65.6	KY	70.0	ND	86.7
AK	72.3	LA	54.3	OH	72.3
AZ	72.4	ME	79.0	OK	75.5
AR	76.6	MD	73.1	OR	71.6
CA	67.7	MA	79.7	PA	78.5
CO	74.5	MI	69.9	RI	73.6
CT	78.6	MN	89.5	SC	61.2
DE	68.0	MS	61.7	SD	84.2
DC	59.5	MO	72.5	TN	67.8
FL	61.2	MT	84.9	TX	65.9
GA	64.0	NE	86.3	UT	79.0
HI	76.1	NV	77.4	VT	80.9
ID	79.7	NH	76.2	VA	73.6
IL	77.5	NJ	82.1	WA	73.1
IN	75.3	NM	69.5	WV	77.5
IA	85.9	NY	64.4	WI	82.5
KS	81.1	NC	68.4	WY	81.7

Suppose we consider a group consisting of one high school senior from each state.

(a) Using all of the data, compute the mean and standard deviation. These values will be used for μ and σ.

(b) You will be selecting a random sample of size 8 from the list. Find the standard error of the sample mean. Select the sample and compute its mean and standard deviation.

(c) Compare the means from (a) and (b). What is the probability of getting a sample mean equal to or larger than the one actually found?

7-42 Assuming that all scores on the final exam discussed in Problem 7-39 are normally distributed with mean μ and standard deviation σ as calculated in Problem 7-39(a), answer the following questions.

(a) The central 50% of the scores fall between what two values?

(b) What is the probability that a randomly selected score is within 30 points of the mean score?

(c) What is the probability that a randomly selected score is 80 or higher?

CASE MBA Income and Stature

Various statistical populations are associated with an MBA degree. Three Slippery Rock University undergraduates majoring in geography, Georgia Maine, Tex York, and Virginia Washington, are compiling a demographic profile. The subjects of their study are former MBA students who have just completed their first year in the working world.

Georgia sent out questionnaires to a random sample of recent graduates. Tex is particularly interested in MBA salaries (including bonuses and other monetary perquisites). Using the sample data from the completed questionnaires, Tex constructed the sample histogram in Figure 7-16. He then calculated the *sample* mean and variance for the salaries. Although he cannot know the levels of the population counterparts, some judgmental adjustments were made to arrive at $\mu = \$29,000$ and $\sigma = \$12,000$. Tex wants to use these values to form various probabilistic assessments.

Virginia believes that persons with an MBA are not only motivationally different from other graduate alumni but physically distinct as well. To begin her study, Virginia investigated sample heights. Using the sample data, she constructed the histograms in Figure 7-17. From these results, Virginia used the following values to make probability evaluations.

$$\mu = 70'' \qquad \sigma = 2.6'' \qquad \text{(men)}$$

$$\mu = 67'' \qquad \sigma = 2.3'' \qquad \text{(women)}$$

At this point, the undergraduates need some statistical expertise. You have volunteered to answer their questions concerning statistics.

QUESTIONS

1. Tex asks you to determine probabilities for the salary of a typical MBA selected at random. Comment on the appropriateness of using the normal distribution for this purpose.

2. You assure Tex that the normal distribution may be used to establish probabilities for the mean salary of any sample group randomly selected from the underlying population.

    (a) Comment on why you may comfortably make such assurances even though the population frequency curve will most likely resemble the histogram in Figure 7-16.

    (b) Suppose that another random sample of size $n = 9$ is selected from the salary population. Determine the following probabilities.

     (1) $\Pr[\bar{X} \geq \$40,000]$ (3) $\Pr[\bar{X} \leq \$26,000]$

     (2) $\Pr[\$27,000 \leq \bar{X} \leq \$30,000]$ (4) $\Pr[\bar{X} > \$31,000]$

```
   Class Interval              Frequency
     for Salary         ------------------------------------------------
                         0    10   20   30   40   50   60   70   80   90
10000. under 15000.      0    :
15000. under 20000.     28    :**************
20000. under 25000.     62    :*******************************
25000. under 30000.     52    :**************************
30000. under 35000.     20    :***********
35000. under 40000.     16    :********
40000. under 45000.      6    :***
45000. under 50000.      4    :**
50000. under 55000.      2    :*
55000. under 60000.      2    :*
60000. under 65000.      0    :
65000. under 70000.      2    :*
70000. under 75000.      2    :*
75000. under 80000.      2    :*
80000. under 85000.      2    :*
85000. under 90000.      0    :
```

Note: Figure generated on an IBM PC using EasyStat.

FIGURE 7-16 Sample histogram for the salaries of former MBA students.

(c) Assume that $n = 100$. Determine the above probabilities.
(d) Compare your answers to (b) and (c). What might you conclude regarding the use of a larger sample size?

3. Virginia asks you to determine various probabilities for the heights of a typical MBA selected at random.
(a) You inform Virginia that there are typical *male* MBA heights and typical *female* MBA heights. But, probabilities should be reported separately. Explain.
(b) Comment on why you may find normal distributions suitable for this purpose in spite of the obstacles you faced with salary.

4. Determine the following probabilities for the height of a randomly selected male MBA.
(a) $\Pr[X \geq 73'']$ (b) $\Pr[X \leq 66'']$

5. Determine the above probabilities for the height of a randomly selected female MBA.

6. Suppose that the sample selected is exactly half men and half women. Consider the mean height of the entire sample, with sexes mixed.
(a) Although it may not be very meaningful, the normal distribution may be used to determine probabilities for the sample mean height (with sexes mixed). Why?
(b) When a bimodal population is formed from two component populations, the resulting population mean will be a weighted average of the two separate population means, according to the proportional sizes of the two groups. Suppose that Virginia combines the heights of men and women MBAs. Regardless of the proportional represen-

```
Class Interval              Frequency (Men)           Frequency (Women)
for Height (inches)     --------------------      --------------------
                         0    10   20   30          0    10   20   30
   60. under 61.      0   :                     0   :
   61. under 62.      0   :                     1   :*
   62. under 63.      1   :*                    2   :*
   63. under 64.      1   :*                    5   :***
   64. under 65.      2   :*                   12   :******
   65. under 66.      4   :**                  15   :********
   66. under 67.      3   :**                  21   :***********
   67. under 68.     10   :*****               15   :********
   68. under 69.     12   :******              13   :*******
   69. under 70.     17   :********            5   :***
   70. under 71.     15   :********            4   :**
   71. under 72.     16   :********            5   :***
   72. under 73.     11   :******              2   :*
   73. under 74.      3   :**                   0   :
   74. under 75.      1   :*                    0   :
   75. under 76.      4   :**                   0   :
   76. under 77.      0   :                     0   :
```

Note: Figure generated on an IBM PC using EasyStat.

FIGURE 7-17 Sample histograms for the heights of former MBA students.

tation of the sexes, her combined population is assumed to have a standard deviation of 3″ (an approximation). Virginia plans to select a random sample of $n = 25$ heights. Assume that the combined population is half men's heights and half women's heights.

(1) Find the mean height of the combined population.
(2) Determine $\Pr[\bar{X} \geq 70″]$.
(3) Determine $\Pr[\bar{X} \leq 68″]$.

(c) Repeat (b) assuming instead that 90% of the combined population observations are men's heights.

(d) Repeat (b) assuming instead that 25% of the combined population observations are men's heights.

7-6 OPTIONAL TOPIC: SAMPLING DISTRIBUTION OF $\bar{X}$ WHEN THE POPULATION IS SMALL

We have established that for independent sample observations, the standard error of $\bar{X}$ may be obtained from the expression $\sigma_{\bar{X}} = \sigma/\sqrt{n}$. Observations are always independent when sampling with replacement, but we usually sample *without replacement*. When populations are large compared to sample size, the probability distributions for successive observations barely change when earlier items are removed. In these cases, we can generally assume independence between observations.

But when the population is small compared to sample size, this fact must be reflected in calculating $\sigma_{\bar{X}}$.

STANDARD ERROR OF $\bar{X}$ (small populations)

$$\sigma_{\bar{X}} = \frac{\sigma}{\sqrt{n}} \sqrt{\frac{N - n}{N - 1}}$$

where σ = population standard deviation, N = population size, and n = sample size.

FINITE POPULATION CORRECTION FACTOR

The term $\sqrt{(N - n)/(N - 1)}$ is referred to as the **finite population correction factor**. When n is small in relation to N, the factor is very close to 1. Thus, the standard error obtained from a sample without replacement is close in value to one obtained from a sample with replacement. Note that the numerator in the expression will never be greater than the denominator, so that $\sigma_{\bar{X}}$ will be smaller when a sample is taken without replacement. *In practice, the finite population correction is usually ignored whenever n is less than 10% of N.*

For samples from small populations, the normal distribution approximately describes the sampling distribution of $\bar{X}$, even though the observations are not independent. As an illustration, consider a survey of incomes in two cities. City A has a population of $N = 10,000$; city B has a population of $N = 2,500$. A standard deviation of $\sigma = \$1,500$ is assumed to be common to both populations. A sample of $n = 1,000$ is taken from each. The following calculation provides the standard error of $\bar{X}$ for city A.

$$\sigma_{\bar{X}} = \frac{\$1,500}{\sqrt{1,000}} \sqrt{\frac{10,000 - 1,000}{10,000 - 1}} = \$45.00$$

Analogously, for city B,

$$\sigma_{\bar{X}} = \frac{\$1,500}{\sqrt{1,000}} \sqrt{\frac{2,500 - 1,000}{2,500 - 1}} = \$36.75$$

Note that the standard error of $\bar{X}$ for city B is smaller than that for city A. This is to be expected, because B is a smaller city. But the standard error of $\bar{X}$ for city A is only about 23% greater, although its population is four times as large.

The probability that $\bar{X}$ *exceeds* the mean by 100 or more can be calculated for each city. For A,

$$z = \frac{\bar{x} - \mu}{\sigma_{\bar{X}}} = \frac{100}{45.00} = 2.22$$

$$\Pr[\bar{X} - \mu \geq 100] = .5000 - .4868 = .0132$$

and for B,

$$z = \frac{100}{36.75} = 2.72$$

$$\Pr[\bar{X} - \mu \geq 100] = .5000 - .4967 = .0033$$

In either case, the probability for obtaining a sample mean that exceeds the respective mean by $100 or more is relatively small. However, the same sample size provides about the same protection against obtaining extremely large sample values in *both* cities, regardless of the size of either.

When n is small in relation to N, the finite population correction factor approaches 1. Thus, a sample of $n = 1,000$ would yield almost the same finite population factor for a population of $N = 100,000$ that it would for one of $N = 1,000,000$ (.9949 versus .9995). Thus, if the standard deviations of the two populations are identical, there would be an imperceptible difference in the respective values of $\sigma_{\bar{X}}$, and the probabilities for possible sample results would be nearly identical. In this case, a sample of $n = 1,000$ would be almost as reliable in a large population as in a population one-tenth its size. This is why we concluded in Chapter 4 that a sample of Alaska voters in a presidential election poll would have to be about the same size as a sample of California voters for the sample results to be equally reliable.

OPTIONAL EXERCISES

7-43 A sample of $n = 100$ families is selected at random from the community of Dog Patch. Assume that there are $N = 500$ families in the entire town. The population standard deviation is known to be $\sigma = \$700$.
(a) Calculate the standard error of the sample mean family income.
(b) Then take a random sample of the same size from the residents of Metropolis. Assume $N = 1,000,000$ and that the same level applies for σ as before. Calculate the value for $\sigma_{\bar{X}}$.

7-44 A random sample of 100 soldiers is selected without replacement from a regiment of 900 men. The mean regiment height is 71 inches, with a standard deviation of 2.5 inches. Determine the probabilities for the following sample mean heights.
(a) between 71 and 71.4 inches.   (c) greater than 71.6 inches.
(b) less than 70.5 inches.   (d) between 70.7 and 71.5 inches.

7-45 The unemployment rates experienced by $N = 210$ medium-sized cities in one year have a mean of $\mu = 7\%$ and a standard deviation of $\sigma = 2\%$. A random sample of 25 of these cities is selected.
(a) Calculate the standard error of the sample mean.
(b) Determine the probability that the sample mean
    (1) exceeds 8%.   (3) is between 6.5% and 7.5%.
    (2) is smaller than 6.5%.   (4) is between 6.0% and 6.5%.

7-46 A customs official wishes to estimate the mean weight of each of three batches of copper ingots obtained from different smelters. $N = 500$ ingots have arrived from Chile, $N = 1,000$ from Bolivia, and $N = 700$ from Arizona. Samples of $n = 100$ ingots from each batch are weighed. Each smelter is assumed to produce batches of ingots with a mean weight of $\mu = 100$ pounds and a standard deviation of $\sigma = 5$ pounds.

(a) Determine the probability that the sample mean of each batch lies between 99 and 101 pounds.

(b) Using the same sample size, determine the analogous probability values when the sample means are obtained from batches ten times as large.

(c) Do your answers differ significantly between smelters? Explain.

7-47 Suppose that the customs official in Exercise 7-46 establishes a rule to enable him to decide when an entire batch of ingots should be individually weighed. Because it is such a time-consuming procedure, he wants to weigh the ingots only when there is strong sample evidence that they are underweight.

Assume that an acceptable batch of $N = 1,000$ ingots has a mean weight of $\mu = 100$ pounds, but that the official does not know this value. He takes a sample of $n = 200$ and calculates $\bar{X}$. Suppose that the batch standard deviation is $\sigma = 5$ pounds. The official must consider three decision rules.

(1) Accept batch (do not weigh all 1,000 ingots) if $\bar{X} \geq 100$ pounds.
(2) Accept batch if $\bar{X} \geq 99.5$ pounds.
(3) Accept batch if $\bar{X} \geq 99.0$ pounds.

(a) Determine the probability according to each of these decision rules that the customs official will accept the batch without weighing all the ingots.

(b) If he prefers the rule that maximizes the probability for not weighing all 1,000 ingots, which rule should he choose?

CHAPTER 8

STATISTICAL ESTIMATION

BEFORE READING THIS CHAPTER, MAKE SURE YOU UNDERSTAND:

How to avoid bias in selecting samples and how sampling error arises (Chapter 4).

How to find probabilities for possible results of a random sample (Chapter 6).

The properties of the sampling distribution of the mean (Chapter 6).

About the binomial distribution and its role as the sampling distribution of the proportion (Chapter 6).

About the normal distribution and how to use the normal curve to obtain probabilities for the sample mean (Chapter 7).

How the binomial distribution may be approximated by the normal curve in finding probabilities for the sample proportion (Chapter 7).

AFTER READING THIS CHAPTER, YOU WILL UNDERSTAND:

About estimation and estimators.

What properties are desirable for an estimator.

What two forms are taken by estimates.

About confidence intervals for the mean, and how they are used and constructed.

About the Student *t* distribution and its role in constructing confidence intervals for the mean.

When the Student *t* distribution should be used instead of the normal distribution.

How to use the normal distribution used in constructing confidence intervals for the proportion.

What considerations are important in establishing a sample size.

In this chapter, we will be concerned with the kinds of estimates we make from sample data and the procedures we use to make these estimates. Problems of estimation are crucial to practically every statistical application. This is especially true in business decision making, where often only sample results are available for establishing vital information. For example, samples are used to estimate a product's share of the market—a useful number for many important marketing decisions. Also, statistical estimates provide management with the average times required to complete various production operations, which allows for intelligent planning and better day-to-day control. Similarly, sample data yield median earnings of subscribers to various magazines, a demographic feature useful to merchandisers in choosing where to place advertisements. Estimation problems are perhaps most difficult in economic planning, where the impact of policies can affect the lives of literally every person in an entire nation.

8-1 ESTIMATORS AND ESTIMATES

Using samples to estimate a population parameter is one of the more common forms of statistical inference. A sample statistic that serves this purpose is called an **estimator**. An important segment of statistical theory is concerned with finding statistics that are appropriate estimators. For instance, the sample mean is a particularly good estimator for the population mean. We will learn why this is so.

THE ESTIMATION PROCESS

Parameter estimation requires a great deal of planning. First, we must choose an estimator. Then a major concern is to control the sampling error. The choice of a sampling method—judgment or convenience sampling, or some version of random sampling—will affect this. Our discussion will center on random samples because we know they are free from sampling bias. We also know that small samples tend to be less reliable, so that sampling error can be controlled by using a sufficiently large sample. A practical consideration is to balance the level of reliability, which is influenced by sampling error, against the costs of obtaining the sample.

Due to chance, the value of the sample statistic we obtain may not be close to the population parameter. But unless we take a census of the population, we cannot determine the true parameter value. Therefore, statisticians must be able to assess the reliability of their results even though they can only theoretically determine what values are reasonable.

We are presently concerned only with estimates based on samples taken from already existing populations or from identifiable target populations. This excludes predictions based on other kinds of information—most notably, economic forecasts based on time-series data. For example, although sampling may be involved in forecasting the gross national product, the major role is played by other factors, such as judgment, current trends, contemplated changes in government policies, and the state of international affairs. Some procedures useful in making such predictions will be discussed in Chapter 10. Another category of excluded predictions concerns parameters of some future population. For example, the median annual family income for the United States in the year 2000 cannot be estimated from the usual sample, because the elementary units cannot be presently defined and the variate values themselves lie in the future.

Statistical estimates take two basic forms.

POINT ESTIMATES

You are probably most familiar with the **point estimate**. For example, you may recall the following statements.

> "The mean height of adult males is 5'9"."
> "The proportion of voters approving the president is .40."
> "Our car averages 35 miles per gallon in highway driving."

To be statistically valid, each of the values in these statements must have been obtained in a sampling investigation where the respective findings gave the following computed values: $\bar{X} = 5'9''$, $P = .40$, and $\bar{X} = 35$ mpg.

One drawback to point estimates is that too often they are assumed to be precise and correct. Indeed, lay persons will often believe point estimates to be the levels of the population parameters themselves. You should by now know better! Nevertheless, you will encounter occasions where a point estimate is the preferred form.

INTERVAL ESTIMATES

A sounder way to report findings is to use the **interval estimate**. This type of estimate places the unknown parameter between two limits. Consider the following examples.

> $5'8'' - 5'10''$ for the mean height μ of adult males
> $.35 - .45$ for the proportion π of voters approving the president
> $28.75 - 39.23$ for the mean gasoline mileage μ

An interval estimate acknowledges that the sampling procedure is prone to some error, so that any computed statistic may fall above or below its population parameter target.

It also shows very simply the degree of precision achieved by the results obtained.

Because it represents a range of possible values, an interval estimate implies the presence of uncertainty. It is ordinarily accompanied by a statement indicating the likelihood that the parameter being estimated actually does lie within the stated interval.

There are several ways to symbolically represent the interval estimate. The one adopted in this book is an **inequality**. For example, the population mean height for a group of men would be reported in the form

$$5'8'' \leq \mu \leq 5'10''$$

Some statisticians favor "strict" inequalities, using $<$ instead of $\leq$. Another method is to state the endpoints only—either in parentheses, $(5'8'', 5'10'')$, or with a dash, $5'8'' - 5'10''$.

It is often convenient to adopt the notation for measurement tolerances, really a more compact form of the inequality. This notation applies to most interval estimates, which are usually symmetrical around a point estimator midpoint. For example, the inequality $5'8'' \leq \mu \leq 5'10''$ can be represented equivalently as

$$\mu = 5'9'' \pm 1'' \quad \textit{measurement tolerance}$$

Whether a point or an interval estimate is to be made depends on the objective of the statistical study. Interval estimates would be unsuitable to a manufacturer as the basis for placing orders for raw materials, for the supplier cannot accept an order for "something between 2,000 and 3,000 units." Likewise, knowing only that the wattage of a stereo amplifier lies between 50 and 80 makes it difficult to compare that model to other brands. But the superiority of an interval estimate is evident in many kinds of planning or reporting. For example, knowing that next year's sales might lie between 10,000 and 11,000 units, a company president is able to draw up a realistic budget taking into account uncertainties about the sales level. He can visualize the best and worst cases, and thereby obtain a reasonable basis for evaluating the risks involved.

CREDIBILITY AND PRECISION IN ESTIMATION

There are two considerations in establishing the endpoints of an interval estimate. One is the **level of precision** obtained. The other involves the **credibility** of the estimate. You can improve each of these features at the expense of the other, but you can attain improvements in *both* precision and credibility only by increasing the quality of the sample itself.

STATISTICS AROUND US

Credibility vs. Precision—How Tall Are Marlborough Men?

Suppose you are asked to construct an interval estimate of the mean height of adult males in Marlborough County. You would obviously agree that the following estimate is totally believable.

$$4' \leq \mu \leq 8'$$

Indeed, almost any knowledgeable person would accept it as true regardless of what (if any) sample evidence were obtained.

You could take a sample of size 1, measure that person, and from your finding report a very precise result, such as the following

$$5'8.33'' \leq \mu \leq 5'8.34''$$

Although precise to one-hundredth of an inch, this result is not very likely to be true and would be believed by few people.

Although totally credible, the first interval is too wide to be of any practical use. A narrower, more precise interval would be mandatory. The second interval is very precise, but not credible. It is useless as well.

In the next section of this chapter you will see how an interval estimate may be constructed using only the information contained in sample data. In doing this, the statistical investigator has some flexibility in making a trade-off between precision and credibility.

CHOOSING AN ESTIMATOR

Several alternative statistics can be used as estimators. For instance, we can use one of three sample statistics—the mean, median, or mode—to estimate the population mean. We may think that the sample mean is the most suitable estimator, but how can we substantiate our choice?

The most desirable feature of an estimator is that it has a value close to the unknown value of the population parameter. Under certain circumstances, the sample mean, median, and mode will each have a value that lies close to the population mean. The basic questions are therefore: Which statistic will be the most reliable estimator? And which will require the least expenditure of resources in terms of sample size? An important ancillary question is: Is there an easily applied theoretical procedure for determining the probability that the value obtained for the estimator statistic will lie sufficiently close to the parameter?

CRITERIA FOR STATISTICS USED AS ESTIMATORS

Three criteria have been developed to compare statistics in terms of their worth in estimating a parameter. One determines whether there is a tendency, on the average, for the statistic to assume values close to the parameter in question. Another considers the reliability of the estimator. The third indicates whether this reliability improves as sample size increases.

UNBIASED ESTIMATORS

An unbiased estimator is a statistic that has an expected value equal to the population parameter being estimated. A statistic that does not, on the average, tend to yield values equal to the parameter is said to be biased. The sample mean $\bar{X}$ is an unbiased estimator of the population mean μ, because we have established that

$$E(\bar{X}) = \mu$$

Likewise, the sample proportion P is an unbiased estimator of the population proportion π, since $E(P) = \pi$.

Unbiasedness explains why we define the sample variance s^2 as

$$s^2 = \frac{\sum (X - \bar{X})^2}{n - 1}$$

Here, the divisor is $n - 1$ instead of n. It can be proved that s^2 defined using the $n - 1$ divisor is an unbiased estimator of σ^2, since

$$E(s^2) = \sigma^2$$

An intuitive reason why $n - 1$ is used as the divisor is because it provides a somewhat larger value for the sample variance than the *n* divisor. The estimator that results from using s^2 is larger, reflecting the fact that a sample is ordinarily less diverse than its population (the part is rarely more varied than the whole).

EFFICIENT ESTIMATORS

One statistic is a more efficient estimator than another if its standard error is smaller for the same sample size. The sample median is an unbiased estimator of μ when the population is normally distributed. But its standard error is 1.2533 times as great as that of the sample mean. This implies that the sample mean is a more efficient estimator of μ than the sample median. Medians of samples taken from normally distributed populations tend to be more unlike each other than means of the same samples. Thus, the sample mean is always a more reliable estimator of μ.

MAXIMUM LIKELIHOOD ESTIMATORS

The most efficient estimator among all the unbiased ones is the maximum likelihood estimator. The sample mean is an example of a maximum likelihood estimator.

CONSISTENT ESTIMATORS

A statistic is a consistent estimator of a parameter if the probability that it will be close to the parameter's true value approaches unity with increasing sample size. In general, *a statistic whose standard error becomes smaller as n becomes larger will be consistent.* In other words, a consistent estimator is more reliable when larger samples are used.

Both $\bar{X}$ and P are consistent estimators, since

$$\sigma_{\bar{X}} = \frac{\sigma}{\sqrt{n}} \quad \text{and} \quad \sigma_P = \sqrt{\frac{\pi(1 - \pi)}{n}}$$

both become smaller as *n* increases.

Consistency alone does not guarantee reliable sample results; reliability can be achieved only by increasing the sample size. But consistency is a necessary condition if a larger sample is to be more reliable. The net effect is that the use of a consistent estimator allows the statistician to buy greater reliability for the price of a larger sample.

The criteria do not always clearly indicate which statistic will be the most reliable estimator. Usually, the better of any two estimators that are both unbiased and consistent is the more efficient. But if the better statistic is cumbersome or theoretically difficult to apply, the second choice is generally used.

COMMONLY USED ESTIMATORS

We have seen that $\bar{X}$ is the most desirable estimator of μ, because it is unbiased, consistent, and more efficient than other estimators, including the sample median. $\bar{X}$ also has a readily obtainable *normal* sampling distribution when the sample is sufficiently large. As we will see in this chapter, knowing the sampling distribution enables us to select a large enough sample to achieve an estimate with a desired level of reliability. It also allows us to qualify the estimate that we actually obtain after the sample results have been collected and tabulated.

The sample variance s^2 is an unbiased and consistent estimator of the population variance σ^2. We can take the square root of s^2 to estimate the population standard deviation, since σ is the square root of σ^2. In the following example, the sample standard deviation is calculated as $s = 62.65$ words per page. This figure can then be used to estimate σ, the standard deviation of words per page for the entire book.

EXAMPLE: ESTIMATING THE LENGTH OF A BOOK

A publisher wishes to determine the number of words in a 600-page book. An estimate of the mean number of words per page μ is obtained by counting the number of words on each of 30 randomly selected pages. The results are shown in Table 8-1. What are the estimates of μ and the total number of words?

SOLUTION: The sample mean number of words per page is computed in Table 8-1 to be $\bar{X} = 356$. The estimate of μ is 356 words per page. This results in an estimate of

$$356 \times 600 = 213,600$$

words in the entire book.

TABLE 8-1 Estimating the Number of Words in a Book

Number of Words X	X²	Number of Words X	X²
383	146,689	175	30,625
325	105,625	278	77,284
411	168,921	351	123,201
416	173,056	423	178,929
395	156,025	327	106,929
372	138,384	381	145,161
293	85,849	317	100,489
361	130,321	362	131,044
216	46,656	338	114,244
431	185,761	411	168,921
406	164,836	371	137,641
394	155,236	393	154,449
402	161,604	388	150,544
376	141,376	295	87,025
268	71,824	421	177,241
		Totals 10,680	3,915,890

$$\bar{X} = \sum X/n = 10,680/30 = 356 \text{ words}$$

$$s = \sqrt{(\sum X^2 - n\bar{X}^2)/(n-1)} = \sqrt{(3,915,890 - 30(356)^2)/29}$$

$$= \sqrt{3,924.48} = 62.65 \text{ words}$$

The population proportion π of elementary units that have a particular attribute can be estimated by the corresponding sample proportion P. We know that $E(P) = \pi$, so that P is an unbiased estimator of π. It is also consistent.

STATISTICS AROUND US

Buying on Impulse

A consumer information service measured the tendency of the average shopper to purchase whatever she or he picks up, whether it is needed or not. Shoppers in a random sample prepared detailed shopping lists. At the store, testers followed each sample shopper and recorded each item touched. The items on the shopper's original list were compared to those purchased. The number of items bought but not on the list was added to the number of items touched but not bought. This sum represented the total number of impulse items not included in the original list.

The proportion P of impulse items bought was then found for every sample shopper. One woman accrued a total of 132 impulse items; of these, she purchased 48. Her value of P was therefore determined to be

$$P = \frac{48}{132} = .364$$

which may be taken as an estimate of the actual proportion of impulse items she would buy under similar circumstances.

The average proportion of impulse purchases was estimated to be .55. The consumer service therefore advised its clients to keep their hands on their carts and rely on their initial grocery buying decisions.

EXERCISES

8-1 For each of the following situations, indicate whether or not a sample may be selected from some population to make a current estimate. Explain.
(a) An estimate is to be made of the mean annual lifetime earnings of recent college graduates.
(b) The taste preferences of the potential buyers of a new product not currently on the market are to be determined.
(c) The responses of heart patients to a new drug, previously untried on humans, are to be measured.
(d) The Federal Power Commission wishes to estimate the kilowatt-hour usage by customers at the end of the coming decade.

8-2 A survey is taken of Trim Cuts hairstyling franchises to determine annual earnings. A random sample of $n = 10$ shops resulted in the following figures (in thousands of dollars, rounded).

15	5	2	7	25	19	11	9	13	42

(a) Find a point estimate of the mean expenditures for all shops as a group.
(b) Find a point estimate of the standard deviation of earnings for the population.
(c) Estimate the proportion of earnings in excess of $10,000.
(d) Estimate the proportion of earnings under $5,000.

8-3 For each of the following parameters, indicate whether you would use a point estimate or an interval estimate. Explain.

(a) The mean age of product buyers, to be used in comparing alternative advertising plans.

(b) The proportion of an evening's television viewing population watching a particular program, to be presented to advertisers as evidence of the program's drawing power.

(c) The mean pH value (a measure of acidity) of intermediary ingredients in a chemical process, so that a formula can be developed that indicates the amount of neutralizing agent to apply.

(d) The median income of doctors, to be published in a government report.

8-4 Tossing a die twice in succession can be viewed as taking a random sample of $n = 2$ with replacement from a population of six observable values (corresponding to the number of dots showing on each side of the die).

(a) Calculate the range of this population.

(b) We define the **sample range** to be the difference between the highest and the lowest values obtained from the two tosses. The sampling distribution of the sample range is provided in the table below. Calculate the expected value of the sample range.

(c) Compare your answers in (a) and (b). Do you conclude that the sample range is an unbiased estimator of the population range? Explain.

Possible Sample Range	Elementary Events	Probability
0	(1,1) (2,2) (3,3) (4,4) (5,5) (6,6)	6/36
1	(1,2) (2,1) (2,3) (3,2) (3,4) (4,3) (4,5) (5,4) (5,6) (6,5)	10/36
2	(1,3) (3,1) (2,4) (4,2) (3,5) (5,3) (4,6) (6,4)	8/36
3	(1,4) (4,1) (2,5) (5,2) (3,6) (6,3)	6/36
4	(1,5) (5,1) (2,6) (6,2)	4/36
5	(1,6) (6,1)	2/36
		36/36

population standard deviation

8-2 INTERVAL ESTIMATES OF THE MEAN WHEN σ IS KNOWN

Estimates of means are very important. The popular form in most statistical applications is the interval estimate because it acknowledges sampling error. The interval end points make it obvious that the sample results are imprecise. In making estimates of the mean we can put our knowledge of the normal distribution to practical use in quantifying the estimation process in terms of probability.

At the planning stage, statistical investigators can specify their precision and credibility targets before collecting actual data. The actual estimate is found in the later data analysis stage of a sampling study, after the sample results are already known. At that time, $\bar{X}$ has already been calculated and there is no uncertainty about the *sample*. (The *population* uncertainty will persist, however.) That computed mean provides the estimate of the unknown μ, becoming the *center* of the interval estimate. We now see how to establish the end points.

Let's return for now to the planning stage (before the sample results are known). The sample size is n and we assume that the value for the population *central limit therom*

standard deviation σ is known. We know that $\sigma_{\bar{X}} = \sigma/\sqrt{n}$, and the central limit theorem allows us to use the normal curve to determine probabilities for the level of $\bar{X}$. The probability is .90 that $\bar{X}$ will fall within $\pm$ 1.64 standard deviations of μ.

$$\Pr[\mu - 1.64\sigma_{\bar{X}} \le \bar{X} \le \mu + 1.64\sigma_{\bar{X}}] = .90$$

Figure 8-1 shows how the above probability incorporates the middle 90% area of the normal curve for $\bar{X}$, leaving a .05 probability area in each of the two tails. The lower tail begins at a point that is 1.64 standard deviations below μ, the other beginning the same distance above μ. When expressed in standard deviation units, the points where the tails start correspond to the **critical normal deviate** $z_{.05}$. Here, $z_{.05} = 1.64$, and we can restate the above probability expression as

$$\Pr[\mu - z_{.05}\sigma_{\bar{X}} \le \bar{X} \le \mu + z_{.05}\sigma_{\bar{X}}] = .90$$

We can transform the above inequality by rearranging the terms inside the brackets, so that we obtain

$$\Pr[\bar{X} - z_{.05}\sigma_{\bar{X}} \le \mu\mu \le \bar{X} + z_{.05}\sigma_{\bar{X}}] = .90$$

There is a .90 probability interval inside the brackets, which may be expressed as either

$$\bar{X} - z_{.05}\sigma_{\bar{X}} \le \mu \le \bar{X} + z_{.05}\sigma_{\bar{X}}$$

or as

$$\mu = \bar{X} \pm z_{.05}\sigma_{\bar{X}}$$

Similar intervals might correspond to other probability levels than .90. Letting $1 - \alpha$ (one minus lowercase Greek *alpha*) denote the designated probability, each tail will have an area $\alpha/2$. The critical normal deviate may then be expressed as $z_{\alpha/2}$. Figure 8-1 shows the case when $1 - \alpha = .90$ with $\alpha/2 = .05$.

The critical normal deviate for any specified upper tail area may be read from Appendix Table E. For instance, $z_{.025} = 1.96$ and $z_{.01} = 2.33$.

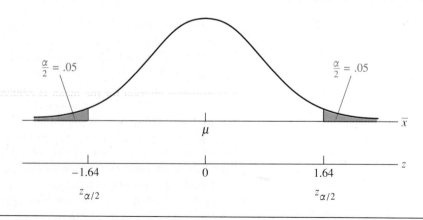

FIGURE 8-1 Illustration of critical normal deviate.

Investigators use an expression similar to the above in calculating the interval estimate.

CONFIDENCE AND MEANING OF THE INTERVAL ESTIMATE

Estimates can be made only *after* the sample data have been collected. At that time it is too late to express a probability that the sample will place μ inside $\bar{X} \pm z_{\alpha/2}\sigma_{\bar{X}}$. The sample mean is then a calculated and known quantity, and it may or may not be close enough to μ. (And, you will ordinarily never know if it is.)

Statisticians use a related concept when expressing their less than perfect certainty regarding the still unknown μ. This is the **confidence level** for which we make the following

DEFINITION: The **confidence level** is the percentage of interval estimates—obtained from many repeated samples, each of size n, from the same population—that will contain the actual value of the parameter being estimated. Although a single sample is ordinarily selected from the population, the confidence level is expressed as a percentage.

For any specified decimal α, the confidence level percentage may be determined from

$$\text{Confidence level} = 100(1 - \alpha)\%$$

And, for the confidence level percentage, the decimal α may be determined from

$$\alpha = 1 - (\text{confidence level } \%)/100\%$$

Figure 8-2 illustrates the concepts underlying the confidence level. A sampling investigation yielding an interval estimate of the mean with 90% confidence can be expected to be correct only 90% of the time. In 100 repetitions of the sampling procedure, about 90 of the constructed intervals, each centered on the computed $\bar{X}$, will contain μ. About 10 will be untrue—the entire interval lying above or below μ. Usually only one sample of n observations is taken, and the *statistician never knows whether the reported interval is true*. This situation can be improved either by raising the confidence level (using a bigger $z_{\alpha/2}$), which reduces the precision, or by increasing the sample size.

The interval estimate is referred to as a **confidence interval**. The level of confidence determines the value of $z_{\alpha/2}$ to be used, with greater confidence resulting in wider confidence intervals.

CONSTRUCTING THE CONFIDENCE INTERVAL

A confidence interval for the mean is centered on the computed value of $\bar{X}$. The following expression is used to calculate the $100(1 - \alpha)\%$

CONFIDENCE INTERVAL ESTIMATE OF THE MEAN WHEN σ IS KNOWN

$$\mu = \bar{X} \pm z_{\alpha/2}\sigma_{\bar{X}} \quad \text{or} \quad \bar{X} - z_{\alpha/2}\sigma_{\bar{X}} \leq \mu \leq \bar{X} + z_{\alpha/2}\sigma_{\bar{X}}$$

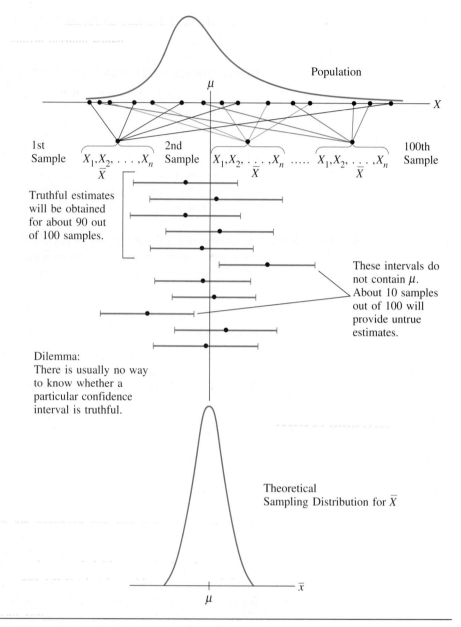

Population

μ

X

1st
Sample $X_1, X_2, \ldots, X_n$ 2nd Sample $X_1, X_2, \ldots, X_n$ ..... $X_1, X_2, \ldots, X_n$ 100th Sample
$\overline{X}$ $\overline{X}$ $\overline{X}$

Truthful estimates
will be obtained
for about 90 out
of 100 samples.

These intervals do
not contain μ.
About 10 samples
out of 100 will
provide untrue
estimates.

Dilemma:
There is usually no way
to know whether a
particular confidence
interval is truthful.

Theoretical
Sampling Distribution for $\overline{X}$

μ $\overline{x}$

FIGURE 8-2 Illustration of the confidence interval concept.

where the standard error of $\overline{X}$ is

$$\sigma_{\overline{X}} = \frac{\sigma}{\sqrt{n}}$$

and σ must be specified in advance.*

*When the sample size n is large in relation to the population size N, the finite population correction factor should be used to calculate the standard error.

$$\sigma_{\overline{X}} = \frac{\sigma}{\sqrt{n}} \sqrt{\frac{N-n}{N-1}}$$

ILLUSTRATION: FAMILY INCOMES

To illustrate how a confidence interval estimate is obtained, we will assume that a sample of $n = 100$ families is selected from the population of a large city and that the sample mean income is $\bar{X} = \$15,549.63$. We have *prior knowledge* that the standard deviation of the population of family incomes is $\sigma = \$5,000$. We wish to determine a 99% confidence interval estimate of the true population mean μ.

Using $\alpha = 1 - .99 = .01$, from Appendix Table E the required normal deviate is $z_{\alpha/2} = z_{.005} = 2.57$. The standard error of $\bar{X}$ is

$$\sigma_{\bar{X}} = \frac{\$5,000}{\sqrt{100}} = \$500$$

and the 99% confidence interval estimate is

$$\mu = \bar{X} \pm z_{\alpha/2}\sigma_{\bar{X}} = \$15,549.63 \pm 2.57(\$500)$$
$$= \$15,549.63 \pm \$1,285.00$$

and

$$\$14,264.63 \leq \mu \leq \$16,834.63$$

We *cannot* say there is a .99 probability that the stated interval contains μ. (It either does or does not, but we do not know which case applies.) For the above 99% confidence interval we give the following proper

INTERPRETATION: If we repeated the same procedure often, each time selecting a different sample of 100 families from the same population, then 99 out of every 100 similar intervals we obtained would, on the average, contain μ.

FEATURES DESIRED IN A CONFIDENCE INTERVAL

Although both credibility and precision are desirable features in a confidence interval estimate, they are competing goals. For a fixed sample size, a reduction in the interval width, which causes greater precision, can be achieved only at the expense of reducing z, which lowers the confidence level. Conversely, greater confidence can be obtained only at the expense of precision. Thus, a confidence interval may be very precise but not at all credible, or vice versa. For example, if $z_{\alpha/2}$ is .5 in estimating the mean family income, then the confidence interval would be

$$\mu = \$15,549.63 \pm .5(500) = \$15,549.63 \pm 250$$

or

$$\$15,299.63 \leq \mu \leq \$15,799.63$$

which is more precise than before, but the confidence level would be only 38%. Likewise, increasing the confidence level to 99.8%, so that $\alpha = 1 - .998 = .002$ and $z_{.001} = 3.08$, would yield the less precise interval estimate

$$\mu = \$15,549.63 \pm 3.08(500) = \$15,549.63 \pm \$1,540$$

or

$$\$14,009.63 \leq \mu \leq \$17,089.63$$

The only way to increase both confidence and precision is to collect a larger sample at the start. For example, suppose that $n = 1,000$ families are selected and that the *same* sample mean is calculated. The standard error of $\bar{X}$ would then be

$$\sigma_{\bar{X}} = \frac{\$5,000}{\sqrt{1,000}} = \$158.11$$

and the 99.8% confidence interval would be

$$\mu = \$15,549.63 \pm 3.08(\$158.11) = \$15,549.63 \pm \$486.98$$

or

$$\$15,062.65 \le \mu \le \$16,036.61$$

This is a *more precise* interval with a *greater confidence level* than the one originally obtained.

But the larger sample might not be the best to use. The cost of collecting the data must be weighed against the value of the information thereby obtained. More will be said about this later in the chapter.

COMPUTER-GENERATED CONFIDENCE INTERVALS

A confidence interval estimate may be constructed with computer assistance. Although, once the hardest job (calculating the sample mean $\bar{X}$) has been done, there is little advantage to using a computer. Some software packages will supply the confidence interval endpoints immediately on request.

To illustrate, suppose that a random sample of student car owners is selected, and the following annual insurance premiums are reported.

$520 $725 $615 $435 $266 $498

The population standard deviation is assumed to be $\sigma = \$100$. Figure 8-3 shows the computer printout obtained from a computer run using the above data.

The computed value of the sample mean is $\bar{X} = \$508.20$. Although it is not used in constructing the confidence interval, the printout provides the *sample* standard deviation of $s = \$153.90$. This should not be confused with the given value of $\sigma = \$100$ for the *population* standard deviation. (Although s is *expected* to be equal to σ, an actual sample result will ordinarily differ, perhaps considerably so, from the expected level.) Figure 8-3 also reports $\sigma_{\bar{X}} = 40.8$, which is computed by dividing σ (not s) by the square root of the sample size. The end points of the 95% confidence interval are ($428.0, $588.3), or

$$\$428.00 \le \mu \le \$588.30$$

(If you are computing by hand, your results may differ slightly from the ones above due to rounding.)

EXERCISES

8-5 The Kryptonite Corporation personnel director wishes to estimate the mean scores for a proposed aptitude test that may be used in screening applicants for clerical positions. The population standard deviation is assumed to be

```
MTB > retrieve 'Shelf'
MTB > AOVOneway c1-c4.
```

```
ANALYSIS OF VARIANCE
SOURCE      DF        SS        MS        F        p
FACTOR       3     412.63    137.54    19.07    0.000
ERROR       26     187.53      7.21
TOTAL       29     600.17
```

```
                                    INDIVIDUAL 95 PCT CI'S FOR MEAN
                                    BASED ON POOLED STDEV
 LEVEL        N     MEAN      STDEV  ---+---------+---------+---------+---
Two-Foot      5    15.200     3.033                 (-----*-----)
Four-Ft.      7     9.143     2.193    (----*----)
Split        10    13.000     2.625            (----*---)
Corner        8    19.375     2.925                             (---*----)
                                    ---+---------+---------+---------+---
POOLED STDEV =     2.686           8.0      12.0      16.0      20.0
```

Note: Figure generated on an IBM PC using Minitab®.

FIGURE 8-3 Computer printout of the confidence interval for sample insurance premiums.

$\sigma = 15$. For a sample of $n = 100$ applicants, the sample mean score is $\bar{X} = 75.6$. Construct a 95% confidence interval estimate of the true mean.

8-6 A random sample of 100 package weights is selected. The population standard deviation is assumed to be .5 ounces. The sample mean is $\bar{X} = 15.9$ ounces. Construct a 95% <u>confidence interval estimate</u> of the mean weight for the items in the entire population.

8-7 The production superintendent for a pharmaceutical manufacturer knows from past history that a particular capsule is produced with varying mean impurity levels, depending on how well the control mechanism performs. The variability in capsule impurities remains nearly constant, so that, regardless of μ, the standard deviation is assumed to be $\sigma = 2.5$ parts per million (ppm). Construct a 95% confidence interval estimate of the true population mean impurity level for the following sample results.
(a) $n = 100$; $\bar{X} = 125.6$ ppm   (c) $n = 200$; $\bar{X} = 148.9$ ppm
(b) $n = 25$; $\bar{X} = 153.4$ ppm   (d) $n = 500$; $\bar{X} = 206.4$ ppm

8-8 The VBM board of directors is evaluating the performance of the corporation president in order to decide whether to retain him. One director proposes that each director rate the president—on a scale from 1 to 5—as to the quality of his performance in five areas: (1) sales growth, (2) personnel relations, (3) operating efficiencies achieved, (4) attainment of profit potential, and (5) successful new-product development. The ratings will be summarized in terms of frequency distributions, with the mean rating calculated for each category and submitted to the directors at the next meeting, when a vote on retention will take place. The board agrees to the procedure.

The chairman is concerned with the average ratings. He is worried about their precision and wonders what level of confidence should be attached to the results. A trustee who happens to be an expert in statistics diplomatically informs the chairman that these considerations are irrelevant. Explain the basis for the expert's stand.

8-9 A CPA auditing trainee wishes to estimate the errors in accounts payable vouchers. The errors are assumed to have a standard deviation of $2. In the following cases, suppose that the sample mean error is $10.

(a) For a sample of size $n = 100$, construct interval estimates of the true mean error level when the confidence level is (1) 90%, (2) 95%, (3) 99%, (4) 99.9%.

(b) Construct 95% confidence interval estimates when the sample size is (1) $n = 10$, (2) $n = 25$, (3) $n = 150$, and (4) $n = 500$.

8-10 *Computer exercise.* The following price/earnings ratios have been obtained for a sample of NYSE stocks selected on a particular day.

| 15.3 | 9.7 | 12.4 | 23.0 | 62.3 | 9.5 | 5.3 | 8.6 | 29.7 | 43.4 |

Assume that $\sigma = 10$. Construct a 90% confidence interval estimate of the mean price/earnings ratio.

8-11 *Computer exercise.* The following annual inventory turnovers have been obtained for a sample of retail gift stores.

| 2.7 | 5.8 | 6.4 | 1.9 | 3.8 | 3.6 | 4.3 | 4.5 |

Assume that $\sigma = .50$. Construct a 95% confidence interval estimate of the mean annual inventory turnover for the population.

8-3 INTERVAL ESTIMATES OF THE MEAN WHEN σ IS UNKNOWN

In Section 8-2, we constructed confidence interval estimates of the mean when the population standard deviation σ is *known*. But often when μ is unknown, the level of σ may not be known either. In those cases, σ must be estimated with μ. The sample standard deviation s is used for that purpose.

The normal distribution is theoretically *not* correct for making inferences about μ when σ is also unknown. This presents a statistical dilemma and creates the need for a new sampling distribution.

THE STUDENT t DISTRIBUTION

W. S. Gosset first studied this dilemma in the early 1900s. Because his employer, a brewery, forbade him to publish, he chose the nom de plume "Student." Gosset derived a probability distribution, now referred to as the Student t distribution, for a random variable t. Whenever the population being sampled is normally distributed,

$$t = \frac{\bar{X} - \mu}{s/\sqrt{n}}$$

In practice, however, the t distribution may be used when samples are taken from any population that is not highly skewed.

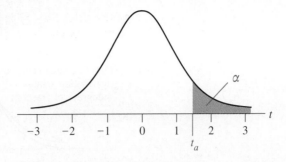

FIGURE 8-4 The Student t distribution.

Like the normal distribution, the Student t distribution has a relative frequency curve that is bell-shaped and symmetrical, as shown in Figure 8-4. The single parameter that determines the shape of its curve is called the *number of degrees of freedom*, which is $n - 1$ (because for a fixed value of $\bar{X}$, there are only $n - 1$ "free choices" for the values of the n observations used to calculate $\bar{X}$ and s).

To determine the probability that t exceeds some value, we must consult the table of areas under the Student t distribution in Appendix Table F. There is a separate distribution—and therefore a separate set of values—for each number of degrees of freedom; these appear in separate rows in the table. It is traditional to use α to represent the upper tail area. The values in the body of the table are the points t_α corresponding to the respective upper tail area α (column) and degrees of freedom (row). To find the point that corresponds to a given upper tail area t_α, so that

$$\Pr[t \geq t_\alpha] = \alpha$$

we read down the column headed by the probability value α, stop at the row corresponding to the number of degrees of freedom, and read the desired t_α value. (Like the normal curve table, there is no need to list separate entries for the left-hand portion of the t curve.) A partial reproduction of Appendix Table F will be helpful.

Degrees of Freedom	Upper Tail Area α									
	.4	.25	.1	.05	.025	.01	.005	.0025	.001	.0005
1	0.325	1.000	3.078	6.314	12.706	31.821	63.657	127.32	318.31	636.62
2	.289	.816	1.886	2.920	4.303	6.965	9.925	14.089	22.327	31.598
3	.277	.765	1.638	2.353	3.182	4.541	5.841	7.453	10.214	12.924
4	.271	.741	1.533	2.132	2.776	3.747	4.604	5.598	7.173	8.610
5	0.267	0.727	1.476	2.015	2.571	3.365	4.032	4.773	5.893	6.869
6	.265	.718	1.440	1.943	2.447	3.143	3.707	4.317	5.208	5.959
7	.263	.711	1.415	1.895	2.365	2.998	3.499	4.029	4.785	5.408
8	.262	.706	1.397	1.860	2.306	2.896	3.355	3.833	4.501	5.041
9	.261	.703	1.383	1.833	2.262	2.821	3.250	3.690	4.297	4.781
10	0.260	0.700	1.372	1.812	2.228	2.764	3.169	3.581	4.144	4.587
11	.260	.697	1.363	1.796	2.201	2.718	3.106	3.497	4.025	4.437
12	.259	.695	1.356	1.782	2.179	2.681	3.055	3.428	3.930	4.318

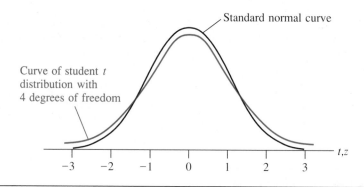

FIGURE 8-5 A comparison of the relative frequency curves for the standard normal distribution and the Student t distribution.

For example, suppose that we wish to find $t_{.01}$ (the value for which the probability is .01 that t is greater than or equal to that value) and that the number of degrees of freedom is 20. From Appendix Table F, $t_{.01} = 2.528$. So

$$\Pr[t \geq 2.528] = .01$$

Figure 8-5 shows the standard normal curve and the t distribution curve when the number of degrees of freedom is 4. Note that the normal curve falls below the t curve for values lying in the tails. This reflects the fact that the t distribution assigns higher probabilities to outcomes of extreme value than the normal distribution does, due to the extra element of uncertainty arising from the unknown value of σ.

A theoretical requirement of the Student t distribution is that the *population* itself be normally distributed. (It is ordinarily acceptable, however, to still employ the Student t as long as the underlying population is unimodal and not highly skewed.) The normal curve comes into play in another more practical way. *For large sample sizes, the Student t distribution tends to coincide with the standard normal distribution.*

CONSTRUCTING THE CONFIDENCE INTERVAL

A confidence interval falls on two sides of the sample mean, which is the center. Thus, two tails are excluded, each of area $\alpha/2$, and the matching critical value $t_{\alpha/2}$ is used in constructing the $100(1 - \alpha)\%$

CONFIDENCE INTERVAL ESTIMATE OF THE MEAN WHEN σ IS UNKNOWN

$$\mu = \bar{X} \pm t_{\alpha/2}\frac{s}{\sqrt{n}} \quad \text{or} \quad \bar{X} - t_{\alpha/2}\frac{s}{\sqrt{n}} \leq \mu \leq \bar{X} + t_{\alpha/2}\frac{s}{\sqrt{n}}$$

To illustrate, we construct a 90% confidence interval estimate of μ, using $\alpha = 1 - .90 = .10$ and $t_{\alpha/2} = t_{.05}$. The results obtained from a survey having

$n = 25$ observations provide $\bar{X} = 10.0$ and $s = 5.0$. The degrees of freedom is $n - 1 = 24$, and, from Appendix Table F, $t_{.05} = 1.711$. The 90% confidence interval estimate of μ is

$$\mu = \bar{X} \pm t_{.05}\frac{s}{\sqrt{n}} = 10 \pm 1.711\frac{5.0}{\sqrt{25}}$$

$$= 10 \pm 1.7$$

so that

$$8.3 \leq \mu \leq 11.7$$

EXAMPLE: ESTIMATING MEAN LOST PRODUCTION TIME

The production manager of Black and Becker is concerned that too little attention has been paid to the cost of labor lost due to stamping machine breakdowns. In the one year in which the plant has been in operation, the stamping machine has failed nine times. Table 8-2 shows the direct labor hours lost for each breakdown. An estimate of the mean number of labor hours lost per breakdown is to be obtained. This estimate may then be multiplied by the expected number of breakdowns per year to obtain an estimate of the hours that will be lost annually in the future.

The production manager desires a 95% confidence interval to estimate μ, the mean labor hours lost.

TABLE 8-2 Labor Hours Lost Due to Stamping Machine Breakdowns

Labor Hours Lost	
X	**X²**
205	42,025
1,123	1,261,129
528	278,784
359	128,881
1,421	2,019,241
723	522,729
57	3,249
172	29,584
25	625
Totals 4,613	4,286,247

$\bar{X} = \sum X/n = 4{,}613/9 = 512.56$ hours

$s = \sqrt{(\sum X^2 - n\bar{X}^2)/(n - 1)} = \sqrt{(4{,}286{,}247 - 9(512.56)^2)/8}$

$= 490.1$ hours

SOLUTION: The number of degrees of freedom is $9 - 1 = 8$. Using $\alpha = 1 - .95 = .05$, Appendix Table F provides $t_{\alpha/2} = t_{.025} = 2.306$. The following confidence interval is obtained:

$$512.56 - 2.306(490.1)/\sqrt{9} \leq \mu \leq 512.56 + 2.306(490.1)/\sqrt{9}$$

so that

$$\mu = 512.56 \pm 376.72$$

and

$$135.84 \le \mu \le 889.28 \text{ hours}$$

Notice that the confidence interval is quite wide, which is expected with a large sample standard deviation and a small sample size.

COMPUTER-GENERATED CONFIDENCE INTERVALS

As with the estimates in Section 8-2, a computer may be used to construct confidence intervals. Figure 8-6 shows the printout obtained from a computer run using the above data. Except for rounding, exactly the same results have been obtained as before when computing by hand.

CONFIDENCE INTERVALS WHEN *n* IS LARGE

The Student *t* distribution applies for $(\bar{X} - \mu)/(s/\sqrt{n})$ when σ is unknown—regardless of the sample size—for most populations encountered in business applications. When constructing intervals by hand, there are some special difficulties that arise from tabular limitations. Appendix Table F leaves gaps. It jumps from 30 degrees of freedom to 40, then from 40 degrees of freedom to 60, and finally from 60 degrees of freedom to 120. There is one row for each, with the last row in the table corresponding to an infinite number for the degrees of freedom.

When constructing confidence intervals, the gaps can be filled by using *linear interpolation* to approximate the missing critical values. But, for simplicity, this book uses the nearest tabled entry when Appendix Table F does not list values for a particular number of degrees of freedom. Thus, we use the entry in row 30 when the degrees of freedom are 31, 32, 33, or 34, and the entry in row 40 when the degrees of freedom are 36, 37, 38, or 39. If the number of degrees of freedom is exactly in the middle (e.g., 35), the entries in the neighboring rows are averaged. When the number of degrees of freedom exceeds 120, use the *t* from the

```
MTB > set c1
      205,1123,528,359,1421,723,57,172,25
MTB > end
MTB > name c1 'Turnover'
MTB > tinterval 95 percent c1
```

	N	MEAN	STDEV	SE MEAN	95.0 PERCENT C.I.
turnover	6	512.556	490.131	163.377	(135.705, 889.406)

Note: Figure generated on an IBM PC using Minitab®.

FIGURE 8-6 Computer printout of the confidence interval for the sample data in Table 8-2.

∞ row. (You may find slight differences between computer results and hand constructions, since computers obtain more accurate critical values of t.)

If n is large enough to generate degrees of freedom greater than 120, the $t_{\alpha/2}$ values in Appendix Table F are identical to the $z_{\alpha/2}$ critical normal deviates in Appendix Table E. This reflects the property that in the limiting case the Student t and standard normal curves coincide. For this reason, t and z are interchangeable when n is large.

EXAMPLE: ESTIMATING MEAN BILL PAYMENT TIMES

The Million Bank operates a credit card system and wishes to establish policy for mailing customer bills. The time of month must be identified that provides the shortest average time to receipt of cash payment. Three samples of customers are randomly selected, one group to be billed on the 5th of the month, another on the 15th, and the final group on the 25th. In order to avoid any bias due to the transition in billing cycle, figures from the fourth month under the new dates constitute the samples. A total of $n = 500$ customers are selected for each sample group. The following results are obtained.

5th of Month	15th of Month	25th of Month
$\bar{X} = 18.30$ days	$\bar{X} = 17.41$ days	$\bar{X} = 5.42$ days
$s = 6.2$	$s = 5.8$	$s = 2.3$

Interval estimates are to be found using a 99% level of confidence.

SOLUTION: First, find α:

$$\alpha = 1 - (99\%)/(100\%)$$
$$= 1 - .99 = .01$$
$$\alpha/2 = .005$$

Since the number of degrees of freedom exceeds 120, the critical value from the ∞ row of Appendix Table F is used. This value is $t_{.005} = 2.576$.

For the 5th of the month, the confidence interval is

$$18.30 - \frac{2.576(6.2)}{\sqrt{500}} \le \mu \le 18.30 + \frac{2.576(6.2)}{\sqrt{500}}$$

or

$$\mu = 18.30 \pm .71$$

so that

$$17.59 \le \mu \le 19.01 \text{ days} \qquad \text{(for 5th)}$$

Analogously, the following confidence intervals have been obtained for the other groups.

$$\mu = 17.41 \pm .67 \quad \text{or} \quad 16.74 \le \mu \le 18.08 \text{ days} \qquad \text{(for 15th)}$$

$$\mu = 5.42 \pm .26 \quad \text{or} \quad 5.16 \le \mu \le 5.68 \text{ days} \qquad \text{(for 25th)}$$

Note that there is so little difference between the results for the 5th and 15th that the confidence intervals overlap. Of the three times of the month, the 25th appears to be the superior billing time. By switching its billing cycle, so that bills are mailed on the 25th instead of at the end of the month, the bank *might* (remember, *we do not know* μ) be able to reduce the average collection time from its present 10 days to some value between 5.17 and 5.68 days, thereby allowing the firm to have longer use of the funds received.

EXERCISES

8-12 Determine the value t_α that corresponds to the following upper tail areas of the Student t distribution.

	(a)	(b)	(c)	(d)	(e)
α	.05	.01	.025	.01	.005
Degrees of freedom	10	13	21	120	30

8-13 Construct 95% confidence interval estimates of the means of populations yielding the following sample results.
(a) $n = 6$; $\bar{X} = \$8.00$; $s = \$2.50$
(b) $n = 15$; $\bar{X} = 15.03$ minutes; $s = .52$ minutes
(c) $n = 25$; $\bar{X} = 27.30$ pounds; $s = 2.56$ pounds

8-14 Construct 99% confidence intervals for (a), (b), and (c) in Exercise 8-13.

8-15 Shirley Smart measures the heights of 35 men in her statistics class. She assumes that the data represent a random sample of all male students in her state. From the data, she calculates $\bar{X} = 70.2''$ and $s = 2.44''$. Construct a 95% confidence interval estimate of the population mean height.

8-16 Rock of Gibraltar Insurance Company is revising its rate schedules. A staff actuary wishes to estimate the average size of claims resulting from fire damage in apartment complexes with between 10 and 20 units. The current year's claim settlements are to be used as a sample. Considering the 19 claim settlements for buildings in this category, the average claim size was $73,249, with a standard deviation of $37,246. Construct a 90% confidence interval estimate of the mean claim size.

8-17 The manager of the Nogales Ritz desires to improve the level of room service by increasing personnel. To justify the increase, she must estimate the mean waiting time experienced by guests before being served. From a random sample of $n = 100$ orders, the sample mean waiting time was established at 30.3 minutes, with a standard deviation of 8.2 minutes. Construct a 99% confidence interval that the manager can use to estimate the actual mean waiting time.

8-18 The Wear-Ever Corporation tested the tread life of a sample of $n = 50$ radial tires. The sample results yielded $\bar{X} = 52,346$ miles and $s = 2,911$ miles.
(a) Construct a 99% confidence interval estimate of the mean tread life.
(b) What is the interpretation of the interval constructed in (a)?

8-19 A hospital administrator intends to improve the level of emergency room service by increasing support personnel. To justify the increase, he must estimate the mean time that patients must wait before being attended to by a physician. For a random sample of $n = 100$ previously recorded emergencies, the sample mean waiting time was 70.3 minutes, with a standard deviation of 28.2 minutes. Construct a 99% confidence interval that the administrator can use to estimate the actual mean waiting time.

8-20 DanDee Assemblers currently trains its chassis assemblers on the job. It has been proposed that new employees be given one week of formal training. To test the quality of the training program, the output rate of ten trainees (Group A) was compared to that of ten new employees receiving on-the-job training (Group B). Each trainee from Group A was matched with one from Group B, based on aptitude test scores. After training, each person was given a specific number of chassis to wire, and the completion time was recorded. For each of the $n = 10$ pairs of assemblers, the time of the trainee from Group A was subtracted from that of the matching trainee from Group B. The sample results yielded $\bar{X} = 3$ minutes and $s = 2$ minutes.

(a) Construct a 95% confidence interval estimate of the mean time difference.

(b) If there is no difference between the two training methods and if the population standard deviation is $\sigma = 2$, use the normal distribution to determine the probability that the sample mean will be 3 or more.

8-21 *Computer exercise.* The following weights (in pounds) have been obtained for a random sample of Dogpatch men.

183	203	148
146	192	159
157	176	165

(a) Compute the sample mean and standard deviation.

(b) Construct a 95% confidence interval estimate of the population mean weight.

8-22 *Computer exercise.* Lily Gilding Company will estimate the mean amount of gold consumed per batch in a plating operation. The following quantities (in ounces) have been obtained for a random sample of 15 batches.

.25	.18	.24	.19	.20
.23	.27	.21	.23	.21
.19	.22	.20	.25	.25

(a) Compute the sample mean and standard deviation.

(b) Construct a 95% confidence interval estimate of the mean gold consumption.

8-23 *Computer exercise.* The Block-Nock tax preparation service provided the following data for the amount of time (in minutes) taken to complete client interviews.

8	12	26	10	23	21
16	22	18	17	36	9

You may assume these data are a representative sample of all client interview times.

(a) Compute the sample mean and standard deviation.

(b) Construct a 99% confidence interval estimate of the population mean interview time.

8-4 INTERVAL ESTIMATES OF THE POPULATION PROPORTION

We can estimate the population proportion π by an interval, using the sample proportion P, in much the same way that we can estimate μ, using $\bar{X}$. To estimate π, we take advantage of the normal approximation to the binomial sampling distribution of P (which we learned in Chapter 7 is allowable only for certain sample sizes).

We will use P to estimate π by an interval in the form

$$P - z_{\alpha/2}\sigma_P \leq \pi \leq P + z_{\alpha/2}\sigma_P$$

Again, we do not know the value of σ_P, because it depends on π—the value we are estimating. So we must determine the value of σ_P from the sample results. We therefore replace π with P in

$$\sigma_P = \sqrt{\frac{\pi(1 - \pi)}{n}}$$

to obtain the point estimate

$$\sqrt{\frac{P(1 - P)}{n}}$$

We can then use this substitution in expressing the $100(1 - \alpha)\%$

CONFIDENCE INTERVAL ESTIMATE OF THE POPULATION PROPORTION

$$\pi = P \pm z_{\alpha/2}\sqrt{\frac{P(1 - P)}{n}}$$

or

$$P - z_{\alpha/2}\sqrt{\frac{P(1 - P)}{n}} \leq \pi \leq P + z_{\alpha/2}\sqrt{\frac{P(1 - P)}{n}}$$

EXAMPLE: PREFERENCE FOR CANNED CORN

To estimate the proportion of buyers who preferred the quality of their canned corn, Yellow Giant researchers randomly selected a panel of $n = 100$ persons. Each panelist was given three cans of brand X and three cans of brand Y, with the labels removed. The testers were asked to rate each can of corn on the basis of four factors: tenderness, sweetness, consistency, and color. The brand receiving the highest aggregate score by a tester was the preferred one. The following test results were obtained.

Number preferring brand X:	59
Number preferring brand Y:	37
Number of ties:	4
Total	100

A 99% confidence interval is desired in estimating π, the proportion of the buying population preferring brand X.

SOLUTION: The critical normal deviate when $\alpha = 1 - .99 = .01$ obtained from Appendix Table E is $z_{\alpha/2} = z_{.005} = 2.57$. The sample proportion of buyers preferring brand X is $P = 59/100 = .59$. The 99% confidence interval is

$$\pi = .59 \pm 2.57 \sqrt{\frac{.59(1 - .59)}{100}}$$

$$\pi = .59 \pm 0.13$$

so that

$$.46 \leq \pi \leq .72$$

EXERCISES

8-24 Construct a 95% confidence interval for the proportion of defective items in large shipments yielding the following sample results.
(a) $n = 1,000$; $P = .2$ (b) $n = 2,000$; $P = .04$ (c) $n = 500$; $P = .01$

8-25 In a poll taken to estimate the president's current popularity, each person in a random sample of $n = 1,000$ voters was asked to agree with one of the following statements.

"The president is doing a good job."
"The president is doing a poor job."
"I have no opinion."

A proportion of .59 chose the first statement. Assuming that the actual number of voters is quite large, construct a 95% confidence interval for the population proportion of voters who will choose the first statement.

8-26 The Eureka Lumber Mill cuts redwood logs removed from a very large reforested area into boards of specified dimensions. The individual pieces of board are then sorted by grade. The proportion of boards that are of a high enough quality to be merchandised is to be estimated. A sample of 100 boards from various logs is taken for this purpose.
(a) Suppose that the sample proportion of quality grade boards is .5. Construct a 99% confidence interval estimate of the proportion of all lumber that will be cut and placed in this category.
(b) Suppose that the sample proportion of quality grade boards is .4. Construct a 95% confidence interval estimate of the proportion of all lumber that will be cut and placed in this category.

8-27 The highway patrol director in a certain state has ordered a crackdown on drunk drivers. To see if this safety campaign is working, the director has

ordered a sampling study to estimate the proportion of all fatal traffic accidents caused by drinking. In a random sample of $n = 100$ accidents, 42%
were attributed to alcohol. Assuming that the accident population is large,
construct a 95% confidence interval for the population proportion.

8-28 The Skinny Tinny Company adjusts the settings of a sheet metal roller
whenever the proportion π of overthick sheets is .015 or greater. The true
level of π is unknown but is periodically estimated from samples of 100
sheets.
(a) In one sample there were 4 overthick sheets. Construct the corresponding 95% confidence interval estimate of π.
(b) Using the normal approximation, determine the probability for getting
as many or more thick sheets as in (a) when the true level of π is .01.

8-29 A printer has negotiated a contract with Centralia Bell to print directories.
Because disgruntled customers whose names are misspelled or listed with
the number of, say, a local mortuary will complain bitterly for a whole year,
the telephone company is anxious to minimize directory errors. Its contract
therefore states that the printer must forfeit $100 for every page that con-
tains errors introduced in the printing process.

Counting the errors in a completed directory is an onerous chore. The
majority are found by customer complaint, and most of these turn out not
to be the printer's fault. Thus, a sample will be taken to determine what
penalty fee to charge the printer. It is so difficult to find errors that many
persons must search for them independently. A company accountant selects
a sample of 50 pages from a 600-page directory and asks 20 people in succession to review each page for errors. An estimate is to be made of the
proportion π of pages that contain errors.
(a) Construct a 99.8% confidence interval estimate of π if $P = .37$.
(b) The contract specifies that the estimate of π must be a point estimate.
What are the losses to the printer if the estimate is too large by .02?
(c) Determine the probability that the estimator P will be .37 or over if the
actual error rate is only $\pi = .35$.

8-5 CHOOSING THE SAMPLE SIZE AND
SELECTING THE ESTIMATOR

In this section we consider two important issues in statistical planning. We begin
by considering the choice of sample size, which can be viewed as an economic
consideration. The n actually used might be dictated by funding or other outside
circumstances. But we will see that it can be selected in order to meet reliability
and error targets. A related issue is the choice of estimator. As we shall see, sometimes we have a choice whether to estimate a mean quantity using a sample mean
or using a sample proportion.

ERROR AND RELIABILITY

Costs are usually incurred when an estimate is erroneous. In many statistical
applications, it is quite difficult to place a monetary value on the results of an

incorrect estimate. Ideally, a sample size should be chosen that achieves the most desirable balance between the chances of making errors, the costs of those errors, and the costs of sampling. Figure 8-7 illustrates the concepts involved in finding the optimal sample size, which minimizes the total cost of sampling. The costs of collecting the sample data increase with n. But larger samples are more reliable, so that the losses from chance sampling error decline. The total cost of sampling—the sum of collection costs and error costs—will achieve a minimum value for some optimal n. This is the sample size that should be used.

Due to the difficulties associated with finding the costs of sampling error, the procedure illustrated in Figure 8-7 is not usually used. Instead, we focus on a number that separates insignificant errors from decidedly undesirable ones. This

STATISTICS AROUND US

Airlines Sharing Ticket Revenues

Lake Airlines is a small regional carrier feeding the larger airlines. Passengers purchasing a ticket for a cross-country trip are issued a single ticket for the entire journey at the point of embarkation. Lake is entitled to keep only its portion of the revenue and must forfeit shares to the other airlines involved. The reverse occurs for passengers originating with other airlines who use Lake for a single leg. In these cases, Lake must collect its share of the ticket revenue from the other airline. At the end of each month, the airlines balance their accounts based on a detailed enumeration of the inter-airline tickets collected. This has proved to be a very costly and time consuming process.

A consulting statistician has suggested that the airlines balance their accounts by means of random samples of collected tickets, arguing that only a small portion of the tickets must then be analyzed. There would be a certain amount of risk, however, for the samples obtained could provide erroneous figures.

Using a sample has drawbacks. Because of chance sampling error, Lake's claims against other airlines will be understated in some months and overstated in others. Viewing the long-run average or expected revenue losses as the cost of sampling error, the statistician has computed (by a procedure too detailed to discuss here) the costs for various sample sizes.

Sample Size n	Cost of Collecting Sample	Sampling Error Costs	Total Cost of Sampling
100	$ 100	$40,222	$40,322
1,000	1,000	13,059	14,059
5,000	5,000	5,666	10,666
5,200	5,200	5,454	10,654
6,000	6,000	5,202	11,202
10,000	10,000	4,028	14,028

Assuming that each sample ticket processed costs Lake $1, the costs of sampling have also been calculated. The sample size yielding the minimum cost to Lake is about $n = 5,200$.

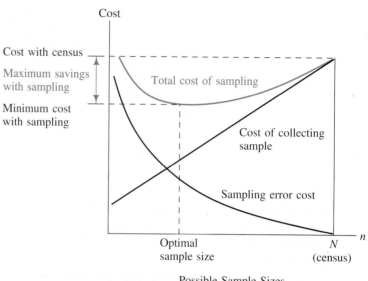

FIGURE 8-7 Relationships among sampling costs.

is called the **tolerable error level**. Accepting some error is the price we pay for using a sample instead of a census.

We denote the tolerable error—the maximum amount the estimate should extend above or below the parameter—by e, which is a number in the same units as the parameter being estimated. As applied in traditional statistics, we define an estimate's reliability in terms of e.

DEFINITION: The **reliability** associated with using $\overline{X}$ to estimate μ is the probability that $\overline{X}$ differs from μ by no more than the tolerable error level e, or

$$\text{Reliability} = \Pr[\mu - e \le \overline{X} \le \mu + e]$$

Figure 8-8 illustrates the relationships among reliability, tolerable error, and the sampling distribution of $\overline{X}$ when reliability is .95. The shaded area provides the probability that $\overline{X}$ will lie within $\mu \pm e$.

For a fixed e, only one normal curve has a shape that provides the desired area. If the reliability is lowered to .80, another curve, shown in Figure 8-9, applies. Note that compared with the curve in Figure 8-8, this second curve is flatter and exhibits more variability, so that it must have a larger value of $\sigma_{\overline{X}}$.

Thus, for any specified tolerable error and corresponding reliability, there is a unique level of $\sigma_{\overline{X}}$. Since $\sigma_{\overline{X}} = \sigma/\sqrt{n}$ and σ is *a fixed value*, only the sample size n can be adjusted to achieve the required level of $\sigma_{\overline{X}}$. This means that a given e and reliability require a unique value of n.

STEPS FOR FINDING THE REQUIRED SAMPLE SIZE TO ESTIMATE THE MEAN

To illustrate how to determine the appropriate sample size to use in estimating the mean, consider the problem faced by a government pension analyst who wishes to estimate the mean age at which federal employees retire.

FIGURE 8-8 Relationships among reliability, tolerable error, and the sampling distribution of $\bar{X}$ when reliability (shaded area) = .95.

STEP 1

Set a tolerable error level e. The same units apply to e as to the observed units. The analyst chooses $e = .5$ year as adequate precision for the estimate.

STEP 2

Set a target reliability probability $1 - \alpha$ and find $z_{\alpha/2}$. Although the analyst would like to be certain of achieving the desired precision, such perfection cannot be achieved using a sample. She determines that a reliability of .95 will suffice with $\alpha = 1 - .95 = .05$. Appendix Table E provides the critical normal deviate of $z_{\alpha/2} = z_{.025} = 1.96$.

FIGURE 8-9 Relationships among reliability, tolerable error, and the sampling distribution of $\bar{X}$ when reliability (shaded area) = .80.

STEP 3

Establish a value for the population standard deviation σ. Ordinarily, this value must be a *guess*. As an aid, a value from a similar study may be used for σ. The analyst is aware that in a recent study of postal employee retirements, the sample standard deviation for the age of retirement was 3.5 years. Believing that a similar age dispersion applies to federal employees, she uses σ = 3.5 years.

STEP 4

Calculate the required sample size n:

REQUIRED SAMPLE SIZE FOR ESTIMATING THE MEAN

$$n = \frac{z_{\alpha/2}^2 \sigma^2}{e^2}$$

Using the values

$$e = .5 \qquad z_{.025} = 1.96 \qquad \sigma = 3.5$$

the pension analyst finds the required sample size.

$$n = \frac{(1.96)^2 (3.5)^2}{(.5)^2} = 188.2, \text{ or } 189$$

(When *n* is fractional, the next larger whole number is chosen.)

THREE INFLUENCES ON SAMPLE SIZE

1. **The required sample size is directly proportional to the population variance.** A larger sample size will be required for a population with high dispersion than for a population that exhibits little variability.

2. **The required sample size is inversely proportional to the square of the tolerable error.** Thus, if we reduce *e* by one-half, we need four times as large a sample if reliability remains constant. Similarly, if we increase *e* ten times, the sample size will be 1/100th as large.

3. **The required sample size is directly related to the square of the critical normal deviate $z_{\alpha/2}$.** Thus, doubling *z* will require *n* to be four times as large. We cannot say that doubling *z* will ordinarily raise reliability by a factor of 2, however, because *z* does not have a linear relationship to normal curve areas. For example, decreasing *z* from 2.57 to 1.28 (a reduction in *z* of about one-half, so that *n* is about one-fourth as large) lowers the reliability from .99 to .80 (not quite a 20% drop).

The choices of *e* and *z* are interrelated, because the targeted reliability usually depends on the selected tolerable error. Because the tolerable error serves merely as a convenient cutoff point between serious and insignificant errors, its choice may be inseparable from the selection of the reliability level.

EXAMPLE: ESTIMATING MEAN LEG INSEAM AND FOOT LENGTH

A consultant is helping a clothing conglomerate establish improved standards for sizing products. One division makes pants, and another shoes. A key measure for sizing pants is the leg inseam length, and a counterpart in making shoes is the foot length. The respective population mean values will be estimated from sample mean measurements of two separate groups of randomly selected men. Using related air force anthropometric data, the following planning values have been obtained for the respective standard deviations.

$$\sigma = 1.75'' \text{ (inseam)} \quad \text{and} \quad \sigma = .45'' \text{ (foot length)}$$

To find the desired sample sizes, the tolerable error is $e = .10''$ and the reliability target is .99.

SOLUTION: For $\alpha = 1 - .99 = .01$, Appendix Table E provides a critical normal deviate value of $z_{\alpha/2} = z_{.005} = 2.57$. The desired sample sizes are thus

Inseam

$$n = \frac{(2.57)^2(1.75'')^2}{(.10'')^2}$$

$$= 2{,}023$$

Foot Length

$$n = \frac{(2.57)^2(.45'')^2}{(.10'')^2}$$

$$= 134$$

Notice that the n needed for estimating mean leg inseam length is about 16 times as great as the sample size needed to estimate mean foot length. This is because, in absolute terms, leg inseams are considerably more varied than foot lengths, with σ for the former being nearly 4 times as great. Our n formula shows that the required n must be about $(4)^2 = 16$ times as great for leg inseams as feet.

Although the above calculations do not reflect it, the consultant would probably want different es for sizing pants and shoes, accounting for the differences in the relative sizes of legs and feet. He may feel that precision of $\pm .10''$ may be adequate for sizing pant legs, but that a smaller tolerable error of $\pm .01''$ would be better for making shoes. [As an exercise, you might want to find the corresponding n for estimating mean foot length.]

FINDING A PLANNING ESTIMATE OF σ

The choice of sample size takes place in the planning stage of the sampling study before any sample data are collected. Like μ, the population standard deviation σ is ordinarily unknown and to be estimated. A planning level must be assumed for σ in order to calculate the desired n. Should this quantity be too big or too small, the computed level of n will result in undersampling (giving poor reliability or too much error) or in oversampling (being unnecessarily costly).

A statistician can sometimes use a planning σ estimated from another study involving a similar population having observations of about the same magnitude. The air force data in the above example were suitable for this purpose. But what if no such data exist?

A reasonably close "ballpark" level of σ is needed for planning purposes. One satisfactory method is purely judgmental. This is based on a feature of all normal curves.

Recall that normally distributed populations will have over 99.7% of their values falling within $\pm 3\sigma$ of the mean. Only about one out of a thousand population observations will fall below $\mu - 3\sigma$ or above $\mu + 3\sigma$. These quantities are roughly the .1st percentile and the 99.9th percentile. Those quantities span a range approximately equal to six standard deviations. Once these two quantities are specified, a planning value of σ may be computed from

$$\text{Planning } \sigma = \frac{99.9\text{th} - .1\text{st Percentiles}}{6}$$

Of course, if an investigator does not precisely know the above percentiles, she cannot be assured that her σ will be correct. But this indirect approach is easier than directly pulling a σ "from thin air."

EXAMPLE: ESTIMATING MEAN INCOME OF ACCOUNTANTS
You are asked to obtain the sample size necessary to estimate the mean income of accountants. First, you must get a planning σ. After some introspection, you can find a dollar figure at or below which about one accountant out of a thousand will earn in a year. At the high end, you can exercise similar judgment to find a 99.9% point.

SOLUTION: A student, Bob S., chose $15,000, reasoning that figure to be the lowest offer anyone received in the last recruiting season at his school. Another student, Lisa L., chose $22,000 because the most junior analyst in her father's CPA firm earns that much.

Bob chose $150,000 as his 99.9th percentile, simply because it seemed appropriate. He said, "Many lawyers earn over $100,000, but accountants are not so wealthy. The richest few should make upwards of $150,000." Lisa reads her father's trade journals, reasons that the high-earners must be partners in big firms, and remembers that one such partner makes $200,000. She chooses that amount.

The two students calculated the following planning standard deviations.

Bob	Lisa
$\sigma = \dfrac{150,000 - 15,000}{6}$	$\sigma = \dfrac{200,000 - 22,000}{6}$
$= \$22,500$	$= \$29,667$

Using $e = \$5,000$ and $z_{.025} = 1.96$, their desired sample sizes are

$$n = \frac{(22,500)^2(1.96)^2}{(5,000)^2} \qquad n = \frac{(29,667)^2(1.96)^2}{(5,000)^2}$$

$$= 78 \qquad\qquad = 136$$

The underlying populations may not have a normal distribution. (In the above example, the population would be positively skewed.) But Chebyshev's theorem tells us that σ should be close to one computed from the above expression. That is because a substantial percentage of any population will lie within $\mu \pm 3\sigma$, falling inside a 6σ central range. Actual experimentation would be necessary to find a better value of σ.

When the costs of error and sampling are high, under- or oversampling can be serious. A two-stage sampling scheme that involves a small preliminary *pilot sample* might then be appropriate. The resulting sample standard deviation s can then be used as a point estimator of σ and as the planning value in computing the desired n.

STEPS FOR FINDING THE REQUIRED SAMPLE SIZE TO ESTIMATE THE PROPORTION

Using the same type of analysis that we applied to the sample mean, we can find the number of observations required to estimate a population proportion from its sample counterpart. The roles of tolerable error and reliability, as they affect n, are completely analogous. Tolerable error e represents the maximum allowable deviation between π and its estimator P, and e is expressed as a *decimal fraction*. Reliability is the probability that P differs from π by no more than e.

We follow the same procedure for finding the required sample size as we did before. To illustrate, we will consider the problem at a gas company, where there is a continual discrepancy between the cubic feet of gas leaving the storage tanks and the actual consumption reported by company meter readers. Some of the discrepancy may be caused by inaccurate meters and minor leaks, but much of it is believed to be due to the inattention of the meter readers. The proportion of misread meters is to be estimated for each reader. A sample of homes from each meter reader's route is selected to be audited. A company supervisor, whose presence is unknown, will follow each reader on a portion of his or her route and reread the meters. Later, the figures will be compared.

STEP 1
Set a tolerance error level e. This will be a decimal fraction. A tolerable error of $e = .02$ is chosen.

STEP 2
Set a target reliability probability and find α and $z_{\alpha/2}$. A reliability of .90 is considered adequate. The critical normal deviate is $z_{.05} = 1.64$.

STEP 3
Establish a preliminary value for the population proportion π. Initially, it is assumed that 10% of the readings are in error. The preliminary value of the population proportion is therefore $\pi = .10$. (The true value of π remains unknown.)

STEP 4
Calculate the required sample size n:

REQUIRED SAMPLE SIZE FOR ESTIMATING THE PROPORTION

$$n = \frac{z_{\alpha/2}^2 \pi (1 - \pi)}{e^2}$$

Using the values

$$e = .02 \qquad z = 1.64 \qquad \pi = .10$$

the required sample size is

$$n = \frac{(1.64)^2(.10)(1 - .10)}{(.02)^2} = 605.16, \text{ or } 606$$

There may be insufficient knowledge for "ballparking" π. In that case, a preliminary value of $\pi = .50$ might be used. The resulting n is then guaranteed to meet error and reliability targets.

CHOOSING THE ESTIMATOR

The choice of statistical estimator is ordinarily dictated by circumstance. Most of the time we will use $\bar{X}$ as the estimator of μ, s to find σ, and P to get π. But there are situations when P might indirectly serve as the basis for estimating μ. As we shall see, in those cases it could actually be more expensive to use $\bar{X}$ to directly estimate μ.

ILLUSTRATION: WORK SAMPLING

One very important concern of production management is work measurement. Because of the great expense involved in collecting the required data, statistical tools have been developed to make the task more efficient.

A generation ago, procedures for obtaining measurements involved stop-watch methods that required continuous monitoring. Sometimes there was one watcher for each worker, so that the cost of gathering the data was high. The development of a statistical technique called **work sampling** relieved management of the burden of the stopwatch and at the same time removed the worker from its purported tyranny.

The classical procedure for finding the mean time to assemble a bumper on a car required that the worker be watched continuously and the installation times be duly recorded. If a sample of 20 completion times was required, each of about 10 minutes duration, about 200 minutes—or half a day—would be spent by the timer watching just this one worker. If ten workers in the automobile assembly plant install bumpers, and a sample is to be obtained for each, the timer must spend about 5 days measuring this one operation.

Work sampling is an alternative to continuous work measurement that can achieve a manyfold increase in the efficiency of the observer. The advantage of work sampling is that the same information obtainable from continuous observation may be achieved instead by many more shorter observations or "glimpses" taken randomly at scattered moments for an extended duration. Suppose that for a week the observer simply walks by the bumper installation station, making a note of what the worker is doing at that moment. It would be possible to do this many times, placing a check mark on a tally sheet for the particular task being performed at that instant. When the tallies have been accumulated at the end of the week, they would form the basis for estimating the proportion of time a worker spends at each task. The underlying principle of work sampling is that *the amount of time spent in a particular state of activity is proportional to the number of observations made of that state.*

Let us suppose that 100 observations have been made of an automobile bumper assembler; 86 times he was busy installing, and the rest of the time he was idle. Let us take this figure to calculate $P = 86/100 = .86$, which is a point estimate of the actual proportion of time π that the employee was busy installing bumpers. Assuming that all observations were made during the 35 hours in which the installer was officially on station and that he installed 222 bumpers, we may estimate the mean time taken for an installation.

The total time actually spent installing is estimated to be

$$35(.86) = 30.1 \text{ hours}$$

By dividing the time duration by the number of cars completed, the mean installation time μ may be estimated to be

$$\frac{30.1}{222} = .136 \text{ hour per bumper}$$

$$= 8.2 \text{ minutes per bumper}$$

This is the same type of result that would have been obtained through many hours of continuous observation of the single worker. But the 100 work sampling observations represent only minutes of the observer's time. On each pass through the plants he may collect tally marks for dozens of workers, each of whom performs a variety of tasks. Tallies would be obtained at all hours of the day and for every day of the week. No worker need feel uncomfortable about being watched, and the observer need carry no stopwatch.

The above results are only estimates. The same would be true for stopwatch timing. But work sampling is free of the many sources of potential bias of stopwatch studies. Thus, the results may be both more reliable and cheaper.

To find the number of work sampling observations required to estimate the mean time the worker takes to install bumpers, a very "rough" estimate would first have to be made of π. Suppose that we use $\pi = .80$. If a 5% tolerable error is desired with a 95% reliability, then $e = .05$ and $z_{.025} = 1.96$. We obtain

$$n = \frac{(1.96)^2(.8)(1 - .8)}{(.05)^2} = 245.86, \text{ or } 246$$

We may compare this value to the number of stopwatch observations necessary to estimate μ, the mean bumper installation time. Suppose that we know this worker's standard deviation to be $\sigma = 2$ minutes per bumper. With a true value of μ near 8 minutes, a 5% tolerable error would correspond to $8(.05) = .4$ minute. Using $e = .4$ and $z_{.025} = 1.96$, the required sample size would be

$$n = \frac{(1.96)^2(2)^2}{(.4)^2} = 96.04, \text{ or } 97$$

The number of continuous stopwatch observations would be 97 as compared to 246 for work sampling. But recall that the latter would take a few seconds each, whereas the former require several minutes each.

RELIABILITY VERSUS CONFIDENCE AND TOLERABLE ERROR VERSUS PRECISION

It may prove helpful at this point to clarify the key concepts that have been introduced in this chapter. An obvious question is: What is the difference between reliability and confidence? Another might be: How do we distinguish between tolerable error and precision? In both cases, aren't we really dealing with two terms that are synonymous?

In one sense, confidence and reliability mean the same thing. But the distinction between these concepts is that they apply in *different stages* of a sampling study. The notion of reliability is mainly a concern in the *planning stage*, where an appropriate sample size is chosen to satisfy the statistical analyst's goals. Greater reliability may only be achieved either by increasing the sample size, and hence the data collection costs, or by reducing the tolerable error level. In selecting a reliability level, the statistician seeks to find a satisfactory balance between risks of error and cost. The concept of confidence applies in the last phase of a sampling study—the *data analysis and conclusions stage*. At this final point in an investigation, the statistician is concerned with communicating results, so that the overriding concern is with *credibility*. Although often of the same value, the reliability need not be equal to the reported confidence level. Indeed, there are instances when the sample size *n* is not under the statistician's control, so that reliability considerations do not even enter into the planning.

We have already encountered the notion of precision in constructing confidence intervals. As the limits of the interval estimate become narrower, we can say that the resulting estimate becomes more precise. Like confidence, precision applies in the final stage of a sampling study. At this point in time, all sample data have been collected and precision can be improved only by a compensating reduction in confidence, or vice versa. The tolerable error level, on the other hand, is merely a convenient point of demarcation that separates serious errors from those that may be acceptable. It is used only in the planning stage and, with reliability, serves primarily to guide the statistician in selecting an appropriate sample size. Only when the reliability coincidentally equals the confidence level, and the planning guess as to σ or π is on target, will tolerable error be of equal magnitude to reported precision.

EXERCISES

8-30 The mean time required by Dearborn automobile assemblers to hang a car door is to be estimated. Assuming a standard deviation of 10 seconds, determine the required sample size under the following conditions.

(a) The desired reliability of being in error by no more than 1 second (in either direction) is .99.

(b) The desired reliability is .95 for a tolerable error of 1 second.

(c) A reliability of .99 is desired with a tolerable error of 2 seconds. How does the sample size you obtain compare with your answer to (a)?

(d) Answer (a), assuming that $\sigma = 20$ seconds. By how much does the sample size increase or decrease?

8-31 The Kryptonite Corporation purchasing manager orders supplies from many vendors and has the following policy. The quality of each shipment is to be estimated by means of a sample that will always include 10% of the items, regardless of the size of the shipment. Do you think this is good policy? Explain.

8-32 The following percentiles have been obtained by judgment. Find, in each case, a planning guess for the population standard deviation.

	(a)	(b)	(c)	(d)
.1st	56"	$20,000	− 20%	.97"
99.9th	80"	$200,000	220%	1.03"

8-33 An operations research analyst for Centralia Bank wishes to estimate the mean transaction time for a new ATM system. He judges it an almost certainty that 10 seconds will be required and that a transaction will seldom take more than 100 seconds. He wants to achieve 99% reliability and plus or minus one-second precision. How many sample transactions must he monitor?

8-34 The cost of obtaining the sample in Exercise 8-30 is $1.50 per observation.
(a) For a tolerable error of 1 second, find the reliability that can be achieved by an expenditure of $300.
(b) For a reliability of .95, find the tolerable error that must correspond to an expenditure of $300.

8-35 An Ace Widgets quality control manager has a flexible sampling policy. Because there are different quality requirements for different parts, there is a separate policy for each type of part. For example, a pressure seal used on some assemblies must be able to withstand a maximum load of 5,000 pounds per square inch (psi) before bursting. If the mean maximum load of a sample of seals taken from a shipment is less than 5,000 psi, then the entire shipment must be rejected.

The sampling policy for this item requires that a sample be large enough so that the probability that the sample mean differs from the population mean by no more than 10 psi (in either direction) is equal to .95. Historically, it has been established that the standard deviation for bursting pressures of this seal is 100 psi.
(a) Find the required sample size.
(b) If the true mean maximum bursting pressure of the seals in a shipment is actually $\mu = 5{,}010$ psi, use your sample size in (a) to determine the probability that the shipment will be rejected.

8-36 A VBM engineer wishes to determine how many extra batteries to include in the power supply so that a satellite's useful life will be likely to exceed minimum specifications. A random sample of a particular type of battery is selected for testing. The engineer wishes to find the sample size that will provide an estimate of the true proportion π of batteries whose performance will be satisfactory to an accuracy of $e = .05$ with a .95 reliability. We will assume that the population of batteries is quite large.
(a) If π is initially assumed to be .5, find the necessary sample size.
(b) After testing the number of batteries found in (a), only 250 prove satisfactory. What is the point estimate of π? If this were the true value of π, how many more batteries were tested unnecessarily?

8-37 A waiter at Bon Appétit has been observed at 200 random times while on his station. The following tabulation provides the frequency distribution for the tasks he was performing at each observation.

Cleaning tables	10
Taking orders	35
Walking	57
Placing orders	8
Preparing food	20
Picking up orders	15
Delivering orders	10
Calculating bills	10
Preparing or delivering drinks	35

If during the time period over which he was observed he worked a total of 25 hours, exclusive of idle time, and served a total of 1,000 customers, estimate the mean time (in minutes) spent on each of the above tasks per customer.

SUMMARY

1. What are estimation, estimate, and estimator?

Estimation is the simplest form of inferential statistics, which uses known sample evidence to draw conclusions regarding unknown population characteristics. An **estimate** is a numerical value assigned to the unknown population parameter. In statistical investigations, the calculated value of a sample statistic serves as the estimate. That statistic is referred to as the **estimator** of the unknown parameter.

2. What are desirable properties for an estimator?

There are several properties that are desirable for estimators. One is **unbiasedness**, so that the expected value of the estimator is equal to the parameter being estimated. A **consistent** estimator achieves improved reliability and precision as the sample size becomes larger. The more **efficient** of two estimators reaches the investigator's reliability and precision goals with the smaller sample size.

3. What are the two forms of estimates?

Estimates take two forms. The **point estimate** is a single numerical quantity. Statisticians prefer the **interval estimate**, which acknowledges that some sampling error is unavoidable. The statistical art balances precision (interval width) against credibility while at the same time not devoting too many resources to collecting the sample data.

4. What are confidence intervals for the mean, and how are they used and constructed?

Interval estimates are qualified by a **confidence level**, a value stating how often the estimation procedure would provide a truthful solution if it were conducted over and over again with new samples. The estimate itself is called a **confidence interval**. A confidence interval estimate of the population mean is centered on the computed $\bar{X}$.

There are two main ways for finding the endpoints of a confidence interval for μ. When the population standard deviation is known, the following expression is used to construct the $100(1 - \alpha)\%$ confidence interval

$$\mu = \bar{X} \pm z_{\alpha/2}\sigma_{\bar{X}} \qquad (\sigma \text{ known})$$

where $\sigma_{\bar{X}} = \sigma/\sqrt{n}$ is the standard error of $\bar{X}$ and $z_{\alpha/2}$ is the normal deviate that corresponds.

5. **What is the Student t distribution, and what is its role in constructing confidence intervals for the mean?**
   When the population standard deviation is unknown, use the critical value $t_{\alpha/2}$ for the **Student t distribution** in place of the normal deviate, and estimate σ using the computed sample standard deviation s. The following expression applies.

$$\mu = \bar{X} \pm t_{\alpha/2}\frac{s}{\sqrt{n}} \qquad (\sigma \text{ unknown})$$

   The Student t distribution is characterized by a single parameter, the *number of degrees of freedom*. Its density function provides a bell-shaped curve resembling the normal curve. It applies to the random variable

$$t = \frac{\bar{X} - \mu}{s/\sqrt{n}}$$

   which involves two uncertain quantities, $\bar{X}$ and s.

6. **When should the Student t distribution be used instead of the normal distribution?**
   The Student t allows us to make inferences about the mean when the population standard deviation σ is unknown. The normal curve for $\bar{X}$, on the other hand, is based on a stipulated value for σ. When the sample size is large, the normal and Student t distributions tend to coincide, and the normal curve is generally applied whenever the sample size is too large to retrieve an accurate $t_{\alpha/2}$ value from the table.

7. **How is the normal distribution used in constructing confidence intervals for the proportion?**
   The normal approximation also extends to constructing confidence intervals for the population proportion where

$$\pi = P \pm z_{\alpha/2}\sqrt{\frac{P(1 - P)}{n}}$$

8. **What are the considerations in establishing a sample size, and how can a level for n be established in an objective and systematic manner?**
   The *choice of sample size* is an important issue. This may be computed ahead of time. For estimating μ, three quantities determine the appropriate n. These are the **tolerable error** level e, the desired **reliability** level for the estimate, and a good *guess* for σ. The reliability corresponds to the probability $1 - \alpha$ that the estimate will fall within a distance of $\pm e$ from its target. Both the tolerable error and reliability are arbitrary choices that reflect sampling costs and the investigator's attitudes toward the risks involved. The reliability gives rise to the **critical normal deviate** $z_{\alpha/2}$. The following expression is used to compute the required sample size.

$$n = \frac{z_{\alpha/2}^2 \sigma^2}{e^2} \quad \text{(for estimating } \mu)$$

The required sample size for estimating the proportion is found in a similar fashion. A good *guess* is made for π (the quantity being estimated) and the required sample size is calculated using

$$n = \frac{z_{\alpha/2}^2 \pi(1 - \pi)}{e^2} \quad \text{(for estimating } \pi)$$

REAL-LIFE STATISTICAL CHALLENGE

Applying Statistical Estimation to the Automobile Dream List

We will now apply statistical estimation methods to the set of "dream machines," using the 232 autos listed in Table 4-2. Table 8-3 shows the sample means and standard deviations found in Chapter 6 for three samples of size 5 and one of size 15.

Now we can construct a 90 percent confidence interval for mean highway mileage using our first sample of five randomly selected automobiles. The confidence interval is:

$$\mu = 28.00 \pm 2.132(2.12/\sqrt{5})$$

$$\mu = 28.00 \pm 2.02$$

so that

$$25.98 \le \mu \le 30.02$$

Now let's consider an example of statistical estimation using the sample proportion. Our population data shows a total of 99, or 43 percent, of the automobiles tested had manual transmissions. We can construct a 95 percent confidence interval for that same proportion of automobiles using the first 15 randomly selected automobiles. (Refer to Table 6-20.) P is equal to 7/15 or .47. The confidence interval is

$$\pi = .47 \pm (1.96)(.13)$$

$$\pi = .47 \pm .25$$

so that

$$.22 \le \pi \le .72$$

In Chapter 9 we will apply these results to the topic of hypothesis testing.

DISCUSSION QUESTIONS

1. Construct and compare the 90 percent confidence intervals for mean mileage using the results for samples (2) and (3).

TABLE 8-3 Sample Means and Standard Deviations for Engine Displacement (liters) and Mileage

	Sample 1 n = 5		Sample 2 n = 5		Sample 3 n = 5		Combined n = 15	
	Disp.	MPG	Disp.	MPG	Disp.	MPG	Disp.	MPG
Mean	2.50	28.00	3.32	27.40	3.10	24.00	2.97	26.47
Standard Deviation	0.67	2.12	1.90	5.03	1.22	5.34	1.31	4.47

2. Construct the 90 percent confidence interval for mean mileage using the combined sample results. Compare this to the intervals found in Question 1.

3. Construct and compare the 95 percent confidence intervals for the proportion of manual transmissions using the results from samples (1)-(3).

4. Develop another example estimating the combined sample proportion. Compare your results to the population data.

REVIEW EXERCISES

8-38 Woody Mills estimates the mean number of square feet of scrap and wasted wood per log in the manufacture of one-half-inch exterior plywood from a random sample of 100 logs of various sizes. Each log's volume was carefully measured, and the theoretical number of square feet of plywood was computed. This value was compared to the actual quantity achieved at the end of production, and the wood loss was calculated. When the study data were assembled, the sample mean and the standard deviation were computed as $\bar{X} = 1,246$ square feet and $s = 114.6$ square feet, respectively. Construct a 95% confidence interval estimate of the mean wood loss.

8-39 In estimating the mean time taken by a sheetrocker to nail one 8-foot sheet already in place, a sample of $n = 25$ observations were taken at random times. The worker was found to be nailing during just 5 of these observations.

(a) Make a point estimate of the proportion of all working time spent nailing.

(b) During the 200-minute span of time covering the observations, the sheetrocker hung 20 sheets. Make a point estimate of the mean time per sheet to do the nailing.

8-40 An engineer for BugOff Chemical Company estimates the mean number of gallons of a key ingredient that are wasted in the manufacturing of a ton of pesticide. She selects a random sample of 100 tons and computes the results to be $\bar{X} = 5.4$ gallons and $s = .42$ gallons. Construct a 95% confidence interval of the mean waste.

8-41 *Computer exercise.* The following rates of return were obtained by holding several common stocks for one year. You may assume that these data are a representative sample of a large population of historical rates of return.

| 5 | − 4 | 10 | 15 | 11 | 25 | − 5 | 17 |
| − 5 | 0 | 8 | 12 | 14 | 8 | 1 | 5 |

(a) Compute the sample mean and standard deviation.
(b) Construct a 95% confidence interval estimate of the population mean rate of return.

8-42 *Computer exercise.* The following salaries were obtained for a sample of ten executive secretaries.

| $35,000 | $67,500 | $51,500 | $53,000 | $38,000 |
| $42,000 | $29,500 | $31,500 | $46,000 | $37,500 |

(a) Find the value of an efficient, unbiased, and consistent estimator of the mean of the salaries of all executive secretaries.
(b) Find the value of an unbiased and consistent estimator of the variance of the salaries.
(c) Find the value of an unbiased estimator of the proportion of salaries above $40,000.

8-43 The respective proportions of viewers watching each of the earliest prime time television programs on one network on four successive nights are to be estimated within a tolerance of ±.01, so that there is a 95% chance this precision will be achieved (reliability = .95). The sample proportion P is to be used. Find the required sample sizes for each of the following daily population proportions.
(a) Tuesday: .3   (c) Thursday: .5
(b) Wednesday: .6   (d) Friday: .1

8-44 A psychologist has designed a new aptitude test for life insurance companies to use to screen applicants for beginning actuarial positions. To estimate the mean score achieved by all future applicants who will eventually take the test, the psychologist has administered it to nine persons. The sample mean and the standard deviation have been calculated as $\bar{X} = 83.7$ and $s = 12.9$ points, respectively. Construct the confidence interval estimates of the mean for each of the following levels of confidence.
(a) 99%   (b) 95%   (c) 90%   (d) 99.5%

8-45 The mean time to failure of Try-Hard batteries is estimated from a sample of 100 test items taken from a large population. Sample results provide $\bar{X} = 57.4$ hours and $s = 11.1$ hours. Construct a 99% confidence interval estimate of the population mean time to failure.

8-46 A random sample of $n = 100$ widths for two-by-fours is selected. The sample results yield $\bar{X} = 3.5$ inches and $s = .1$ inches. Construct a 95% confidence interval estimate of the boards in the entire shipment.

8-47 A pharmaceutical house wants to estimate the mean number of milligrams (mg) of drug its machinery inserts into each capsule in four different sizes of pills. In each case, a standard deviation of 1 mg is assumed and a reliability of 95% is desired. However, the amount of error tolerated varies with pill size. Find the following required sample sizes.
(a) tiny pills: .05 mg error   (c) medium pills: .2 mg error
(b) small pills: .1 mg error   (d) large pills: .5 mg error

8-48 Unified Airways is estimating the mean distance traveled annually by its first-class business travelers. From a random sample of $n = 100$ it was determined that $\bar{X} = 76,400$ and $s = 5,250$ miles. Construct a 95% confidence interval estimate of the mean distance traveled.

8-49 The work sampling example in Chapter 4 shows how work sampling can be used to allocate the expense of data entry. Suppose that two departments in a company have data entry. Three alternatives are possible for determining the charges assigned to the respective departments. (1) Detailed record keeping (census) at a cost of $200 per day. (2) Stopwatch sampling to estimate the mean daily data entry time per operator for Department A; then estimating the total daily time for Department A by multiplying this sample mean by the number of operators. (Department B's usage can then be estimated from employee timeclock records.) (3) Work sampling to estimate the proportion of all data entry time for Department A, which when applied to total daily data entry time yields an estimate equivalent to that in (2).

(a) Suppose that the daily operator data entry time for Department A, determined by stopwatch sampling, has a standard deviation of $\sigma = .5$ hour. A .95 reliability probability is desired, with a tolerable error of $e = .08$ hour. Find the required sample size n.

(b) Suppose that the proportion of time spent on Department A, determined by a work sampling study, is presumed to be $\pi = .50$ (a guess). A .95 reliability probability is desired, with a tolerable error of $e = .02$. Determine the required number of observations n.

(c) Suppose that each stopwatch observation costs $1.00, but that each work sampling observation costs only $.05. Determine the daily cost of each method. Which one is least expensive?

STATISTICS IN PRACTICE

8-50 Using the master class data list developed in Exercise 1-19, answer the following (ignoring any finite population corrections).

(a) Select a quantitative variable and *assume* an appropriate value for σ. Then randomly select $n = 4$ observations. Using the normal distribution, construct a 90 percent confidence interval for the mean assuming that σ is known.

(b) Using the same sample observations as in (a), use the Student t distribution to construct a 95 percent confidence interval for the mean.

(c) Comment on differences between the results achieved in (a) and (b).

(d) Select a sample of $n = 5$ observations of a qualitative variable from the data set. Construct a 99 percent confidence interval for the proportion having a particular attribute. If the confidence level were lowered to 90 percent, what would that interval be?

8-51 Repeat Exercise 8-50 using your group's class data list developed in Exercise 1-21.

8-52 In Exercise 6-55 you were asked to go to a local store or other retail outlet and collect data for the number of customer arrivals during each of several one-minute intervals. Treating those data as *sample* observations, construct a 95 percent confidence interval for the mean number of arrivals per minute. Comment on your results.

8-53 Consider genetic diversity in your class and develop a set of questions based on some personal characteristics. Possible factors would be gender, eye color, handedness, ability to roll tongue, and color blindness.
  (a) Collect the data. For each variable, these may be assumed to be random samples from the respective general populations.
  (b) Construct a 90 percent confidence interval estimate of the proportion of the general population possessing the ability to roll their tongues.
  (c) Construct a 95 percent confidence interval estimate of the proportion of persons who are right-handed.

8-54 Who do you want for President? If the election were held today, which candidate would you vote for? Research the most recent pre-election opinion poll from your local newspaper.
  (a) Comment on that poll in terms of the investigator's use of statistical estimation methods.
  (b) Using the question as it was worded in the newspaper report, conduct your own poll. Then construct a 90 percent confidence interval for the proportion favoring a particular candidate.
  (c) Comment on the validity of your results.

8-55 Using the final exam data in Table 3-13, answer the following questions.
  (a) Select a random sample of size 9. Construct a 95% confidence interval estimate for the mean. Assume σ is the value you obtained in Exercise 7-39(a).
  (b) Select another random sample of size 9. Construct a 95% confidence interval estimate of the mean. Assume σ is unknown.
  (c) Comment on the results obtained in (a) and (b).

8-56 Using the library spending data given in Exercise 7-40, answer the following questions.
  (a) Find the required sample size so that the probability that the sample mean differs from the population mean by no more than $4 (in either direction) is equal to .90. Assume σ is the value you obtained in Exercise 7-40(a).
  (b) Using the sample size found in (a), collect a random sample and construct a 90% confidence interval estimate of the mean. (Ignore any finite correction factor.)

8-57 Using the graduation rate data given in Exercise 7-41, answer the following questions.
  (a) Find the desired sample size so that the probability that the sample mean differs from the population mean by no more than 4% (in either direction) is equal to .80. Assume an appropriate value for σ.
  (b) Using the sample size found in (a), collect a random sample and construct an 80% confidence interval estimate of the mean. Assume here that σ is unknown.

8-58 Toss a coin 50 times and record your results. Determine the proportion of times, P, that heads appears. Construct a 99% confidence interval estimate for π.

CASE Brown and Becker's Budget

Brown and Becker is a consumer products manufacturer. The president has requested budgetary input for the next fiscal year. The head of new product development must generate data for the required funding. This will be done on a product-by-product basis, as if those items are already in existence, already part of the company's regular product mix.

One of the largest cost components for new products is direct manufacturing labor, used almost exclusively in assembling products supplied by Asian vendors. Forecast levels of direct labor will be based partly on the estimated productivity of existing products. For the electronics group, the following specialized data have been obtained for sample production runs.

Units	Direct Labor Cost	Units	Direct Labor Cost
5,240	$ 65,720	12,500	$105,200
8,330	79,249	5,550	49,720
1,125	13,450	3,355	42,060
24,360	261,420	15,610	163,400
8,550	91,050	1,500	17,400

The above data will be helpful in establishing the forecast cost of a new cellular modem.

The ultimate budgetary impact of the cellular modem will depend on the unit sales volume. The demand for the product will remain uncertain until it is on the market, the price has been established, and the marketing plan is in place. Several statistical samples will provide management with information regarding these factors.

QUESTIONS

1. Discuss the advantages of using a point estimate to forecast the labor cost segment of the budget for new product manufacturing. Why might management also require an interval estimate?

2. Convert the sample direct labor cost data to direct labor cost per unit. Calculate the sample mean and standard deviation of the cost per unit.

3. Construct a 95% confidence interval estimate of the mean direct labor cost per unit of all of the electronics group items.

4. Suppose that the unit direct labor cost of assembling cellular modems is estimated to be double that of the sample products. What is the point estimate of this cost component?

5. The product demand will depend, to a great extent, on the proportion of the market targeted to buy the product. Suppose that the modem will cost $100. A sample of potential users is asked if they would buy one, and the data obtained will be used to estimate the true proportion of would-be buyers.

(a) Using a guess of .10 for the population proportion, how large must the sample size be for the sample proportion to fall within .02 of the population parameter with probability .95?

(b) If you are unable to guess where the population proportion will fall, select a sample size that guarantees achieving or exceeding the above specifications.

6. For a sample similar to the one above, the quantity of interest is the most a potential customer would be willing to pay for a cellular modem. Management feels that almost nobody would pay $500, but that nearly everybody would be willing to pay $20. The sample size must be chosen to obtain sample responses.

(a) Suggest an appropriate planning guess for the population standard deviation.

(b) Using your answer to (a), what sample size is necessary if the population mean maximum price is to be estimated within plus or minus $10, with reliability .95?

(c) Suppose that the management can only afford a sample of $n = 100$, and that the standard deviation given in (a) applies.

(1) What is the resulting reliability if the tolerable error level remains at $10?

(2) What is the resulting tolerable error level if the reliability probability .95 remains unchanged?

7. A sample of $n = 100$ is selected to estimate the proportion in Question 5. Four of the sample persons said that they would buy a $100 cellular modem. Construct a 95% confidence interval estimate of the true proportion of the market targeted to buy that priced modem.

8. A sample of $n = 15$ persons is selected for estimating the mean maximum price of the modem. The following results have been obtained.

$100	$50	$200	$700	$10	$300	$150	$250
$75	$150	$50	$350	$400	$250	$90	

(a) Calculate the sample mean and standard deviation.

(b) Construct a 95% confidence interval estimate of the population mean maximum price.

9. Discuss any further sample information that management might find useful in establishing the budget for cellular modems.

8-6 OPTIONAL TOPIC I: ESTIMATING THE DIFFERENCE BETWEEN MEANS

The simplest two-sample inference involves estimating the difference between two population parameters. We begin by constructing a confidence interval estimate of the difference between the two population means.

For convenience, we will designate the populations as *A* and *B*.

POPULATION MEANS

$$\mu_A = \text{Mean of population } A$$
$$\mu_B = \text{Mean of population } B$$

The population that is presumed to have the larger mean is usually denoted by A, although this designation is completely arbitrary. The difference between population means $\mu_A - \mu_B$ may be estimated from the sample results. To do this, the observations may be made either independently or by matching pairs.

INDEPENDENT SAMPLES

It is a simpler procedure to select the sample observations independently. Sample means from the respective populations are denoted by $\bar{X}_A$ and $\bar{X}_B$. As an unbiased estimator of $\mu_A - \mu_B$, we use the

DIFFERENCE BETWEEN THE SAMPLE MEANS

$$d = \bar{X}_A - \bar{X}_B$$

The samples may vary in size.

The sampling distributions of $\bar{X}_A$ and $\bar{X}_B$ may be approximated by the normal curve for sufficiently large samples. Because the samples are selected independently, d will also be approximately normally distributed, with mean $\mu_A - \mu_B$ and standard deviation

$$\sigma_d = \sqrt{\frac{\sigma_A^2}{n_A} + \frac{\sigma_B^2}{n_B}}$$

where σ_A^2 and σ_B^2 are the population variances.*

Ordinarily, the values of σ_A and σ_B are unknown. Two parallel procedures apply for estimating $\mu_A - \mu_B$, depending on the sample sizes.

---

*Here, we make use of the fact that $\bar{X}_A$ and $\bar{X}_B$ are independent random variables, so that the variance of their sum or difference equals the sum of the individual variances.

$$\sigma_d^2 = \sigma^2(\bar{X}_A - \bar{X}_B) = \sigma^2(\bar{X}_A) + \sigma^2(\bar{X}_B) = \frac{\sigma_A^2}{n_A} + \frac{\sigma_B^2}{n_B}$$

Large Sample Sizes

When n_A and n_B are both greater than or equal to 30, the following expression is used as an estimator of σ_d.

$$s_d = \sqrt{\frac{s_A^2}{n_A} + \frac{s_B^2}{n_B}}$$

We are now ready to construct the confidence interval estimate of the difference between population means. We select a normal deviate z corresponding to the desired confidence level, so that we estimate the difference between population means by the interval

$$\mu_A - \mu_B = d \pm z s_d$$

However, it is more convenient to use the following expression to compute the $100(1 - \alpha)\%$

CONFIDENCE INTERVAL FOR THE DIFFERENCE BETWEEN MEANS USING INDEPENDENT SAMPLES (large *n*'s)

$$\mu_A - \mu_B = \bar{X}_A - \bar{X}_B \pm z_{\alpha/2} \sqrt{\frac{s_A^2}{n_A} + \frac{s_B^2}{n_B}}$$

EXAMPLE: MEASURING THE ADVANTAGE OF SHELF POSITION

A large greeting card chain conducted an experiment to estimate the mean sales advantage due to favorable location of promotional cards. In group *A* stores, the cards were interspersed within the regular line. In group *B* stores, the same promotional cards were located in a separate special location. Sales of those cards were recorded for two independent random samples. The following data apply.

$$n_A = 50 \qquad n_B = 100$$
$$\bar{X}_A = \$1{,}257 \qquad \bar{X}_B = \$928$$
$$s_A = \$152 \qquad s_B = \$129$$

Find the 95% confidence interval estimate for $\mu_A - \mu_B$.

SOLUTION: Using $z_{.025} = 1.96$, the following 95% confidence interval estimate applies to the difference in mean sales for all stores where promotional cards were displayed.

$$\mu_A - \mu_B = \$1{,}257 - \$928 \pm 1.96 \sqrt{\frac{(152)^2}{50} + \frac{(129)^2}{100}}$$

$$= \$329 \pm 49$$

or

$$\$280 \leq \mu_A - \mu_B \leq \$378$$

With 95% confidence, promotional card sales are on the average between $280 and $378 higher when interspersed with regular cards.

SMALL SAMPLE SIZES

When $n_A < 30$ or $n_B < 30$, the Student t distribution is used to estimate the difference between population means. The key theoretical assumption is that *both populations must have the same variance*. We must assume that $\sigma_A^2 = \sigma_B^2 = \sigma^2$. We express the standard error of d in a slightly different form than before.

$$\sigma_d = \sqrt{\frac{\sigma^2}{n_A} + \frac{\sigma^2}{n_B}} = \sigma\sqrt{\frac{1}{n_A} + \frac{1}{n_B}}$$

To fulfill this requirement, s_A^2 and s_B^2 must serve as unbiased estimators of σ^2. We obtain an even better estimate of σ^2 by pooling the sample results. Thus, σ_d may be estimated by taking the square root of a weighted average of the sample variances, providing the following expression for the

STANDARD ERROR OF THE DIFFERENCE IN SAMPLE MEANS (small n's)

$$s_{d\text{-small}} = \sqrt{\frac{(n_A - 1)s_A^2 + (n_B - 1)s_B^2}{n_A + n_B - 2}}\sqrt{\frac{1}{n_A} + \frac{1}{n_B}}$$

(Note that the denominator of the first term has been reduced by 2 to yield an unbiased estimator.)

The following expression is used to compute the $100(1 - \alpha)\%$

CONFIDENCE INTERVAL FOR THE DIFFERENCE BETWEEN MEANS USING INDEPENDENT SAMPLES (small n's)

$$\mu_A - \mu_B = \bar{X}_A - \bar{X}_B \pm t_{\alpha/2}s_{d\text{-small}}$$

We find $t_{\alpha/2}$ from Appendix Table F using the α that corresponds to the confidence level. The number of degrees of freedom is $n_A + n_B - 2$. In effect, the combined sample size $n_A + n_B$ must be reduced by 2, because one degree of freedom is lost in calculating each of the two sample variances.

EXAMPLE: COST SAVINGS FOR AUTOMATED TELLERS

A large bank estimated the cost per transaction for customer cash withdrawals from checking accounts. The mean cost of human teller processing is μ_A, while that for automated teller processing is μ_B. Using the weekly costs per transaction for $n_A = 10$ branches and for $n_B = 15$ automated teller sites, the bank obtained the following data.

$$\bar{X}_A = \$.13 \qquad \bar{X}_B = \$.09$$
$$s_A = \$.021 \qquad s_B = \$.018$$

Find the 90% confidence interval estimate of the difference in mean costs.

SOLUTION: Using $t_{.05} = 1.714$, from Appendix Table F for $10 + 15 - 2 = 23$ degrees of freedom, we find the following

$$\mu_A - \mu_B = \$.13 - \$.09 \pm 1.714 \sqrt{\frac{(10-1)(.021)^2 + (15-1)(.018)^2}{10 + 15 - 2}} \sqrt{\frac{1}{10} + \frac{1}{15}}$$

$$= \$.04 \pm .013$$

or

$$\$.027 \le \mu_A - \mu_B \le \$.053$$

With 90% confidence, the mean cost savings for automated tellers lie between $.027 and $.053 per transaction.

OPTIONAL EXERCISES

8-59 The dean of the business school at State University wishes to compare the GMAT scores of his graduate students to those of nonbusiness students. Scores have been obtained for two independent random samples. The following data apply.

Business Students	Nonbusiness Students
$n_A = 100$	$n_B = 150$
$\bar{X}_A = 620.1$	$\bar{X}_B = 576.4$
$s_A^2 = 1,874$	$s_B^2 = 2,057$

Construct a 95% confidence interval for the difference between population means.

8-60 Independent random samples have been obtained for the fuel consumption (miles per gallon) of two car models. The following results apply.

Car A	Car B
$n_A = 10$	$n_B = 10$
$\bar{X}_A = 24$	$\bar{X}_B = 22.5$
$s_A^2 = 2$	$s_B^2 = 2.5$

Construct a 95% confidence interval estimate of the difference between mean fuel consumptions.

8-61 CompTell Corporation has collected independent random samples for the transaction times (seconds) of two computer teleprocessing monitors. The following data apply.

Monitor A				Monitor B			
12.7	13.4	14.5	11.7	9.8	10.4	12.6	13.7
10.6	11.4	12.2	13.7	12.3	11.7	12.1	10.8
14.1	13.3	12.6	12.2	12.6	11.9	10.1	9.9
11.3	12.5	12.3	13.7	12.3	12.1	11.6	10.8
15.1	13.7	12.5	14.4	13.1	11.5	10.9	11.4
12.5	13.3	13.3	14.5	10.2	10.4	12.7	12.6
12.5	13.3	13.5	12.5	11.2	11.7	12.4	13.1
10.7	10.5	12.4	11.9	11.0	12.0	13.1	12.0
12.0	13.5	14.1					

Construct a 99% confidence interval estimate of the difference between mean processing times.

8-62 The following student GPA data have been obtained for matched pairs randomly selected from two populations at Old Ivy University. Group A consists of students who work less than 20 hours a week. Group B consists of students who hold full-time jobs.

A	B	A	B	A	B	A	B
3.65	3.71	2.84	2.75	3.22	3.15	3.61	3.40
3.25	2.96	2.86	2.91	3.11	2.95	3.55	3.35
3.33	3.17	3.55	3.51	4.00	3.86	3.74	3.55
2.54	2.27	2.85	2.62	3.45	3.28	3.61	3.48
3.44	3.42	3.65	3.51	3.12	2.88	3.05	3.12
3.14	3.02	3.67	3.50	3.24	3.18	3.15	2.91
3.29	3.17	3.64	3.52	3.78	3.42	3.20	2.95
2.65	2.90	2.85	2.69	3.53	3.37	3.15	3.11
3.22	2.84	3.55	3.65	3.52	3.44		

Construct a 95% confidence interval for the difference between mean GPA for all students in the respective populations.

8-63 Mirror Images collected the following annual operating cost sample for two high-volume copiers.

Copier A			Copier B		
$12,366	$12,575	$13,589	$ 7,024	$11,115	$10,443
11,950	13,820	12,276	18,203	6,450	4,255
11,786	12,479	13,125	12,357	19,204	4,158
12,659			23,425	3,718	8,295
			6,225	4,870	9,146

(a) Compute the mean and standard deviation for each sample.
(b) Construct a 95% confidence interval estimate of the difference between mean costs for the two copiers.

8-7 OPTIONAL TOPIC II: DATA ANALYSIS USING RESAMPLING SIMULATION

The concepts and procedures presented in Chapter 8 are *traditional statistics.* Those methods originated before World War II, long before modern computers existed. Today's widespread availability of computers and software packages allows us to take an alternative approach called **resampling.**

The focus of resampling is **data analysis.** The procedure is light on mathematical theory, relying heavily on manipulations and computations originating with the sample data themselves. Those observations provide a surrogate for the underlying population, whose true characteristics remain unknown and must be dealt with, as in traditional statistics, through inferences. As its name implies, resampling involves taking a succession of samples from this surrogate population. In essence the sampling process is *simulated* over and over again with the objective of drawing meaningful conclusions regarding the true population. All findings are based on the original sample data, so that investigators using these procedures must virtually lift themselves by their bootstraps. This is why the resampling procedure is sometimes referred to as **statistical bootstrapping.**

THE PROCEDURE

The process is extremely simple. The imaginary surrogate population is what would be obtained by copying the value for each observation onto a million slips of paper, so that altogether there are *n* times one million values in the surrogate population, each having its own slip of paper. Imagine a hopper into which the slips are dropped and then mixed thoroughly. We may then draw a random selection of those slips and record the sample values, mimicking how the original sample values were obtained from the original population. To avoid confusion with the original data, we will now call the new values a **resample.** Many separate resamples, each of size *n,* must ordinarily be selected in reaching a meaningful conclusion.

As a practical matter, the actual physical generation of millions of slips of paper would be cumbersome and very expensive. Instead, the entire process is duplicated paperlessly on the computer using **Monte Carlo simulation.** Computer-generated random numbers are used to determine the values that go into each resample, so that each of the original sample observations is equally likely to be selected each time. To simplify things further, there are only *n* values being resampled *with replacement,* producing virtually the same effect as actually making random selections using *n* million slips and values.

We illustrate the procedure using the sample lost production times listed in Table 8-2.

Original sample value	205	1,123	528	359	1,421	723	57	172	25
Represented by random digit	1	2	3	4	5	6	7	8	9

A resample is built by taking 9 random digits read from a list of random numbers. In doing this, we skip any 0s, and use the above assignment to match the data value to the successive random number.

The following results are obtained for the first resample.

Random digit	4	7	6	6	5	9	8	7	2
Resample value	359	57	723	723	1,421	25	172	57	1,123

$$\bar{X} = \frac{359 + 57 + 723 + 723 + 1,421 + 25 + 172 + 57 + 1,123}{9} = 437.44$$

Notice that random numbers 6 and 7 both appear twice, while no 1 or 3 is obtained. The data values 723 and 57 each occur twice in the resample, while 205 and 528 do not. The next 9 random numbers give a different set of values for the second resample.

Random digit	8	1	3	6	5	9	4	3	7
Resample value	172	1,123	528	723	1,421	25	359	528	57

$$\bar{X} = \frac{172 + 1,123 + 528 + 723 + 1,421 + 25 + 359 + 528 + 57}{9} = 548.44$$

Like the random numbers determining them, successive resamples will vary, each no more likely to resemble a particular resample than the original data themselves. Such variability is what we would expect with repeated random samples taken from the original population. The collection of resamples should tell us much the same story about the underlying population that a similar set of actual samples would. But the computer makes it far easier, faster, and cheaper to do this with resamples.

RESAMPLING WITH THE COMPUTER

With the help of a computer, the resampling process is drastically simplified. In just a few seconds of personal computer time 1,000 resamples with $n = 9$ were generated. These are summarized in Figure 8-10. That computer run was made with a readily available MS-DOS PC program, *Resampling Stats.* This program requires only a short set of command instructions and the original sample data values. The instructions tell the program to repeat a series of commands 1,000 times. A random resample is created each time from the original values and the mean computed. That set of $\bar{X}$s can be summarized in several ways, including a complete histogram like that shown in Figure 8-10. We may use those computed means to draw an inference about the underlying population.

Recall in Section 8-3 we used the original sample data to construct a 95% confidence interval estimate of the unknown population mean μ:

$$135.84 \le \mu \le 889.28 \text{ hours}$$

An interpretation of this interval is that if the original sampling process were to be repeated many times, then about 95% of similarly constructed intervals would bracket the true level for μ, while 5% would lie totally above or totally below the true level.

Resampling provides an analogous interval estimate for μ. This is accomplished by finding limits within which any stated percentage of the 1,000 computed resample means happened to fall. Those findings are called a **resampling interval**

FIGURE 8-10 Details of *Resampling Stats* run for lost production times.

estimate of μ. To get a 95% resampling interval estimate of the mean lost production time, *Resampling Stats* sifts through the 1,000 resample means generated to find the 2.5 percentile (239) as the lower limit and the 97.5 percentile (831.06) as the upper limit, so that it reports

95% resampling interval estimate of $\mu = (239, 831.06)$

Since it summarizes what was *actually achieved* in 1,000 resamples, you may find the interpretation of this interval is to be more concrete than that of the standard confidence interval.

RESAMPLING AND TRADITIONAL STATISTICS COMPARED

The resampling procedure has the advantage of being simple. Conclusions are reached using exactly the same information (original sample data) as with traditional statistics. Sampling error is inherent in both procedures. The major drawback to the bootstrapping approach has until recently been the computational demands. Personal computers have eliminated that limitation and, paradoxically, make it sometimes easier to use than traditional methods. Its main advantages are conceptual simplicity and ease of use. Traditional statistical procedures have the advantage of rich mathematical theory and can usually be applied without computer help.

But statistical theory itself can create burdens. For instance, the limits of the confidence interval are based on critical values for the Student t distribution. That distribution is theoretically correct only when the parent population is assumed to be normally distributed. The sample data themselves cannot absolutely confirm the normality assumption, weakening the case for using the traditional confidence interval.

OPTIONAL EXERCISES

8-64 Refer to the salary data for executive secretaries in Exercise 8-42. Using a random number assignment such that 1 corresponds to the lowest possible sample salary, 2 to the second lowest, and so on up to 0 for the highest, determine (by hand) the resample values for each of the following sets of random numbers and compute the resample means.
(a) 6 5 4 8 6 1 3 2 0 1
(b) 9 9 8 7 3 5 6 6 4 0
(c) 3 4 4 0 7 6 7 8 5 0

8-65 *Computer Exercise.* Refer to the salary data for executive secretaries in Exercise 8-42. Using *Resampling Stats,* generate 1,000 resamples of size 10, computing the mean for each. Obtain a 95% resampling interval estimate of the true population mean salary.

8-66 *Computer Exercise.* Using the lost production time sample data in Figure 8-10, generate 1,000 resamples of size 9, computing the median for each. (Duplicate the *Resampling Stats* instructions, replacing the command MEAN B C by the command MEDIAN B C.) Obtain a 95% resampling interval estimate of the true population median salary.

8-67 *Computer Exercise.* Refer to the lost production time sample data in Figure 8-10.
(a) Generate 5,000 resamples of size 9, computing the mean for each. (Duplicate the *Resampling Stats* instructions, replacing the command REPEAT 1000 with REPEAT 5000.) Obtain a histogram and a 95% resampling interval estimate of the true population median salary.
(b) Compare this interval to the one obtained in the text. Should they differ by much?
(c) Compare the histogram obtained to the one in Figure 8-10. What do you notice?

8-68 *Computer Exercise.* Use the lost production time sample data in Figure 8-10.
(a) Using *Resampling Stats,* generate for each of the following cases 1,000 resamples, computing the mean for each. Obtain in each case a 95% resampling interval estimate of the true population mean salary and a histogram.
(1) Use a sample size of $n = 25$. (The original data will still be the initial 9 data values. Change the SAMPLE 9 A B command to SAMPLE 25 A B.)
(2) Use instead a sample size of $n = 100$.
(b) What are the important differences between (1) and (2)? What may you conclude regarding sample size and estimating precision?

CHAPTER 9

HYPOTHESIS TESTING

BEFORE READING THIS CHAPTER, MAKE SURE YOU UNDERSTAND:

How to avoid bias in selecting samples and how sampling error arises (Chapter 4).

The properties of the sampling distribution of the mean and proportion (Chapter 6).

How to use the normal curve to obtain probabilities for the sample mean and proportion (Chapter 7).

About confidence intervals and how they are used and constructed (Chapter 8).

When the Student *t* distribution should be used instead of the normal distribution (Chapter 8).

What considerations are important in establishing a sample size (Chapter 8).

AFTER READING THIS CHAPTER, YOU WILL UNDERSTAND:

About hypothesis testing and how it may be used in decision making.

How the hypothesis testing approach deals with sampling error.

The basic forms of a hypothesis test.

How decisions are reached when testing hypotheses.

About the two basic hypothesis testing procedures and when *z* or *t* should be used.

About the significance level of a test and how it relates to the decision rule and error probabilities.

We have encountered one form of statistical inference, estimation, and we are now ready for another type of inference, **hypothesis testing**. Since it culminates in a decision, the latter is the more dynamic form. Statistical testing is based on two opposite assumptions called **hypotheses** regarding populations that have some unknown features. This chapter considers the most common hypothesis tests involving assumed levels for population parameters. Later chapters consider other forms of hypotheses used to compare two or more populations, pertaining to the manner in which two variables are related, concerned with the structure of the population frequency distribution, or involving tests for randomness of data.

To set the stage, we begin with hypothesis tests for the unknown level of the population mean. Such an evaluation is helpful when there are two complementary actions, the outcomes of which depend on the unknown μ. For example, a supervisor can adjust controls whenever the mean output exceeds some prescribed level. Since the unknown μ cannot be known, the final action must depend on sample data. The sample mean is used as the **test statistic**, with adjustment taking place only if the computed $\bar{X}$ exceeds some critical value.

Unfortunately, the supervisor can never know if a shutdown was really necessary, since samples can give false readings. We can control but never eliminate the underlying sampling error. Unlike estimation, where precision and reliability are the major concerns, hypothesis testing focuses on a **decision rule** that balances the probabilities for taking incorrect actions. A good rule allows the supervisor to keep small the chance of unnecessarily adjusting controls while avoiding leaving bad controls in operation too long. Errors of omission and errors of commission can be managed through hypothesis testing when there has been a judicious choice of decision rule.

9-1 BASIC CONCEPTS OF HYPOTHESIS TESTING: TESTING A NEW DRUG

We will develop the many concepts that link hypotheses together via an extensive illustration based on whether or not the government should approve the manufacturing of a new drug.

A dietary supplement is being tested to determine if it can dissolve cholesterol deposits in arteries. A major cause of coronary ailments is hardening of the arteries caused by the accumulation of cholesterol. The Food and Drug Administration will not allow the product to be marketed unless there is strong evidence that it is effective. A sample of 100 middle-aged men have been selected for the test, and each man is given a standard daily dosage of the supplement. At the end of the experiment, the change in each man's cholesterol level is recorded.

On the basis of the sampling experiment, a government administrator must decide between two courses of action.

1. Release the supplement for public use.
2. Delay the supplement (and request further research).

Some risks are involved due to uncertainty regarding the supplement's true effectiveness (the sample may not be representative of the population as a whole).

THE NULL AND ALTERNATIVE HYPOTHESES

The possible effectiveness states of the supplement are referred to as *hypotheses*. Because the drug administrator is considering only two possibilities—ineffective versus effective—the following hypotheses apply.

1. The supplement is ineffective.
2. The supplement is effective.

The true effectiveness of the supplement is defined by the population of the percentage reduction in cholesterol levels experienced by all middle-aged men who took the supplement. We summarize effectiveness in terms of the population mean.

$$\mu = \text{Population mean percentage reduction in cholesterol levels}$$

The government will classify the drug as effective only if it produces more than a 20% improvement ($\mu > 20\%$). The percentage reduction constitutes a *target population* that does not exist until (and will not exist unless) the supplement is widely available. However, it is still possible to draw a sample from this "imaginary" population.

The first hypothesis is customarily referred to as the null hypothesis. Here, "null" represents no change from the natural variation in cholesterol level. In terms of the population mean μ, we use the following expression for the

NULL HYPOTHESIS

$$H_0: \mu \le 20\% \qquad \text{(Supplement is ineffective.)}$$

The second hypothesis is called the alternative hypothesis. We express the

ALTERNATIVE HYPOTHESIS

$$H_A: \mu > 20\% \qquad \text{(Supplement is effective.)}$$

The hypotheses are formulated so that H_0 and H_A are opposites: When one is true, the other is false.

To achieve another special notation in hypothesis testing, we add the subscript 0 to the symbol for the population parameter. In the present example, this gives

$$\mu_0 = 20\%$$

which is the **pivotal value** of the population mean. In general, the null hypothesis holds for all levels of μ that are equal to μ_0 or that fall on one side of this value, and the alternative hypothesis applies otherwise. Unfortunately, we do not know which side actually applies, because the true value of μ remains unknown.

MAKING THE DECISION

The decision as to whether or not to release the dietary supplement coincides with the test results obtained for the sample patients. This decision is based on the value of

$$\bar{X} = \text{Sample mean percentage reduction in cholesterol levels}$$

We refer to $\bar{X}$ as the **test statistic**.

The chosen action must be consistent with the sample evidence. The two choices may be expressed in terms of the following hypotheses.

1. Release the supplement. Conclude that the null hypothesis is false (the supplement is effective). This is expressed as *reject* the null hypothesis.

2. Delay the supplement. Conclude that the null hypothesis is true (the supplement is ineffective). This is expressed as *accept* the null hypothesis.

The government administrator will release the supplement for public use if it provides a large mean reduction $\bar{X}$ in the cholesterol levels of the sample patients, because this result would seem to deny H_0. Similarly, she will delay the supplement's introduction if $\bar{X}$ is small and the supplement has not been very effective during the sample test—evidence that tends to confirm H_0.

In effect, the administrator will decide what action to take when she sets the point of demarcation for $\bar{X}$. For now, we suppose that the value 22 is chosen. This value is commonly referred to as the **critical value** or the **acceptance number**. The test statistic is then used to formulate a decision rule. A decision rule allows us to translate sample evidence into a plan for choosing a course of action.

DECISION RULE

Accept H_0 if $\bar{X} \leq 22$ (Delay the supplement.)

Reject H_0 if $\bar{X} > 22$ (Release the supplement.)

The decision rule identifies **acceptance and rejection regions** for the possible value of $\bar{X}$, which can be illustrated as

Accept H_0 (Delay the supplement.)	Reject H_0 (Release the supplement.)

$\bar{X}$

22

Having established the decision rule, the ultimate action taken by the government agency will be determined by the observed sample results. The computed value of $\bar{X}$ will fall within either the acceptance or the rejection region, and H_0 will be accepted or rejected accordingly. When H_0 is *rejected*, the results are said to be **statistically significant**. Here, we use the word *significant* in a special sense. All hypothesis-testing results are important, but the test is statistically significant only when the null hypothesis is *rejected*.

The structure of the decision is shown in Table 9-1. Two courses of action are considered: *Delay* or *release* the supplement. There are also two population states: The supplement is either *ineffective* or *effective*. For each combination of an action and a supplement quality, the outcome represents a correct decision or an error. Two correct decisions are (1) *accept* a true null hypothesis (delay an ineffective supplement) and (2) *reject* a false null hypothesis (release an effective supplement). The decision rule may also result in two errors.

TYPE I ERROR

Reject H_0 when it is true   (Release an ineffective supplement.)

TYPE II ERROR

Accept H_0 when it is false   (Delay an effective supplement.)

TABLE 9-1 The Decision Structure for the Dietary Supplement

Possible Population States	Course of Action	
	Accept Null Hypothesis If $\bar{X} \le 22$ (Delay the supplement.)	**Reject Null Hypothesis** If $\bar{X} \ge 22$ (Release the supplement.)
Null Hypothesis True $\mu \le 20$ (μ_0) (Supplement is ineffective.)	**Correct Decision** Probability $= 1 - \alpha$ (Delay the ineffective supplement.)	**Type I Error** Probability $= \alpha$ Significance level $= \alpha$ (Release the ineffective supplement.)
Null Hypothesis False $\mu > 20$ (μ_0) (Supplement is effective.)	**Type II Error** Probability $= \beta$ (Delay the effective supplement.)	**Correct Decision** Probability $= 1 - \beta$ (Release the effective supplement.)

To evaluate the decision rule, we find the probability for committing each error. It is conventional to denote the probabilities for these errors by α and β (the lower case Greek *beta*).

ERROR PROBABILITIES

$$\alpha = \Pr[\text{Type I error}] \;\;= \Pr[\textit{Reject } H_0 | H_0 \text{ is true}]$$
$$\beta = \Pr[\text{Type II error}] = \Pr[\textit{Accept } H_0 | H_0 \text{ is false}]$$

The value α is also called the **significance level** of the test.

FINDING THE ERROR PROBABILITIES

How good is the choice of 22 as the critical value? When establishing the decision rule, the decision maker's attitude toward the two types of errors should be reflected in the levels of the α and β probabilities.

To find α, we consider the case when the null hypothesis is true: the population mean μ is ≤ 20. The null hypothesis holds for any value of $\mu = 20$ or less, such as 0, 9.7, or 17.5. We focus on the extreme possibility, when the pivotal value of μ_0 applies, and set the population mean at $\mu = 20$.

The normal curve at the top of the following figure shows the sampling distribution of $\bar{X}$ when the null hypothesis is true and $\mu = \mu_0$ exactly. Although we do not know its actual value, for purposes of illustration we assume that the population standard deviation for reduction in cholesterol levels is $\sigma = 10$. The probability for the Type I error (the shaded area to the right of 22 under the top curve) is

$$\alpha = \Pr[\bar{X} > 22 | H_0 \text{ is true } (\mu = \mu_0 = 20)] = .5 - .4772 = .0228$$

When the null hypothesis is false, a different sampling distribution of $\bar{X}$ applies, as shown in the bottom curve. The dietary supplement is effective for any mean percentage reduction in cholesterol levels greater than 20. In our illustration, $\mu = 23.5$ (and the population standard deviation is assumed to be the same as before). The corresponding probability for the Type II error (the shaded area to the left of 22 under the bottom curve) is

$$\beta = \Pr[\bar{X} \leq 22 | H_0 \text{ is false } (\mu = 23.5)] = .5 - .4332 = .0668$$

A similar β probability can be obtained for any other level of μ greater than 20. For instance, when $\mu = 24.5$ is used, we obtain $\beta = .0062$.

Of course, the number of ways for H_0 to be false is unlimited, and μ might assume any level, with a different β applicable to each. A fundamental dilemma of hypothesis testing is balancing the targeted α with the family of possible βs. This is accomplished by choosing an appropriate decision rule.

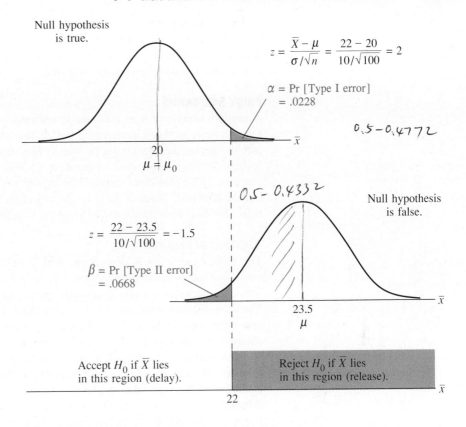

Null hypothesis
is true.

$$z = \frac{\overline{X} - \mu}{\sigma/\sqrt{n}} = \frac{22 - 20}{10/\sqrt{100}} = 2$$

$\alpha = \text{Pr [Type I error]}$
$= .0228$

$0.5 - 0.4772$

20
$\mu = \mu_0$

$0.5 - 0.4332$

Null hypothesis
is false.

$$z = \frac{22 - 23.5}{10/\sqrt{100}} = -1.5$$

$\beta = \text{Pr [Type II error]}$
$= .0668$

23.5
μ

Accept H_0 if $\overline{X}$ lies
in this region (delay).

Reject H_0 if $\overline{X}$ lies
in this region (release).

22

CHOOSING THE DECISION RULE

In hypothesis-testing situations, the decision maker's only real choice is selecting the decision rule. In testing the dietary supplement, the administrator could use a different critical value, such as 23 or 24. Different α and β probabilities would then apply. An ideal decision rule provides a balance between α and β.

In general, the Type I error (rejecting the null hypothesis when it is true) is more serious. In our example, the Type I error is to release an ineffective supplement, because great care is taken in the United States to avoid marketing any drug or food additive that could have serious undesirable side effects. **Decision rules are usually selected to guarantee a target level for α.**

Avoiding the Type I error by keeping α small tends to increase the chances of committing a Type II error (accepting a false null hypothesis). Delaying an effective supplement could result in deaths that could have been prevented by the use of an anticholesterol agent. Both the α and β error probabilities can be kept tolerably small by using a large sample size.

MAKING THE DECISION

Up to this point, our perspective with the dietary supplement decision has been from the planning stage of the sampling investigation. Recall that the planning stage occurs before data have been collected, and it is at that time when the hypotheses are formulated, the sample size is fixed (perhaps by the constraints of a budget), and the decision rule is established in accordance with the prescribed

α. Only after all of this will the sample observations be made.

In the dietary supplement decision, the action taken depends on what sample results are obtained. Consider the following hypothetical scenarios that might apply once the data have been collected.

FIRST SCENARIO

A random sample of $n = 100$ men is selected, administered the supplement, and their cholesterol levels determined before and after the experiment. For each subject the percentage reduction is found. The mean percentage reduction in cholesterol levels is computed to be $\bar{X} = 25.7\%$. This result exceeds the critical value of 22%, providing statistically significant evidence that the supplement is indeed effective. Since $\bar{X}$ falls in the rejection region, the administrator would *reject* her null hypothesis and *release* the supplement for public use.

SECOND SCENARIO

The same experiment is performed, with little change in cholesterol levels. The computed mean percentage reduction is only $\bar{X} = 17.4\%$. This is not strong evidence in support of an effective supplement, and $\bar{X}$ falls in the acceptance region. The administrator must *accept* H_0, concluding that the supplement is ineffective, and *delay* its introduction until further research has been completed. (That same action would be required for any computed level for $\bar{X}$ that is ≤ 22, such as 15.1, 19.2, or even 21.9.) Since H_0 is accepted, the test results are not statistically significant. The administrator should be aware of the β probabilities that this decision is incorrect (since in spite of the sample results μ might nevertheless be bigger than 20).

FORMULATING HYPOTHESES

The null and alternative hypotheses are opposites: When one is true, the other is false. This allows us to consider just two actions and two outcomes for each hypothesis, depending on whether H_0 is true or false. One area of potential confusion is deciding which hypothesis to label H_0. In earlier statistical applications, the null hypothesis corresponded to the assumption that no change occurs, which accounts for the adjective *null*. For example, in testing a drug, the usual hypoth-

---

STATISTICS AROUND US

Testing Grade Point Averages

A college president wants to show that special admissions students have lower grade point averages (GPAs) than regular students, whose mean GPA is 2.75. Letting μ represent the mean GPA of the special admissions, the following hypotheses apply.

$$H_0: \mu \geq 2.75 \quad \text{(GPAs are as high.)}$$
$$H_A: \mu < 2.75 \quad \text{(GPAs are lower.)}$$

The null hypothesis places $\mu \geq 2.75$, since this is what the decision maker wishes to disprove.

esis would be that it yields little or no improvement over nature. The H_0 used in the dietary supplement illustration corresponds to this designation. Another frequently used guideline is to designate the hypothesis that the decision maker wishes to disprove as H_0. *A common practice is to designate as H_0 the hypothesis for which rejection when true is the more serious error.* Thus, the Type I error would be worse than the Type II error. In the dietary supplement illustration, the decision rule was chosen so that this happened to be the case.

The Statistics Around Us box on page 388 and the earlier dietary supplement illustration have hypotheses that place μ to one side of the pivotal level. A statistical investigation involving such hypotheses is referred to as a **one-sided test**. A second form, described below, has hypotheses used in a **two-sided test**.

The Statistics Around Us box on page 390 shows that designation of the null hypothesis can vary with the decision making context.

STATISTICS AROUND US

Testing Cannery Machinery

A cannery inspector must determine whether or not cans are being filled with a mean $\mu = 16$ ounces of tomato paste. Machinery must be adjusted if the cans are being overfilled or underfilled. The inspector uses the following hypotheses.

H_0: $\mu = 16$ ounces   (Machinery is satisfactory.)
H_A: $\mu \neq 16$ ounces   (Machinery must be adjusted.)

The null hypothesis is $\mu = 16$ ounces, so that the machinery is assumed to be satisfactory. The Type I error of rejecting H_0 when it is true (unnecessarily adjusting the machinery when it is satisfactory) is the more serious error. The alternative hypothesis states that $\mu \neq$ (is not equal to) 16 ounces. This can also be stated as $\mu > 16$ ounces (cans are being overfilled) or $\mu < 16$ ounces (cans are being underfilled). This is an example of a *two-sided alternative*.

EXERCISES

9-1 A new slow-dissolving aspirin tablet is being evaluated. The null hypothesis is that the tablet dissolves too fast, with a mean dissolving time of $\mu \leq 10$ seconds. The new aspirin will replace the old one if the sample mean $\overline{X} > 12$ seconds; otherwise, the old tablet will continue to be marketed.

Express the null and alternative hypotheses as inequalities involving μ. Then, construct an appropriate hypothesis-testing decision table similar to Table 9-1. Be sure to identify the Type I and Type II errors. (Do *not* try to find the values of α and β.)

9-2 For each of the following situations, indicate the Type I and Type II errors and the correct decisions.
(a) H_0: New system is not better than the old one.
    (1) Adopt new system when new one is better.

STATISTICS AROUND US

Producers, Consumers, and Blenders

A **producer** of lightbulbs must decide whether or not to ship a production batch to its regular customers or to scrap it and sell it as "seconds." The bulbs in any batch may be predominantly good ones with a long mean lifetime μ, or mainly bad ones with a short μ. Ideally, the regular customers would get nothing but good batches, and the bad bulbs would all be scrapped. But since the producer will decide a batch's disposition from sample data, there are two errors.

1. Some good batches will be scrapped.
2. Some bad batches will be shipped.

Producers tend (perhaps shortsightedly) to view the first error as more serious. The null hypothesis would then be that any particular batch is good, so that in terms of mean lifetime μ,

$$H_0: \mu \geq \mu_0$$

where μ_0 might be the advertised "minimum" lifetime.

The **consumer** of the lightbulbs can refuse or buy any particular shipment. This choice will be based on a sample inspection by the receiving-department. The following two errors apply.

1. Some of the time a bad shipment will be bought.
2. Some of the time a good shipment will be refused.

Consumers are less concerned about inconveniencing suppliers than acquiring defective merchandise, so they judge the first error to be more serious. The null hypothesis is thus that the shipment is bad. In terms of mean lifetime,

$$H_0: \mu \leq \mu_0$$

where μ_0 might be a barely tolerable mean lifetime.

To achieve color consistency, a **blender** of Scotch whiskey wants to ensure a balance between the levels of dark and light whiskeys. The mixing process is designed so that any batch of barrels yields a mean color index of 100. When the true level for μ is lower, dark ingredients should be added; when it is higher, light additives should be included. Unfortunately, not all barrels can be opened, and μ can't be known. Some batches will be unnecessarily darkened, others improperly lightened. These errors are equally serious, and the following simple null hypothesis applies.

$$H_0: \mu = \mu_0$$

The value $\mu_0 = 100$ would be appropriate here.

(2) Retain old system when new one is better.
(3) Retain old system when new one is not better.
(4) Adopt new system when new one is not better.
(b) H_0: New product is satisfactory.
  (1) Introduce new product when unsatisfactory.
  (2) Do not introduce new product when unsatisfactory.
  (3) Do not introduce new product when satisfactory.
  (4) Introduce new product when satisfactory.
(c) H_0: Batch of transistors is of good quality.
  (1) Reject good-quality batch.
  (2) Accept good-quality batch.
  (3) Reject poor-quality batch.
  (4) Accept poor-quality batch.

9-3 Indicate whether the following statements are true or false. If false, explain why.
(a) A Type II error is the same as accepting the alternative hypothesis when it is false.
(b) Either a Type I or a Type II error must occur.
(c) The significance level is the probability of rejecting the null hypothesis when it is true.

9-4 For each of the following hypothesis-testing situations, state the Type I and Type II errors in nonstatistical terms (for example, releasing a poor drug or delaying a good drug).
(a) The null hypothesis is that a new manufacturing process is no improvement over the existing one. If sample evidence indicates that it is better, the new process will be adopted.
(b) A union is negotiating with management for a 4-day workweek with 9-hour working days at a slightly higher wage. The union argues that efficiency and morale will be improved, thereby increasing output. Choosing as its null hypothesis that productivity will not increase, management will sign the contract if there is adequate evidence that the union claims are true. Otherwise, some hard negotiating sessions will follow.
(c) The objective of a statistical study is to determine whether a stronger consumer protection law is favored by more voters than the present one. Taking as its null hypothesis that the new law does not meet greater voter approval, a consumer action group will lobby for the new law if there is significant evidence to the contrary.

9-5 A university introduces a new degree program.
(a) What null and alternative hypotheses are being tested if the Type I error is to incorrectly conclude that the program will succeed?
(b) What hypotheses are being tested if the Type II error is to incorrectly conclude that the program will succeed?

9-6 In testing the hypotheses

$$H_0: \mu \le \mu_0 \quad \text{and} \quad H_A: \mu > \mu_0$$

use $\mu_0 = 150$.

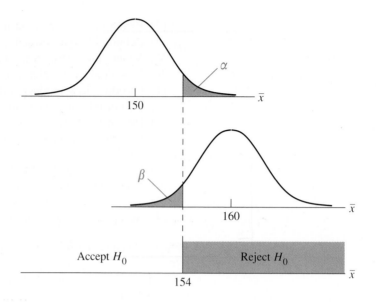

Suppose that the population standard deviation is $\sigma = 30$ and a sample of $n = 100$ is used. Find the Type I error probability α when $\mu = 150$ and the Type II error probability β when $\mu = 160$. Assume that the following decision rule applies.

$$Accept\ H_0\ if\ \bar{X} \leq 154$$

$$Reject\ H_0\ if\ \bar{X} > 154$$

9-7 Repeat Exercise 9-6 using 156 as the critical value. Is the new α larger or smaller? Is the new β larger or smaller?

9-8 Repeat Exercise 9-6 using a larger sample of $n = 200$. Is the new α larger or smaller? Is the new β larger or smaller?

9-2 TESTING THE MEAN

Now that we have mastered the basic concepts of hypothesis testing, we are ready to apply the procedure. The sampling study begins with the formulation of the hypotheses. After the decision maker establishes a Type I error probability α (significance level) and an appropriate sample size n, everything that follows is largely mechanical. The sample data are collected, and a critical value corresponding to the desired value of α is found. The computed value of the test statistic is then compared to the critical value, and the decision rule indicates the appropriate course of action.

THE HYPOTHESIS-TESTING STEPS

To simplify hypothesis testing with the mean, a five-step procedure will be used.

STEP 1
Formulate the null and alternative hypotheses. The decision parameter is the unknown population mean μ. A pivotal level μ_0 is used to define H_0 and H_A.

ONE-SIDED TESTS

The more serious error establishes which side of μ_0 to include under H_0. One of the following two null hypotheses applies.

$$\mu \leq \mu_0 \quad \text{or} \quad \mu \geq \mu_0$$

There are two types of errors.

1. Taking the wrong action when $\mu \leq \mu_0$.
2. Taking the wrong action when $\mu \geq \mu_0$.

The null hypothesis is H_0: $\mu \leq \mu_0$ if the first error is more serious, and H_0:$\mu \geq \mu_0$ if the second error is more serious.

TWO-SIDED TESTS

In a two-sided test, the following null hypothesis applies.

$$H_0{:}\mu = \mu_0$$

Since H_0 is false when $\mu < \mu_0$ and when $\mu > \mu_0$, the testing of the null hypothesis is two-sided.

STEP 2

Select the test statistic and procedure. In testing the mean, $\bar{X}$ is the natural test statistic. When the population standard deviation σ is known, the normal distribution is used as the sampling distribution for $\bar{X}$. Hypothesis testing procedures are developed using probability concepts for the normal distribution. But, when σ is unknown, the testing procedures must instead be based on the

STUDENT *t* TEST STATISTIC (σ unknown)

$$t = \frac{\bar{X} - \mu_0}{s/\sqrt{n}}$$

There are two types of testing procedures, depending on the nature of the decisions to be made. The **single-decision procedure** tests H_0 just once. The **recurring-decisions procedure** applies when there are a series of decisions to be made, so that H_0 is accepted or rejected over and over again. Both the choice of the test statistic and the form of the decision rule differ under the two procedures.

A recurring-decisions procedure uses one decision rule many times, possibly to be applied by different investigators at various places. The test statistic should be easy to compute and readily understood by all participants. To keep the procedure simple, the population standard deviation value is stipulated for all test applications, so that σ is treated as a *known* quantity.

When σ is known, there are two versions of the decision rule. Both versions utilize the fact that $\bar{X}$ has a normal sampling distribution. The **detailed decision**

rule compares the computed mean $\bar{X}$ to one or two critical values expressed on the same numerical scale. The **abbreviated decision rule** compares instead the computed values of the normal deviate z to one or two values read from the normal curve table. The two versions are used widely and lead to identical results.

A single-decision procedure requires no stipulation on the value of the population standard deviation, and σ may remain *unknown*. In this case, the Student t serves as the test statistic and the decision rule is based on it.

STEP 3

Establish the significance level and identify the acceptance and rejection regions. The probability α of the more serious Type I error, also referred to as the significance level, is prescribed in advance. Figure 9-1 summarizes the three basic test forms. How H_0 is expressed determines which form applies. Each is labeled according to which part of the sampling distribution curve overlaps the rejection region for the computed test statistic values. A test form is either lower-tailed, upper-tailed, or two-sided. The acceptance and rejection regions are defined by the critical value of the test statistic.

In testing the mean when σ is known, these regions are determined by the **critical normal deviate** z_α (or $z_{\alpha/2}$) for which the normal curve upper tail area is α (or $\alpha/2$). When σ is unknown, the critical value of the Student t statistic t_α (or $t_{\alpha/2}$) is used instead.

When a recurring-decisions procedure applies, so that σ is known and $\bar{X}$ serves as the test statistic, the critical normal deviate is used in conjunction with a *detailed decision rule* to compute the

CRITICAL VALUES OF THE SAMPLE MEAN (σ known)

Lower-tailed tests ($H_0: \mu \geq \mu_0$)   Upper-tailed tests ($H_0: \mu \leq \mu_0$)

$$\bar{X}^* = \mu_0 - z_\alpha \sigma_{\bar{X}} \qquad \bar{X}^* = \mu_0 + z_\alpha \sigma_{\bar{X}}$$

Two-sided tests ($H_0: \mu = \mu_0$)

$$\bar{X}_1^* = \mu_0 - z_{\alpha/2} \sigma_{\bar{X}} \quad \text{and} \quad \bar{X}_2^* = \mu_0 + z_{\alpha/2} \sigma_{\bar{X}}$$

The computed standard error of $\bar{X}$ is*

$$\sigma_{\bar{X}} = \frac{\sigma}{\sqrt{n}}$$

The *abbreviated decision rule* requires computing the

*When the sample size n is large in relation to the population size N, the finite population correction factor is used to compute $\sigma_{\bar{X}}$.

$$\sigma_{\bar{X}} = \frac{\sigma}{\sqrt{n}} \sqrt{\frac{N-n}{N-1}}$$

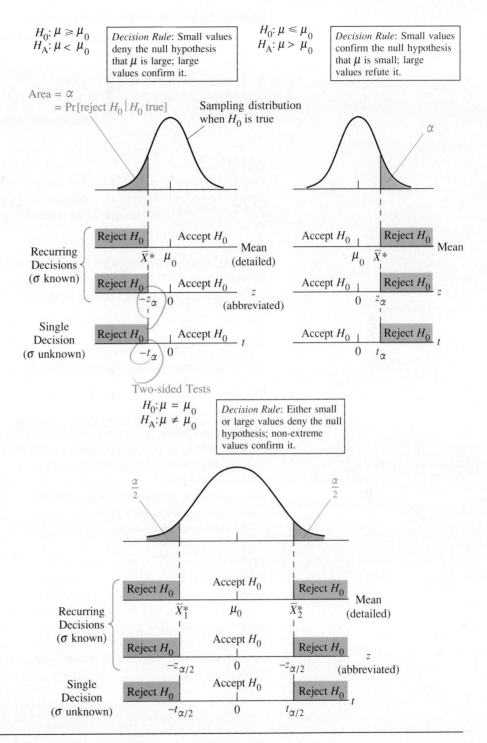

FIGURE 9-1 Three forms of hypothesis testing for the mean.

NORMAL DEVIATE FOR SAMPLE RESULTS (σ known)

$$z = \frac{\bar{X} - \mu_0}{\sigma_{\bar{X}}}$$

STEP 4

Collect the sample and compute the value of the test statistic. This step occurs during the second stage of the statistical sampling study. No revisions to steps 1–3 should be made during or after collecting sample data.

STEP 5

Make the decision. The decision rule established in Step 3 makes the final choice automatic. H_0 must be accepted if the computed value of the test statistic falls in the acceptance region and rejected otherwise.

UPPER-TAILED TESTS

Two detailed illustrations of upper-tailed tests for the mean follow.

SINGLE DECISION: TESTING AUDITING SOFTWARE

Consider how hypothesis testing may be used to evaluate a new software package.

Baskin and Shells is testing a new software package to be used in auditing field sites assisted by a portable personal computer. The test involves a team of two auditors who each examine identical data and complete workups. Judged equally skillful, one member uses the traditional manual procedures, the other the personal computer. A random sample of eight sites have been examined. The teammates switch roles at each new job.

The following steps apply.

STEP 1

Formulate the null and alternative hypotheses. Baskin and Shells will adopt the proposed software and use it in portable personal computers system-wide if the present test shows that doing so is a significant improvement over manual field auditing methods. The most serious error would be to do this when in fact there is not a time savings under computerized auditing. Letting μ represent the actual mean time savings using the computers in field auditing workups, the following hypotheses apply.

$H_0: \mu \leq 0$ (Personal computer software does not save time.)
$H_A: \mu > 0$ (Personal computer software saves time.)

The pivotal level of the population mean is $\mu_0 = 0$.

STEP 2

Select the test statistic and procedure. The firm's decision is made just once. The Student t therefore serves as the test statistic.

STEP 3

Establish the significance level and identify the acceptance and rejection regions. Management wants good protection against the very undesirable Type I error of adopting computerized field auditing when it won't be faster on the average. A small significance level of $\alpha = .01$ is thus chosen. The resulting test is upper-tailed. Using $8 - 1 = 7$ degrees of freedom, Appendix Table F provides the critical value $t_\alpha = t_{.01} = 2.998$. The acceptance and rejection regions are shown below.

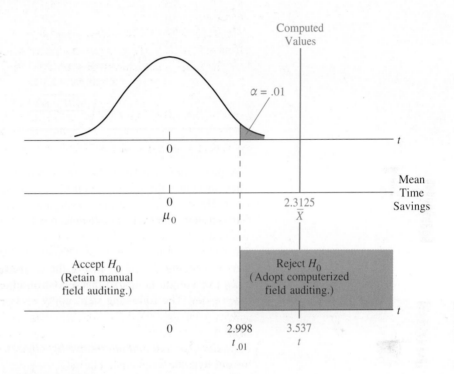

STEP 4

Collect the sample and compute the value of the test statistic. The workup completion times are provided in Table 9-2. To obtain the time savings using the computer, the latter completion times are subtracted from the manual times. The computed value of the test statistic is

$$t = \frac{2.3125 - 0}{1.849/\sqrt{8}} = 3.537$$

STEP 5

Make the decision. Since the computed value of the test statistic falls in the rejection region, the firm must *reject* the null hypothesis that computerized field auditing yields no time savings. Baskin and Shells will adopt a policy of using personal computers with the tested software.

RECURRING DECISIONS: ADJUSTING MIXING CONTROLS

Consider how hypothesis testing may be used to establish a permanent testing policy for monitoring production.

TABLE 9-2 Test Results of Auditing Software for Personal Computers

Site	Completion Time Manual Procedure	Completion Time Personal Computer	Difference X	X^2
1	4.1 hours	1.7 hours	+2.4 hours	5.76
2	9.5	6.2	+3.3	10.89
3	12.3	13.5	−1.2	1.44
4	18.4	14.8	+3.6	12.96
5	7.5	5.0	+2.5	6.25
6	3.4	3.0	+.4	.16
7	6.5	3.5	+3.0	9.00
8	12.5	8.0	+4.5	20.25
			+18.5	66.71

$$\bar{X} = 18.5/8 = 2.3125$$

$$s = \sqrt{\frac{66.71 - 8(2.3125)^2}{8 - 1}} = 1.849$$

A production superintendent for a pharmaceutical manufacturer must decide when to adjust the mixing controls for the final stage of production of a pain killer. He wants to base these everyday decisions on the mean weight of inert materials per tablet. The desired mean value μ is .5 milligram (mg) for each tablet, although a lower level would be satisfactory. A decision rule needs to be found that technicians may use to determine whether or not to adjust control settings, thereby keeping the mean within the desired limit. A new sample of tablets is taken every eight hours, so that a control-adjustment decision can be made three times a day. The following steps apply.

STEP 1
Formulate the null and alternative hypotheses. The superintendent selects the following hypotheses.

$$H_0: \mu \le .5\text{mg} \qquad \text{(Weight is within desired limit.)}$$
$$H_A: \mu > .5\text{mg} \qquad \text{(Weight is above desired limit.)}$$

The pivotal level of the mean material weight is $\mu_0 = .5$mg per tablet.

The above designation provides a Type I error of unnecessarily adjusting controls when the mean actually falls within the desired limit. The Type II error is failing to adjust controls when the mean level of inert materials is intolerably high. The first error is judged to be more serious.

STEP 2
Select the test statistic and procedure. The sample mean weight $\bar{X}$ serves as the test statistic. From previous testing, the superintendent establishes a value of $\sigma = .2$ mg for the population standard deviation. The standard deviation is assumed to be stable even though the mean fluctuates, and σ is therefore treated as a *known* quantity.

STEP 3
Establish the significance level and identify the acceptance and rejection regions. The superintendent decides that a 5% significance level will adequately protect

against the undesirable Type I error. To keep the incidence of the Type II error low, he relies on a fairly substantial sample size of $n = 25$ tablets.

The standard error of $\bar{X}$ is

$$\sigma_{\bar{X}} = \frac{.2}{\sqrt{25}} = .04 \text{ mg}$$

Since a *large* $\bar{X}$ refutes the null hypothesis that the mean level of inert materials falls within the desired limit, the resulting test is *upper-tailed*. Using the significance level of $\alpha = .05$, the critical normal deviate, from Appendix Table E, is $z_{.05} = 1.64$. The critical value of the sample mean is

$$\bar{X}^* = .5 + 1.64(.04) = .566 \text{ mg}$$

The acceptance and rejection regions are shown in the figure that follows.

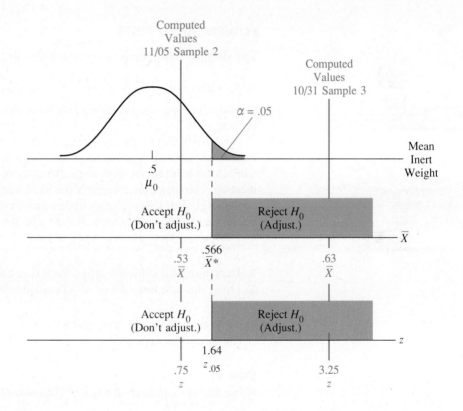

STEP 4

Collect the sample and compute the value of the test statistic. This step is conducted every eight hours. The mean weight of inert materials is computed for each 25-tablet sample.

STEP 5

Make the decision. As in Step 4, a decision is made every eight hours in accordance with the decision rule.

When implemented, the test is run three times daily using a different sample of tablets each time. Two results are illustrated above. On 10/31 during the swing shift, the computed value of the sample mean is $\bar{X} = .63$ mg. Since $\bar{X}$ falls within the rejection region, the null hypothesis must be *rejected* and the controls adjusted. The opposite conclusion is reached on 11/05 during the day shift. The computed value of the sample mean is found to be $\bar{X} = .53$ mg. Since the value falls within the acceptance region, the null hypothesis, for that shift, must be *accepted*, and no control adjustments are made.

The same conclusions may be reached using an abbreviated decision rule. If the computed normal deviate falls above $z_\alpha = z_{.05} = 1.64$, the null hypothesis must be rejected; otherwise it is accepted. We have

10/31 Sample 3   11/05 Sample 2

$$z = \frac{.63 - .5}{.04} = 3.25 \qquad z = \frac{.53 - .5}{.04} = .75$$

Reject H_0 *Accept* H_0

LOWER-TAILED TESTS

Two detailed illustrations of lower-tailed tests for the sample mean follow.

SINGLE DECISION: FINE TUNING AN EMPLOYMENT SCREENING TEST

Consider how hypothesis testing may be used to evaluate an employment screening test.

The Variety Galore Stores have redesigned their employment screening examination for sales clerk positions to eliminate sex bias. Management must decide whether to decrease the new test's difficulty or to adopt it without further modification. The major uncertainty is the mean score μ to be achieved by the clerical applicant pool. If μ is as high or higher than the historical mean score of 70 points, the revised test is easy enough. Should μ be lower, the new test is too hard. Since μ is unknown, there are two types of errors.

1. Decreasing the difficulty when the test is easy enough.
2. Using the new test without modification when it is too hard.

The first error is judged least desirable.
The following steps apply.

STEP 1
Formulate the null and alternative hypotheses. The following hypotheses apply.

$H_0: \mu \geq 70$ (Test is easy enough.)
$H_A: \mu < 70$ (Test needs difficulty decreased.)

The pivotal level of the mean score is $\mu_0 = 70$.

STEP 2
Select the test statistic and procedure. The new test is administered to a random sample of $n = 100$ applicants for the clerical positions. This is a one-time decision. The population standard deviation σ of all the test scores remains unknown, and the Student t serves as the test statistic.

STEP 3

Establish the significance level and identify the acceptance and rejection regions. Although a tiny significance level such as $\alpha = .01$ would be ideal, that would be accompanied by unacceptably high chances of adopting the test with no changes when it is too easy. Management decides that a better balance would be achieved between the Types I and II errors if they set the significance level at the higher level of $\alpha = .05$. Using $100 - 1 = 99$ degrees of freedom, Appendix Table F provides the nearest critical value of $t_{.05} = 1.658$. Since a low value of the sample mean test score $\bar{X}$ refutes the null hypothesis, the test is lower-tailed. Thus, a negative value of t lying below -1.658, will lead to rejection of H_0. The acceptance and rejection regions are shown in the figure that follows.

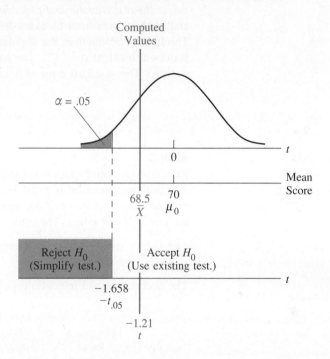

STEP 4

Collect the sample and compute the value of the test statistic. The computed value of the sample mean is $\bar{X} = 68.5$ points, and the value of the sample standard deviation is $s = 12.4$. The computed value of the test statistic t is

$$t = \frac{68.5 - 70}{12.4/\sqrt{100}} = -1.21$$

STEP 5

Make the decision. Since t falls within the acceptance region, the null hypothesis must be *accepted* and the existing test must be used without modification.

RECURRING DECISIONS: TESTING TAPE THICKNESS

Consider how hypothesis testing may be used to evaluate a new laser control.

Scotty Adhesives has installed a new laser control to determine when a roll of cellophane tape has reached the desired thickness. To exceed labeling requirements by an acceptable margin, the mean length μ of individual rolls must be at least 525 inches. Otherwise the control mechanism needs to be replaced.

The following steps apply.

STEP 1

Formulate the null and alternative hypotheses. The following hypotheses apply.

$$H_0: \mu \geq 525'' \qquad \text{(Control is working properly.)}$$
$$H_A: \mu < 525'' \qquad \text{(Control needs replacement.)}$$

The pivotal level of the mean length is $\mu_0 = 525''$ per roll.

STEP 2

Select the test statistic and procedure. A random sample of $n = 50$ rolls is tested and each is measured to exact length. The sample mean $\bar{X}$ is then computed. Throughout production, the population standard deviation is assumed to be at the historical level of $\sigma = 12''$. The sample mean $\bar{X}$ may therefore serve as the test statistic. The standard error of $\bar{X}$ is

$$\sigma_{\bar{X}} = \frac{12''}{\sqrt{50}} = 1.70''$$

STEP 3

Establish the significance level and identify the acceptance and rejection regions. A significance level of $\alpha = .01$ is chosen. Appendix Table E provides the critical normal deviate of $z_{.01} = 2.33$. Since a low value of $\bar{X}$ refutes the null hypothesis the test is lower tailed. The critical value for the sample mean is

$$\bar{X}^* = 525'' - 2.33(1.70) = 521.04''$$

The acceptance and rejection regions are shown below.

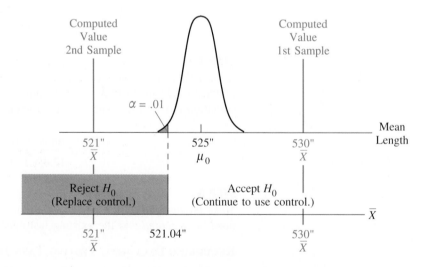

STEP 4

Collect the sample and compute the value of the test statistic. Samples are taken periodically. The computed mean value of the *first* sample is $\bar{X} = 530''$.

STEP 5

Make the decision. Since the first $\bar{X}$ falls within the acceptance region, H_0 must be *accepted* and the control must remain in operation.

A second sample yields a computed mean of value $\bar{X} = 521''$. Since $\bar{X}$ now falls within the rejection region, H_0 must be *rejected* and the control replaced.

TWO-SIDED TESTS

Two detailed illustrations of two-sided tests using a single-decision and a recurring-decisions procedure follow.

SINGLE DECISION: QUALITY CONTROL IN FOOD PROCESSING

Consider how a two-sided hypothesis test may be used to maintain quality control in food production.

A food company advertises that there are 105 chunks of beef in every 15-ounce can of its chili. To verify that its standards are being met in chili production, periodic checks of product quality are made by measuring the quantity of beef in several random samples of 15-ounce cans of chili.

Management cannot be sure that 105 chunks of beef will be added to every can, and can control only the *mean number* of chunks per can.

If current production has a lower mean than 105, remedial action is to be taken. However, because beef is by far the most expensive chili ingredient, a mean higher than 105 will also require remedial action. The management wishes to avoid both high and low extreme values in the mean beef quantity. A sample of $n = 100$ cans is tested.

STEP 1

Formulate the null and alternative hypotheses. The following hypotheses apply.

$$H_0: \mu = 105 \quad \text{(No correction is required.)}$$
$$H_A: \mu \neq 105 \quad \text{(Correction is required.)}$$

Here, $\mu_0 = 105$ beef chunks. The two-sided alternative hypothesis states that the quantity of beef differs from μ_0, so that either $\mu > 105$ (too much beef) or $\mu < 105$ (too little beef).

STEP 2

Select the test statistic and procedure. Since the population standard deviation σ is unknown, $\bar{X}$ cannot serve as the test statistic. The Student t is used instead.

STEP 3

Establish the significance level and identify the acceptance and rejection regions. There are two ways the Type I error may occur: to unnecessarily correct for overfilling or for underfilling. Management desires a significance level of $\alpha = .05$. This is split: Half of the value is assigned to the left tail and half to the right tail. Using $100 - 1 = 99$ degrees of freedom, Appendix Table F provides the nearest critical value of $t_{\alpha/2} = t_{.025} = 1.98$. The acceptance and rejection regions are shown in the following figure.

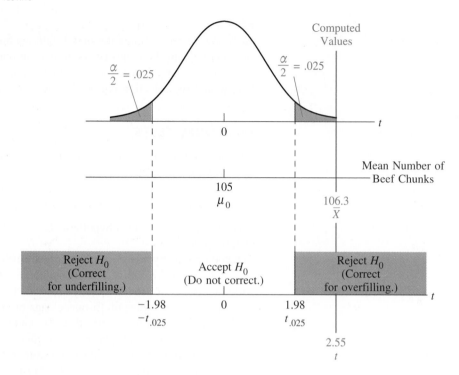

STEP 4

Collect the sample and compute the value of the test statistic. The computed value of the sample mean is $\bar{X} = 106.3$ beef chunks, and the value of the standard deviation is $s = 5.1$ beef chunks. The computed value of the test statistic is

$$t = \frac{\bar{X} - \mu_0}{s/\sqrt{n}} = \frac{106.3 - 105}{5.1/\sqrt{100}} = 2.55$$

STEP 5

Make the decision. Since t falls in the upper rejection region, the null hypothesis must be *rejected.* The test results are significant at the 5% level, and the management must take corrective action to remedy overfilling.

RECURRING DECISIONS: QUALITY CONTROL IN RECEIVING SHIPMENTS

Consider how hypothesis testing may be used to establish a routine maintenance policy.

A brass fixture manufacturer is reformulating its policy for receiving shipments of one-hundred pound ingots. It is too expensive to continue weighing all ingots, since they would have to all be unpackaged. Instead, a sample mean is computed for $n = 100$ ingots, and the shipment will be accepted without further weighing if the computed value is within the limits determined below.

The following steps apply.

STEP 1

Formulate the null and alternative hypotheses. The following hypotheses apply.

$$H_0: \mu = 100 \text{ lbs}$$
$$H_A: \mu \neq 100 \text{ lbs}$$

The pivotal level of the mean ingot weight is $\mu_0 = 100$ lbs. Management uses a two-sided test because the final billing from the smelter is adjusted according to shipment weight when received.

STEP 2
Select the test statistic and procedure. From previous experience, the standard deviation in ingot weights has been firmly established at $\sigma = 2$ lbs. The sample mean $\bar{X}$ may therefore serve as the test statistic. The standard error of $\bar{X}$ is

$$\sigma_{\bar{X}} = \frac{2}{\sqrt{100}} = .2 \text{ lb}$$

STEP 3
Establish the significance level and identify the acceptance and rejection regions. Management has to separately weigh each ingot in a rejected shipment, which is quite costly because of the necessary unpackaging. The significance level has therefore been set at $\alpha = .01$ to keep the incidence of unnecessary weighings low. The critical normal deviate is $z_{\alpha/2} = z_{.005} = 2.57$. The critical values of the sample mean are

$$\bar{X}_1^* = 100 - 2.57(.2) = 99.49 \text{ lbs}$$
$$\bar{X}_2^* = 100 + 2.57(.2) = 100.51 \text{ lbs}$$

The acceptance and rejection regions are shown below.

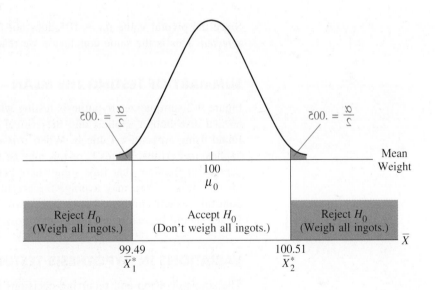

STEP 4
Collect the sample and compute the value of the test statistic. A sample mean is computed for each shipment.

STEP 5
Make the decision. If a computed mean value such as $\bar{X} = 100.2$ lbs falls within the acceptance region, the shipment would be *accepted* without further weighing.

Should a shipment yield a sample mean falling within one of the rejection regions, such as $\bar{X} = 98.7$ lbs or $\bar{X} = 101.1$ lbs, it would be *rejected* and all ingots weighed.

HYPOTHESIS TESTING AND CONFIDENCE INTERVALS

Two-sided hypothesis tests are related to statistical estimation with confidence intervals. We can approach the testing procedure by first constructing a $100(1 - \alpha)\%$ confidence interval from the sample results. If μ_0 falls inside the interval, the null hypothesis must be accepted; otherwise, it is rejected.

Here, α represents the proportion of similarly constructed intervals (found in duplicated sampling experiments) that fail to bracket μ_0 when it is the true mean. This interpretation means that the Type I error of rejecting H_0 when it is true occurs at frequency α.

In the previous quality control illustration, $\bar{X} = 106.3$ beef chunks, $s = 5.1$, and $n = 100$. Using these data to construct a 95% confidence interval gives

$$\mu = \bar{X} \pm t_{\alpha/2}\frac{s}{\sqrt{n}}$$

$$= 106.3 \pm 1.98\frac{5.1}{\sqrt{100}}$$

$$= 106.3 \pm 1.0$$

or

$$105.3 \le \mu \le 107.3 \text{ beef chunks}$$

Since the pivotal value $\mu_0 = 105$ does not fall within this interval, H_0 must be *rejected*. This is the same conclusion we reached earlier.

SUMMARY OF TESTING THE MEAN

Figure 9-2 summarizes hypothesis testing with the mean. When σ is known, the normal distribution applies, and the critical normal deviates z_α or $z_{\alpha/2}$ may be found using Appendix Table E. When σ is unknown, the Student t distribution applies, and critical values t_α or $t_{\alpha/2}$ may be found using Appendix Table F. (For degrees of freedom that falls somewhere between the listed tabled values, read the one nearest. You may average the neighboring values if the degrees of freedom falls exactly midway between the two. For large sample sizes, the critical-values should be read from the df $= \infty$ row.)

VARIATIONS IN HYPOTHESIS-TESTING PROCEDURES

The single-decision and recurring-decisions procedures are useful in sorting situations and choosing an appropriate course of action. A common convention is to simply specify whether or not σ is known. When σ is unknown, the entire hypothesis-testing procedure may be referred to as a **t-test**. Likewise, when σ is known, the procedure may be referred to as a **z-test**, since it is based on the normal curve.

Not only does the terminology vary, but the procedure may differ also. Two important variations follow.

SIGNIFICANCE OF RESULTS

Instead of concluding that you must either *accept* H_0 or *reject* H_0, and then take the corresponding action, another common approach is to *make no decision at all*. In this case, a conclusion is reached in terms of one of the following statements.

1. The test results are not significant at the α level.
   (equivalent to *accept* H_0)

2. The test results are significant at the α level.
   (equivalent to *reject* H_0)

This type of reporting is often found in research publications when no specific decision needs to be made. One shortcut is not to mention alpha, which is generally understood to be some conventional level, such as .01.

PROBABILITY FOR GETTING THE SAME RESULT

In published research, when no decision is needed, the reader may be allowed to select a significance level. No level is stipulated for α. Instead, a probability value is determined that establishes the likelihood of getting the reported result were the null hypothesis to actually be true. *Readers draw their own conclusions.*

COMPUTER-ASSISTED HYPOTHESIS TESTING

As with the estimating procedures in Chapter 8, statistical testing may be done with the assistance of a computer. Here, again, computing $\bar{X}$ and s is the hardest part. If the computations have already been done (either by hand, with a calculator, or using a computer), it is very easy to do the rest by hand.

Computer software packages can do various amounts of the work. Many provide just the computed values of $\bar{X}$ and s. The Minitab® software package does a bit more.

t-TEST WHEN σ IS UNKNOWN

Figure 9-3 displays the computer printout of the auditing software data given in Table 9-2. Minitab computes the same values of $\bar{X}$ and s that we found earlier, and reports the *estimated* value of $\sigma_{\bar{X}}$ (s divided by $\sqrt{n}$). The computed value of the test statistic $t = 3.54$, (found previously) is also given. Finally, notice that the **prob. value** of .0047 is provided. This number expresses the likelihood of getting sample results identical to or more extreme than those actually obtained.

z-TEST WHEN σ IS KNOWN

The computer printout of a *z*-test is similar to that of a *t*-test. The level of σ must be provided with the input. Consider, again, the control-adjustment decision for the production of a pain killer. Figure 9-4 displays the computer printout for the sample results for a particular 8-hour shift. The computed value of the test statistic is $z = 1.08$. Since this value falls below the critical normal deviate of $z_{.05} = 1.64$, the null hypothesis must be *accepted*, and the mixing controls are not adjusted. (The same conclusion may be reached by noting that the computer-generated prob. value of .14 exceeds the desired $\alpha = .05$ significance level.)

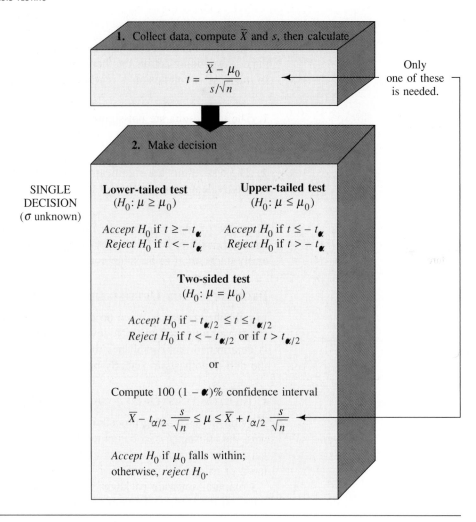

FIGURE 9-2 Summary of hypothesis-testing procedures with the mean.

```
MTB > set c1
      2.4, 3.3, -1.2, 3.6, 2.5, 0.4, 3.0, 4.5
MTB > end
MTB > name c1 'Time Sav'
MTB > ttest mu=0 c1;
SUBC> alternative=+1.


TEST OF MU = 0.000 VS MU G.T. 0.000

                N      MEAN    STDEV  SE MEAN         T    P VALUE
Time Sav        8     2.312    1.849    0.654      3.54    0.00475
```

Note: Figure generated on an IBM PC using Minitab®.

FIGURE 9-3 Computer printout for the auditing software hypothesis test.

1. Compute $\sigma_{\overline{X}}$, find critical value, and establish decision rule

Lower-tailed test $(H_0: \mu > \mu_0)$

$$\overline{X}^* = \mu_0 - z_\alpha \sigma_{\overline{X}}$$

Accept H_0 if $\overline{X} \geq \overline{X}^*$ (if $z \geq -z_\alpha$)
Reject H_0 if $\overline{X} < \overline{X}^*$ (if $z < -z_\alpha$)

Upper-tailed test $(H_0: \mu < \mu_0)$

$$\overline{X}^* = \mu_0 - z_\alpha \sigma_{\overline{X}}$$

Accept H_0 if $\overline{X} \leq \overline{X}^*$ (if $z \leq z_\alpha$)
Reject H_0 if $\overline{X} > \overline{X}^*$ (if $z > z_\alpha$)

Two-sided test $(H_0: \mu = \mu_0)$

$$\overline{X}_1^* = \mu_0 - z_{\alpha/2} \sigma_{\overline{X}}$$
$$\overline{X}_2^* = \mu_0 + z_{\alpha/2} \sigma_{\overline{X}}$$

Accept H_0 if $\overline{X}_1^* \leq \overline{X} \leq \overline{X}_2^*$ (if $-z_{\alpha/2} \leq z \leq z_{\alpha/2}$)

Reject H_0 if $\overline{X} < \overline{X}_1^*$ (if $z < -z_{\alpha/2}$
or if $\overline{X} > \overline{X}_2^*$ or if $z > z_{\alpha/2}$)

RECURRING
DECISIONS
(σ known)

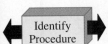
Identify
Procedure

When $n < .10N$:

$$\sigma_{\overline{X}} = \frac{\sigma}{\sqrt{n}}$$

When $n > .10N$:

$$\sigma_{\overline{X}} = \frac{\sigma}{\sqrt{n}} \sqrt{\frac{N-n}{N-1}}$$

2. Collect data, compute $\overline{X}$, and decide using

$$\overline{X} \text{ directly or } z = \frac{\overline{X} - \mu_0}{\sigma_{\overline{X}}}$$

EXERCISES

9-9 In testing the hypotheses

$$H_0: \mu \leq \mu_0 \quad \text{and} \quad H_A: \mu > \mu_0$$

using $\mu_0 = 100$, the desired Type I error probability is $\alpha = .10$. The values $\overline{X} = 102.6$ and $s = 25$ have been computed for a sample of $n = 100$.
(a) Is this a lower- or an upper-tailed test? Sketch this situation; include an appropriate Student t curve.
(b) Find the critical value t_α and indicate the acceptance and rejection regions on your sketch.
(c) Compute the value of the Student t test statistic and indicate in which region it falls. Should the null hypothesis be accepted or rejected?

9-10 In testing the hypotheses

$$H_0: \mu \leq 160 \quad \text{and} \quad H_A: \mu > 160$$

```
MTB > set c1
      .33, .45, .67, .85, .23, .49, 1.01, .76, .41, .30, .25
      .66, .74, .52, .49, .37, .46, .55, .60, .82, .44, .53
      .25, .67, .73
MTB > end
MTB > name c1 'Inert Wt'
MTB > ztest mu=.5, sigma=.2, c1;
SUBC> alternative=+1.
```

```
TTEST OF MU = 0.5000 VS MU G.T. 0.5000
THE ASSUMED SIGMA = 0.2000


              N        MEAN      STDEV     SE MEAN         Z    P VALUE
Inert Wt     25      0.5432     0.2055      0.0400      1.08       0.14
```

Note: Figure generated on an IBM PC using Minitab®.

FIGURE 9-4 Computer printout for a sample of tablets.

a significance level of $\alpha = .05$ is desired. The test is upper-tailed, as shown below.

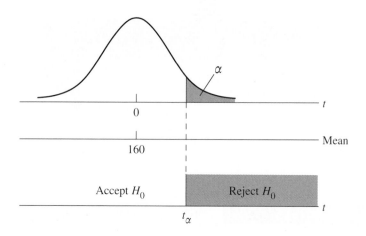

The values $\bar{X} = 170$ and $s = 30$ have been computed for a sample of $n = 25$. Complete the hypothesis-testing steps to determine whether the null hypothesis should be accepted or rejected.

9-11 In testing the hypotheses

$$H_0: \mu \geq \mu_0 \quad \text{and} \quad H_A: \mu < \mu_0$$

using $\mu_0 = 30$, the desired Type I error probability is $\alpha = .05$. The values $\bar{X} = 25$ and $s = 10$ have been computed for a sample of $n = 100$. Referring to Exercise 9-9, answer (a), (b), and (c).

9-12 A Yellow Giant cannery inspector insists that the mean weight of ingredients in 16-ounce cans be precisely accurate. If the mean weight falls above or below this figure, some remedial action is taken. The inspector assumes that the standard deviation is $\sigma = .3$ ounces. A significance level of $\alpha = .05$ is established for a sampling test, so that the Type I error (taking unnecessary action) is expected 5% of the time. Each hour, a sample of $n = 25$ cans is taken, each can is opened, and the contents are weighed.

(a) Perform the hypothesis-testing Steps 1–3.

(b) Should the inspector take remedial action if (1) $\bar{X} = 15.9$ ounces; (2) $\bar{X} = 16.2$ ounces?

9-13 In testing the hypotheses

$$H_0: \mu = \mu_0 (= 0) \quad \text{and} \quad H_A: \mu \neq \mu_0$$

the values $\bar{X} = 1.2$ and $s = 9.5$ have been computed for a sample of $n = 100$. At the significance level of $\alpha = .05$, should the null hypothesis be accepted or rejected?

9-14 The output of a chemical process for manufacturing Snail Hail is monitored by taking a sample of $n = 25$ vials to determine the level of impurities. The null hypothesis is that the mean level is exactly .05 gram per liter. If the mean level of impurities in the sample is too high, the process will be stopped and the tanks will be purged; if the sample mean is too low, the process will also be stopped and the valves will be readjusted. Otherwise, the process will continue. The test is two-sided, as shown below.

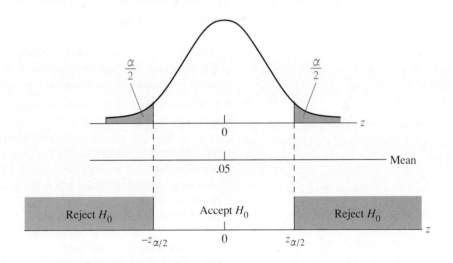

Assume that the population standard deviation is $\sigma = .02$ gram per liter. Sample results provide $\bar{X} = .064$ gram. At a significance level of $\alpha = .01$, should the process be stopped? If so, what type of remedial action is required?

9-15 For each of the following two-sided testing situations, construct a 95% confidence interval for μ. Decide whether H_0 must be accepted or rejected.

(a) $\mu_0 = 10;\ \bar{X} = 10.1;\ s = .3;\ n = 100$

(b) $\mu_0 = .72;\ \bar{X} = .705;\ s = .13;\ n = 169$

(c) $\mu_0 = 0;\ \bar{X} = -.7;\ s = 2.5;\ n = 625$

9-16 In packaging Snow White soap powder, the desired weight is 5 lbs. If the true population mean value μ is above or below this amount, the machinery needs to be adjusted. Management has decided that unnecessary adjustments occur no more than 5% of the time.

Each day a random sample of 100 boxes is selected, and then, based on the sample mean weight, a decision is made whether to leave the equipment alone or to adjust it. Suppose that $\bar{X}$ is 5.1 lbs. and $\sigma = .5$ lbs. What action should be taken?

9-17 Satcom Corporation will use a new power cell in future communications satellites if sample evidence refutes the null hypothesis that it exhibits a mean-time-between-failure no greater than the present cell, which is rated at $\mu = 550$ hours. A sample test of 100 new cells provides a sample mean of $\bar{X} = 565$ hours and a standard deviation of $s = 200$ hours.

Assuming a significance level of 5%, perform all the hypothesis-testing steps. Should the new power cell be used?

9-18 Huey-Packer is evaluating an experimental tuning stand as a possible substitute for the present manual method of calibrating electronic timing devices. The stand will be acquired only if it can calibrate the devices in a mean time μ of less than 15 minutes. A sample of 50 units is to be tested, and nothing is known regarding the population of calibration times.

(a) Assuming a maximum chance of $\alpha = .01$ for acquiring the tuning stand when it takes 15 minutes or longer to complete calibration, express the decision rule.

(b) Test results provide a mean calibration time of 13.5 minutes, and a standard deviation of 3.4 minutes. What action should be taken?

9-19 A special paper has a desired thickness of .05 millimeter. If the mean value differs from this amount, the processing machinery requires adjustment. The value $\bar{X} = .051$ mm has been computed for a sample of $n = 100$ sheets. The assumed standard deviation is $\sigma = .002$ mm. At the $\alpha = .05$ significance level, should the machinery be adjusted or left alone?

9-20 A Wheel-Rite plant produces bearings with a specified 1-inch mean diameter. The standard deviation for all bearings produced is known to be .01 inch. A decision rule is to be established for determining when to correct for oversized or undersized items. This choice is based on a sample of 100 bearings, and the assumption is made that there is only an $\alpha = .01$ chance of taking corrective action when the production process is exactly meeting its mean target.

(a) Formulate the null hypothesis.

(b) What test statistic is appropriate?

(c) Express the decision rule.

(d) What action should be taken if (1) $\bar{X} = .993''$; (2) $\bar{X} = 1.0023''$?

9-21 A structural engineer is testing the strength of a newly designed steel beam required in cantilever construction. As his null hypothesis, he assumes that the mean strength will be at most as great as the 100,000 pounds per square inch (psi) for traditional beams. A test sample of $n = 9$ new beams has provided $\bar{X} = 105,000$ psi and $s = 10,000$ psi. At the $\alpha = .05$ significance level, should the engineer accept or reject his null hypothesis?

9-22 The product manager for Exonex wants to determine the time in which an experimental drug cures a skin disease. If management concludes that the drug yields a mean cure-time advantage over traditional treatment of more than 2 days, research will continue with the present formulation. Otherwise, a new formulation will be adopted for further testing. The drug will be administered to a sample of $n = 25$ persons and the cure-time advantage determined for each. The Type I error probability has been set at $\alpha = .05$ for switching to a new formulation when the present one achieves the desired advantage.

(a) Formulate the null hypothesis. Indicate which test statistic applies, and determine its critical value. Express the decision rule.

(b) Suppose the sample results for the cure-time advantage are $\bar{X} = 1.6$ days and $s = .4$ day. What action should the manager take?

9-23 P. J. Willy periodically checks the output of a chemical process to determine the level of impurities in the final product. If it contains too many impurities, the product will be reclassified; if it contains too few, an expensive catalyst is being consumed in undesirably large quantities. The process is designed to tolerate impurities of $\mu = .05$ gram per liter. Regardless of the mean impurity level, the historical standard deviation of .025 gram per liter applies.

The level of impurities in a sample of $n = 100$ 1-liter vials is measured at random times during each 4-hour period. The process is stopped if there are too many impurities (the tanks are purged) or too few impurities (the control valves are readjusted). The chief engineer will accept a Type I error probability of $\alpha = .01$ for unnecessarily stopping the process when the true mean level of impurities is at the target level.

(a) Perform hypothesis-testing Steps 1–3.

(b) What action should be taken in the following cases?

(1) At 8 A.M., $\bar{X} = .042$.

(2) At 12:30 P.M., $\bar{X} = .052$.

(3) At 5 P.M., $\bar{X} = .056$.

9-24 Your friend owns a retail store where she plans to give individual arriving customers a short verbal "commercial" message regarding the products for sale. Your friend asks you to determine if this will boost the mean sales transaction level μ, currently at $5.00. You may assume that the standard deviation per transaction is $1.00 and that the population is of unlimited size. You will monitor a random sample of $n = 200$ customers given this special treatment and determine the amount purchased by each.

(a) Your friend will adopt a policy of giving messages if sample evidence indicates that sales will improve. She wants most to avoid adopting this policy when the mean sales transaction won't improve. Formulate the null and alternative hypotheses.

(b) Suppose you wish to protect your friend with a probability of $\alpha = .05$ against rejecting the null hypothesis when it is true. Compute the critical value of the sample mean, and express the decision rule.

(c) You collect the sample data. What action should you take if (1) $\bar{X} = 5.37; (2) $\bar{X} = 5.05; (3) $\bar{X} = 4.97; (4) $\bar{X} = 5.20?

9-25 The Sour Grapes Winery is evaluating a modified fermentation process that involves higher temperatures than its present method. Since the new procedure requires specially designed controls, it has been judged economic only if production batches ferment faster than the mean time of 30 hours under the present system. If that isn't supported by testing, the present process will be continued. The test will involve 50 pilot batches to be run under the modified procedure.

(a) The more serious error is to adopt the modified process when it isn't actually the faster one. Express the null hypothesis in terms of the mean fermentation time μ.

(b) The standard deviation in fermentation time is unknown. Assuming a significance level of $\alpha = .01$, express the decision rule.

(c) Suppose the sample results are $\bar{X} = 29.5$ hours and $s = 4.91$ hours. What action should be taken?

9-26 The superintendent of a Deluxe Printing Company plant selects random samples of 100 rolls of paper from every large batch. The average length of the rolls in any shipment is unknown, although the standard deviation in lengths is assumed to always be $\sigma = 50$ feet. His null hypothesis is that $\mu \geq 525$ feet (satisfactory batch) and his alternative hypothesis is that $\mu < 525$ feet (short batch). Any shipment the superintendent believes to be short will be made into 100-foot rolls. Those believed to be satisfactory will be shipped.

Unfortunately, there is no way to be certain about the batch quality. A decision rule needs to be formulated to determine the action for each batch. This should be done, so that satisfactory batches are rendered just 1% of the time.

(a) What type of action is taken when H_0 is (1) accepted; (2) rejected?

(b) What is the significance level? Specify the appropriate test statistic and decision rule.

(c) For each of the following sample results, decide whether the null hypothesis should be accepted or rejected and the appropriate action to take.

(1) $\bar{X} = 514'$ (2) $\bar{X} = 530'$ (3) $\bar{X} = 521'$ (4) $\bar{X} = 508'$

9-27 *Computer exercise.* The accounting firm of Ernest & Whitney achieved the following percentage savings in audit time by using a new computer system for examining transactions.

80	10	37	26
45	29	44	5

(a) Compute the sample mean and standard deviation.

(b) At the $\alpha = .05$ significance level, can the firm conclude that the computer system will yield some level of savings in auditing time?

9-28 *Computer exercise.* You want to test the null hypothesis that the true mean family income in Blahsburg falls at or below $20,000. Assume that the standard deviation is $\sigma = \$2,500$. The following sample results have been obtained.

$19,874	$23,496	$33,520	$17,442	$19,002	$21,003
$37,720	$41,352	$17,246	$18,010	$19,240	$22,207

(a) Find the normal deviate statistic and the prob. value.

(b) Should the null hypothesis be accepted or rejected? Explain.

9-29 *Computer exercise.* A professor obtained the following sample differences in basic mathematics scores.

-7	-13	25	7	8	9	10	12	21	2
0	-2	-10	8	6	12	13	15	1	7

Each value was found by subtracting a student's standardized test score at the beginning of the semester from that achieved at the end. The standard deviation in differences is assumed to be 5 points.

(a) Perform a z-test to evaluate the null hypothesis that mean scores are the same at the beginning and the end of the semester (zero difference). At the 5% significance level, what should you conclude?

(b) Construct a 95% confidence interval for the mean score difference. Is this result consistent with your answer to (a)? Explain.

9-30 *Computer exercise.* The following Wear-Ever tire mileage data (in thousands of miles) have been obtained for a new tread design.

62.3	44.4	49.2	63.3	47.6	60.1
37.4	55.8	57.5	58.3	56.2	54.3

(a) Compute the sample mean and standard deviation.

(b) At the $\alpha = .05$ significance level, should you accept or reject the null hypothesis that, on the average, tires with the new tread will last 50 thousand miles or more?

9-3 TESTING THE PROPORTION

Tests of the proportion are used extensively in statistical applications. The proportion is important in a variety of managerial situations. In quality assurance, testing establishes whether the level of defectives in a shipment or from a production process is too high or too low. In marketing decisions, it is the proportion of product users in various categories that influences whether to change a product or its package, to enter a market, or to modify advertising.

The testing procedures for the proportion are similar to those for the mean. Ordinarily the sample proportion P serves as the test statistic in evaluations of π. The normal approximation closely approximates the sampling distribution for P for many situations, depending on the size for n and π.

USING *P* AS THE TEST STATISTIC

Tests of the proportion are categorized in the same way as those for the mean. The hypotheses and decision rules take the following forms.

Lower-tailed tests ($H_0: \pi \geq \pi_0$)   Upper-tailed tests ($H_0: \pi \leq \pi_0$)

Accept H_0 if $P \geq P^*$ *Accept H_0 if $P \leq P^*$*

Reject H_0 if $P < P^*$ *Reject H_0 if $P > P^*$*

Two-sided tests ($H_0: \pi = \pi_0$)

Accept H_0 if $P_1^* \leq P \leq P_2^*$

Reject H_0 if $P < P_1^*$ or   if $P > P_2^*$

The sampling distribution of P is approximated by a normal curve having mean $E(P) = \pi$ and standard error $\sigma_P = \sqrt{\pi(1 - \pi)/n}$. Critical normal deviates are used in the same manner as in testing the mean. The following expressions are used to find the

CRITICAL VALUES OF THE PROPORTION

Lower-tailed tests   Upper-tailed tests

$$P^* = \pi_0 - z_\alpha \sqrt{\frac{\pi_0(1 - \pi_0)}{n}} \qquad P^* = \pi_0 + z_\alpha \sqrt{\frac{\pi_0(1 - \pi_0)}{n}}$$

Two-sided tests

$$P_1^* = \pi_0 - z_{\alpha/2} \sqrt{\frac{\pi_0(1 - \pi_0)}{n}} \quad \text{and} \quad P_2^* = \pi_0 + z_{\alpha/2} \sqrt{\frac{\pi_0(1 - \pi_0)}{n}}$$

Some investigators prefer to use instead the normal deviate as the test statistic. That quantity is computed by subtracting π_0 from the computed P and dividing by the standard error.

NORMAL DEVIATE FOR TESTING THE PROPORTION

$$z = \frac{P - \pi_0}{\sqrt{\pi_0(1 - \pi_0)/n}}$$

The hypothesis-testing steps are discussed in the following illustration.

ILLUSTRATION: CONTROLLING ERRORS IN TELEPHONE DIRECTORIES

Liberty Bell Telephone publishes its telephone directory once a year. The state public utilities commission has established very strict quality guidelines. The greatest source of error is in preprocessing, not in typesetting. Historically, Liberty Bell has simply checked the directory against billing records for proper name, address, and telephone number. A new, more expensive procedure involves pasting each listing on the bill itself and asking customers to verify their own entry, placing a check mark by each correct item or making any necessary changes. This procedure will only work if a high proportion of customers respond, since expensive follow-up contacts are required for nonresponders.

A random sample of $n = 1,000$ customers has been selected for a test mailing to determine if the proportion π of responses received would be practical. If the sample response rate is sufficiently high, the new procedure will be adopted. Otherwise, the present method will be retained.

The following steps apply.

STEP 1

Formulate the null and alternative hypotheses. The new system is judged to be practical if at least 90% of the customers supply acknowledgement or corrections of their listings. The following hypotheses apply.

$$H_0: \pi \geq .90 \qquad \text{(New procedure is practical.)}$$
$$H_A: \pi < .90 \qquad \text{(New procedure is impractical.)}$$

The pivotal level for the population proportion of responders is $\pi_0 = .90$. The null hypothesis is designated in such a way that the more serious error corresponds to the Type I error: retaining the old preprocessing check when the new procedure would be practical.

STEP 2

Select the test statistic and procedure. The sample proportion P serves as the test statistic.

STEP 3

Establish the significance level and identify the acceptance and rejection regions. Liberty Bell management will tolerate only a 1% chance of retaining the old method when the new procedure would be practical. Using $\alpha = .01$, the critical normal deviate is $z_\alpha = z_{.01} = 2.33$ for this lower-tailed test. The critical value for P is

$$P^* = .90 - 2.33 \sqrt{\frac{.90(1 - .90)}{1,000}} = .878$$

The acceptance and rejection regions are shown in the figure that follows.

STEP 4

Collect the sample and compute the value of the test statistic. Only 791 listing responses were obtained from the sample mailing. The computed value of the test statistic is

$$P = \frac{791}{1,000} = .791$$

STEP 5

Make the decision. Since P falls within the rejection region, the test results are statistically significant. Liberty Bell management must *reject* the null hypothesis that the new procedure would be practical, and retain the old method.

The above test could have been performed using the normal deviate z instead of P as the test statistic. In that case, the computed value of z is

$$z = \frac{.791 - .90}{\sqrt{.90(1 - .90)/1,000}} = -11.49$$

Since z falls below $-z_\alpha = -2.33$, in the rejection region, the same conclusion is reached as before.

EXERCISES

9-31 In testing the hypotheses

$$H_0\colon \pi \le \pi_0 \ (= .5) \quad \text{and} \quad H_A\colon \pi > \pi_0$$

the desired Type I error probability is $\alpha = .10$. The value $P = .55$ has been computed for a sample of $n = 100$. Complete the hypothesis-testing steps to determine whether the null hypothesis should be accepted or rejected.

9-32 A quality control inspector at ChipMont tests random samples of $n = 100$ from the items in each shipment received from suppliers. If the proportion P of defective items is sufficiently low, the shipment is accepted; otherwise, it is rejected. The null hypothesis is that the true proportion of defectives in a shipment does not exceed the standard: $\pi \le \pi_0$. In all cases, the significance level is $\alpha = .05$.
(a) Is this a lower- or an upper-tailed test?
(b) For each of the following situations, decide whether the shipment will be accepted or rejected.
(1) $\pi_0 = .05$; $P = .08$
(2) $\pi_0 = .10$; $P = .08$
(3) $\pi_0 = .01$; $P = .04$

9-33 A statistician is testing the null hypothesis that exactly half of all MBAs continue their formal education by taking courses within ten years of graduation. Using a sample of 200 persons, she found that 111 had taken coursework since receiving their MBA. At the $\alpha = .05$ significance level, should the statistician accept or reject her null hypothesis?

9-34 A professional group claims that at least 40% of all engineers employed by aerospace firms switch jobs within three years of being hired. The alternative hypothesis is that the rate of job changing is below 40%. At the $\alpha = .01$ significance level, should the claim be accepted or rejected if the sample results show that 25 out of $n = 100$ engineers changed jobs?

9-35 Liberty Bell Telephone policy is to add an information operator to the pool whenever sample data indicate that all operators are busy an excessive proportion of the time. A Type I error probability of $\alpha = .05$ has been established for unnecessarily adding an operator when the pool is busy 50% of the time or less. A sample of $n = 20$ observations will be made at random times.

(a) The sample proportion of time busy P serves as the test statistic. Express the decision rule.

(b) What action should be taken if all operators are busy during 65% of the sample observation times?

9-36 A sample of $n = 100$ items has been selected at random from a large incoming shipment. The null hypothesis is that the proportion defective is at most .05. The sample proportion defective is .06. At the $\alpha = .05$ significance level, should the null hypothesis be accepted or rejected?

9-4 SELECTING THE TEST

SOME IMPORTANT QUESTIONS

We have covered the basic concepts of hypothesis testing that apply to means and proportions. It is now time to consider some fundamental questions.

1. *What other test statistics can we use?* Many test statistics other than $\bar{X}$ and P can be applied to hypothesis-testing situations. Usually, the nature of the test determines the type of test statistic to be employed. In later chapters, we will learn to use many new statistics to compare the parameters of two or more populations. In lieu of testing with $\bar{X}$, a number of so-called **nonparametric tests** (to be described in Chapter 19) may be used.

2. *How can we determine which test statistic will work best?* Often, we must choose from several alternative procedures. Perhaps the most important factor to consider in making this choice is the relative efficiency of each test.

3. *How can we evaluate a particular decision rule in terms of the protection it provides against both kinds of incorrect decisions, the Type I and Type II errors?* Both types of decision errors should be avoided. But we have seen that when the choice is based on sample data, some probability for each error (α and β) must be tolerated. Ordinarily, only α—the probability for committing the more serious Type I error—is explicitly considered in selecting a decision rule. But the statistician may revise the initial decision rule if it proves to be inadequate in protecting against the Type II error.

4. *What assumptions underlie the proposed testing procedure, and how do they affect its applicability?* The t test assumes that the population itself is normally distributed. Just how critical is such an assumption? At one extreme, an assumption can limit a test so severely that it cannot be applied to many decision-making situations. On the other hand, an assumption may prove to be relatively unimportant. A test that basically accomplishes what it is intended to do even when a requirement is not exactly met is said to be **robust** with respect to a violation of that assumption.

THE POWER CURVE

Usually there are several possible values of β, the Type II error probability. Remember that β is the probability for accepting H_0 when H_0 is false (and H_A is true). Using the alternative hypothesis $H_A: \mu > 20$ in our dietary supplement illustration, we can compute a different β for any particular level of μ greater than 20. On page 386, we computed $\beta = .0668$ when $\mu = 23.5$. Some other values are

$$\beta = .8413 \text{ when } \mu = 21$$

$$\beta = .5000 \text{ when } \mu = 22$$

$$\beta = .0228 \text{ when } \mu = 24$$

These probabilities are represented as points on the graph in Figure 9-5. The curve connecting the points is called a **power curve**. The height of the curve provides the probability $(1 - \beta)$ for rejecting the null hypothesis at the indicated possible level for μ.

The power curve can be useful in evaluating a hypothesis test. The usual hypothesis-testing procedure begins with a prescribed significance level α (the Type I error probability) and set sample size n. These parameters fix the levels of the β probabilities.

The decision maker may study the power curve and conclude that the βs are higher than the desired levels. In our dietary supplement illustration, two remedies are available.

1. Raise the significance level α, so that there is a higher Type I error probability for releasing an ineffective supplement. This shifts the critical value of the test statistic, lowering all the βs and providing a lower Type II error probability for delaying an effective supplement for each μ.

2. Increase the sample size n. This will decrease both the α and β probabilities for all levels of μ.

EFFICIENCY AND POWER

The choice of a test statistic is an important issue in advanced applications of hypothesis-testing theory. In many decision situations, a number of statistical tests can be performed. For instance, rather than find the actual levels of cholesterol reduction in patients treated in the dietary supplement illustration, the statistician could simply determine the proportion P of patients who achieved a major reduction in their cholesterol levels. Instead, the more detailed measure $\bar{X}$—the mean percentage reduction in cholesterol levels—was chosen. Generally, $\bar{X}$ provides more information than P, so that $\bar{X}$ is a more efficient test statistic than P. Thus, for the same sample size and Type I error probability α, the decision rule obtained for $\bar{X}$ should provide smaller Type II error probabilities β (and higher probabilities for rejecting H_0 when it is false). In this case, the $\bar{X}$-test is said to be more **powerful** than the P-test.

9-5 LIMITATIONS OF HYPOTHESIS-TESTING PROCEDURES

In this chapter we presented the *classical* statistical decision analysis. Its applicability to the rather large class of decision problems faced by the modern manager is limited in several ways. Paramount among these is the dependence on

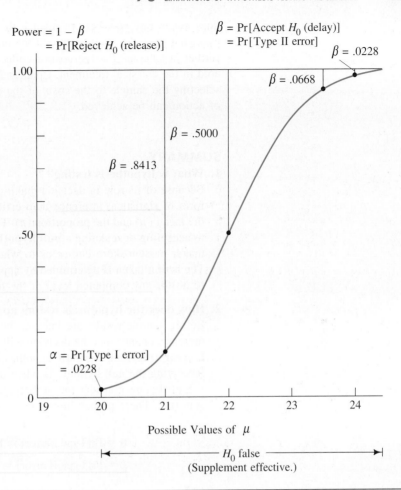

Power = $1 - \beta$
= Pr[Reject H_0 (release)]

β = Pr[Accept H_0 (delay)]
= Pr[Type II error]

$\beta = .0228$

$\beta = .0668$

$\beta = .5000$

$\beta = .8413$

α = Pr[Type I error]
= .0228

Possible Values of μ

H_0 false
(Supplement effective.)

FIGURE 9-5 Power curve for the dietary supplement decision.

samples for obtaining supportive or contradictory evidence. Many significant decisions must be made without first taking a sample, because a sample is too costly or simply unobtainable. For example, in deciding whether to drill for oil, the wildcatter does not collect direct sample evidence by drilling holes at random as the basis for rejecting or accepting the null hypothesis that there is oil. The only way such evidence may be obtained is to sink the shaft, and this can be done only after the decision has already been made to drill. What evidence is obtained must be of an indirect nature, such as results of geological surveys, seismic tests, and nearby drilling experience. Another limitation of hypothesis testing is its restricted applicability to decisions involving two alternatives when so many decisions involve choosing among a multitude of alternatives.

Even when classical hypothesis testing is applicable, there are improvements that can be made. One is to expand the process so that more information can be utilized. For instance, the fact that certain values of the population decision parameter may be more likely than others can be used by the decision maker to reduce the probability for an incorrect decision. Methods for doing this will be described in Chapter 28. A further limitation of the classical approach is that it does not in any way help to resolve the problem faced by a decision maker in assessing the risks associated with the incorrect decisions; this subject is covered further in Chapter 25. The cost of collecting the sample is not explicitly considered in the classical treatment. Chapter 27 shows how we can relate the costs of selecting the sample to the costs of the ensuing risks, so that an optimal course of action can be achieved.

SUMMARY

1. **What is hypothesis testing?**
   Because of its role in decision making, **hypothesis testing** is a more dynamic form of statistical inference than estimation. This chapter considers tests for the mean (μ) and the proportion (π). There are two possible actions, equivalent to accepting or rejecting a **null hypothesis** (H_0). While uncertain, the decision maker must make a choice as to whether or not the null hypothesis is true. The action taken is determined by applying a **decision rule** that specifies what to do for any computed level of the **test statistic**, $\bar{X}$ or P, or z or t.

2. **How does the hypothesis testing approach deal with sampling error?**
   Before sample results are known, the test statistic is a random variable, and there is a chance that the decision will be incorrect—resulting in either a **Type I error** (rejecting the null hypothesis when it is true) or a **Type II error** (accepting the null hypothesis when it is false).

   Statisticians consider the probabilities for these errors when setting a decision rule. These probabilities are

   $$\alpha = \Pr[\text{Type I error}] = \Pr[\textit{reject } H_0 | H_0 \text{ true}]$$
   $$\beta = \Pr[\text{Type II error}] = \Pr[\textit{accept } H_0 | H_0 \text{ false}]$$

   You ordinarily designate H_0 so that the more undesirable outcome corresponds to the Type I error.

3. **What are the basic forms of a hypothesis test?**
   The **pivotal parameter level** is denoted by μ_0 in testing the mean and by π_0 in testing the proportion. That value establishes the center of the sampling distribution for the test statistic, and this center is assumed to apply under the extreme case of the null hypothesis. Depending on the form of H_0, the procedure may be a **one-sided test** or a **two-sided test**. One-sided tests may be **lower-tailed** or **upper-tailed**. The following classifications apply.

Lower-tailed test	Upper-tailed test	Two-sided test
$H_0: \mu \geq \mu_0$	$H_0: \mu \leq \mu_0$	$H_0: \mu = \mu_0$
$\pi \geq \pi_0$	$\pi \leq \pi_0$	$\pi = \pi_0$

For an upper-tailed test, the Type I probability α corresponds to an area in the upper tail of the curve for the sampling distribution of the test statistic, and for a lower-tailed test, it corresponds to an area in the lower tail. For a two-sided test, α is equal to the sum of the matching areas in both tails.

4. **How are decisions reached when testing hypotheses?**

   The decision will be made depending on where the computed level of the test statistic falls. The point(s) of demarcation is (are) the **critical value(s)**. It separates the **acceptance region** from the **rejection region**. The form and placement of these regions is determined by the above test classifications.

5. **What are the two basic hypothesis testing procedures for the mean, and when should *z* or *t* be used?**

   In testing the mean, there is a basic dichotomy that depends on knowledge of the population standard deviation.

   When σ is unknown, the *Student t statistic* is used to test the hypothesis. It is convenient to designate such a test as a **single-decision procedure**. It is also referred to as a ***t*-test**.

   When σ is known, the normal distribution applies for $\bar{X}$. The decision rule then is based on the **critical normal deviate**, z_α or $z_{\alpha/2}$. Ordinarily, more than one decision is made with the same rule when σ is known, and it is convenient to classify this test of the mean as a **recurring-decisions procedure**. There are two versions of the procedure. A **detailed decision rule** involves the critical value(s) of $\bar{X}$ that falls above or below μ_0 at a distance of z_α or $z_{\alpha/2}$ times $\sigma_{\bar{X}}$. An **abbreviated decision rule** compares the computed z to the critical normal deviate. The ***z*-test** is another common designation for a test of the mean when σ is known.

6. **What is the significance level of a test, and how does it relate to the decision rule and error probabilities?**

   Once the null hypothesis is formulated, the decision maker must choose a value for α. This is the **significance level**. The critical value is positioned in accordance with α. A statistical decision rule guarantees that the Type I error probability will equal the significance level. But that rule may provide inadequate protection against the Type II error. Probabilities β for the latter vary, depending on the pivotal level μ_0 or π_0. The adequacy of the decision rule is sometimes assessed by examining the **power curve**.

REAL-LIFE STATISTICAL CHALLENGE

Applying Hypothesis Testing to the Automobile Dream List

In Chapter 8 concepts about statistical estimation were used to analyze populations for 232 autos. We will now apply hypothesis testing methods to the set of "dream machines."

Let us assume that the list of 15 cars in Table 6-20 represents a sample of the cars purchased by a firm for business use. To control costs, the company might be concerned whether the fleet mileage is above certain standards. We will determine for management whether the mileage is significantly above 20 miles per gallon. Our null hypothesis is:

$$H_0\text{: } \mu \leq 20 \qquad \text{(Mileage level is too low)}$$

REAL-LIFE STATISTICAL CHALLENGE

Our alternative hypothesis is:

$$H_A: \mu > 20 \qquad \text{(Mileage level is satisfactory)}$$

The Student t test statistic is used:

$$t = \frac{\bar{X} - \mu_0}{s/\sqrt{n}}$$

For the sample of 15 automobiles $\bar{X} = 26.47$ mpg and $s = 4.47$. The computed t value is:

$$t = \frac{26.47 - 20}{4.47/\sqrt{15}} = 5.60$$

Using significance level $\alpha = .01$ the critical value is $t_{.01} = 2.624$ for $(15 - 1) = 14$ degrees of freedom. Since $t = 5.60$ exceeds the critical value we can *reject* the null hypothesis and conclude that the gasoline mileage level is satisfactory.

The choice of the pivotal value and the level of significance was arbitrary. For example a pivotal value $\mu_0 = 25$ miles per gallon would have yielded $t = 1.27$; and at $\mu_0 = 24$ mpg, $t = 2.13$. In these two cases the null hypothesis would be accepted when $\alpha = .01$. For $\alpha = .05$, the critical value becomes $t_{.05} = 1.761$; we would reject the null hypothesis when $\mu_0 = 24$ (but not when $\mu_0 = 25$).

DISCUSSION QUESTIONS

1. Develop another hypothesis test using the mean gas mileage.
2. Comment on the impact on your test in Question 1 from altering the pivotal value or the sample size.
3. Develop two examples of hypothesis tests using the engine displacement data.
4. Develop a hypothesis for testing the proportion (for example: proportion of cars with manual transmissions, or various combinations of car type, large, midsize, etc.).

REVIEW EXERCISES

9-37 For each of the following situations, find the Type I error probability α that corresponds to the stated decision rule. In all cases, use a sample of $n = 100$.
(a) *Accept H_0 if $\bar{X} \geq 12$ Reject H_0 if $\bar{X} < 12$ $\mu_0 = 14$ and $\sigma = 18$*
(b) *Accept H_0 if $\bar{X} \leq 100$ Reject H_0 if $\bar{X} > 100$ $\mu_0 = 97$ and $\sigma = 20$*

9-38 For each of the following hypothesis-testing situations, $n = 100$ and $\alpha = .05$. In each case, decide whether H_0 should be accepted or rejected.
(a) $H_0: \mu \geq 25$; $H_A: \mu < 25$; $\bar{X} = 23.0$; $s = 4.7$.
(b) $H_0: \mu \leq 14.7$; $H_A: \mu > 14.7$; $\bar{X} = 15.3$; $s = 1.5$.
(c) $H_0: \mu = 168$; $H_A: \mu \neq 168$; $\bar{X} = 169$; $s = .92$.

9-39 The mean length of a random sample of $n = 20$ rolls of wire is $\bar{X} = 2,031$ meters(m), with a standard deviation of $s = 47$ m. The null hypothesis that

$\mu \geq 2,000$ m is to be tested. Assuming that $\alpha = .01$, should the null hypothesis be accepted or rejected?

9-40 You are asked to determine whether to accept or reject the null hypothesis that the mean processing time μ for special orders is less than or equal to 10 minutes. There will be a very large number of such orders processed, and you may assume that the standard deviation is 2 minutes per order (the same value that applies to regular orders). A sample of $n = 100$ special orders have been timed.
(a) Formulate the null and alternative hypotheses.
(b) Suppose you wish to protect yourself with a probability of $\alpha = .01$ against rejecting the null hypothesis when it is true. Compute the critical value of the sample mean, and express the decision rule.
(c) Collect the sample data. What action must be taken if (1) $\bar{X} = 10.62$ min; (2) $\bar{X} = 10.47$ min; (3) $\bar{X} = 10.25$ min?

9-41 A presidential candidate plans to campaign in only those primaries that he is preferred by at least 20% of the voters in his party. A random sample of 100 voter preferences is obtained from each state. In each case, the null hypothesis is that the state meets the 20% criterion. The desired Type I error probability is $\alpha = .05$. Decide whether the null hypothesis should be accepted or rejected in each of the following states. Also decide whether or not the candidate will enter the campaign in each of these states.

State	Number Preferring Candidate
(a) New Hampshire	12
(b) Florida	23
(c) Wisconsin	15
(d) Massachusetts	10

9-42 Gizmo Corporation will be manufacturing a bearing with a specified 1/2-inch diameter. The standard deviation in diameter is unknown, and corrective action will be taken based on a sample of 100 items measured.
(a) Formulate the null hypothesis.
(b) What test statistic is appropriate?
(c) Using $\alpha = .01$, express the decision rule.
(d) What action should be taken: (1) if $\bar{X} = .497''$ and $s = .0075''$? (2) if $\bar{X} = .508''$ and $s = .013''$?

9-43 Ace Assemblers is reviewing its employment screening procedures for detail work. Several new persons, none having prior experience, have been hired. They have all been given a manual dexterity test. An investigator wishes to test the null hypothesis that the mean test score μ of newly hired inexperienced persons is just as high as that of the company's experienced workers, for which it has been established that the mean is 81.

Only 15 inexperienced persons take the test. They achieve a mean score of $\bar{X} = 78.3$ with a standard deviation of $s = 5$. At a significance level of $\alpha = .05$, should the null hypothesis be accepted or rejected?

9-44 The Fruty Tooty product manager wishes to determine whether or not to change the package design for the cereal. She feels that it will be worth the bother only if more than 60% of nonusers prefer the new box to the old one. She most wants to avoid changing the box when the preference proportion π is smaller, so that her null hypothesis is $\pi \leq .60$.

The manager selects a random sample of $n = 100$ persons who don't buy Fruty Tooty. She wants to protect herself at the 5% significance level against incorrectly rejecting the null hypothesis when it is true. She finds that 73 sample respondents prefer the new box. What action should she take?

9-45 To assess the time required to cure a disease using an experimental drug, it is administered to a sample of $n = 25$ persons. The pharmaceutical company is basing its decision to continue or terminate its research on whether or not the drug is deemed effective. The desired Type I error probability is $\alpha = .01$ for not continuing the research when the drug actually yields a mean advantage in cure time of at least two days over the present treatment time. If the sample results for the cure-time advantage are $\bar{X} = 1.5$ and $s = .5$ day, should the null hypothesis be accepted or rejected? Should the drug experiment be continued or terminated?

9-46 The plant manager of Very Wide Shoe Company wishes to determine whether or not the sizing department's work is satisfactory. Due to ordinary variability, a shoe does not fall into a precise size category like $8\frac{1}{2}$EEE. Finished shoes must be individually measured and then classified to the nearest appropriate size. To determine whether or not to take corrective action, the manager asks that a sample of 100 randomly selected shoes be meticulously resized. The proportion of shoes that were originally correctly sized is to be determined. As his null hypothesis, the manager assumes that the true proportion of all shoes incorrectly sized is $\leq .05$, the desirable level. He must construct a decision rule that rejects this hypothesis when it is true with a probability of .05.

The sample results show that $P = .062$. Should the null hypothesis be accepted or rejected? Should corrective action be taken?

9-47 A personal director for Kryptonite Corporation wishes to give her standard screening examination to some recent job applicants to decide whether or not today's job seekers achieve higher scores than applicants did ten years ago. If they do, she will use a new examination in the future. The test is to be administered to a random sample of $n = 25$ persons. In analyzing the results, the director wishes to allow only a 1% chance of incorrectly changing procedures when the actual mean screening examination score is ≤ 86, the historical mean figure ten years ago. If the sample group achieves a mean score of 88, with a standard deviation of 10 points, should the present screening examination be retained or changed?

9-48 The VBM personnel manager is testing the physical aptitude of college graduates to determine whether or not they score higher than high school graduates. If they do, the new test will be used in the future to screen college graduates, as well as nongraduates, applying for nonmanagement positions. The test is administered to a random sample of $n = 25$ persons. Management wants only an $\alpha = .05$ chance of incorrectly changing screening procedures when the actual mean aptitude test score is ≤ 86, the historical mean for high school graduates.

(a) Formulate the null hypothesis. Indicate which test statistic applies, and compute its critical value. Express the decision rule.

(b) Suppose the sample results are $\bar{X} = 88$ and $s = 10$. What action should the manager take?

9-49 Consider populations comprising all statistics students. Using as sample data the master class list developed in Exercise 1-19, answer the following. (Note: Be sure to show all your intermediate steps. You may use intermediate answers you developed in earlier chapters to avoid unnecessary effort.)

(a) Test the population for the mean of one of your variables, using either an upper- or lower-tailed test.

(b) Test the population mean of one of your variables, using a two-tailed test.

(c) Test for the population proportion of one of your variables for either an upper- or lower-tailed test.

(d) Perform a hypothesis test for a population proportion using a two-tailed test.

9-50 Repeat Exercise 9-49 using as sample data your group's class data from Exercise 1-21.

9-51 In Exercise 6-55 you were asked to go to a local store or other retail outlet and collect data for the number of arrivals during one minute intervals. Develop a hypothesis test to aid the store manager in decision making.

9-52 Using the data set from Exercise 8-53 based on genetic diversity you may assume that 70 percent of the population possess the ability to roll their tongues and that 90 percent of the people are right-handed. Test whether the data you gathered are significantly different from the population proportion for (a) hand preference and (b) tongue rolling. Comment on your results.

9-53 Who do you want for President? If the election were held today, which candidate would you vote for? Research the most recent pre-election opinion poll from your local newspaper. Comment on the most recent poll in terms of the pollster's use of statistical estimation methods. Conduct your own poll, using the question as it was worded for the nationwide poll. Do your results differ significantly from the national results?

9-54 Consider the final exam data in Table 3-13. If these data comprise only a random sample of scores from the instructor's final exam, test the null hypothesis that the exam is too easy (that is, $\mu \geq 70$) at the 5% level of significance. *Note:* Be sure to show all of your intermediate steps. You may use intermediate answers you developed in earlier chapters.

9-55 Refer to the coin toss data you obtained in your solution to Exercise 8-58. Test the null hypothesis that the coin you tossed was fair (that is, $\pi = .50$) at the 1% level of significance. You may use intermediate answers you developed in earlier chapters.

9-56 Refer to the die cube results you obtained in your solution to Exercise 6-57. Test to see if your sample mean results are consistent with the mean obtained by rolling a fair die cube 100 times at the 10% level of significance. *Note:* Refer to Section 6-2 for the expected value (mean) and standard deviation for rolling a fair die cube.

9-57 Refer to the graduation rate data given in Exercise 7-41. Using the sample results obtained in your solution, test the null hypothesis that the average graduation rate is at most 74% at the 1% level of significance. Assume that σ is unknown. *Note:* Be sure to show all of your intermediate steps.

CASE SynerGentex

SynerGentex is a pharmaceutical company specializing in drugs and hormones synthesized through "genetic engineering" using bacterial media. All areas of the company use statistics in a variety of ways and to meet distinct needs. The statistical applications may be conveniently categorized into one of the following four groupings.

1. To determine whether or not a new product or approach is even worth pursuing.

2. To establish the efficacy of a new drug or chemical.

3. To assess the deleterious impact ("side effects") of a new drug or chemical.

4. To settle issues of implementation of promising products, such as effective dosages.

Group 1 applications are strictly in-house investigations and the information thereby gleaned is proprietary. The remaining statistical applications often involve outside entities, such as universities, institutes, other firms and researchers, and government regulators.

Examples of each type of application are given in the following Questions.

QUESTIONS

1. SynerGentex wants to determine if a sizable market exists for a new drug to treat a rare genetic disease. Management will provide the required funding for the development of the substance if a high enough proportion of physicians would potentially prescribe the drug when it is known to give noticeable symptom relief. A sample of 25 potential prescribers were given a brief hypothetical description of the proposed drug, and 19 responded positively. The company will proceed if they can reject the null hypothesis that, at most, half of all treating doctors would prescribe the drug. At the 5% significance level, what action should SynerGentex take?

2. A synthetic steroid for treatment of an induced allergic skin rash is evaluated in terms of the time it takes to clear up the problem. The null hypothesis is that the mean clearing time is at least as long as that of a conventional treatment, known to be 96 hours. If the hypothesis is

rejected, the steroid will be passed on to the next phase of testing; otherwise, it will be reformulated. The following sample clearing times have been obtained. At the $\alpha = .01$ significance level, what action should be taken?

| 22 | 37 | 41 | 55 | 69 | 115 | 138 | 61 | 204 |

3. A new substance is being tested for carcinogenic effects. The research is performed by administering the chemical to laboratory rats at a dosage that would be hundreds of times the anticipated human equivalent. The following results have been obtained for three treatment levels.

(a)	(b)	(c)
100 × Human	**500 × Human**	**1,000 × Human**
7 tumorous	18 tumorous	21 tumorous
54 healthy	49 healthy	54 healthy
$H_0: \pi \le .05$	$H_0: \pi \le .10$	$H_0: \pi \le .20$

The results show how many treated rats developed tumors. At a 5% significance level, should the respective null hypotheses be accepted or rejected?

4. A new sleep inducer is being tested to establish a recommended dosage. Again, laboratory rats are used to conduct the research. The null hypothesis is that treated rats will fall to sleep quickly at a mean dosage of $\mu \le .1$ mg. The following intravenous dosage data have been obtained for a sample of rats.

| .15 | .07 | .09 | .22 | .08 | .08 | .11 | .07 | .06 |

At a 5% significance level, what conclusion should be made regarding the true level of μ?

9-6 OPTIONAL TOPIC: HYPOTHESIS TESTS FOR COMPARING TWO MEANS

In addition to estimating the difference between two population means, hypothesis-testing procedures can be used to determine whether or not population *A* values are significantly larger or smaller than population *B* values. These methods permit choices to be made. Thus, an experimental compensation program may be adopted because the statistical test concludes that workers paid under it attain a higher mean productivity than those paid under the existing program. A new drug may be rejected by a hospital staff because its mean relief level does not significantly exceed that of a drug currently in use. The owner of a taxicab fleet may find that sample results indicate a new tire supplier should be awarded a contract because his tires wear longer than the present brand. In each case, sample data are required for both the control and the experimental groups.

In two-sample tests, the null hypothesis may be stated in any one of the following forms.

$$H_0: \mu_A \geq \mu_B \quad \text{or} \quad H_0: \mu_A - \mu_B \geq 0 \qquad \text{(lower-tailed test)}$$
$$H_0: \mu_A \leq \mu_B \quad \text{or} \quad H_0: \mu_A - \mu_B \leq 0 \qquad \text{(upper-tailed test)}$$
$$H_0: \mu_A = \mu_B \quad \text{or} \quad H_0: \mu_A - \mu_B = 0 \qquad \text{(two-sided test)}$$

The equivalent expressions on the right are found by subtracting μ_B on both sides of the original inequalities. As in estimating the difference between two means, two-sample hypothesis tests can be applied to independent samples as well as to matched pairs.

INDEPENDENT SAMPLES

When samples are selected independently, an appropriate test statistic is $d = \bar{X}_A - \bar{X}_B$. As in estimating $\mu_A - \mu_B$, there are two methods for testing H_0, depending on whether the sample sizes are large or small.

Large Sample Sizes

When $n_A \geq 30$ and $n_B \geq 30$, the normal deviate serves as the test statistic. The following expression is used to compute the

NORMAL DEVIATE FOR INDEPENDENT SAMPLES (large *n*'s)

$$z = \frac{d}{s_d} = \frac{\bar{X}_A - \bar{X}_B}{\sqrt{\dfrac{s_A^2}{n_A} + \dfrac{s_B^2}{n_B}}}$$

We will illustrate this procedure by conducting a comparison of automobile exhaust emissions.

Illustration: Testing Exhaust Emissions

In evaluating how effectively a new automobile engine controls exhaust emissions, the U.S. Environment Protection Agency might conduct a sampling study like the one we will describe here. The experimental group (A) consists of a sample of $n_A = 50$ prototype turbocharged engines proposed to replace conventional engines. The control group (B) contains a sample of $n_B = 100$ fuel injection engines equipped with catalytic converters. (Note that different sample sizes were used for the two groups.)

STEP 1

Formulate the null hypothesis. The EPA wishes to use the null hypothesis that the mean sulfur-dioxide emissions level in parts per million (ppm) for all turbocharged engines is at least as great as that for the current fuel injection engines. The following null hypothesis applies.

$$H_0: \mu_A \geq \mu_B$$

STEP 2

Select the test statistic and procedure. The normal deviate z serves as the test statistic.

STEP 3

Establish the significance level and identify the acceptance and rejection regions. Because rejecting the null hypothesis will permit a manufacturer to install the turbocharged engine in all its cars, the EPA has established an $\alpha = .01$ significance level for the test; that is, there is a 1% chance of making the incorrect decision and concluding that turbocharged engines are cleaner than fuel injection engines when the opposite is true. From Appendix Table E, we find $z_{.01} = 2.33$. Because a large negative difference between sample means will refute the null [hypothesis, th]e test is lower-tailed. The acceptance and rejection regions are

[sa]mple *and compute the value of the test statistic.* The following sam-[ple values ha]ve been obtained for sulfur-dioxide emissions.

Turbocharged Engine	**Fuel Injection Engine**
$\bar{X}_A = 25$ ppm	$\bar{X}_B = 30$ ppm
$s_A^2 = 90$	$s_B^2 = 100$

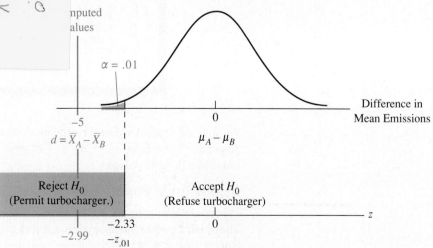

The computed value of the normal deviate z is

$$z = \frac{\bar{X}_A - \bar{X}_B}{\sqrt{\dfrac{s_A^2}{n_A} + \dfrac{s_B^2}{n_B}}} = \frac{25 - 30}{\sqrt{\dfrac{90}{50} + \dfrac{100}{100}}} = -2.99$$

STEP 5

Make the decision. Since $z = -2.99$ falls in the rejection region, the null hypothesis must be *rejected*. The EPA must permit the turbocharged engine to be installed.

The above example involves a lower-tailed test. An upper-tailed test with H_0: $\mu_A \leq \mu_B$ has a rejection region with large positive values of z. A two-sided test (when H_0: $\mu_A = \mu_B$) has a double rejection region.

The two-sided test is often conducted in conjunction with a confidence interval estimate of $\mu_A - \mu_B$. In the beginning of this chapter, we found that the 95% confidence interval for the difference between population mean statistics scores for students using a new book A and students using an old book B is

$$-3.68 \leq \mu_A - \mu_B \leq 8.48$$

Since this interval contains the value 0, the null hypothesis for those data—H_0: $\mu_A = \mu_B$ or $\mu_A - \mu_B = 0$—must be *accepted* at an $\alpha = 1 - .95 = .05$ significance level.

SMALL SAMPLE SIZES

When $n_A < 30$ or $n_B < 30$, the testing procedure is based on the Student t distribution. The following expression is used to compute the

STUDENT t STATISTIC FOR INDEPENDENT SAMPLES (small n's)

$$t = \frac{\bar{X}_A - \bar{X}_B}{\sqrt{\dfrac{(n_A - 1)s_A^2 + (n_B - 1)s_B^2}{n_A + n_B - 2}}\sqrt{\dfrac{1}{n_A} + \dfrac{1}{n_B}}}$$

We find the critical value corresponding to the desired significance level α from Appendix Table F for $n_A + n_B - 2$ degrees of freedom. The following example illustrates this procedure.

ILLUSTRATION: FORMULATING A SOAP

Laboratory researchers for a home products company are formulating a new soap. They plan to recommend version A if it is found to be significantly more effective than version B. The effectiveness of a soap is measured from wash tests by finding the mean percentage reduction in stain area μ.

STEP 1
Formulate the null hypothesis. The researchers assume that version A is not more effective. The following null hypothesis applies.

$$H_0: \mu_A \leq \mu_B$$

STEP 2
Select the test statistic and procedure. The Student t serves as the test statistic because both $n_A = 10$ and $n_B = 15$ are less than 30.

STEP 3
Establish the significance level and identify the acceptance and rejection regions. The researcher chooses an $\alpha = .05$ significance level. For $10 + 15 - 2 = 23$ degrees of freedom, Appendix Table F provides $t_{.05} = 1.714$. Since a large positive value of $d = \bar{X}_A - \bar{X}_B$ will refute the null hypothesis, the test is upper-tailed. The acceptance and rejection regions are shown in the following figure.

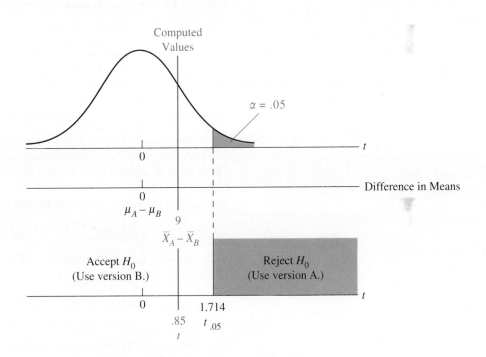

STEP 4
Collect the sample and compute the value of the test statistic. The following sample results have been obtained for each sample.

Version A	Version B
$\bar{X}_A = 45\%$	$\bar{X}_B = 36\%$
$s_A^2 = 706$	$s_B^2 = 654$

The computed value of the test statistic t is

$$t = \frac{45 - 36}{\sqrt{\frac{9(706) + 14(654)}{23}}\sqrt{\frac{1}{10} + \frac{1}{15}}} = .85$$

STEP 5

Make the decision. The computed value $t = .85$ falls within the acceptance region. The null hypothesis that version A is not more effective must be *accepted*.

9-58 Sly Fox is a real estate property manager who wishes to compare net monthly incomes for two different leasing agreements. Plan A has tenants sign for a lower rent but requires them to pay for all small repairs themselves. Plan B has tenants pay more rent but they are not responsible for repairs. As the null hypothesis, the manager assumes that plan B yields at least as great a mean income as plan A. The following data have been obtained for independent random samples of 15 leases each.

Plan A	Plan B
$\bar{X}_A = \$132.45$	$\bar{X}_B = \$128.06$
$s_A^2 = 123$	$s_B^2 = 95$

At a 5% significance level, should the manager reject the null hypothesis?

9-59 To evaluate two alternative assembly procedures, a Hoopla Hoops production manager has gathered independent sample data from pilot runs of both. She wishes to protect herself from erroneously concluding that the procedures are equally fast, in terms of mean assembly times, at an $\alpha = .05$ significance level. She has collected the following data.

$$n_A = 100 \qquad n_B = 100$$

$$\bar{X}_A = 10.8 \text{ minutes} \qquad \bar{X}_B = 10.6 \text{ minutes}$$

$$s_A = .21 \text{ minutes} \qquad s_B = .19 \text{ minutes}$$

What conclusion should the manager reach?

9-60 Refer to the data for teleprocessing transaction times given in Exercise 8-61. Test the null hypothesis that monitor A involves times that are on the average less than or equal to those of monitor B. At a 1% significance level, should you accept or reject H_0?

9-61 To combat aphid infestation, Rich Sod must decide whether he should spray his fruit trees with pesticide or inundate them with ladybugs. He sprays 250 trees and uses ladybugs on another 250 trees. The farmer's null hypothesis is that spraying (A) produces a mean yield at least as great as the yield obtained using natural predators (B). His sample results for spraying provide a mean of 10 bushels of good fruit per tree, with a standard deviation of 3 bushels. Using ladybugs, the mean is 10.5 bushels of good fruit per tree, with a standard deviation of 1 bushel. Should the farmer accept or reject the null hypothesis at a .05 significance level?

9-62 A consumer testing service asks you to compare gas and electric ovens by baking one type of bread in each type of oven. The following baking times have been obtained.

Gas	Electric
$n_A = 10$	$n_B = 12$
$\bar{X}_A = 2.1$ hours	$\bar{X}_B = 2.3$ hours
$s_A = .3$ hours	$s_B = .4$ hours

(a) Construct a 95% confidence interval estimate of the difference in mean baking times for the two ovens.

(b) At an $\alpha = .05$ significance level, should you accept or reject the null hypothesis of identical means?

CHAPTER 10

REGRESSION AND CORRELATION

BEFORE READING THIS CHAPTER, MAKE SURE YOU UNDERSTAND:

The distinction between the sample and population (Chapter 1).

The role of random samples in statistical evaluations (Chapter 4).

About confidence intervals and how they are used and constructed (Chapter 8).

About the basic concepts of hypothesis testing (Chapter 9).

AFTER READING THIS CHAPTER, YOU WILL UNDERSTAND:

How statistics measures and expresses association between variables.

What the correlation coefficient measures and how to compute it.

The role of the regression line and how it is found.

How to summarize the variability about the regression line and measure its quality.

The theoretical assumptions underlying regression analysis.

How to make statistically confident predictions using the regression line.

About the coefficient of determination and the quality of the regression analysis.

The role of the computer in regression and correlation analysis.

In many important business decisions it is necessary to predict the values of unknown variables. A personnel manager is concerned with predicting the success of a job applicant, which may be expressed in terms of the applicant's productivity. A production manager for a chemical company may wish to predict the levels of impurities in a final product. Many economists make predictions of gross national product (GNP). In each case, knowledge of one factor may be used to better predict another factor. The personnel manager may use screening examination scores as the basis for predicting future on-the-job performance. The production manager may use process temperatures or concentrations of ingredient chemicals to forecast impurities. The economist may use current interest rates, unemployment levels, and government spending to make GNP prognostications.

Regression analysis tells us how one variable is related to another by providing an equation that allows us to use the known value of one or more variables to estimate the unknown value of the remaining variable. For instance, an economist may use regression analysis to show how one variable, such as percentage unemployment, can be used to predict the percentage inflation rate. The resulting mathematical relationship provides a graphical display called the Phillips curve. More than one variable can be used to estimate an unknown variable. When several variables are used to make a prediction, the technique is called **multiple regression**. (We will discuss this topic in Chapter 11.)

Correlation analysis tells us the degree to which two variables are related. It is useful in expressing how efficiently one variable has estimated the value of another variable. Correlation analysis can also identify the factors of a multiple-characteristic population that are highly related, either directly or by a common connection to another variable.

10-1 REGRESSION ANALYSIS

The primary goal of regression analysis is to obtain predictions of one variable using the known values of another. These predictions are made by employing an equation such as $Y = a + bX$, which provides the estimate of an unknown variable Y when the value of another variable X is known. Such an expression is referred to as a **regression equation**. Knowing the regression equation, we can readily predict Y from a given X. Unlike the results from ordinary mathematical equations (such as $A = b \times h$ for the area of a rectangle, or interest $= i \times P \times t$, where i is the rate of interest, P is the principal, and t is the time), we cannot be certain about the value of Y that we obtain from the regression equation. This is due to inherent statistical variability. Predictions made from the regression equation are subject to error and are only *estimates* of the true values.

Regression analysis begins with a set of data involving pairs of observed values, one number for each variable. Table 10-1 shows the observations of distances and transportation times for a sample of ten rail shipments made by an automobile parts supplier. These data will be used to arrive at predictions of transit times for future shipments. From these the regression equation will be determined. Because using a sample gives rise to sampling error, the regression equation obtained may not be truly representative of the actual relationship between the variables. In order to reduce the chances of large sampling error, a sample size considerably greater than ten ought to be used. We have taken such a small number here merely for ease in showing calculations.

TABLE 10-1 Sample Observations of Rail Distances and Transportation Times for Ten Shipments by a Parts Supplier

Customer	Rail Distance to Destination X	Transportation Time (days) Y
1. Muller Auto Supply	210	5
2. Taylor Ford	290	7
3. Auto Supply House	350	6
4. Parts 'n Spares	480	11
5. Jones & Sons	490	8
6. A. Hausman	730	11
7. Des Moines Parts	780	12
8. Pete's Parts	850	8
9. Smith Dodge	920	15
10. Gulf Distributors	1,010	12

THE SCATTER DIAGRAM

A first step in regression analysis is to plot the value pairs as points on a **scatter diagram** as Figure 10-1. The horizontal axis corresponds to values of the variable distance, denoted by the letter X. The vertical scale represents values of the variable time, for which we use the designation Y. A point is found for each shipment. For example, the shipment to Jones & Sons, located at a distance of $X = 490$ miles from the plant, took $Y = 8$ days to arrive. This is represented by the point $(X = 490, Y = 8)$ on the graph.

The parts supplier wishes to use the known rail distance to the customers as the basis for predicting an order's unknown transportation time. It is customary to refer to the variable whose value is known as the **independent variable**, the possible values of which are represented on the X axis of the scatter diagram. The variable whose value is being predicted is called the **dependent variable**, the possible magnitudes of which are represented on the Y axis. Thus, rail distance X is the independent variable, because it is determined by the shipment's destination only, whereas the transportation time Y is the dependent variable, because it is in part predictable from rail distance.

These designations follow from simple algebra, where the X axis represents the independent variable, and the Y axis provides values of the dependent variable by means of a function or an equation. Thus, Y is a function of X. The dependence of Y on X does not necessarily mean that Y is *caused* by X. The type of relationship found by regression analysis is a statistical one. (We can find a *statistical* relationship expressing family household expenditures as a dependent variable that is a function of an independent variable, family disposable income. But having money to spend does not mean that appliances will be purchased. A purchase is a voluntary decision that is merely allowed to occur because money has been made available; a purchase need not be made just because there is sufficient income.)

THE DATA AND THE REGRESSION EQUATION

The second step in regression analysis is to find a suitable function to use for the regression equation, so that it will provide the predicted value of Y for a given

FIGURE 10-1 Scatter diagram for shipments by a parts supplier (Values from Table 10-1).

value of X. The clue to finding an appropriate regression equation can be found in the general pattern presented by the points in the scatter diagram. A quick examination of the parts supplier's data in our example indicates that a straight line, like the one shown in Figure 10-2, might be a meaningful summary of the information provided by the sample. This line seems to "fit" the rough scatter pattern of the data points.

A linear relationship between the variables X and Y is the simplest to visualize. The general equation for a straight line is $Y = a + bX$. The constant a is the value of Y obtained when $X = 0$, so that $Y = a + b(0) = a$. Because this is the value of Y at which the line intersects the Y axis, a is usually referred to as the **Y intercept**. The constant b, or the **slope** of the line, represents the change in Y due to a one-unit increase in the value of X. Figure 10-3 shows the line for the equation $Y = 3 + 2X$. Here, the Y intercept is $a = 3$ and the slope is $b = 2$. Y increases by two units for every one-unit change in X.

To review how we determine the value of Y for X, suppose we wish to find the Y that corresponds to $X = 5$. Substituting 5 for X in the expression gives us $Y = 3 + 2(5) = 13$. The same value may be read directly from Figure 10-3 by

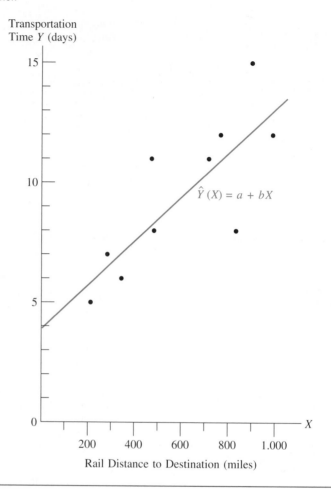

FIGURE 10-2 Fitting a regression line to the parts supplier's data.

following the vertical black line from $X = 5$ to the line relating Y to X. The vertical distance represents the value of Y. Any point on the line, for example $(X = 5, Y = 13)$, can be described by the horizontal distance (5) and the vertical distance (13) from the origin.

The line used to describe the average relationship between the variables X and Y, or the **estimated regression line**, is generally obtained from sample data. The estimated regression line provides an estimate of the mean level of the dependent variable Y when the value of X is specified. We use the symbol $\hat{Y}(X)$ ("Y-hat of X") to represent the values obtained from the linear

ESTIMATED REGRESSION EQUATION

$$\hat{Y}(X) = a + bX$$

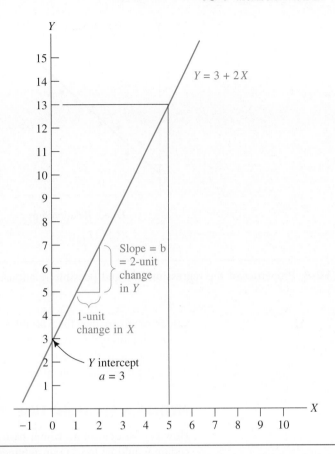

FIGURE 10-3 Slope and Y intercept of a straight line.

The symbol $\hat{Y}(X)$ distinguishes estimates of the dependent variable from the observed data points, which, for simplicity, we denote by the symbol Y. For a specific X, the resulting $\hat{Y}(X)$ is a *predicted* value of the dependent variable. As we will see, the values a and b in this expression are found from sample data and are referred to as **estimated regression coefficients**.

SOME CHARACTERISTICS OF THE REGRESSION LINE

Some important general properties of the regression line and its fit to the data are illustrated in Figure 10-4. First, we will consider the manner in which Y is related to X. There are two basic kinds of regression lines. If the values of the dependent variable Y increase for larger values of the independent variable X, then Y is **directly related** to X, as shown in Figure 10-4(a). Here, the slope of the line is positive, so that $b > 0$; this is because Y will increase as X becomes larger. Figure 10-2 shows that transportation time and rail distance are directly related variables. Other examples of directly related variables are age and salary (during employment years), weight and daily caloric intake, and the number of passengers and the quantity of luggage on commercial aircraft flights. In Figure 10-4(b), the slope of the regression line is negative and $b < 0$. Here, Y becomes smaller for larger

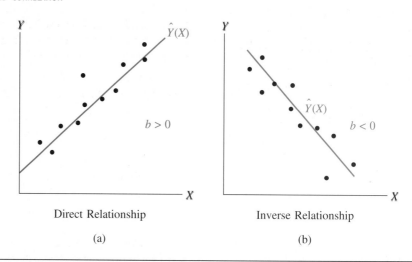

FIGURE 10-4 Properties of the regression line and possible relationships between variables.

values of X, so that the variables X and Y are **inversely related**. Examples of inverse relationships include remaining tire tread and miles driven, crop damage by insects and the quantity of insecticide applied, and the typical economic demand curve where quantity demanded decreases as price increases.

FITTING A STRAIGHT LINE TO THE DATA

How do we determine which particular regression line to use? One simple procedure would be to use our judgment in positioning a straightedge until it appears to summarize the linear pattern of the scatter diagram, and then draw the line. We can find the equation of this regression line by reading its Y intercept and slope directly from the graph. Although this procedure may be adequate for some applications, estimates of Y obtained in this way are often crude. A major drawback to using freehand methods in fitting a line is that two persons will usually draw different lines to represent the same data. Freehand fitting can therefore create unnecessary controversy about the conclusions of the data analysis. Another serious objection is that statistical methodology cannot be used to qualify the estimation errors (by confidence limits, for instance).

These difficulties can be overcome by using a statistical method to fit the line to the data. The most common technique is the **method of least squares**, which we will discuss in Section 10-3. From many different viewpoints, this procedure provides the best possible fit to a set of data and thereby the best possible predictions.

EXERCISES

10-1 On graph paper, plot the following regression lines and indicate whether X and Y are directly or inversely related.
(a) $\hat{Y}(X) = -5 + 2X$ (b) $\hat{Y}(X) = 5 + 3X$ (c) $\hat{Y}(X) = 20 - 2X$

10-2 An economist has established that personal income X may be used to predict personal consumption Y by the relationship $\hat{Y}(X) = -24.0 + .94X$ (billions of dollars). For each of the following levels of personal income, calculate the predicted value for personal consumption.

(a) $300 billion   (b) $500 billion   (c) $700 billion.

10-3 The following data represent the years in practice and the annual income (thousands of dollars) for a random sample of certified public accountants.

Years	Income	Years	Income
5	40	3	20
15	40	6	30
24	90	12	30
16	70	27	70
19	60	13	50

Treat income as the dependent variable.

(a) Plot the scatter diagram for the data.

(b) The following estimated regression lines have been recommended. Plot each line on your graph.

(1) $\hat{Y}(X) = 0 + 1X$ (3) $\hat{Y}(X) = 100 - 3X$
(2) $\hat{Y}(X) = 40 + 0X$ (4) $\hat{Y}(X) = 20 + 2X$

(c) Which regression line appears to provide the best fit?

10-4 Consider the two variables, family savings and income. For each of the following studies, indicate which of these two variables would be independent and which would be dependent.

(a) A bank wishes to predict the increase in its time deposits due to a 10% increase in the salaries of state employees, whose incomes are known.

(b) A mutual fund wishes to use its customers' stock purchases (a form of savings) to predict their incomes. This information will be used by salespersons to identify leads for increased business.

(c) An economist wishes to forecast increases in savings due to inflationary wage settlements.

10-2 CORRELATION ANALYSIS

Regression analysis provides an equation for estimating the value of one variable from the value of another variable. Correlation analysis is used to measure the *degree* to which two variables are related—to show how closely two variables can move together.

Correlation analysis is a useful auxiliary tool in regression analysis, because it can indicate how well the regression line explains the relationship between variables. Correlation is used instead of regression when the only question is how strongly two variables are related. One application is isolating statistically related characteristics of a population to explain their differences. For example, a pharmacologist may wish to identify the chemicals that can be formulated into a drug to alleviate various symptoms of a particular disease, such as anemia, pain, and poor appetite. A high positive correlation between dosage X of a specific chemical and appetite Y (measured by the quantity of food consumed) may make the chemical a good candidate for inclusion in the final drug.

ILLUSTRATION: BASEBALL SUPERSTAR SALARIES AND PERFORMANCE

We again use the baseball superstar data first introduced in Chapter 6. Figure 10-5 shows scatter diagrams of selected variables from the data set in Table 10-2, which gives various performance statistics for players paid salaries of at least $2,000,000 in the 1991 baseball season. The positively sloping regression line in

(a) Strong positive correlation (batters)

(c) Near perfect correlation (batters)

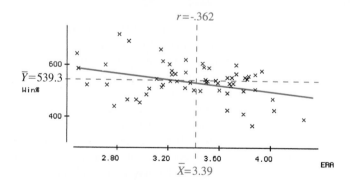

(e) Weak negative correlation (pitchers)

FIGURE 10-5 Scatter diagrams and correlations for baseball superstars. (Graphs generated with Minitab®.)

(a) points up, since a player's runs batted in (RBI) ordinarily increase as his number of home runs becomes greater. A different set of variables X and Y applies to the negatively sloping line in (e). That line points down, reflecting the tendency for a pitcher's winning percentage to drop as his earned run average (ERA) rises

(b) Weak positive correlation (batters)

(d) Near zero correlation (batters)

(f) Strong negative correlation (batters)

FIGURE 10-5 (con't)

TABLE 10-2 Baseball Superstar Data for Players Having 1991 Salaries of at Least $2,000,000

1 Player	2 Salary ($1,000)	3 Card Price	4 Posi- tion	5 Games	6 At Bats or Innings	7 Bat. Ave. or ERA	8 RBI or Win%	9 Runs or S. Outs	10 Fielding or Walks	11 Home Runs	12 Put Outs
1 Larry Anderson	2,000	6.00	1	534	819.67	3.15	516	589	254	0	0
2 Kevin Bass	2,000	1.25	7	1,008	3,349	274	428	426	983	85	1,694
3 George Bell	2,150	9.00	7	1,181	4,528	286	740	641	965	202	2,018
4 Bert Blyleven	2,000	60.00	1	667	4,837.33	3.27	540	3,631	1,293	0	0
5 Mike Boddicker	3,167	2.00	1	273	1,802.33	3.66	554	1,180	610	0	0
6 Wade Boggs	2,750	35.00	5	1,338	5,153	346	586	912	963	70	1,468
7 Barry Bonds	2,300	4.00	7	717	2,601	265	337	468	983	117	1,605
8 Bobby Bonilla	2,400	3.00	3	761	2,717	279	426	408	953	98	1,219
9 George Brett	3,675	200.00	5	2,279	8,692	311	1,398	1,382	970	281	5,277
10 Hubie Brooks	2,317	2.50	7	1,351	5,082	274	700	561	951	123	1,600
11 Tom Browning	2,650	2.00	1	220	1,439	3.73	604	774	389	0	0
12 Tom Brunansky	2,650	2.50	7	1,376	4,943	248	712	659	983	224	2,818
13 Tim Burke	2,328	.25	1	388	554.33	2.48	645	370	175	0	0
14 Brett Butler	2,833	2.50	7	1,360	5,001	285	362	850	990	39	3,423
15 Ivan Calderon	2,215	1.00	7	660	2,433	273	323	356	974	81	1,283
16 Tom Candiotti	2,500	.25	1	179	1,166.67	3.69	522	711	388	0	0
17 Jose Canseco	3,500	50.00	7	699	2,644	270	525	425	973	165	1,243
18 Joe Carter	3,792	15.00	3	1,024	3,941	262	646	541	982	175	3,467
19 Jack Clark	3,400	20.00	3	1,773	6,109	270	1,060	1,011	986	38	7,016
20 Will Clark	3,775	5.00	3	736	2,700	302	447	452	992	117	6,588
21 Roger Clemens	2,700	13.00	1	206	1,513	2.89	695	1,424	425	0	0
22 Vince Coleman	3,113	1.50	7	878	3,535	265	217	566	973	15	1,660
23 David Cone	2,350	2.75	1	132	784.67	3.14	663	725	276	0	0
24 Kal Daniels	2,025	6.00	7	507	1,665	300	262	316	980	81	817
25 Ron Darling	2,067	5.00	1	240	1,517.67	3.48	595	1,090	586	0	0
26 Danny Darwin	3,250	.70	1	488	1,913.33	3.40	505	1,265	581	0	0
27 Chili Davis	2,000	1.25	7	874	4,720	267	659	652	970	156	2,553
28 Eric Davis	3,600	15.00	7	767	2,572	272	499	515	985	166	1,709
29 Glenn Davis	3,275	2.00	3	830	3,032	262	518	427	992	166	6,951
30 Mark Davis	3,625	1.50	1	469	927	3.86	368	827	392	0	0
31 Storm Davis	2,367	.70	1	265	1,431	3.93	579	831	523	0	0
32 Andre Dawson	3,325	45.00	7	2,018	7,785	283	1,231	1,130	983	346	4,569
33 Jose DeLeon	2,367	.08	1	233	1,417	3.79	415	1,225	636	0	0
34 Jim Deshaies	2,100	.25	1	155	948	3.50	538	638	358	0	0
35 Bill Doran	2,833	.80	4	1,182	4,323	269	409	621	982	70	2,281
36 Doug Drabek	3,350	1.00	1	157	1,003	3.21	605	577	271	0	0
37 Shawon Dunston	2,100	3.00	6	758	2,768	257	290	340	967	61	1,349
38 Len Dykstra	2,217	2.50	7	783	2,628	281	232	432	990	43	1,728
39 Dennis Eckersly	3,100	20.00	1	604	2,815.33	3.49	547	1,938	659	0	0
40 Nick Esasky	2,100	.70	3	810	2,703	250	427	336	986	122	4,180
41 Steve Farr	2,400	.30	1	320	627	3.33	514	512	249	0	0
42 Sid Fernandez	2,167	6.00	1	199	1,212.33	3.26	569	1,153	491	0	0
43 Tony Fernandez	2,100	6.00	6	1,028	3,952	289	404	510	980	40	1,786
44 Chuck Finley	2,500	.90	1	152	767	3.20	539	544	311	0	0
45 Carlton Fisk	2,455	150.00	2	2,278	8,055	272	1,231	1,220	987	354	10,660
46 John Franco	2,633	1.50	1	448	595.67	2.49	588	423	231	0	0
47 Julio Franco	2,313	6.00	4	1,221	4,720	297	593	680	968	69	2,086
48 Gary Gaetti	2,700	5.00	5	1,361	4,989	256	758	646	965	201	1,166
49 Andres Galarraga	2,485	3.50	3	740	2,707	276	400	360	993	97	6,377
50 Scott Garrelts	2,400	.90	1	344	939.67	3.23	567	695	404	0	0
51 Dwight Gooden	2,467	9.00	1	211	1,523.67	2.82	721	1,391	449	0	0
52 Mike Greenwell	2,650	2.75	7	635	2,256	313	388	326	975	73	1,006
53 Kevin Gross	2,217	.35	1	265	1,469.33	4.02	471	996	583	0	0
54 Kelly Gruber	3,033	8.00	5	686	2,219	266	326	321	956	83	498
55 Mark Gubicza	2,667	1.00	1	215	1,407.33	3.57	543	921	540	0	0
56 Pedro Guerrero	2,283	10.00	3	1,378	4,819	305	812	679	976	206	4,795
57 Tony Gwynn	2,388	20.00	7	1,201	4,651	329	488	696	987	49	2,534
58 Von Hayes	2,200	2.00	7	1,324	4,658	272	646	689	987	139	5,144
59 Dave Henderson	2,625	2.00	7	1,205	3,915	262	537	559	983	147	2,676
60 Rickey Henderson	3,250	200.00	7	1,608	6,013	293	622	1,290	980	166	4,016
61 Tom Henke	2,967	1.25	1	381	517	2.72	527	596	165	0	0
62 Orel Hershiser	3,167	5.00	1	235	1,482.33	2.71	604	1,027	438	0	0
63 Ted Higuera	2,750	1.00	1	181	1,255	3.34	622	986	381	0	0
64 Kent Hrbek	2,600	6.00	3	1,299	4,670	290	803	685	994	223	10,127

(because a higher percentage of runs is given up). Notice that in some diagrams the data scatter adheres closely to the regression line, while in others there is a barely discernable pattern or none apparent.

Before we discuss the details for fitting the regression line in Section 10-3, it will be helpful to first introduce the associated statistical measure.

TABLE 10-2 Continued

1 Player	2 Salary ($1,000)	3 Card Price	4 Posi-tion	5 Games	6 At Bats or Innings	7 Bat. Ave. or ERA	8 RBI or Win%	9 Runs or S. Outs	10 Fielding or Walks	11 Home Runs	12 Put Outs
65 Danny Jackson	2,625	2.50	1	196	1,206.33	3.66	493	737	473	0	0
66 Howard Johnson	2,242	10.00	5	1,023	3,395	256	512	516	937	159	714
67 Wally Joyner	2,100	.80	3	703	2,657	286	422	759	994	93	6,061
68 Jimmie Key	2,217	1.00	1	251	1,269.67	3.47	608	702	301	0	0
69 Mark Langston	3,550	2.25	1	233	1,597.67	3.88	508	1,448	772	0	0
70 Barry Larkin	2,100	.80	6	572	2,125	293	221	314	970	38	846
71 Craig Lefferts	2,042	.20	1	528	762.33	2.95	470	482	227	0	0
72 Charlie Leibrandt	2,183	.50	1	300	1,735	3.71	532	800	513	0	0
73 Greg Maddux	2,425	2.00	1	140	911	3.68	531	540	319	0	0
74 Dennis Martinez	3,348	2.00	1	460	2,711.33	3.82	549	1,423	804	0	0
75 Don Mattingly	3,420	30.00	3	1,117	4,416	317	759	655	995	169	8,769
76 Kirk McCaskill	2,100	.35	1	162	1,043.33	3.80	553	643	382	0	0
77 Roger McDowell	2,200	.40	1	396	611.33	3.05	512	299	211	0	0
78 Willie McGee	3,563	4.00	7	1,193	4,698	297	560	650	977	52	2,744
79 Fred McGriff	2,750	1.00	3	578	1,944	278	305	348	993	125	4,161
80 Mark McGwire	2,875	3.00	3	623	2,173	253	429	355	993	156	4,913
81 Kevin McReynolds	2,267	7.00	7	1,089	3,997	270	621	550	985	167	2,353
82 Kevin Mitchell	3,750	3.00	5	688	2,378	278	412	369	959	135	953
83 Paul Molitor	3,253	50.00	5	1,540	6,246	299	626	1,053	964	131	2,115
84 Jack Morris	3,700	6.00	1	430	3,043.33	3.73	569	1,980	1,086	0	0
85 Dale Murphy	2,500	60.00	7	1,983	7,312	268	1,171	1,125	982	378	5,997
86 Eddie Murray	2,562	45.00	3	2,135	7,997	294	1,373	1,210	993	379	17,030
87 Randy Myers	2,000	.50	1	251	326.67	2.56	525	362	135	0	0
88 Pete O'Brien	2,038	.70	3	1,209	4,271	267	569	526	993	131	9,972
89 Lance Parrish	2,417	30.00	2	1,656	6,066	257	947	765	991	285	8,166
90 Tony Pena	2,350	2.50	2	1,350	4,676	273	528	500	989	89	7,668
91 Pascual Perez	2,100	2.50	1	193	1,170.33	3.45	504	781	320	0	0
92 Dan Plesac	2,267	.30	1	276	353	2.98	458	333	112	0	0
93 Kirby Puckett	3,192	15.00	7	1,070	4,395	320	586	624	989	108	2,915
94 Tim Raines	3,500	9.00	7	1,405	5,305	301	552	934	986	96	2,782
94 Jeff Reardon	2,608	1.25	1	694	943.33	3.03	488	755	320	0	0
96 Dave Righetti	2,500	2.50	1	522	1,136	3.11	548	940	473	0	0
97 Jose Rijo	2,613	1.00	1	193	872	3.60	505	753	399	0	0
98 Cal Ripken Jr.	2,433	18.00	6	1,476	5,655	274	828	871	977	225	4,469
99 Jeff Russell	2,450	.20	1	277	778	4.03	430	476	303	0	0
100 Nolan Ryan	3,300	1,400.00	1	740	4,990.33	3.16	526	5,308	2,614	0	0
101 Bret Saberhagen	2,950	5.00	1	224	1,464	3.23	581	957	286	0	0
102 Ryne Sandberg	2,725	45.00	4	1,389	5,508	287	649	872	988	179	2,606
103 Scott Sanderson	2,175	.30	1	343	1,826.33	3.59	535	1,209	478	0	0
104 Mike Scioscia	2,183	7.00	2	1,205	3,680	262	382	340	987	57	7,017
105 Mike Scott	2,337	10.00	1	345	2,061	3.51	539	1,466	623	0	0
106 Ruben Sierra	2,650	3.50	7	748	2,882	274	470	395	971	114	1,378
107 Bryn Smith	2,133	.25	1	310	1,541.67	3.37	533	916	371	0	0
108 Lee Smith	2,792	1.25	1	650	919.33	2.88	470	923	363	0	0
109 Lonnie Smith	2,042	3.00	7	1,269	4,377	292	427	772	964	77	2,085
110 Ozzie Smith	2,225	45.00	6	1,926	7,019	256	600	910	978	19	3,237
111 Zane Smith	2,225	.35	1	223	1,116.33	3.66	429	652	435	0	0
112 Dave Stewart	3,500	12.00	1	393	1,827.67	3.52	591	1,202	677	0	0
113 Dave Stieb	3,000	10.00	1	390	2,667	3.34	574	1,557	937	0	0
114 Darryl Strawberry	3,800	18.00	7	1,109	3,903	263	733	662	979	252	2,054
115 Rick Sutcliffe	2,275	3.25	1	357	2,130.67	3.83	559	1,412	856	0	0
116 Greg Swindell	2,025	1.00	1	120	805	3.88	567	587	195	0	0
117 Danny Tartabull	2,250	6.00	7	691	2,435	281	435	357	962	121	913
118 Bobby Thigpen	2,417	1.00	1	277	382.33	2.78	444	251	141	0	0
119 Alan Trammell	2,200	50.00	6	1,835	6,702	288	810	1,009	977	152	2,880
120 Andy Van Slyke	2,160	3.00	7	1,098	3,632	270	516	530	985	113	2,626
121 Frank Viola	3,167	10.00	1	307	2,107.67	3.7	555	1,469	608	0	0
122 Bob Welch	3,450	15.00	1	396	2,512.33	3.16	618	1,714	801	0	0
123 Lou Whitaker	2,000	20.00	5	1,827	6,693	274	781	1,040	983	167	3,581
124 Dave Winfield	3,750	50.00	7	2,401	8,896	286	1,516	1,384	981	378	4,668
125 Mike Witt	2,417	.80	1	330	2,062	3.79	502	1,343	690	0	0
126 Matt Young	2,267	.15	1	264	956	4.26	395	666	413	0	0
127 Robin Yount	3,200	200.00	7	2,449	9,494	289	1,201	1,433	970	225	4,827

Source: *New York Times, The Sporting News Official Baseball Register—1991,* and *Sports Collectors Digest Baseball Card Pocket Price Guide.*

THE CORRELATION COEFFICIENT

The direction and overall strength of the linear relationship between X and Y is summarized by the **correlation coefficient**, denoted by the letter r. A strong correlation of $r = .833$ applies in diagram (a) of Figure 10-5, where a player's RBI Y is plotted against his number of home runs X. When two variables are highly correlated, the regression line will provide good predictions of Y using only the known level for X, so that the number of home runs could be used in arriving at accurate forecasts of a player's RBI.

Figure 10-5(b) displays data for variables having a much looser linear fit. There, a batter's salary is the Y and his RBI is now the X; a much lower correlation of $r = .284$ applies. The weak correlation suggests that RBI would not be a very accurate predictor of salary. The data in diagram (c), where number of at bats Y is related to the number of games played X, scatter very tightly about the regression line. The correlation coefficient for (c) is $r = .986$, which is very close to the maximum that r might achieve. A **perfect correlation** is achieved when $r = 1$, in which case all data points would fall exactly on the regression line.

The complete lack of correlation is reflected when $r = 0$. A **zero correlation** is almost reached in Figure 10-5(d), where a player's batting average Y has only an $r = .006$ correlation with his fielding percentage X. There is essentially no statistical relationship between the two variables, and the regression line is flat. Therefore, fielding percentage appears to be worthless in predicting batting average.

The correlation coefficient can be negative, as in Figure 10-5(e), in which the regression line has a negative slope. There a pitcher's winning percentage is the Y and his earned run average (ERA) is the X, which provide a correlation coefficient of $r = -.362$. The negative value reflects that winning pitchers tend to give up fewer runs.

The slope of the regression line and correlation coefficient always have the same sign. The computed value for r always falls between -1 and $+1$.

COMPUTING THE CORRELATION COEFFICIENT

The correlation coefficient may be computed by establishing for each data point a collective measure of the distance separating it from the respective sample means, computed in the usual manner:

$$\bar{X} = \frac{\sum X}{n} \quad \text{and} \quad \bar{Y} = \frac{\sum Y}{n}$$

To illustrate, we will use the scatter diagram in Figure 10-6, which relates RBI Y to home runs X. Consider the player Dave Winfield, who is the 66th batter in the superstar data set. The distances of the data point (X_{66}, Y_{66}) from the respective means are the differences $(X_{66} - \bar{X})$ and $(Y_{66} - \bar{Y})$. A collective distance measure is the product of these

$$(X_{66} - \bar{X})(Y_{66} - \bar{Y})$$

The above product is the area of the rectangle having Dave Winfield at one corner and the point $(\bar{X}, \bar{Y})$ diagonal to it. The $(X - \bar{X})$ and $(Y - \bar{Y})$ differences computed for some players will be negative, if their points lie to the left or below $(\bar{X}, \bar{Y})$.

If you imagine the dashed line at $\bar{X}$ as the north-south axis and the dashed line at $\bar{Y}$ as the east-west axis, then the distance products will be negative for data points lying in the northwest and southeast quadrants and positive for points in

FIGURE 10-6 Scatter diagram for baseball superstar RBI and home runs.

the northeast and southwest quadrants. Positively correlated variables have data points lying predominantly in the northeast and southwest, while negatively correlated ones fall mainly in the northwest and southeast.

The correlation coefficient is based on the average of all distance products. But the distances themselves must be adjusted for scale before determining r. Otherwise, a very big average distance product would be obtained for major league baseball players, and the resulting value could be thousands of times greater than the counterpart measure for younger minor league batters.

All distances are adjusted by dividing by the respective *standard deviations*. These are computed in the usual fashion from the data values separately for each variable:

$$s_X = \sqrt{\frac{\sum (X - \bar{X})^2}{n - 1}} = \sqrt{\frac{\sum X^2 - n\bar{X}^2}{n - 1}}$$

and

$$s_Y = \sqrt{\frac{\sum (Y - \bar{Y})^2}{n - 1}} = \sqrt{\frac{\sum Y^2 - n\bar{Y}^2}{n - 1}}$$

The subscripts X and Y are needed to distinguish between the two variables.

The following transformed distances

$$\frac{(X - \bar{X})}{s_X} \quad \text{and} \quad \frac{(Y - \bar{Y})}{s_Y}$$

are then averaged to compute the correlation coefficient.

$$r = \frac{\sum \left[\frac{(X - \bar{X})}{s_X}\right]\left[\frac{(Y - \bar{Y})}{s_Y}\right]}{n - 1}$$

The following equivalent expression is used to compute the

CORRELATION COEFFICIENT

$$r = \frac{\sum (X - \bar{X})(Y - \bar{Y})}{(n - 1)s_X s_Y}$$

Since the numerator is equal to

$$\sum (X - \bar{X})(Y - \bar{Y}) = \sum XY - n\bar{X}\bar{Y}$$

the following equivalent expression may also be used.

$$r = \frac{\sum XY - n\bar{X}\bar{Y}}{(n - 1)s_X s_Y}$$

When the sample standard deviations are not computed separately, the following expression can also be used.

$$r = \frac{\sum XY - n\bar{X}\bar{Y}}{\sqrt{\left(\sum X^2 - n\bar{X}^2\right)\left(\sum Y^2 - n\bar{Y}^2\right)}}$$

(As we shall see, an alternative procedure is sometimes used to find r using information obtained during regression analysis.)

EXAMPLE: PRICE OF ROOKIE BASEBALL CARD AND PLAYER SALARY

Although a player's *salary* ordinarily expresses his worth to the club's *owner*, an alternative objective measure of worth might apply to the *fans*. We use the player's *rookie baseball card price*. Consider the following superstars having a rookie card valued at least $100 in 1991.

Superstar	Price of Rookie Card	Salary (thousands)
9 George Brett	$ 200	$3,675
45 Carlton Fisk	100	2,455
60 Rickey Henderson	200	3,250
100 Nolan Ryan	1,400	3,300
127 Robin Yount	200	3,200

We will designate price of rookie card as X and the salary as Y, and calculate the correlation coefficient.

SOLUTION: Using $n = 5$, the following calculations apply.

Card Price X	Salary Y	$(X - \bar{X})$	$(X - \bar{X})^2$	$(Y - \bar{Y})$	$(Y - \bar{Y})^2$	$(X - \bar{X})(Y - \bar{Y})$
200	3,675	−220	48,400	499	249,001	−109,780
100	2,455	−320	102,400	−721	519,841	230,700
200	3,250	−220	48,400	74	5,476	−16,280
1,400	3,300	980	960,400	124	15,376	121,520
200	3,200	−220	48,400	24	576	−5,280
2,100	15,880	0	1,208,000	0	790,270	220,900

$$\bar{X} = \frac{2,100}{5} = 420$$

$$\bar{Y} = \frac{15,880}{5} = 3,176$$

$$s_X = \sqrt{\frac{\sum (X - \bar{X})^2}{n - 1}} = \sqrt{\frac{1,208,000}{5 - 1}} = 549.55$$

$$s_Y = \sqrt{\frac{\sum (Y - \bar{Y})^2}{n - 1}} = \sqrt{\frac{790,270}{5 - 1}} = 444.49$$

$$r = \frac{\sum (X - \bar{X})(Y - \bar{Y})}{(n - 1)s_X s_Y} = \frac{220,900}{(5 - 1)(549.55)(444.49)} = .226$$

Although it is not surprising that r is positive, the correlation is a weak one. For these five superstars, owner and fan player valuations are not strongly associated.

Regression or correlation analyses are usually performed using sample data. Inferences may then be made regarding the parent population. The population counterpart to r is the *population* correlation coefficient ρ. That parameter may be estimated using the value for r computed from sample data.

COMPUTING THE CORRELATION COEFFICIENT USING A COMPUTER

The correlation coefficient is ordinarily found using computer assistance. Figure 10-7 shows the correlations for all the baseball superstar batters computed using Minitab.

EXERCISES

10-5 Horatio Dull is a statistics instructor who wants to find the correlation between his students' homework point totals and their average examination scores. The following results have been obtained for a random sample of five students.

Homework Point Total X	Average Examination Score Y
140	90
80	80
90	60
150	80
110	70

```
MTB > Correlation c1-c12.
```

	Player	Salary	Card Pr.	Position	Games	At Bats	Bat.Ave.	RBI
Salary	-0.039							
Card Pr.	0.106	0.308						
Position	-0.013	0.001	0.026					
Games	0.298	0.156	0.654	-0.027				
At Bats	0.276	0.182	0.666	0.012	0.986			
Bat.Ave.	-0.004	0.174	0.216	0.098	0.113	0.166		
RBI	0.203	0.284	0.595	-0.094	0.878	0.881	0.101	
Runs	0.250	0.268	0.735	0.064	0.923	0.942	0.270	0.825
Fielding	0.120	0.067	-0.035	-0.302	0.079	0.057	0.006	0.090
H.Runs	0.181	0.244	0.458	-0.098	0.604	0.603	-0.096	0.833
P.Outs	0.180	0.047	0.245	-0.618	0.455	0.426	0.014	0.534

	Runs	Fielding	H.Runs
Fielding	0.075		
H.Runs	0.573	0.124	
P.Outs	0.375	0.597	0.488

FIGURE 10-7 Minitab output showing correlations between all possible variable pairs for baseball superstar batters.

Calculate the correlation coefficient for the data.

10-6 The following data obtained for sample households in Dogpatch relate the size of the family X to the annual usage Y of a cleaning agent.

Family size X	Bottles Used Y	Family size X	Bottles Used Y
5	2	4	2
8	3	5	3
7	4	5	2
3	2	6	4
2	1	7	5

Calculate the correlation coefficient for the data.

10-7 There are only four baseball superstar catchers listed in Table 10-2. These are indicated by the value 2 as the position in column (4). Compute for the catchers the correlation coefficients for each of the following variable pairs.
(a) Y = salary (2) and X = rookie baseball card price (3)
(b) Y = games played (5) and X = number of putouts (12)
(c) Y = rookie baseball card price (3) and X = number of home runs (11)

10-8 For each of the following situations, indicate whether a correlation analysis, a regression analysis, or both would be appropriate. In each case, give the reasons for your choice.
(a) To choose advertising media, an agency account executive is investigating the relationship between a woman's age and her annual expenditures on a client firm's cosmetics.
(b) A trucker wishes to establish a decision rule that will enable him to

determine when to inspect or replace his tires, based on the number of miles driven.

(c) A government agency wishes to identify which field offices of various sizes (based on number of employees) do not conform to the prevailing pattern of working days lost due to illness.

(d) A research firm conducts attitude surveys in two stages. The first stage identifies coincident factors, such as age and income. The second stage is more detailed and involves a separate study to predict the values of one variable using the known values of other variables associated with it in the initial stage.

10-3 FINDING THE REGRESSION EQUATION

An estimated regression line should fit the sample data. To accomplish this, statisticians use a procedure called the method of least squares.

THE METHOD OF LEAST SQUARES

We will begin by applying the method of least squares to our previous parts supplier's data, which are again plotted in Figure 10-8. The least-squares criterion requires that a line be chosen to fit our data so that the *sum of the squares of the vertical deviations separating the points from the line will be a minimum*. The deviations are represented by the lengths of vertical line segments that connect the points to the estimated regression line in the scatter diagram.

To explain how this procedure may be interpreted, we investigate the shipment to Jones & Sons at a distance of $X = 490$ miles from the supplier's plant. Our data (page 438) show that $Y = 8$ days were required for the shipment to arrive. This transportation time is represented on the graph by the vertical distance to the corresponding data point along the dashed line from the X axis at $X = 490$. The predicted or estimated transportation time for the *next* shipment to Jones & Sons equals the vertical distance all the way up to the regression line, a total of $\hat{Y}(X) = \hat{Y}(490) = 8.4$ days. The difference between the observed transportation time, $Y = 8$ days, and the predicted value for Y is the deviation $Y - \hat{Y}(X) = Y - \hat{Y}(490) = 8 - 8.4 = -.4$ days. This is represented by the colored vertical line segment connecting the point to the regression line. Because the observed value of Y lies below the predicted value, a negative deviation is obtained; if the observed Y lay above the line, the deviation would be positive. The vertical deviation represents the amount of *error associated with using the regression line to predict* a future shipment's transportation time. We want to find the values of a and b that will minimize the sum of the squares of these vertical deviations (or prediction errors).

One reason for minimizing the sum of the *squared* vertical deviations is that some of the deviations are negative and others are positive. For any set of data, a great many lines can be drawn for which the sum of the unsquared deviations is zero, but most of these lines would fit the data poorly.

The sum to be minimized is

$$\sum [Y - \hat{Y}(X)]^2 = \sum [Y - a - bX]^2$$

which involves two unknowns, a and b. Mathematically, it may be shown that

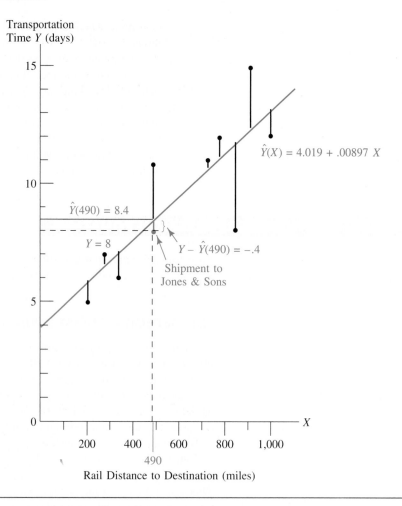

FIGURE 10-8 Fitting the regression line to the parts supplier's data using the method of least squares.

the required values must simultaneously satisfy the following expressions, referred to as the **normal equations**.*

$$\sum Y = na + b\sum X$$

$$\sum XY = a\sum X + b\sum X^2$$

Solving these equations algebraically gives us the following expression for b.

$$b = \frac{n\sum XY - \sum X\sum Y}{n\sum X^2 - (\sum X)^2}$$

We obtain the equation for a by substituting the value of b into the first normal equation. Then

$$a = \frac{1}{n}(\sum Y - b\sum X)$$

*The word *normal* as used here has nothing to do with the normal curve. Rather, *normal equations* receive their name from a mathematical property of linear algebra.

The expressions for a and b can be simplified further by using the mean values $\bar{X} = \left(\sum X\right)/n$ and $\bar{Y} = \left(\sum Y\right)/n$ to compute the

ESTIMATED REGRESSION COEFFICIENTS

$$b = \frac{\sum XY - n\bar{X}\bar{Y}}{\sum X^2 - n\bar{X}^2}$$

$$a = \bar{Y} - b\bar{X}$$

Note that b must be calculated before a.

The advantage of calculating a and b from these expressions is that every step involves computations with values of moderate size. Although this may increase the danger of rounding errors, such errors are usually negligible.

ILLUSTRATION OF THE METHOD

We are now ready to find the regression equation for the parts supplier's regression line obtained from the $n = 10$ observations. In order to evaluate the expressions for a and b, we must perform a set of intermediate calculations (shown in Table 10-3). To find b, we must calculate $\bar{X}$, $\bar{Y}$, $\sum XY$, and $\sum X^2$. Columns for the values of X, Y, XY, and X^2 are used for this purpose. An extra column for the squares of the dependent variable observations, Y^2, is computed for use in later

TABLE 10-3 Intermediate Calculations for Obtaining the Parts Supplier's Estimated Regression Line

(1) Customer	(2) Rail Distance to Destination X	(3) Transportation Time (days) Y	(4) XY	(5) X^2	(6) Y^2
1. Muller Auto Supply	210	5	1,050	44,100	25
2. Taylor Ford	290	7	2,030	84,100	49
3. Auto Supply House	350	6	2,100	122,500	36
4. Parts 'n Spares	480	11	5,280	230,400	121
5. Jones & Sons	490	8	3,920	240,100	64
6. A. Hausman	730	11	8,030	532,900	121
7. Des Moines Parts	780	12	9,360	608,400	144
8. Pete's Parts	850	8	6,800	722,500	64
9. Smith Dodge	920	15	13,800	846,400	225
10. Gulf Distributors	1,010	12	12,120	1,020,100	144
Totals	6,110	95	64,490	4,451,500	993
	$= \sum X$	$= \sum Y$	$= \sum XY$	$= \sum X^2$	$= \sum Y^2$

$$\bar{X} = \frac{\sum X}{n} = \frac{6,110}{10} = 611.0 \qquad \bar{Y} = \frac{\sum Y}{n} = \frac{95}{10} = 9.5$$

discussions of the regression line. Using the intermediate values obtained, we can first find the value of b.

$$b = \frac{\sum XY - n\bar{X}\bar{Y}}{\sum X^2 - n\bar{X}^2} = \frac{64{,}490 - 10(611.0)(9.5)}{4{,}451{,}500 - 10(611.0)^2} = \frac{6{,}445}{718{,}290} = .00897$$

Substituting $b = .00897$, we obtain

$$a = \bar{Y} - b\bar{X} = 9.500 - .00897(611.0)$$
$$= 9.500 - 5.481 = 4.019$$

Thus, we have determined the following equation for the estimated regression line graphed in Figure 10-8.

$$\hat{Y}(X) = 4.019 + .00897X$$

We may now use the above regression equation to predict the transportation time $\hat{Y}(X)$ for a shipment of known rail distance X from the parts supplier's plant. For instance, when $X = 490$, we have

$$\hat{Y}(490) = 4.019 + .00897(490)$$
$$= 8.4 \text{ days}$$

Thus, the prediction for the transportation time to a customer 490 miles away is $Y(490) = 8.4$ days. This is the same value previously read from the graph of the regression line in Figure 10-8.

The least-squares regression line has two important features. First, it goes through the point $(\bar{X}, \bar{Y})$ that corresponds to the mean of the X and Y observations. Second, the sum of the deviations of the Ys from the regression line is zero, or

$$\sum [Y - \hat{Y}(X)] = 0$$

Thus, the positive and negative deviations from the regression line cancel one another, so that the least-squares line goes through the center of the data scatter. This can be a useful check to determine if any miscalculations have been made in finding a and b.

MEANING AND USE OF THE REGRESSION LINE

Once the regression equation has been obtained, predictions or estimates of the dependent variable may be made. For purposes of planning, the parts supplier now has a basis for determining his order-filling priorities, so that there will be a reasonable chance that shipments will be received by customers at the required times. His estimated regression equation is $\hat{Y}(X) = 4.019 + .00897X$. The value $a = 4.019$ is an estimate of the Y intercept. An interpretation of this value is that about 4 days of "overhead" are built into all rail shipments. This roughly corresponds to the time a shipment spends in delivery to and from the railhead, being loaded and unloaded, and waiting between various stages of the shipping process. The slope $b = .00897$ reflects the impact of distance alone on the total transportation time. For each additional mile, an estimated .00897 day is added to the total time. Stated another way, each additional 100 miles of distance adds roughly .9 day to the transportation time. Note that b is positive, indicating that transportation time varies directly with distance—the greater the distance, the longer, on the average, it will take for a shipment to be delivered.

Knowing that Jones & Sons is 490 miles distant, the $\hat{Y}(490) = 8.4$ days may be used as a point estimate of the transportation time required for the shipment. But the proper interpretation of 8.4 days is that *on the average* all future shipments to Jones & Sons will require about this much time in transit. It is an average because the conditions existing for successive shipments to this customer will vary due to a host of factors, such as freight train schedules, total freight to be handled, loading and unloading conditions, and routing of the box car. The times will vary from shipment to shipment. In general, the dependent variable Y will vary for a given X. Furthermore, the same regression equation will be used for other customers at a 490-mile distance; shipments to these others may travel on roads having different characteristics. This leads us to the next important considerations of regression analysis.

MEASURING VARIABILITY IN RESULTS

The fundamental indication of variability provided by the sample data is the measure of the spread or scatter about the estimated regression line. As we have noted, estimates made from the regression line will be more precise when the data are less scattered. Thus, we can investigate the degree of scatter to determine an expression for the error involved making estimates through regression. We wish to employ a measure that fits naturally into the scheme of least-squares regression. Recall that we obtained the Y intercept a and the slope b of the regression line by minimizing $\sum [Y - \hat{Y}(X)]^2$, the *sum* of the squared deviations about the regression line. As we saw in selecting the fundamental measure of a population's variability, the variance is the average of the squared deviations from the mean. This suggests that we can select as our measure of variability the *mean* of the squared deviations about the regression line. The following expression applies.

$$\frac{\sum [Y - \hat{Y}(X)]^2}{n}$$

The square root of the mean squared deviations is referred to as the **standard error of the estimate** about the regression line. As this suggests, we will use it to estimate the true variability in Y. For convenience, we will modify the preceding expression before taking its square root, using as our standard error of the estimate

$$s_{Y \cdot X} = \sqrt{\frac{\sum [Y - \hat{Y}(X)]^2}{n - 2}}$$

The subscript $Y \cdot X$ indicates that the deviations are about the regression line, which provides values of Y for given levels of X. We divide the sum of the squared deviations by $n - 2$, which will make $s_{Y \cdot X}^2$ an unbiased estimator of the true variance of the Y values about the regression line. We subtract 2 from n to indicate that 2 degrees of freedom are lost, since the values of a and b contained in the expression for $\hat{Y}(X)$ have been calculated from the same data.

The standard error of the estimate resembles the standard deviation calculated for the individual Ys.

$$s_Y = \sqrt{\frac{\sum (Y - \overline{Y})^2}{n - 1}} = \sqrt{\frac{\sum Y^2 - n\overline{Y}^2}{n - 1}}$$

Here, X does not appear in the subscript because s_Y makes no reference to the values of X. The sample standard deviation is the square root of the mean of the squared deviations about the center $\overline{Y}$ of the sample: $(Y - \overline{Y})^2$. Thus, s_Y represents the *total variability* in Y. Ordinarily, the deviations about $\overline{Y}$ are larger than their counterparts about the estimated regression line, so that s_Y will be larger than $s_{Y \cdot X}$. Figure 10-9 illustrates this concept. Note that s_Y and $s_{Y \cdot X}$ summarize the dispersions of separate sample frequency distributions.

To compute the standard error for our parts supplier regression, we first have to compute the estimated shipment time $\hat{Y}(X)$, plugging the distance X for each data point into the estimated regression equation. The resulting values are listed in column (4) of Table 10-4. Subtracting each $\hat{Y}(X)$ from its counterpart Y, the *residuals* $Y - \hat{Y}(X)$ in column (5) are then computed. Those quantities are squared

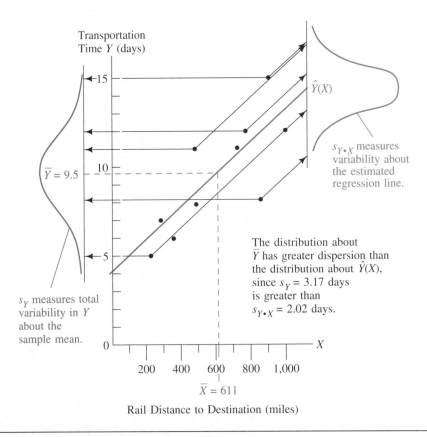

FIGURE 10-9 Illustration of the difference between total variability and variability about the estimated regression line.

TABLE 10-4 Preliminary Computations for Finding Standard Error of the Estimate for the Regression Analysis of the Parts Supplier's Data

(1) Customer	(2) Time Y	(3) Distance X	(4) $\hat{Y}(X) =$ 4.019 + .00897X	(5) Residual $Y - \hat{Y}(X)$	(6) $[Y - \hat{Y}(X)]^2$
1	5	210	5.90	−.90	.8100
2	7	290	6.62	.38	.1444
3	6	350	7.16	−1.16	1.3456
4	11	480	8.32	2.68	7.1824
5	8	490	8.41	−.41	.1681
6	11	730	10.57	.43	.1849
7	12	780	11.01	.99	.9801
8	8	850	11.64	−3.64	13.2496
9	15	920	12.27	2.73	7.4529
10	12	1,010	13.08	−1.08	1.1664
				.02	32.6844

in column (6). Substituting the total of column (6) into the above expression, we have

$$s_{Y \cdot X} = \sqrt{\frac{32.6844}{10 - 2}} = 2.02$$

When knowledge of X is ignored, and no regression line is used, the total variability in Y is summarized by the sample standard deviation s_Y, which we calculate

$$s_Y = \sqrt{\frac{993 - 10(9.5)^2}{10 - 1}} = 3.17 \text{ days}$$

This value of s_Y is larger than the value found for $s_{Y \cdot X}$, reflecting the fact that the variability about the regression line is smaller than the total variation in Y. This is illustrated in Figure 10-9, where the underlying frequency curve for deviations about the estimated regression line is more compact than the one that might be constructed for the Ys without a knowledge of X. Thus, a prediction interval calculated using s_Y would be wider. (Section 10-5 discusses how those intervals are constructed.) A general conclusion is that *predictions tend to be more reliable and accurate when X is used as a predictor than when it is not.*

In calculating $s_{Y \cdot X}$, we sometimes use the following mathematically equivalent

SHORTCUT EXPRESSION FOR THE STANDARD ERROR OF THE ESTIMATE

$$s_{Y \cdot X} = \sqrt{\frac{\sum Y^2 - a\sum Y - b\sum XY}{n - 2}}$$

Using the values obtained previously for a and b and the intermediate calculations from Table 10-3, we have

$$s_{Y \cdot X} = \sqrt{\frac{993 - 4.019(95) - .00897(64{,}490)}{10 - 2}} = 2.02 \text{ days}$$

which is identical to the result found earlier.

COMPUTER-ASSISTED REGRESSION ANALYSIS

We have explained the procedures for finding a regression line using an example in which computations were made by hand with a calculator. In actual practice, most regressions involve such a volume of data that it is cumbersome to take this approach. For this reason, computers have been programmed to compute regression lines. Although the details of operation vary with the computer system and software package available, the essential features of a computer regression are provided in the *EasyStat* program for the IBM PC that accompanies this book. The following illustration provides an example of regression using a computer.

ILLUSTRATION: PREDICTING TIME NEEDED TO DUPLICATE REPORTS

A corporate headquarters uses a duplicating center for preparing copies of company reports. Based on the size of the job, the manager gives service requesters an estimated duplication completion time. In order to improve these projections, the manager requests the help of the statistical department.

Based on a sample of 20 jobs, an analyst obtained the following data.

Job i	Number of Copies X	Completion Time (minutes) Y	Job i	Number of Copies X	Completion Time (minutes) Y
1	150	2.9	11	500	4.2
2	310	3.9	12	200	3.4
3	450	3.9	13	50	.9
4	1,150	8.1	14	920	6.2
5	800	7.1	15	500	5.1
6	200	2.6	16	500	5.4
7	300	4.1	17	400	2.7
8	250	3.3	18	750	5.8
9	910	6.1	19	410	3.5
10	100	1.9	20	200	3.5

Figure 10-10 is a printout for the above regression data generated on a computer using *EasyStat*. The data in the two columns X and Y were first entered onto a computer spreadsheet. During data entry, *EasyStat* allows for backing up to fix errors and for final editing. The data can be saved on a file for retrieval at a later time.

EasyStat operates from a series of menus (not pictured). The first menu selection prints the original data as they appear on the spreadsheet. These values are listed in the top portion of the printout. The second menu selection informs *EasyStat* that column Y contains data for the dependent variable and that one independent variable has values listed in the first column. In an instant, *EasyStat* provides the results displayed in the bottom portion of Figure 10-10.

```
            NO. COPIES X      TIME Y
               150            2.9
               310            3.9
               450            3.9
              1150            8.1
               800            7.1
               200            2.6
               300            4.1
               250            3.3
               910            6.1
               100            1.9
               500            4.2
               200            3.4
                50             .9
               920            6.2
               500            5.1
               500            5.4
               400            2.7
               750            5.8
               410            3.5
               200            3.5

REGRESSION RESULTS
```

Vari-able	Title	Regression Coefficient	Mean	Standard Deviation	Correl. X vs. Y	Standard Error
X1	NO. COPIES X	0.0054638 b	$\bar{x}$ 452.5	s_X 306.81513	0.9331339	0.0004962
Y2	TIME Y		$\bar{Y}$ 4.23	s_Y 1.7965171	r	s_b

```
Intercept                           1.75760926995 a
Standard Error of the Estimate      0.66359944416 sY.X
Coefficient of Determination        0.87073878867 r²
```

Note: Figure generated on an IBM PC using EasyStat.

FIGURE 10-10 Computer printout for the duplicating center illustration.

For convenience, all of the reported values are annotated in color with their symbol. The following regression equation (rounded) applies.

$$\hat{Y}(X) = 1.758 + .00546X$$

The standard error of the estimate is

$$s_{Y \cdot X} = .664$$

EasyStat generates a variety of other output in conjunction with regression. Popular software packages also provide similar information. Figure 10-11 is the scatter diagram obtained for the above data using *Minitab*. The regression line was inserted by hand. (Many software packages do not graphically display the estimated regression line. This is partly because the printers that are widely available do a poor job of printing diagonal lines.)

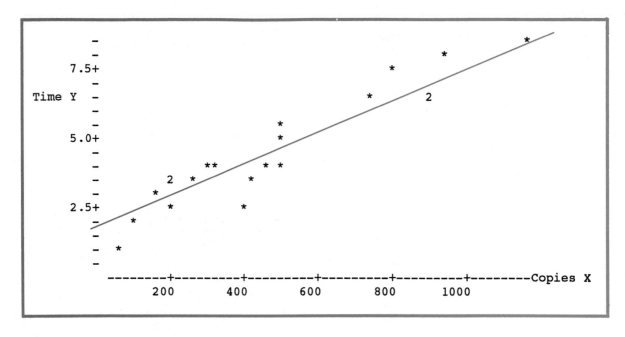

Note: Figure generated on an IBM PC using Minitab®.

FIGURE 10-11 Scatter diagram for the duplicating center illustration.

EXERCISES

10-9 Cost accountant Uriah Heap provided the following sample data for observations obtained during an investigation of the relationship between the volume of an ingredient X and the weight of a production batch Y.

Volume (liters) X	Weight (kilograms) Y	Volume (liters) X	Weight (kilograms) Y
10	61	25	102
24	110	6	38
13	75	10	42
7	47	16	75
9	78	15	91

(a) Determine the estimated regression equation.
(b) Compute, for batch weight, (1) the sample standard deviation and (2) the standard error of the estimate. Does a comparison of these two values indicate that the regression line would be useful in predicting batch weight? Why or why not?

10-10 A statistician for FlyMe Airlines wishes to determine the equation relating destination distance to freight charge for a standard-sized crate. The following data were obtained for a random sample of ten freight invoices.

Distance (hundreds of miles) X	Charge (to nearest dollar) Y
14	68
23	105
9	40
17	79
10	81
22	95
5	31
12	72
6	45
16	93

(a) Plot the scatter diagram for the data.

(b) Using the method of least squares, determine the equation for the estimated regression line.

(c) Check your calculations by computing $\sum [Y - \hat{Y}(X)]$. (Allowing for rounding errors, this should equal zero. If it does not, find your error.) Plot the regression line on your graph.

10-11 A floppy disk drive manufacturer has conducted a regression analysis to estimate the drive lifetime Y (hours) at various force settings X (grams). The regression equation $\hat{Y}(X) = 1{,}300 - 200X$ has been obtained for a sample of $n = 100$ drives that were played at different forces until they were worn out. The standard error of the estimate for drive lifetimes about this line is $s_{Y \cdot X} = 100$ hours.

(a) Plot the regression line on graph paper.

(b) State the meaning of the slope b of the regression line.

(c) Calculate $\hat{Y}(X)$ when $X = 1$, $X = 2$, $X = 3$ grams.

10-12 A food processing manager uses least-squares regression to predict the total cost of Crunchola production runs. The following data apply.

Production Quantity (tons) X	Total Cost (thousands of dollars) Y
400	200
150	85
220	115
500	200
300	140
100	65
150	70
150	65
240	125
350	190

(a) Using the method of least squares, determine the equation for the estimated regression line.

(b) State the meaning of the slope b and intercept a of the regression line.

(c) Using your answer to (a), calculate the predicted value of total cost per production run for the following quantities.
(1) 200   (2) 350   (3) 400

10-13 Consider the baseball superstar first-basemen in Table 10-2. These are identified in column (4) by position number 3. Determine, for the first-basemen only, the estimated regression equation for each of the following variable pairs.
(a) Y = salary (2) and X = number of runs (9)
(b) Y = price of rookie baseball card (3) and X = no. of games played (5)

10-14 Consider the baseball superstar shortstops in Table 10-2. These are identified in column (4) by position number 6. Determine, for the shortstops only, the estimated regression equation for each of the following variable pairs.
(a) Y = salary (2) and X = runs batted in (8)
(b) Y = price of rookie baseball card (3) and X = no. of home runs (11)

10-15 *Computer exercise.* A WaySafe market provided the following data for the number of arriving customers X per hour and the total hourly waiting time Y at the checkout counter.

Number of Customers X	Waiting Time (minutes) Y	Number of Customers X	Waiting Time (minutes) Y
105	44	435	208
511	214	275	138
401	193	55	34
622	299	128	73
330	143	97	52
211	112	187	103
332	155	266	110
322	131		

(a) Determine the estimated regression equation.
(b) Compute for total waiting time, (1) the sample standard deviation, and (2) the standard error of the estimate.

10-16 *Computer exercise.* Ace Widgets provided the following data for the time required to inspect outgoing batches of their deluxe model for various percentages of defective items.

Percentage Defective X	Inspection Time (minutes) Y	Percentage Defective X	Inspection Time (minutes) Y
17	48	10	49
9	50	14	55
12	43	18	63
7	36	19	55
8	45	6	36

(a) Plot the scatter diagram for the data.

(b) Determine the estimated regression equation, and plot the estimated regression line on your graph.

(c) Compute, for inspection time, (1) the sample standard deviation, and (2) the standard error of the estimate.

10-4 ASSUMPTIONS AND PROPERTIES OF LINEAR REGRESSION ANALYSIS

In Section 10-3, we were introduced to the mechanical process of fitting a regression line to the data. In this section, we will examine the assumptions and properties of the theoretical model for regression analysis.

ASSUMPTIONS OF LINEAR REGRESSION ANALYSIS

Suppose that in our parts supplier illustration we consider each possible transportation time Y for *all* shipments, past and future, to customers at a specified distance X from the plant. For this fixed X, the values of Y represent a population, and they will fluctuate and cluster about a central value. Similarly, for any other rail distance X, there will be a corresponding population of Y values. Since the means of these populations depend on the respective values for X, we may represent them symbolically by $\mu_{Y \cdot X}$, where, as before, the subscript $Y \cdot X$ signifies that the values of Y are for a given value of X.

Figure 10-12 illustrates how several populations for Y fit into the context of linear regression. This graph is three dimensional, having an extra axis perpendicular to the XY plane. This vertical axis represents the relative frequency of Y at a specified level X. The curves are drawn with their centers at a distance $\mu_{Y \cdot X}$ from the X axis. Thus, we may refer to $\mu_{Y \cdot X}$ as the **conditional mean** of Y

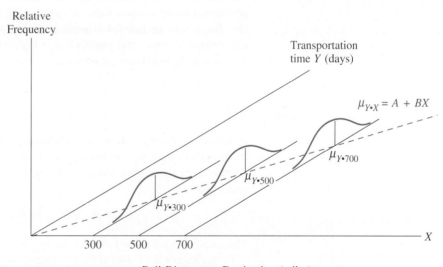

FIGURE 10-12 Populations for Y at various given values of X.

given X. There will be a different frequency curve for each X. Here, we show these curves for all shipments to destinations of $X = 300$, $X = 500$, and $X = 700$ miles. The respective conditional means are denoted by $\mu_{Y \cdot 300}$, $\mu_{Y \cdot 500}$, and $\mu_{Y \cdot 700}$.

In linear regression analysis, the following four theoretical assumptions about the populations for Y apply.

1. All populations have the same standard deviation, denoted by $\sigma_{Y \cdot X}$, no matter what the value of X is.

2. The means $\mu_{Y \cdot X}$ all lie on the same straight line, given by the equation

$$\mu_{Y \cdot X} = A + BX$$

which is the expression of the **true regression line**.

3. Successive sample observations are independent.

4. The value of X is known in advance.

It is convenient to express each observation in terms of the expression

$$Y = A + BX + \varepsilon$$

where ε is the **error term**. Ordinarily, the εs are assumed to be independent and have a normal distribution with mean 0 and standard deviation $\sigma_{Y \cdot X}$. For any specific level of X, the Ys would then be normally distributed with mean $\mu_{Y \cdot X}$ and standard deviation $\sigma_{Y \cdot X}$.

SAMPLING AND REGRESSION ANALYSIS

The true regression line is not usually known. Ordinarily, a regression analysis is performed using *sample* data. A single sample of size n is usually all we ever see. But it will be helpful in understanding the process if we consider a special experiment in which the population is *known* and repeated samples are selected, with regressions performed on each.

For this experiment, the baseball superstar data in Table 10-2 were used. The dependent variable is the price Y of a batter's rookie baseball card; the independent variable is his number of runs X. To avoid wild oscillations from sample to sample, six players having unusually high-priced cards (Brett, Canseco, Fisk, Henderson, Murphy, and Yount) were removed from the population. (The data for these players may be categorized as *outliers*. This concept will be discussed in Section 10-6.) A regression analysis for the population provides the true regression equation.

$$\mu_{Y \cdot X} = -16.2 + .0454X$$

The above is plotted in color as the regression line in Figure 10-13.

In this experiment, 100 separate samples were selected, each with $n = 20$ players, and the respective regression line determined. The following representative results were obtained.

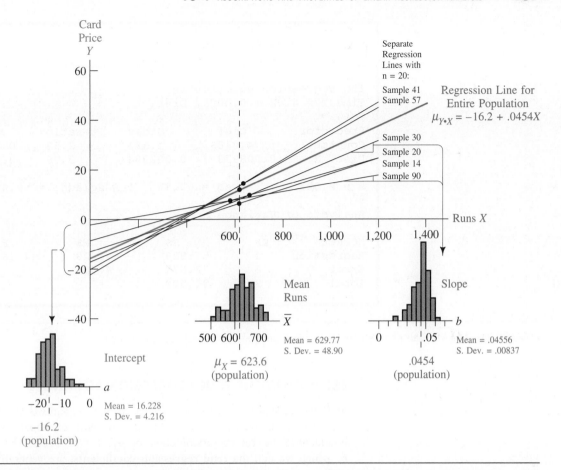

FIGURE 10-13 Results from 100 separate regressions, each using $n = 20$ random observations from truncated population of baseball batter superstars.

Sample 14:	$\hat{Y}(X) = -8.56 + .0275X$	$\bar{X} = 554.60$
Sample 20:	$\hat{Y}(X) = -12.74 + .0321X$	$\bar{X} = 623.55$
Sample 30:	$\hat{Y}(X) = -17.40 + .0408X$	$\bar{X} = 661.05$
Sample 41:	$\hat{Y}(X) = -22.24 + .0577X$	$\bar{X} = 631.10$
Sample 57:	$\hat{Y}(X) = -20.97 + .0557X$	$\bar{X} = 634.05$
Sample 90:	$\hat{Y}(X) = -2.30 + .0167X$	$\bar{X} = 548.60$

Each of the above lines is plotted in Figure 10-13. Notice that the intercepts and slopes vary, as well as the mean level for $\bar{X}$. The regression line for any particular sample can differ substantially from the true regression line.

Histograms are plotted in Figure 10-13 for the intercepts a, slopes b, and sample means $\bar{X}$ for the independent variable. The computed means for each of these lie close in value to their population counterparts. That fact is not a coincidence, and it exhibits an essential feature to the theory underlying regression analysis.

```
MTB > Regress c2 1 c1.
```

```
The regression equation is
Time Y = 4.02 + 0.00897 Dist. X

Predictor        Coef        Stdev      t-ratio         p
Constant        4.018        1.591        2.53       0.036
Dist. X       0.008973     0.002384       3.76       0.006

s = 2.021       R-sq = 63.9%      R-sq(adj) = 59.4%

Analysis of Variance

SOURCE          DF          SS          MS          F          p
Regression      1        57.829      57.829      14.16      0.006
Error           8        32.671       4.084
Total           9        90.500
```

FIGURE 10-14 Minitab printout for regression analysis with parts supplier data.

ESTIMATING THE TRUE REGRESSION EQUATION

We have learned how to use the method of least squares to derive the estimated regression equation $\hat{Y}(X) = a + bX$. Now we will investigate how this equation is related to the true regression equation $\mu_{Y \cdot X} = A + BX$. The values of A and B, which we call the **true regression coefficients**, are generally unknown. We will use $\hat{Y}(X)$ to estimate $\mu_{Y \cdot X}$ in the same way that we used $\bar{X}$ to estimate μ in Chapter 8. The estimated regression equation differs from the true regression equation only in the values of the Y intercept and slope. We can consider a and b, calculated from the sample data, to be point estimates of A and B, respectively.

The calculated values of a and b depend on the sample observations obtained. The equation $\hat{Y}(X) = 4.019 + .00897X$ was determined from the particular transportation times for the sample of ten shipments selected. A regression equation for some other sample of ten shipments would probably have differed—perhaps considerably—from the one we found.

When a and b are calculated by the method of least squares, they are *unbiased estimators* of the true coefficients A and B. This means that if the experiment of collecting samples is repeated a large number of times and the regression line is found by the least-squares method each time, the average value of the Y intercepts a will tend to be close to the true Y intercept A. Likewise, on the average, the values of b will tend to be close to B. As we mentioned in Chapter 8, unbiasedness is a desirable property of an estimator. In addition, the least-squares criterion provides the estimators of smallest variance, making the method of least squares the *most efficient* of all unbiased estimators of linear regression coefficients. Therefore, a and b minimize chance sampling error, so that estimates made from the regression line $\hat{Y}(X) = a + bX$ are the most reliable ones that can be attained for a fixed sample size. The values of a and b obtained by the least-squares method are also *consistent* and *maximum likelihood* estimators of A and B. Recall from Chapter 8 that a consistent estimator becomes progressively closer to the target parameter with increasing sample size. This can be attributed to the sampling distributions of a and b, whose variances decrease with n.

INFERENCES REGARDING REGRESSION COEFFICIENTS

The normality assumption of the error terms permits us to employ statistical theory in establishing sampling distributions for the regression coefficients a and b. For both of these quantities, the Student t statistic may be used to qualify the results obtained. A detailed discussion of how that is done is provided in optional Section 10-9.

Computer programs generally provide computed values for the respective ts under the assumption that the regression line is flat (the case of zero correlation). This is illustrated in Figure 10-14, which provides the *Minitab* computer printout for a regression analysis using the same parts supplier data seen earlier. The constant row provides the values for the intercept a, and the distance row gives the values for the slope b. That t-ratio column provides 3.76 for the slope. The adjacent entry in the p column indicates a prob. value of .006. (That means that under the assumption of a flat regression line there would be only a .6% chance of getting, from a sample of $n = 10$ random shipments, a slope as big or greater than the one actually computed.)

EXERCISES

10-17 Suppose that the theoretical regression line for predicting assembly time Y (minutes) from the number of components X is

$$\mu_{Y \cdot X} = 35.0 + 5.1X$$

Individual Y values may be computed from the above by plugging in a level for X and adding the error term ε. Those error terms are normally distributed with mean zero and standard deviation $\sigma_{Y \cdot X} = 10$. We represent a random normal deviate as z, so that error terms may be generated from

$$\varepsilon = 0 + z\sigma_{Y \cdot X}$$

(a) Complete the following table for 10 levels of X and random normal deviates.

Number of Components X	Theoretical Time $\mu_{Y \cdot X}$	Random Normal Deviate z	Error Term ε	Simulated Actual Time Y
5	_____	−1.13	_____	_____
7	_____	1.09	_____	_____
10	_____	−.30	_____	_____
12	_____	−.95	_____	_____
13	_____	2.14	_____	_____
15	_____	.25	_____	_____
16	_____	.47	_____	_____
20	_____	−.08	_____	_____
22	_____	.53	_____	_____
25	_____	1.22	_____	_____

(b) Plot a scatter diagram using the above levels for Y and their matching value for X.

10-18 *Continuation.*
(a) Plot the *true* regression line on a graph.
(b) Using the above values for Y and X, determine the estimated regression equation.
(c) Plot on the same graph the *estimated* regression line.

10-19 *Continuation.*
(a) Compute $s_{Y \cdot X}$ using the regression results from Exercise 10-18(b).
(b) Why does $s_{Y \cdot X}$ differ from $\sigma_{Y \cdot X}$?

10-20 *Continuation.*
(a) Complete the following table.

(1) Number of Components X	(2) Simulated Actual Time Y	(3) Theoretical Time $\mu_{Y \cdot X}$	(4) Estimated Time $\hat{Y}(X)$	(5) Error Term $\varepsilon = Y - \mu_{Y \cdot X}$	(6) Residual $Y - \hat{Y}(X)$
5					
7					
10					
12					
13					
15					
16					
20					
22					
25					

(b) Compare the values in columns (3) and (4). Should these be identical or not?
(c) Compare the values in columns (5) and (6). Should these be identical or not?

10-5 PREDICTIONS AND STATISTICAL INFERENCES USING THE REGRESSION LINE

We use the estimated regression line to make a variety of inferences, which can be grouped into two broad categories: (1) predictions of the dependent variable and (2) inferences regarding the regression coefficients A and B. Because predictions are made more often, we will discuss them first.

PREDICTIONS USING THE REGRESSION EQUATION

The major goal of regression analysis is to predict Y from the regression line at given levels of X. This may be done either by (1) predicting the value of the conditional mean $\mu_{Y \cdot X}$ or (2) predicting an individual Y value, rather than a mean. As an example of the first kind of prediction, the parts supplier might want to predict the mean transportation time that will be achieved by all shipments over a distance of 500 miles. In this case, $X = 500$, and the best point estimate of $\mu_{Y \cdot X}$ will be the fitted Y value from the regression line.

$$\hat{Y}(500) = a + b(500)$$
$$= 4.019 + .00897(500)$$
$$= 8.50 \text{ days}$$

The computed value 8.50 may also be used to estimate the transportation time for a particular shipment over the same distance. To distinguish an individual value from a mean value, both of which can only be estimated from the sample, we use the special symbol Y_I.

Either kind of estimate will involve sampling error, which can be acknowledged and expressed in terms of confidence intervals. Because of the special nature of regression analysis, the numbers obtained are usually referred to as **prediction intervals**.

PREDICTION INTERVALS FOR THE CONDITIONAL MEAN

We determine prediction intervals in a manner similar to the way we derived confidence intervals in Chapter 8. There, we used

$$\mu = \bar{X} \pm t_{\alpha/2}\frac{s}{\sqrt{n}} \qquad \text{(when } \sigma \text{ is unknown)}$$

where $s/\sqrt{n}$ is the estimator of $\sigma_{\bar{X}}$.

In regression analysis, Y (not X) is the variable being estimated. Intervals of analogous form are required to estimate a conditional mean of Y.

$$\mu_{Y \cdot X} = \hat{Y}(X) \pm t_{\alpha/2} \text{ estimated } \sigma_{\hat{Y}}$$

The standard error of $\hat{Y}(X)$, denoted by $\sigma_{\hat{Y}}$, represents the amount of variability in possible $\hat{Y}(X)$ values at the particular level for X that a prediction is desired. In the context of transportation time, a somewhat different line $\hat{Y}(X) = a + bX$ [such as $\hat{Y}(X) = 3.5 + .011X$ or $\hat{Y}(X) = 4.2 + .009X$] might have fitted the least-squares method if some other random sample of ten shipments had been selected. Thus, for some other sample $\hat{Y}(500)$ might have computed to a value different from 8.50 days. But nevertheless, for each particular value of X, a potential set of $\hat{Y}(X)$ values would have a distribution with a standard deviation of $\sigma_{\hat{Y}}$.

There are two components of the variability in $\hat{Y}(X)$.

$$\sigma_{\hat{Y}}^2 = \begin{array}{c} \text{Variability in the} \\ \text{mean of } Y\text{s} \end{array} + \begin{array}{c} \text{Variability caused by the} \\ \text{distance of } X \text{ from } \bar{X} \end{array}$$

The first source is analogous to the variability in the sample mean, which, as we saw in Chapter 8, depends on the population standard deviation and the sample size. The second source of variation is associated with the distance that X lies from $\bar{X}$. Figure 10-15 shows why this is so. Here, several estimated regression lines have been plotted, each representing different samples of shipments taken from the same population. (Although each sample involves the same Xs and thus

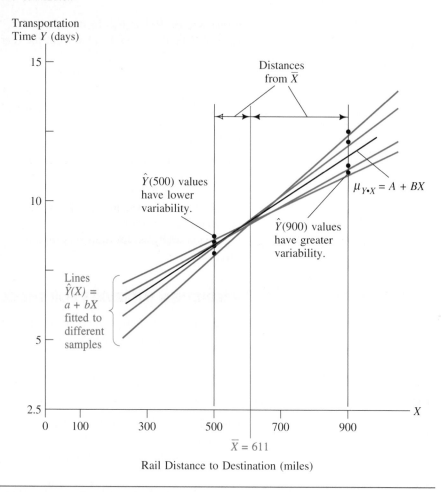

FIGURE 10-15 Illustration of how variability in $\hat{Y}(X)$ increases for larger distances separating X from $\bar{X}$.

the same level for $\bar{X}$, each involves slightly different values for a, b, and $\bar{Y}$.) Note that these lines tend to diverge and that their separations become greater as the distance between X and $\bar{X}$ increases. Therefore, the values of $\hat{Y}(X)$ become more varied the farther X is from $\bar{X}$.

The following expression is used to construct the $100(1 - \alpha)\%$

PREDICTION INTERVAL FOR THE CONDITIONAL MEAN

$$\mu_{Y \cdot X} = \hat{Y}(X) \pm t_{\alpha/2} s_{Y \cdot X} \sqrt{\frac{1}{n} + \frac{(X - \bar{X})^2}{\sum X^2 - n\bar{X}^2}}$$

where $t_{\alpha/2}$ is found from Appendix Table F for $n - 2$ degrees of freedom. (When using Appendix Table F, if the required critical value of t is not listed, use the

FIGURE 10-16 Confidence limits for predictions of mean transportation time.

nearest tabled entry. If the value is exactly in the middle, average the entries in the two neighboring rows. And, when the number of degrees of freedom exceeds 120, use the value of t from the df $= \infty$ row.)

Representing $\mu_{Y \cdot X}$ when $X = 500$ as $\mu_{Y \cdot 500}$, we may construct the 95% prediction interval for the conditional mean transportation time using $10 - 2 = 8$ degrees of freedom. Since $\alpha/2 = .025$, we find that $t_{\alpha/2} = t_{.025} = 2.306$, and therefore

$$\mu_{Y \cdot 500} = \hat{Y}(500) \pm t_{.025}s_{Y \cdot X} \sqrt{\frac{1}{n} + \frac{(500 - \bar{X})^2}{\sum X^2 - n\bar{X}^2}}$$

$$= 8.50 \pm 2.306(2.02) \sqrt{\frac{1}{10} + \frac{(500 - 611)^2}{4,451,500 - 10(611)^2}}$$

$$= 8.50 \pm 1.59$$

or

$$6.91 \leq \mu_{Y \cdot 500} \leq 10.09 \text{ days}$$

We therefore conclude that the transportation time for destinations 500 miles from the plant is *on the average* somewhere between 6.91 and 10.09 days. Our confidence that this statement is correct rests on the procedure used, which provides similar intervals containing the true mean about 95% of the time.

We may calculate 95% prediction intervals for the other values of X, thus obtaining prediction limits for $\mu_{Y \cdot X}$ over the entire range of X. In Figure 10-16, this has been done for the parts supplier's data. Note that the width of the confidence band depends on the distances that the X values lie from the mean.

PREDICTION INTERVALS FOR AN INDIVIDUAL VALUE OF Y GIVEN X

Predicting an individual value of Y given X is similar to predicting the mean. If our parts supplier wished to predict the transportation time for the next shipment over a distance of $X = 500$ miles, then the same point estimate, $\hat{Y}(500) = 8.50$ days, would be made from the regression equation. The following expression provides the $100(1 - \alpha)\%$

PREDICTION INTERVAL FOR AN INDIVIDUAL Y

$$Y_I = \hat{Y}(X) \pm t_{\alpha/2}s_{Y \cdot X} \sqrt{\frac{1}{n} - \frac{(X - \bar{X})^2}{\sum X^2 - n\bar{X}^2} + 1}$$

This expression is the same as the one for $\mu_{Y \cdot X}$, except for the addition of "$+ 1$." This reflects the fact that when $\hat{Y}(X)$ is used to estimate Y_I, a third source of variability is present—the dispersion of individual Y values about the regression line. (Even if the true regression line were known, the Ys at a particular level of X would have a variance of $\sigma^2_{Y \cdot X}$.)

We may now construct a 95% prediction interval for Y_I, using the parts supplier's data when $X = 500$.

$$Y_I = \hat{Y}(500) \pm t_{.025}s_{Y \cdot X} \sqrt{\frac{1}{n} + \frac{(500 - \bar{X})^2}{\sum X^2 - n\bar{X}^2} + 1}$$

$$= 8.50 \pm 2.306(2.02) \sqrt{\frac{1}{10} + \frac{(500 - 611)^2}{4,451,500 - 10(611)^2} + 1}$$

$$= 8.50 \pm 4.92$$

or

$$3.58 \leq Y_I \leq 13.42 \text{ days}$$

Note that this interval is considerably wider than the interval obtained previously for $\mu_{Y \cdot 500}$. This is to be expected, because Y_I is the estimate of the transportation time for *a particular shipment*, not a mean, and the greater width is attributable to the added variability that would be present even if the true regression line were available in making the prediction.

COMPUTER-GENERATED INTERVAL ESTIMATES

The procedures for finding confidence intervals in regression analysis involve computations that are cumbersome to do by hand. Certain computer software packages will generate these estimates concurrently with the regression. Figure 10-17 displays a computer printout for the above estimates. Notice that, in the figure, the quantity $\hat{Y}(500) = 8.504$ days is referred to as the "Fit." The *Minitab* software package provides 95% prediction intervals. The first, narrower interval applies to $\mu_{Y \cdot X}$; the second interval applies to Y_I.

```
MTB > Regress 'Time Y' on 1 'Dist.X';
SUBC> predict 500.
```

```
The regression equation is
Time Y = 4.02 + 0.00897 Dist. X


    Fit   Stdev.Fit        95% C.I.          95% P.I.
   8.504     0.692    ( 6.909, 10.100)  ( 3.577, 13.431)
```

Note: Figure generated on an IBM PC using Minitab®.

FIGURE 10-17 Portion of a computer printout for the parts supplier illustration.

INFERENCES REGARDING THE SLOPE OF THE REGRESSION LINE

Second in importance to prediction intervals are inferences regarding the slope B of the true regression line. This is especially true in statistical applications where the underlying relationship between X and Y is more important than predicting Y at a particular level for X. For example, much economic theory relies on regression analysis to substantiate hypothetical models requiring supply and demand curves. The *coefficients* of these demand and supply equations—not the predicted quantities for a given price—are our main interest. Similarly, a metallurgist might use regression analysis to develop a mathematical relationship between alloy concentrations and strength properties. He might be more concerned with predicting how much extra shearing force is needed to break a metal for each unit increase in alloy material than with predicting a particular force (that is, he might wish to estimate B rather than $\mu_{Y \cdot X}$).

A prediction interval can be constructed for B, and hypotheses regarding the true level of B can be tested. An optional discussion of these procedures appears in Section 10-9.

EXERCISES

10-21 The estimated regression line $\hat{Y}(X) = 150 + .1X$ provides the yield (bushels) per acre of corn when X pounds of nitrate fertilizer are applied. This result was obtained for a sample of $n = 100$ acres for which $s_{Y \cdot X} = 5$ bushels. Construct the 95% prediction intervals for $\mu_{Y \cdot X}$ and Y_I when $X = 50$ pounds. Assume that $\bar{X} = 50$ pounds.

10-22 The relationship between the total weight Y (pounds) of luggage stored in an aircraft's baggage compartment and the number of passengers X on the flight manifest is $\hat{Y}(X) = 250 + 27X$. Airport superintendents will use this equation to determine how much additional freight can be stored safely on a flight, after considering the fuel load and the weight of the passengers themselves. The data have been obtained for a sample of $n = 25$ flights. The sample results yield $s_{Y \cdot X} = 100$ pounds, $s_Y = 300$ pounds, $\sum X^2 = 64,000$, and $\bar{X} = 50$. Construct the 95% prediction intervals for $\mu_{Y \cdot X}$ and Y_I when (a) $X = 50$; (b) $X = 75$; (c) $X = 100$.

10-23 Refer to the Crunchola data given in Exercise 10-12 and to your answers. Construct the 95% prediction intervals for (a) the mean total cost of production runs of 200 tons and (b) the cost of an individual run of 400 tons.

10-24 Refer to the FlyMe Airlines' data given in Exercise 10-10 and to your answers. Construct the 99% prediction intervals for (a) the mean freight charge for shipments over a distance of six hundred miles and (b) the freight charge for an individual shipment over a distance of nine hundred miles.

10-25 *Computer exercise.*   Refer to the WaySafe customer data given in Exercise 10-15 and to your answers. Construct the 95% prediction intervals for (a) the mean customer waiting time and (b) an individual's waiting time when the number of hourly arrivals is (1) 100, (2) 200, and (3) 300 customers.

10-26 *Computer excercise.*   Refer to the Ace Widgets inspection data given in Exercise 10-16 and to your answers. Construct the 95% prediction intervals for (a) the mean inspection time and (b) an individual inspection time when the percentage of defectives is (1) 7, (2) 10, and (3) 15.

10-27 The credit manager of a department store has determined that the regression equation for a customer credit rating index X and the proportion of customers Y who eventually incur bad debts is $\hat{Y}(X) = .09 - .002X$. The index values range from 0 to 40. A sample of $n = 25$ is selected. The sample results yield $\sum X^2 = 23{,}000$, $s_{Y \cdot X} = .02$, and $\bar{X} = 30$.
(a) Construct the 90% prediction interval for the mean proportion of customers with ratings of $X = 20$ who will incur bad debts.
(b) The proper interpretation of Y_I in this case is the *probability* that a particular individual will incur a bad debt. Construct the 90% prediction interval for Y_I when $X = 20$.

10-6   ASSESSING THE QUALITY OF REGRESSION ANALYSIS

One way of assessing the overall quality of regression analysis is to measure the strength of the relationship between the dependent and independent variables. Another means of assessment explores whether the data are consistent with the theoretical assumptions of the regression model. An *analysis of residuals* may pinpoint potential trouble spots that tend to weaken or even invalidate the conclusions drawn from regression analysis.

THE COEFFICIENT OF DETERMINATION

In Section 10-2, we saw the degree to which the correlation coefficient indicates the direction and strength of association between X and Y. A related index, the **coefficient of determination**, expresses the amount of variation in the levels of Y that is explained by the regression analysis. As a foundation for understanding this coefficient, we first take the difference between the observed Y and its mean and break it into three *deviations*. To help illustrate, consider, again, the parts supplier's data.

Figure 10-18 shows the regression line found earlier for the parts supplier's original transportation times. Suppose the parts supplier predicts how long the next order will take to ship without using that line. That sample mean would then give a suitable estimate, providing the following

$$\bar{Y} = 9.5 \text{ days} \qquad \text{(prediction without regression)}$$

The estimate ignores how far the shipment will go. Suppose that this shipment goes to Smith Dodge, for which the distance is known to be $X = 920$ miles. This information allows the supplier to make a better forecast,

$$\hat{Y}(920) = 12.3 \text{ days} \qquad \text{(prediction using regression line)}$$

Although the actual time of the next shipment to Smith Dodge is uncertain, it can be represented by the time originally observed in the sample,

$$Y = 15.0 \text{ days} \qquad \text{(observed time)}$$

The first prediction falls wide of the mark, providing a **total deviation** of $Y - \bar{Y} = 15.0 - 9.5 = 5.5$ days, none of which can be explained. The second prediction is better since it yields a smaller prediction error of $Y - \hat{Y}(X) = 15.0 - 12.3 = 2.7$ days. By using the regression line, the total error is reduced by the amount $\hat{Y}(X) - \bar{Y} = 12.3 - 9.5 = 2.8$ days. Thus, part of the total error may be attributed to using the regression line, so that $\hat{Y}(X) - \bar{Y} = 2.8$ days is the **explained deviation**. The remaining portion of the error is due to unidentifiable

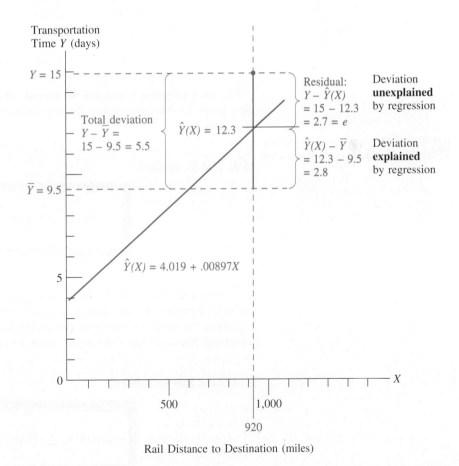

FIGURE 10-18 Illustration of total, explained, and unexplained variation in Y.

causes, so that $Y - \hat{Y}(X) = 2.7$ days is an **unexplained deviation**. The total deviation of the observed Y may then be expressed as

$$[Y - \bar{Y}] = [\hat{Y}(X) - \bar{Y}] + [Y - \hat{Y}(X)]$$

Stated in words, we have

Total deviation = Explained deviation + Unexplained deviation

The unexplained deviations are often referred to as the **residuals** and are defined by the differences

$$e_i = Y_i - \hat{Y}(X_i)$$

The *e*s may be considered as the *observed* errors. Although similar, they differ from the *actual* errors ε of the theoretical model, the values of which remain unknown.

By squaring the above deviations and then summing, we extend the relationship to the entire collection of observations.

$$\begin{array}{ccccc} \text{Total} \\ \text{variation} \end{array} = \begin{array}{c} \text{Explained} \\ \text{variation} \end{array} + \begin{array}{c} \text{Unexplained} \\ \text{variation} \end{array}$$

$$\sum [Y - \bar{Y}]^2 = \sum [\hat{Y}(X) - \bar{Y}]^2 + \sum [Y - \hat{Y}(X)]^2$$

$$SSTO \quad = \quad SSR \quad + \quad SSE$$

The total variation expresses the amount that the individual Ys deviate from their mean $\bar{Y}$ without regard to the regression relationship. The result is referred to as the

TOTAL SUM OF SQUARES

$$SSTO = \sum [Y - \bar{Y}]^2$$

As shown in Figure 10-18, the distance between Y and the regression line at X explains a portion of the deviation in the observed Y from its mean $\bar{Y}$. The explained variation summarizes the collective squared distances between the regression line $\hat{Y}(X)$ and the sample mean $\bar{Y}$. This is expressed by the

REGRESSION SUM OF SQUARES

$$SSR = \sum [\hat{Y}(X) - \bar{Y}]^2$$

The final component of total variation involves the residuals and measures the overall observed error in the sample. This is the

ERROR SUM OF SQUARES

$$SSE = \sum [Y - \hat{Y}(X)]^2$$

The method of least squares selects the regression coefficients a and b, so that the above quantity is minimized. The above term expresses the collective dispersion in Y about the regression line. The regression line leaves those deviations *unexplained*.

Rearranging the terms, the identity

$$\frac{\text{Explained}}{\text{variation}} = \frac{\text{Total}}{\text{variation}} - \frac{\text{Unexplained}}{\text{variation}}$$

$$SSR = SSTO - SSE$$

is used to construct a useful index. Dividing the explained variation by the total variation provides the **coefficient of determination**. The following expression applies.

$$r^2 = \frac{\text{Explained variation}}{\text{Total variation}} = \frac{SSTO - SSE}{SSTO} = \frac{\sum [Y - \bar{Y}]^2 - \sum [Y - \hat{Y}(X)]^2}{\sum [Y - \bar{Y}]^2}$$

An equivalent expression is

$$r^2 = \frac{\text{Explained variation}}{\text{Total variation}} = 1 - \frac{\sum [Y - \hat{Y}(X)]^2}{\sum [Y - \bar{Y}]^2}$$

which may be expressed equivalently as

$$r^2 = 1 - \frac{SSE}{SSTO}$$

The coefficient of determination expresses the proportion of the total variation in Y explained by the regression line. The above summations are the numerators of $s_{Y \cdot X}^2$ and s_Y^2. The following expression is most commonly used in computing the

COEFFICIENT OF DETERMINATION

$$r^2 = 1 - \frac{s_{Y \cdot X}^2}{s_Y^2}\left(\frac{n - 2}{n - 1}\right)$$

For the parts supplier's data, the above expression provides

$$r^2 = 1 - \frac{(2.02)^2}{(3.17)^2}\left(\frac{10 - 2}{10 - 1}\right) = .639$$

The computed value $r^2 = .639$ signifies that 63.9% of the total variation or scatter of transportation time Y about their mean can be explained by the relationship between this variable and the corresponding rail distance X, as estimated by the regression line for X and Y.

The coefficient of determination is computed automatically using the popular software packages. When working by hand, it may be convenient to express the sample coefficient of determination by means of the mathematically equivalent equation

$$r^2 = \frac{a\sum Y + b\sum XY - n\bar{Y}^2}{\sum Y^2 - n\bar{Y}^2}$$

In the parts supplier illustration, we may calculate r^2 using $a = 4.019$, $b = .00897$, and the intermediate calculations from Table 10-3.

$$r^2 = \frac{4.019(95) + .00897(64,490) - 10(9.5)^2}{993 - 10(9.5)^2}$$

$$= \frac{57.78}{90.50} = .64$$

The *population* coefficient of determination is denoted by ρ^2. This parameter ordinarily remains unknown, so that r^2 serves as the point estimate of its population counterpart ρ^2.

RELATION TO THE CORRELATION COEFFICIENT

Choosing r^2 to denote the sample coefficient of determination is no coincidence. The following relationship applies.

Coefficient of determination = (Correlation coefficient)^2

Thus, the absolute value of the correlation coefficient is the square root of the coefficient of determination.

$$|r| = \sqrt{r^2} \quad \text{and} \quad |\rho| = \sqrt{\rho^2}$$

The sign for r or ρ and the slope of the corresponding regression line must agree. Thus, for the parts supplier illustration, the sample correlation coefficient is

$$r = \sqrt{.639} = +.80$$

The above relationship provides another perspective on how the coefficient of determination measures the strength of association between X and Y. In the special case when all the data points fall directly on the regression line, so that there is a perfect correlation and $r = +1$ or $r = -1$, all of the variation in Y is explained and r must be equal to one. At the other extreme, a horizontal regression line is obtained when X and Y exhibit zero correlation, so that all of the variation in Y is unexplained and r^2 must then be equal to zero.

APPROPRIATENESS OF THE MODEL: RESIDUAL ANALYSIS

The residual values computed for the parts supplier's data are listed in Table 10-4. The first step in residual analysis is to construct the scatter plot. Figure 10-19 illustrates the residual scatter diagram for the data given in Table 10-5.

All inferences made from the regression relationship are based on theoretical properties discussed in Section 10-4. Should the underlying population and sampling process deviate from the model described, the regression analysis will be based on false assumptions. Residual analysis can be helpful in uncovering the violations of the model.

The parts supplier's residual data reflect the aforementioned linear relationship, with the individual *e*s falling within a narrow horizontal band. Such a plot has

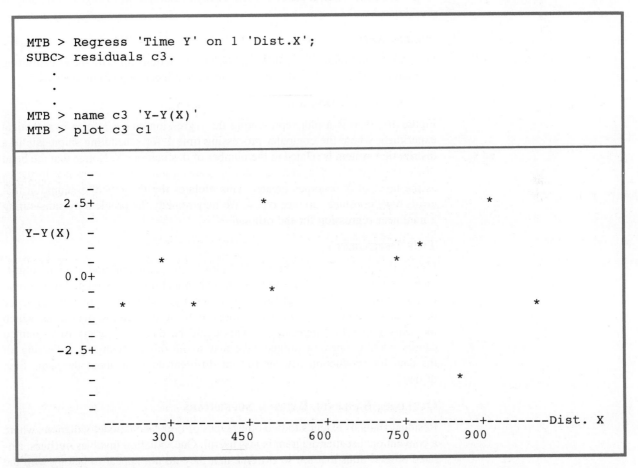

Note: Figure generated on an IBM PC using Minitab®.

FIGURE 10-19 Residual scatter plot for the parts supplier illustration.

TABLE 10-5 Residual Calculations for Parts Supplier's Data

Customer	Rail Distance to Destination X	Transportation Time (days) Y	Predicted Time from Regression Line $\hat{Y}(X) = 4.019 + .00897X$	Residual $e = Y - \hat{Y}(X)$
1	210	5	5.9027	−.9027
2	290	7	6.6203	.3797
3	350	6	7.1585	−1.1585
4	480	11	8.3246	2.6754
5	490	8	8.4143	−.4143
6	730	11	10.5671	.4329
7	780	12	11.0156	.9844
8	850	8	11.6435	−3.6435
9	920	15	12.2714	2.7286
10	1,010	12	13.0787	−1.0787

an appearance ideal for a regression analysis. The three scatter diagrams in Figure 10-20 illustrate other situations where critical assumptions of regression analysis are violated.

NONLINEARITY

Diagram (a) in Figure 10-20 shows a *nonlinear* relationship, with the *e*s exhibiting a pronounced curve. Section 10-8 considers nonlinear regression analysis.

NONCONSTANT VARIANCE

Figure 10-20(b) is a plot representing the regression analysis for a hypothetical experiment where the computer processing time Y for scheduling shipments in a distribution system is related to the number of destinations X. Notice that the band of *e*s gets wider as X increases. This indicates a *nonconstant variance* in the *e*s as the level of X becomes greater. This violates the theoretical assumption that errors have constant variance $\sigma^2_{Y \cdot X}$. We may remedy the problem by substituting a nonlinear regression for the original.

TIME DEPENDENCY

Figure 10-20(c) illustrates the residual plot for a regression model where adjustment time Y for temperature settings in a chemical process is related to the final output volume X of the production batch. The horizontal axis is the *time sequence* of the observation (rather than X). Notice that the *e*s increase over time, which indicates a *lack of independence*. This could be due to a variety of explained causes, such as operator fatigue. (We may avoid this difficulty by collecting all the data for production batches run on different days, at about the same time of day.)

OUTLIERS: BASEBALL BATTING SUPERSTARS

Residual analysis extends to two other types of regression model violations where a conventional scatter diagram is less useful. One violation involves **outliers**, isolated observations that are so extreme that they do not appear to belong with the rest. If an identifiable cause exists (such as a power outage or an absent operator), the data point may be safely discarded.

Figure 10-21 shows the *Minitab* results for a regression analysis with the baseball superstar data from Table 10-2 (batters only). The rookie baseball card price

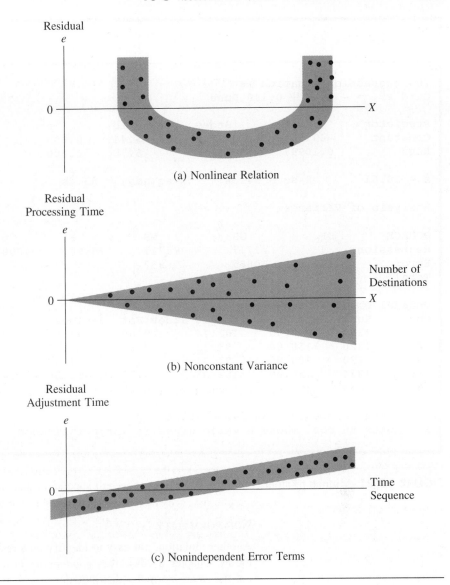

FIGURE 10-20 Residual scatter diagrams reflecting regression model violations.

Y is the dependent variable and the number of runs X is the independent variable. The program output lists the players whose data involve outliers. The outlying players are:

George Brett   Carlton Fisk   Rickey Henderson   Robin Yount

(The data do not show that these players are held in abnormally high esteem by fans because of their longevity, records, all-star performance, and World Series participation. Those extras have given added boost to their card prices.) A fifth listed player, Dave Winfield, is not classified as an outlier because his data point lies closer to the estimated regression line. But because of his high run production, he does have a greater influence on the positioning of that line.

```
MTB > Regress c3 1 c9.

The regression equation is
Card Pr. = - 49.8 + 0.110 Runs

Predictor       Coef       Stdev      t-ratio       p
Constant      -49.841      9.218       -5.41      0.000
Runs          0.10997      0.01257      8.75      0.000

s = 30.61       R-sq = 54.1%      R-sq(adj) = 53.4%

Analysis of Variance

SOURCE        DF          SS          MS          F          p
Regression     1        71717       71717       76.56      0.000
Error         65        60885         937
Total         66       132602

Unusual Observations
Obs.    Runs   Card Pr.      Fit  Stdev.Fit   Residual   St.Resid
  6     1382    200.00    102.14     9.69       97.86      3.37RX    George Brett
 26     1220    150.00     84.32     7.85       65.68      2.22R     Carlton Fisk
 36     1290    200.00     92.02     8.64      107.98      3.68R     Rickey Henderson
 66     1384     50.00    102.36     9.72      -52.36     -1.80 X    Dave Winfield
 67     1433    200.00    107.75    10.29       92.25      3.20RX    Robin Yount

R denotes an obs. with a large st. resid.
X denotes an obs. whose X value gives it large influence.
```

FIGURE 10-21 Minitab printout from regression using baseball superstar data.

NON-NORMALITY

Another violation, not easy to identify on a residual diagram, is non-normality in the *e*s. Chapter 23 describes *goodness-of-fit tests* that may establish whether or not the *e*s are normally distributed.

EXERCISES

10-28 The following data represent disposable personal income and personal consumption expenditures (billions of dollars) for the United States during the five-year period from 1964 through 1968. (Source: *Economic Report of the President*, February 1970.)

Year	Disposable Income X	Consumption Expenditures Y
1964	438	401
1965	473	433
1966	512	466
1967	547	492
1968	590	537

(a) Using the method of least squares, determine the estimated linear regression equation that provides consumption expenditure predictions for specified levels of disposable income.
(b) Is the Y intercept negative or positive? Why do you think this is so?
(c) State the meaning of the slope b of the regression line.
(d) Using your intermediate calculations in (a) and the values found for the estimated regression coefficients, calculate the coefficient of determination.

10-29 To help evaluate the effectiveness of a retraining program, the MakeWave Corporation personnel manager is studying the following results obtained for a sample of $n = 10$ employees. The data in the table that follows provide productivity indexes before and after retraining.
(a) Using the method of least squares, determine the equation for the estimated regression line.
(b) Calculate the sample coefficient of determination.

Student	Prior Score X	Current Score Y
Grace Brown	90	83
Patrick Gray	75	72
Lisa White	80	84
Homer Black	65	76
John Green	85	77
Linda Jones	90	82
Carl Smith	95	95
Freddy Tyler	75	68
Lisa Adams	70	78
Karen Johnson	60	55

(c) What percentage of the total variation in Y is explained by the estimated regression line?

10-30 Refer to the data given in Exercise 10-28.
(a) What percentage of the total variation in Y is explained by the regression line?
(b) Calculate the correlation coefficient.

10-31 Refer to the FlyMe Airlines' data in Exercise 10-10 for the distance X and the freight charge Y of a shipment.
(a) Calculate the sample correlation coefficient directly from the data.
(b) Using your earlier regression results, calculate the sample coefficient of determination.
(c) What percentage of the total variation in freight charge Y is explained by the estimated regression line?

10-32 Refer to the FlyMe Airlines' data given in Exercise 10-10 and to your answers.
(a) Compute, for each observation, the residual values.
(b) Plot the residual scatter diagram for the data.
(c) What do you conclude regarding consistency with the theoretical assumptions of the regression model?

10-33 Repeat Exercise 10-32(a)–(c) for the Crunchola data given in Exercise 10-12.

10-34 *Computer exercise.* Refer to the Ace Widgets data given in Exercise 10-16 and to your answers.
(a) Calculate (1) the sample coefficient of determination and (2) the sample correlation coefficient.
(b) Plot the residual scatter diagram for the data.

10-35 *Computer exercise.* Repeat Exercise 10-34(a) and (b) for the WaySafe customer data given in Exercise 10-15.

10-7 COMMON PITFALLS AND LIMITATIONS OF REGRESSION AND CORRELATION ANALYSIS

There are several pitfalls and limitations associated with linear regression and correlation analysis that should be given special mention. These may be categorized as being due to (1) violations of the theoretical assumptions, (2) improper use of the regression equation and correlation coefficient, and (3) misinterpretation of these coefficients. Regression and correlation are powerful tools, but ludicrous conclusions may be drawn if they are not used properly.

DANGERS OF EXTRAPOLATION IN REGRESSION ANALYSIS

The set of observations used to establish a regression equation covers a limited range of values of the independent variable X. Caution must be exercised in making predictions of the dependent variable Y whenever X falls outside this range. Such predictions are called **extrapolations**.

In the parts supplier illustration, the regression line was determined for ten shipments whose distances ranged from 210 to 1,010 miles. Suppose we wished to use our results to predict the transportation time for a shipment to a customer separated from the plant by 2,000 miles, a distance considerably greater than the largest used in determining the regression line. How reliable would such an extrapolation be?

This depends on whether our assumption of a linear relationship between time and distance is valid for shipments over great distances. There is simply no way to know this without including some longer shipments in the sample. As noted earlier in this chapter, the selection of a straight line was motivated by the general appearance of the data's scatter. Perhaps with a few additional points for distances between 1,000 and 2,000 miles, a curvilinear relationship might provide a better fit.

There may be a good logical basis for assuming that a line will prevail—but then we might expect its slope to be flatter or steeper because of the influence of additional data points. On the other hand, there are reasonably sound arguments that longer distances ought to involve less time-consuming recomposition of trains (adding and removing box cars), so that the additional time per extra mile (that is, the slope of the regression curve) decreases for longer trips.

Regression analysis is limited only to the range of actual observations. These observations—and not qualitative reasoning—are used to quantify the relationship between X and Y. Qualitative reasoning is useful initially in selecting the form of the regression equation (linear versus curvilinear) and later in interpreting the results, but it cannot be used in place of actual observation. We are not ruling out extrapolation here but are merely indicating its potential pitfalls. If there are

beginning interpreting

no data available beyond the range of required predictions, then extrapolation may be the only suitable alternative. Keep in mind that *extrapolation assigns values using a relationship that has been measured for circumstances differing from those for the prediction.*

Circumstances may differ for reasons other than extrapolation. Should the underlying populations change over time—as would be the case for changes in railroad operations or technology—then the regression line would not represent the shipments in subsequent years. Often, a regression analysis is short lived in its applicability because underlying relationships can change over time.

RELEVANCY OF PAST DATA

used history data to forecast future

Care must be taken in using past data to determine a future relationship. Regression analysis is often used in forecasting with time series, which we will discuss in Chapter 12. There the independent variable is time, with the dependent variable *Y* being forecast. The source of data is history, so that often a time span of many years is encompassed by the observed *Y* values. A very serious danger is that the underlying *Y* populations may change character over time. The regression equation assumes that variance in *Y* is constant. Thus, if there is reason to believe that the values of *Y* are becoming more or less volatile over time, a critical assumption of regression analysis is violated. In addition to difficulties with the variance, the observations over the years are usually statistically *dependent* violating another assumption of regression theory. The net effect of such violations is that probabilistic interpretations of inferences are invalid and cannot be used.

Because relationships are apt to change over time, special care should be taken when past data are used to predict a future value of the dependent variable. The hazards are most pronounced in forecasting with time series, but similar difficulties may arise whenever the data are collected over a long time period. This would be the case in attempting to express the cost of a production run by means of a regression line relating it to quantity produced.

A very useful result of such an analysis is identification of fixed and variable cost components, so that the *Y* intercept is the estimated fixed cost per production run, while the slope of the regression line provides an estimate of variable costs per unit. Since production runs may be infrequent, obtaining sufficient data points for predictions precise enough to be useful may require historical experience from several years. But during this period, a great many changes—in labor and material costs, in efficiency (due to technological improvements), or in facilities—can cause unknown changes in the relationship between cost and production volume.

The regression assumptions presume that the same conditions prevail at all levels of production, which is probably not the case. For example, low production volumes may predominate in early time periods, with higher volumes in later years. The slope of the regression line obtained may be unduly steep, exaggerating the true cost–volume relationship if prices have been increasing over the duration. If there is inflation, labor rates and per-unit material prices will rise with time, so that all basic historical accounting data ought to be recalculated at present wage and price levels prior to regression analysis, if that is at all possible.

CORRELATION AND CAUSALITY

The correlation coefficient measures only the strength of *association* between two variables. This is a statistical relationship, and a large positive or negative value of r does not indicate that a high value of one variable necessarily *causes* the other variable to be large. Examples of nonsense or *spurious* correlations abound.

relationship

Regression and correlation analysis only provides a *statistical* relationship between two variables. It cannot tell us whether the values of X cause the values of Y. There may be a cause-and-effect relationship, but not necessarily. Possibly there is not even a logical reason for a relationship. (Although for any practical problem there is ordinarily some reasonable connection.) Often the relationship between two variables may be explained by their interactions with a common factor. Thus, we might find that a straight line provides a very close fit to the scatter diagram that relates the number of major oil slicks polluting our coasts to the number of electrical power failures. Clearly, one set of events is not caused by the other, but both may be explained by a common linkage: the demand for energy.

STATISTICS AROUND US

Sperm Whales and Stock Prices

Consider the correlation between the number of sperm whales Y caught between 1964 and 1968 and *Standard and Poor's Price Index* for 500 stocks X during the same time period. In the following table, $r = -.89$ is calculated, indicating a high negative correlation between X and Y. How do we interpret this result? Clearly, there is no apparent logical connection between whaling and the New York Stock Exchange prices of common stocks. The values of X and Y have simply moved in opposite directions by approximately the same relative amounts for the five years considered. Statistically, large values of X have occurred with small values of Y, and vice versa. Obviously, r does not measure **causality** here, because we cannot say that increasing stock prices have caused a decline in the number of sperm whales caught, or the reverse.

Year	Number of Whales Caught (thousands) X	Standard and Poor's Price Index Y	X²	Y²	XY
1964	29	81	841	6,561	2,349
1965	25	88	625	7,744	2,200
1966	27	85	729	7,225	2,295
1967	26	92	676	8,464	2,392
1968	24	99	576	9,801	2,376
Totals	131	445	3,447	39,795	11,612
	$= \sum X$	$= \sum Y$	$= \sum X^2$	$= \sum Y^2$	$= \sum XY$

$$\bar{X} = 26.2 \qquad \bar{Y} = 89$$

$$r = \frac{\sum XY - n\bar{X}\bar{Y}}{\sqrt{(\sum X^2 - n\bar{X}^2)(\sum Y^2 - n\bar{Y}^2)}} = \frac{11,612 - 5(26.2)(89)}{\sqrt{[3,447 - 5(26.2)^2][39,795 - 5(89)^2]}} = -.89$$

Sources: *Yearbook of Fishery Statistics,* Food and Agricultural Organization, United Nations; *Economic Report of the President,* February 1970.

SUMMARY

1. **How does statistics measure and express *association* between two or more variables?**

   Regression and correlation analyses are concerned with the *association* between two or more variables, each representing a separate quantitative population. The relationship between two variables may be suggested graphically by the **scatter diagram**.

2. **How is the correlation coefficient computed and what does it measure?**

   The **correlation coefficient**

   $$r = \frac{\sum (X - \bar{X})(Y - \bar{Y})}{(n - 1)s_X s_Y}$$

   measures the <u>strength and direction of the relationship between X and Y. This value can help determine when there exists a potentially useful linear relationship between two variables.</u> **Perfect correlation** is approached as r becomes near to 1 or -1. X and Y are **uncorrelated** whenever $r = 0$.

3. **What is the role of the regression line and how is its equation found?**

   Regression analysis predicts the level of the **dependent variable** Y when only the value of the **independent variable** X is known. You compute the predicted Y by plugging a specific X into the **estimated regression equation**

   $$\hat{Y}(X) = a + bX$$

   This is also called the **estimated regression line**, which you establish by the **method of least squares** from the sample data. The Y intercept a and the slope b are the **regression coefficients**, found by the following equations.

   $$b = \frac{n\sum XY - \left(\sum X\right)\left(\sum Y\right)}{n\sum X^2 - \left(\sum X\right)^2} = \frac{\sum XY - n\bar{X}\bar{Y}}{\sum X^2 - n\bar{X}^2}$$

   $$a = \bar{Y} - b\bar{X}$$

   These values describe the regression line that best fits the data.

4. **How do we summarize the amount of variability in Y about the regression line and thereby achieve an important measure of the overall quality of the regression analysis?**

   $S_{Y\cdot X\cdot}$

   The overall quality of the regression line is reflected by the **standard error of the estimate**

   $$s_{Y\cdot X} = \sqrt{\frac{\sum [Y - \hat{Y}(X)]^2}{n - 2}}$$

   This quantity reflects the capacity of the regression line to "explain" some of the variability in values of Y. <u>A satisfactory regression line will yield a value of $s_{Y\cdot X}$ that is considerably smaller than the sample standard deviation of Y, s_Y.</u>

5. **What are the theoretical assumptions underlying regression analysis?**

   The theory underlying regression and correlation assumes that X and Y may be related by a **true regression line**

   $$\mu_{Y \cdot X} = A + BX$$

   that can only be estimated by the sample results. The height of this line $\mu_{Y \cdot X}$ at any given level of X is called the **conditional mean** of the underlying population of Y values assumed to exist for that X.

   Any inferences made rest upon further theoretical assumptions, among which are the normality and independence of **error terms** ε and constant variance $\sigma_{Y \cdot X}^2$ in Y populations, regardless of X. An analysis of **residuals** $e = Y - \hat{Y}(X)$ can help to assess how well those assumptions are met.

6. **How can we use the regression equation to make predictions with statistical confidence?**

   Several statistical inferences may be made in conjunction with regression analysis. Especially important to business applications are **prediction intervals**. These are confidence intervals for estimating either the **conditional mean** $\mu_{Y \cdot X}$ or an individual value Y_I, both of which have a common point estimate — the height $\hat{Y}(X)$ of the estimated regression line at the given level of X. The interval for $\mu_{Y \cdot X}$ is narrower, and the width of both depends on the distance separating X from its mean $\overline{X}$.

7. **What other inferences may be made in regression analysis?**

   Estimates or tests may also be made regarding the **true regression coefficients** A and B (using the sample counterparts a and b) and the **population correlation coefficient** ρ.

8. **What is the coefficient of determination and how does it relate to the quality of the regression analysis?**

   The overall quality of the regression analysis may be summarized by the **coefficient of determination**, r^2.

   $$r^2 = 1 - \frac{s_{Y \cdot X}^2}{s_Y^2}\left(\frac{n - 2}{n - 1}\right)$$

   The coefficient of determination expresses the proportion of the variability in Y that is explained by the regression line.

9. **What is the role of the computer in regression analysis?**

   Computer assistance is especially valuable in regression analysis because of the large volume of calculations needed. Popular software packages will not only find the estimated regression equation and plot scatter diagrams, but they may compute r, r^2, $s_{Y \cdot X}$, and most information needed for making inferences.

REAL-LIFE STATISTICAL CHALLENGE

Regression and Correlation Applied to the Automobile Dream List

In Chapter 9 hypothesis testing concepts were used to help analyze various populations for 232 autos. We will now apply regression and correlation testing methods to the set of "dream machines."

What factors could determine mileage? Weight of the vehicle? Transmission type? Driving skill? Engine size? To keep things simple we will investigate how gasoline mileage varies with engine size.

Using gasoline mileage Y as the dependent variable and engine size X as the independent variable, the regression equation for the population is:

$$\mu_{Y \cdot X} = 36.40 - 3.32X$$

The results are not really surprising—cars with bigger engines generally have lower mileage ratings.

In Chapter 6 three samples of $n = 5$ and one sample of $n = 15$ were described in Tables 6-19 and 6-20. The regression data for those samples are shown in Table 10-6. Observe how the slopes for the subgroups are similar to the overall population.

DISCUSSION QUESTIONS

1. Graph the regression lines for the population and the combined sample (15 cars). Comment on what you observe.

2. Graph the regression lines for all four samples. What do you observe?

3. Using the data for the combined sample, calculate the 95 percent prediction interval for the conditional mean of Y when $X = \bar{X}$.

4. Using the data for the combined sample, calculate the 95 percent prediction interval for an individual value of Y given X when $X = \bar{X}$.

TABLE 10-6 Regression Results for the 1990 Automobiles Mileage Data by Engine Displacement (X) and Highway Mileage (Y) per Gallon

| | Regression Results | | | |
	First Sample	Second Sample	Third Sample	Combined
Constant	33.34	34.82	33.15	33.56
Stand. Error of Est.	1.82	3.12	4.55	3.32
R Squared	0.45	0.71	0.46	0.49
No. of Observations	5	5	5	15
Degrees of Freedom	3	3	3	13
Slope	−2.13	−2.23	−2.95	−2.39
Stand. Error of Coeff.	1.36	0.82	1.86	0.68

REVIEW EXERCISES

10-36 The Dean at Old Ivy provided the following data for the number of outside activities X and the GPA Y for a sample of ten students.

Number of Activities X	GPA Y	Number of Activities X	GPA Y
10	3.9	3	2.8
0	3.1	4	3.3
5	3.4	5	2.6
2	2.8	4	2.5
0	1.9	3	3.2

(a) Determine the estimated regression line for predicting a student's GPA from the number of his or her activities.
(b) Compute, for GPA, (1) the sample standard deviation and (2) the standard error of the estimate.
(c) Compute (1) the sample coefficeint of determination and (2) the sample correlation coefficient.
(d) What is the predicted GPA of a student who has the following number of activities?
(1) 5   (2) 2   (3) 4   (4)10

10-37 A security analyst wants to be convinced that the efficiency of capital utilization, expressed by the annual turnover of inventory, actually does have an effect on a manufacturer's earnings. The following data have been obtained for a sample of five firms selected at random.

Company	Inventory Turnover X	Earnings as a Percentage of Sales Y
A	3	10
B	4	8
C	5	12
D	6	15
E	7	13

Calculate the correlation coefficient.

10-38 A California rancher has kept records over the past $n = 10$ years of the amount of rainfall X (inches) in his county and of the number of alfalfa bales Y he has had to buy to supplement grazing grass for his herd until he has been able to sell his excess cattle. The following estimated regression line has been obtained: $\hat{Y}(X) = 20{,}000 - 500X$. The rancher has calculated $s_Y = 1{,}000$ bales, $s_{Y \cdot X} = 500$ bales, and $\sum X^2 = 2{,}500$. The mean rainfall for the time period considered has been $\bar{X} = 15$ inches. To arrange bank financing, the rancher wishes to predict how much alfalfa he must buy for the remainder of the current year. Since the dry season has arrived, he knows how much rain has fallen. Construct the 95% prediction intervals for the required number of bales if this year's rainfall is (a) 15, (b) 20, and (c) 10 inches.

10-39 An economist has established that personal income X may be used to predict personal savings Y by the relationship $\hat{Y}(X) = 24.0 + .06X$ (billions of dollars). For each of the following levels of personal income, calculate the predicted value of personal savings.
(a) $300 billion   (b) $500 billion   (c) $700 billion

10-40 BugOff Chemical Company determined the estimated regression line for total ingredient cost of chemical batches of size X (thousands of liters) to be $\hat{Y}(X) = \$30,000 + \$5,000X$. This result was obtained for a sample of $n = 100$ production runs, for which $s_{Y \cdot X} = \$400$ and $\bar{X} = 10$ thousand liters.
(a) Construct the 95% prediction interval for the conditional mean batch cost $\mu_{Y \cdot X}$ when $X = 10$ thousand liters.
(b) Construct the 99% prediction interval for the total cost of the next 10-thousand-liter batch.

10-41 A Fast-Gro agronomist believes that over a limited range of fertilizer levels X (gallons per acre) she can obtain a prediction of crop yield Y (bushels per acre) using the method of least squares. For a sample of $n = 25$ plots, she has established that $\hat{Y}(X) = 50 + .05X$, with $s_Y = 8$ and $s_{Y \cdot X} = 2$ bushels per acre; $\bar{X} = 210$ gallons, and $\sum X^2 = 1,105,000$. Construct the 95% prediction intervals for (a) the mean bushels per acre when the level of fertilizer applied is 200 gallons and (b) the yield of an individual 1-acre plot with the same amount of fertilizer as in (a).

STATISTICS IN PRACTICE

10-42 Consider the populations comprising all statistics students. Using as sample data the master class data list developed in Exercise 1-19, answer the following. (Note: Be sure to show all your intermediate steps. You may use intermediate answers you developed in earlier chapters to avoid unnecessary effort. If needed gather additional data such as weight, age, commute time to work or distance to work.)
(a) Select one variable as the independent variable X and one as the dependent variable Y.
(b) Determine the estimated regression equation.
(c) For the dependent variable determine the sample standard deviation and the standard error of the estimate.
(d) Calculate the sample coefficient of determination and the sample correlation coefficient.
(e) Predict the value of the dependent variable for four different independent variable values (see Exercise 10-36 as an example).
(f) Demonstrate how to calculate the 95 percent prediction interval for the conditional mean when $X = \bar{X}$.
(g) Demonstrate how to calculate the 95 percent prediction interval for an individual value of Y given X when $X = \bar{X}$.

10-43 Repeat Exercise 10-42 using your group's class data from Exercise 1-21.

10-44 Carry out a hypothesis test for the results you found in either Exercise 10-42 or 10-43. (See Section 10-9 for additional details.)

10-45 Exercise 10-36 asked you to examine the relationship between the number of outside activities and a student's GPA. Select several of your classmates (groups of at least five would work best) and list the number of outside activities and your GPAs.
(a) Add your data to the "Old Ivy" data and recalculate the estimated regression equation for predicting a student's GPA from the number of his or her activities.
(b) Compute for the GPA the sample standard deviation and the standard error of the estimate.
(c) Compute the sample coefficient of determination and the sample correlation coefficient.
(d) What is the predicted GPA for each of your group members?
(e) If you previously answered Exercise 10-36, compare the answers and comment on any similarities or differences.

10-46 *Comparing Commute Time and Distance to Work.* The following data is from a sample of graduate students who work in the Silicon Valley (San Jose, Calif.) and attend school at night.

Commute Time (Min.)	Distance (Kilometers)	Data (Rounded) (Miles)
20	8	5
20	13	8
35	21	13
45	26	16
25	24	15
30	28	17
20	20	12
45	54	33
30	28	17
15	4	3
10	8	5
20	8	5
35	31	19
35	37	23
25	18	11
5	3	2

(a) Calculate the estimated regression line for predicting a student's commute time given the distance traveled to work.
(b) Compute for the commute time the sample standard deviation and the standard error of the estimate.
(c) Compute the sample coefficient of determination and the sample correlation coefficient.
(d) What is the predicted commute time for someone living 12 miles from the office?

10-47 Refer to the NFL quarterback data in Table 3-10. Assume that these 12 quarterbacks constitute a random sample of all NFL quarterbacks.
  (a) Calculate the estimated regression equation for predicting the number of touchdowns (TD), given the percentage of passes completed (Pct. Comp.).
  (b) Compute for the dependent variable the sample standard deviation and the standard error of the estimate.
  (c) Compute the sample coefficient of determination and the sample correlation coefficient.
  (d) What is the predicted number of touchdowns for a quarterback completing 62% of his passes?

10-48 Refer to the data in Exercises 7-40 and 7-41. The following questions are designed to investigate whether or not there is a relationship between per capita library spending and the high school graduation rates for the states in 1991.
  (a) Select a random sample of size 8 from the states.
  (b) Using your sample, calculate the estimated regression line for predicting high school graduation rate, given per capita library spending.
  (c) Compute for the dependent variable the sample standard deviation and the standard error of the estimate.
  (d) Compute the sample coefficient of determination. What percentage of the variation in high school graduation rate is explained by the estimated regression line?

10-49 Consider the following random sample of exam scores from 9 students from Table 3-13, which now includes the grades received on the midterm exam (100 points possible).

Student No.	Midterm Score	Final Exam
42	43	24
61	36	34
86	65	49
24	89	87
37	82	73
13	90	95
51	43	10
31	75	75
18	87	86

Source: Janet Anaya, Fall 1993.

  (a) Calculate the estimated regression line for predicting the final exam score given the midterm exam score.
  (b) For the dependent variable determine the sample standard deviation and the standard error of the estimate.
  (c) Compute the sample coefficient of determination and the sample correlation coefficient.
  (d) Construct the 95% prediction interval for the conditional mean when $X = \overline{X}$.

(e) Construct the 95% prediction interval for an individual value of Y, given X when $X = \bar{X}$.

10-50 Consider the SAT score data in Table 2-17. Assume that this information constitutes a random sample of all SAT average scores.
(a) Calculate the estimated regression line for predicting the average male SAT math score, given the average male SAT verbal score.
(b) Compute for the dependent variable the sample standard deviation and the standard error of the estimate.
(c) Compute the sample coefficient of determination and the sample correlation coefficient. Comment.

CASE La Boutique Fantasque

Anna Respighi runs a gift shop located in the Gentrytown Mall. The shop, La Boutique Fantasque, specializes in merchandise with a ballet theme, including objets d'art, music boxes, and figurines. Anna has hired a study group of statistics students from the local college campus to help her answer important questions about her store.

The store's 19X1 operating statements provide the following data.

Month	Wages	Utilities	Sales Volume
January	$1,500	$200	$26,000
February	2,200	250	31,500
March	1,850	225	27,450
April	1,920	185	26,450
May	2,350	195	42,440
June	1,750	210	21,010
July	1,660	195	18,075
August	1,550	180	16,350
September	1,620	200	19,330
October	2,050	210	25,370
November	2,250	235	32,340
December	3,150	305	58,730

Anna buys her merchandise from various suppliers and marks it up, so that after paying for all the freight, damage, shrinkage, and obsolescence costs, she achieves an average gross margin of 50%. Thus, for a $20 sale her cost of goods will be $10. Anna's lease requires that she pay a monthly minimum of $2,000 plus 10% of any sales over $40,000. All of her other costs, except rent, wages, and utilities, take 10% from each sales dollar.

QUESTIONS

1. Using the above data, determine the estimated regression equations for predicting (a) wages and (b) utilities from sales volume.

2. Calculate the coefficients of determination for the above equations. Comment on the quality of each regression.

3. Using the estimated regression equation found in Question 1(a), comment on the suitability of a prediction interval for mean wages.

4. Anna needs to forecast her operating profit for 19X2. She projects that month-by-month sales will be 20% higher than their 19X1 levels.
   (a) Determine her projected sales for each month of 19X2.
   (b) Using the estimated regression equations found in Question 1, predict (1) wages and (2) utilities for each month of 19X2.
   (c) Using the forcasted sales data, compute the predicted levels of rent and other costs for each month. Then, compute Anna's predicted monthly operating profit.
   (d) What will Anna's projected operating profit be for the year of 19X2?

10-8 OPTIONAL TOPIC I: NONLINEAR REGRESSION ANALYSIS

It must be emphasized that a straight line is not always an appropriate function relating Y to X. The scatter diagrams in Figure 10-22 illustrate cases for which various types of nonlinear functions fit the data more closely. Notice that all the functions are curves. Such relationships between X and Y are called **curvilinear** relationships.

Figure 10-22(a) shows the relationship between crop yield Y and quantity X of fertilizer applied. The curve fits data obtained for test plots to which various amounts of fertilizer have been applied. As the amount of fertilizer increases to a certain point, it proves beneficial in increasing the harvest. But beyond this point, the benefits become negative, because additional fertilizer burns plant roots and causes the crop yield to decline. The greatest increases in Y occur for small values of X, with Y increasing at a decreasing rate. The peak value of Y may be referred to as the "point of negative returns," after which Y decreases at an increasing rate. This curve expressing Y as a function of X has the shape of an inverted U. A regression equation in the form $Y = a + bX - X^2$ could be used here.

This is contrasted to the U-shaped curve in Figure 10-22(b), where the incremental or marginal cost Y of production is plotted against volume X. This regression equation assumes the form $Y = a + bX + cX^2$. Here, data points have been obtained for the various levels of production activity in a plant. At low levels of plant activity, all factors of production are employed less efficiently. But as volume increases, the cost of additional units declines as factors are employed more efficiently. Increases in efficiency become less pronounced, until a point is reached after which extra production can be handled—but less efficiently than before—and marginal costs begin to rise.

In Figure 10-22(c), the size Y of a population of *Drosophila* (fruit flies) is shown as a function of the number of generations X since the colony was established. The data points represent observations made after successive hatchings. There are no natural checks on the population growth, because the flies are reared in an artificial environment. The curve obtained is an exponential or geometric growth curve, so that Y is related to X by an expression like $Y = a^X$ or $Y = X^c$. Plots for the world's human population growth during the past several centuries assume the same basic shape. With exponential growth, Y increases at an increasing rate for larger values of X.

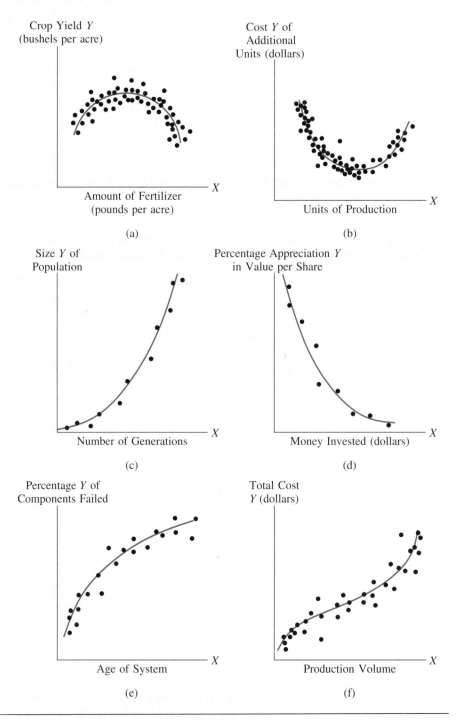

FIGURE 10-22 Scatter diagrams for examples of curvilinear relationships.

This is contrasted to the negative exponential curve in Figure 10-22(d), where the percentage appreciation Y in the value of each share of a mutual fund is plotted against the total money invested X by the fund. The points represent several successful mutual funds at various stages of growth. The appropriate regression equation would be in the form $Y = ae^{-bX}$. Negative exponential curves correspond to values of Y that decrease at a decreasing rate as X becomes larger. A rationale for such a result is that a small mutual fund can be highly selective in choosing its portfolio, giving it the opportunity to buy small company stocks that may appreciate greatly. But as the fund grows larger, it cannot buy as heavily into the rather limited number of small, growing companies and must invest more money in the stocks of larger, less promising firms.

Figure 10-22(e) shows a logarithmic curve relating the percentage Y of the original components of a particular type that have failed to the age X of the system. The points were obtained from the histories of several systems. Some components survive almost indefinitely, but most original components fail early. Here, values of Y increase at a decreasing rate as X becomes larger. We can express Y in terms of X by using the equation $Y = a + b \log(1 + X)$.

In Figure 10-22(f), the total cost Y of production for a plant over a particular time period is plotted against the associated levels of production activity X. These points are fitted by a curve that shows total cost increasing at a decreasing rate as greater volumes of production are achieved. Beyond a point of diminishing returns for X, the larger volume reduces incremental efficiency, and the curve shows the values of Y increasing at an increasing rate.

Throughout this chapter, we have considered only linear relationships. The procedure we use to determine the particular line that best fits the data is called *linear regression analysis*. One reason for our emphasis on linear equations is that they are easier to explain. The methods of analysis are also simpler and may be directly extended to curvilinear relationships. Straight lines are useful for describing a great many phenomena, so they are among the most common regression relationships.

SOLVING BY TRANSFORMATION OF VARIABLES

Linear regression analysis may be used to solve some nonlinear problems by first making a transformation of the variables. The dependent variable may be transformed using logarithms, so that $\log(Y)$ becomes the independent variable. The predicted values can then be converted back to original units by taking the antilogarithm. In Chapter 12 we will see in more detail how this may be done in conjunction with time-series analysis.

With the use of a computer, either X or Y may be transformed easily and followed by a linear regression analysis performed on the new variables. In doing this, the least-squares method minimizes the sum of the vertical deviations in the *transformed* units. But then the assumptions of the underlying model may not apply, so that care must be taken when making inferences.

FITTING A POLYNOMIAL

In Chapter 11, we will investigate in detail *multiple regression*. The procedures involved may be adapted to a simple nonlinear regression analysis involving just one predictor X. The estimated regression equation

$$\hat{Y}(X) = a + b_1X + b_2X^2 + b_3X^3 + \cdots$$

may be found by treating $X^2, X^3, \ldots$ as separate independent variables. The resulting regression equation is a **polynomial**.

10-51 Plot the scatter diagram for each of the following sets of data. Sketch the shape of the regression curve that seems to be the best fit for each relationship.

(a)		(b)		(c)	
Number of Workers X	**Output per Labor Hour** Y	**Number of Units** X	**Total Cost** Y	**Minutes between Rest** X	**Pounds Lifted per Minute** Y
5	10	600	$11,000	5.5	350
8	4	50	3,100	9.6	230
1	3	470	10,200	2.4	540
1	2	910	15,700	4.4	390
1	7	160	6,300	.5	910
8	8	950	19,500	7.9	220
7	10	690	13,900	2.0	680
10	2	90	1,800	3.3	590
3	5	310	8,800	13.1	90
3	8	1,000	25,700	4.2	520

10-9 OPTIONAL TOPIC II:
INFERENCES REGARDING REGRESSION COEFFICIENTS

In some applications of regression analysis, the major concern is not predictions but instead the nature of the regression equation itself. The slope and intercept of the true regression equation

$$\mu_{Y \cdot X} = A + BX$$

can be estimated or tested, so that inferences regarding A or B could be made. Such investigations are usually limited to the slope B.

CONFIDENCE INTERVAL ESTIMATE OF B

An unbiased estimate of slope B of the true regression line may be obtained from its sample counterpart b. We construct the $100(1 - \alpha)\%$

CONFIDENCE INTERVAL ESTIMATE OF SLOPE

$$B = b \pm t_{\alpha/2} \frac{s_{Y \cdot X}}{\sqrt{\sum X^2 - n\bar{X}^2}}$$

where $t_{\alpha/2}$ is found from Appendix Table F for $n - 2$ degrees of freedom.*

We may use our parts supplier illustration to apply this procedure. Suppose that a 95% confidence interval is desired for the true regression coefficient B. Using $\alpha = .05$ and $10 - 2 = 8$ degrees of freedom, we have, from Appendix Table F, $t_{\alpha/2} = t_{.025} = 2.306$. Using the intermediate calculations from Table 10-3 and the values previously determined for b and $s_{Y \cdot X}$, we construct the following 95% confidence interval.

$$B = .00897 \pm 2.306 \frac{2.02}{\sqrt{4,451,500 - 10(611)^2}} = .00897 \pm .00550$$

or

$$.00347 \le B \le .01447$$

This means that we are 95% confident that the true value of B, the mean number of days required for transporting a shipment each additional mile, falls between .00347 and .01447. (Repeating this procedure for 100 different samples, then, about 95% of the time we will construct an interval containing the true value of B.)

This interval estimate of B is not very precise and would probably be of little use to the parts supplier. As with the confidence interval for the population mean discussed in Chapter 8, precision can be increased by using a large sample—considerably larger than the one used in this illustration.

TESTING HYPOTHESES ABOUT B

We may extend hypothesis testing to inferences about B. Ordinarily, the fact of greatest importance in testing for the value of B is whether it equals zero. Figure 10-23 illustrates a regression line having zero slope. Note that no matter what the value of X, $\mu_{Y \cdot X}$ remains at A, parallel to the X axis. Thus, if $B = 0$, then since the population distributions of Y have the same mean and variance, we may

---

*Here we use the principle that

$$B = b \pm t_{\alpha/2} \text{ (estimated } \sigma_b)$$

It can be established that

$$\sigma_b = \frac{\sigma_{Y \cdot X}}{\sqrt{\sum X^2 - n\bar{X}^2}}$$

Using $s_{Y \cdot X}$ in place of $\sigma_{Y \cdot X}$, we obtain an estimate of the standard error s_b for b.

usually conclude that the Y distributions are identical for all values of X. This means that there is no statistical relationship between X and Y. Thus, if $B = 0$, regression analysis will be of no value in making predictions of Y.

The following hypotheses apply for a two-sided testing situation.

$$H_0: B = 0 \quad \text{and} \quad H_A: B \neq 0$$

If we choose $\alpha = .05$ (to match the previous confidence level) as our significance level, then we only need to determine if our confidence interval contains the point $B = 0$. If it does not, we must reject the null hypothesis. Since the lower limit of the 95% confidence interval calculated previously is .00347, a number greater than $B = 0$, the null hypothesis must be *rejected* at a .05 significance level. We conclude that rail distance does affect transportation time.

It may be appropriate instead to employ an upper-tailed test with $H_0: B \leq 0$ and $H_A: B > 0$. This would be better if Y varies directly with X, as seems natural in the case of transportation time and distance. The first step is to calculate the

STUDENT *t* STATISTIC FOR THE SLOPE

$$t = \frac{b - 0}{s_b} = \frac{b}{\dfrac{s_{Y \cdot X}}{\sqrt{\sum X^2 - n\overline{X}^2}}}$$

The computed value is then compared to the critical value t_α that corresponds to the prescribed significance level α. If t is smaller than t_α the null hypothesis is accepted. The opposite is true for a lower-tailed test, where the alternative is that $B < 0$ (the case when Y bears an inverse relationship to X).

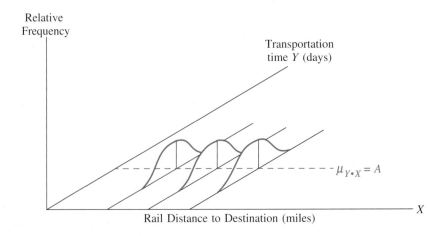

FIGURE 10-23 Illustration of a true regression line having zero slope, so that X and Y are uncorrelated.

We may illustrate the one-sided test using the parts supplier's results. For example, using $\alpha = .005$ and $10 - 2 = 8$ degrees of freedom, from Appendix Table F we obtain the critical value $t_{.005} = 3.355$. The computed value of the test statistic is

$$t = \frac{.00897}{\dfrac{2.02}{\sqrt{4{,}451{,}500 - 10(611)^2}}} = 3.769$$

Since $t = 3.769$ exceeds 3.355, the null hypothesis must be *rejected* at the significance level of $\alpha = .005$. This indicates that the slope of the true regression line is greater than zero.

USING B TO MAKE STATISTICAL INFERENCES ABOUT ρ

The population correlation coefficient ρ is the square root of the population coefficient of determination. The latter is defined as 1 minus the ratio of the variance of Y about the true regression line to the variance of Y about its mean. In order to make probability statements regarding ρ, *both* X and Y must be treated as random variables. Correlation theory requires this before we can qualify inferences about ρ. When using r as the estimator, one additional restrictive—and often unrealistic—assumption is ordinarily made to avoid mathematical difficulties in finding the sampling distribution of r. This is that X and Y have a particular joint probability distribution called the **bivariate normal distribution**. Since

```
MTB > Regress 'Time Y' 1 'Copies X'

The regression equation is
Time Y = 1.76 + 0.00546 Copies X

Predictor        Coef        Stdev     t-ratio         p
Constant       1.7576       0.2691        6.53     0.000
Copies X    0.0054638    0.0004962       11.01     0.000

s = 0.6636       R-sq = 87.1%      R-sq(adj) = 86.4%

Analysis of Variance

SOURCE          DF           SS           MS          F         p
Regression       1       53.395       53.395     121.25     0.000
Error           18        7.927        0.440
Total           19       61.322
```

Note: Figure generated on an IBM PC using Minitab®.

FIGURE 10-24 Computer printout for the duplicating center illustration.

discussion of this distribution is beyond the scope of this book, we cannot describe the sampling distribution of r or discuss construction of the confidence interval estimates of ρ.

The far more common inference desired is a test to decide whether $\rho = 0$— that is, whether there is any statistical relationship at all between X and Y. For this purpose, we may substitute the test regarding the slope of the regression line. Recall that a slope of zero for the regression line indicates a zero correlation. Thus, a test of whether $B = 0$ may be used to reject or to accept the null hypothesis $\rho = 0$. *A test rejecting the null hypothesis that $B = 0$ will also reject the assumption that $\rho = 0$.*

COMPUTER-ASSISTED INFERENCES ABOUT REGRESSION COEFFICIENTS

As with prediction intervals, the computations needed to make inferences about B are burdensome. Fortunately, the popular software packages often provide the necessary information as part of regression analysis. Consider the printout in Figure 10-24 for the regression analysis of the duplicating center illustration.

The applicable values regarding inferences about the slope are found in the "Copies X" row. Listed first is the value $b = .00546$ (rounded). Next, we find the value of the standard error to be .0004962. The computed value $t = 11.01$ follows for the null hypothesis that $B = 0$. The achieved result has a prob. value of zero, to three places of accuracy.

The printout also provides analogous information for making inferences about the intercept A. The corresponding values appear in the "Constant" row.

The bottom portion of the printout contains other information, the meaning and use of which will be described in Chapter 11.

OPTIONAL EXERCISES

10-52 Refer to the information given in Exercise 10-22.
  (a) Construct a 99% confidence interval estimate of the slope B of the true regression line.
  (b) In testing H_0 that $B = 0$ against the two-sided alternative that $B \neq 0$, should the null hypothesis be accepted or rejected at the .01 significance level?
  (c) In testing H_0 that $B \leq 0$ against the one-sided alternative that $B > 0$, should the null hypothesis be accepted or rejected at the .01 significance level?

10-53 Refer to the information given in Exercise 10-27.

(a) Construct a 95% confidence interval estimate of the slope B of the true regression line.

(b) In testing H_0 that $B = 0$ against the two-sided alternative that $B \neq 0$, should the null hypothesis be accepted or rejected at the .05 significance level?

(c) In testing H_0 that $B \geq 0$ against the one-sided alternative that $B < 0$, should the null hypothesis be accepted or rejected at the .05 significance level?

CHAPTER 11

MULTIPLE REGRESSION AND
CORRELATION

BEFORE READING THIS CHAPTER, MAKE SURE YOU UNDERSTAND:

The distinction between the sample and population (Chapter 1).

The role of random samples in statistical evaluations (Chapter 4).

About confidence intervals and how they are used and constructed (Chapter 8).

About the basic concepts of hypothesis testing (Chapter 9).

The basic concepts of regression and correlation analysis (Chapter 10).

AFTER READING THIS CHAPTER, YOU WILL UNDERSTAND:

What the difference is between multiple regression and simple regression.

How to establish the multiple regression equation.

What assumptions underlie multiple regression analysis and what potential pitfalls may be encountered.

What inferences may be made with multiple regression analysis.

How to assess the overall quality of a regression analysis.

How to find a predictive regression model.

How dummy variables can be used in conjunction with multiple regression.

In Chapter 10, we learned to construct a regression equation to make predictions of a dependent variable when the value of a single independent variable is known. The techniques we used there are referred to as **simple regression and correlation analysis**. We have already noted that such predictions may be too imprecise for practical application, because a substantial amount of the variation in Y cannot be explained by X. In this chapter, these techniques will be expanded to include **multiple regression and correlation analysis**, which involves *several* independent predictor variables. The total variation in Y can then be explained by two or more variables, which permits us to make a more precise prediction in many situations than is possible in simple regression analysis.

The essential advantage in using two or more independent variables is that it allows greater use of available information. For example, a regression line expressing a new store's sales in terms of the population of the city it serves should yield a poorer sales forecast than an equation that also considers median income, number of nearby competitors, and the local unemployment rate. A plant manager ought to predict more precisely the cost of processing a new order if he considers, in addition to the size of that order, the total volume of orders, his current manpower level, or the production capacity of available equipment. A marketing manager ought to gauge more finely the sales response to a magazine advertisement by considering, in addition to its circulation, the demographical features of its readers, such as median age, median income, or proportion of urban readers.

11-1 LINEAR MULTIPLE REGRESSION INVOLVING THREE VARIABLES

In linear multiple regression analysis, we extend simple linear regression analysis to consider two or more independent variables. In the case of two independent variables, denoted by X_1 and X_2, we use the

ESTIMATED MULTIPLE REGRESSION EQUATION

$$\hat{Y} = a + b_1 X_1 + b_2 X_2$$

As before, $\hat{Y}$ denotes values of Y calculated from the estimated regression equation. Here, we must consider two independent variables and one dependent variable, or a total of three variables. The sample data will consist of three values for each sample unit observed, so that a scatter diagram for these observations will be three–dimensional.

REGRESSION IN THREE DIMENSIONS

To explain how sample data can be portrayed in three dimensions, we will use the analogy of the walls and the floor of a room. Letting a corner of the room represent the situation when all three variables have a value of zero, the data

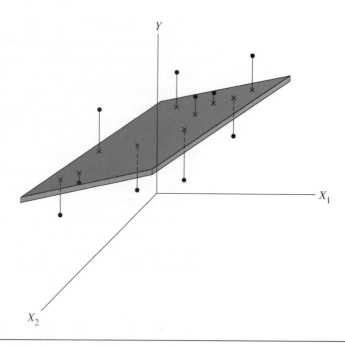

FIGURE 11-1 Scatter diagram and regression plane for multiple regression using three variables.

points may be represented by marbles suspended in space at various distances from the floor and the two walls. A marble's height above the floor can be the value of Y for that observation. Its distance along the right wall can represent the observed value of X_1, and its distance along the left wall can express the value of X_2. Figure 11-1 is a pictorial representation of one three-dimensional scatter for a hypothetical set of data.

The estimated multiple regression equation corresponds to a **plane**,* which must be slanted in the way that provides the best fit to the sample data. This results in a three-dimensional surface called the **regression plane**. Choosing this plane is analogous to determining how to position a pane of glass through the suspended marbles so that its incline approximates that of the pattern of scatter. Of course, everyone should obtain the same regression plane, so we will adapt the method of least squares to three dimensions.

The constants a, b_1, and b_2 in the equation of the regression plane $\hat{Y} = a + b_1 X_1 + b_2 X_2$ are called the **estimated regression coefficients**. As with $\hat{Y}(X) = a + bX$, a is the value of Y where the regression plane intersects the Y axis, so that we still refer to a as the Y intercept. However, the interpretations of b_1 and b_2 are somewhat different in multiple regression. The constant b_1 expresses the net change in Y for a one-unit increase in X_1, holding X_2 at a constant value. We can view b_1 as the slope of the edges obtained by slicing the

*Although Y is related to X_1 and X_2 by a plane instead of a line, we still say that the relationship is linear. The three-dimensional extension of a two-dimensional line is a plane. Although a line can also exist in three dimensions, it is defined as the intersection of two planes. Thus, a three-dimensional line is like a point in two dimensions, which can be defined by the intersection of two lines.

regression plane with cuts made parallel to the X_1 axis at a distance X_2 from the origin. Likewise, b_2 is the net change in X_2, holding X_1 constant. Because b_1 or b_2 by itself only indicates part of the total movement in Y in response to increases in its respective independent variable, b_1 and b_2 are referred to as **estimated partial regression coefficients**.

ILLUSTRATION: PREDICTING COLLEGE GPA

For example, suppose that college grade point average (GPA) Y (on a scale of 4) is related to high school GPA, denoted by X_1, and Scholastic Aptitude Test (SAT) score X_2 (hundreds of points) by the equation $\hat{Y} = -1.8 + .8X_1 + .3X_2$. Here $a = -1.8$, so that the regression plane cuts the Y axis at $Y = -1.8$. The regression coefficient $b_1 = .8$ signifies that a student's college GPA can be predicted to be .8 point higher for each additional point in her high school GPA, regardless of how well she has done on the SAT. The constant $b_2 = .3$ indicates that each additional 100 points on the SAT is estimated to add .3 point to a student's college GPA, no matter what her high school GPA. Thus, a "straight A" high school student (GPA = 4.0) scoring 750 on the SAT would have a predicted college GPA of

$$\hat{Y} = -1.8 + .8(4.0) + .3(7.5) = 3.65$$

which is an "A minus" average. Because the sample of students used to obtain the above regression equation will exhibit individual differences in background, motivation, study load, high school grading levels, and so forth, we cannot assume that this particular student will necessarily achieve a 3.65 GPA. As noted in Chapter 10, we must account for variability in Y, both inherent and due to sampling error.

11-2 MULTIPLE REGRESSION USING
THE METHOD OF LEAST SQUARES

Mathematically, we use the method of least squares to position the regression plane so that the sum of the squared vertical deviations from its surface to the data points is minimized. The dots in Figure 11-1 represent the observed data points, and the vertical deviations of these points from the plane are shown as line segments. The crosses indicate the corresponding points on the regression plane that have identical values of X_1 and X_2. The height of a cross above the X_1X_2 plane (or the floor in our analog) represents the value of $\hat{Y}$ computed from $\hat{Y} = a + b_1X_1 + b_2X_2$. The deviation between the observed and the computed heights, $Y - \hat{Y}$, will be positive for dots lying above the regression plane and negative for dots lying below, so that the method of least squares minimizes

$$\sum (Y - \hat{Y})^2$$

As in simple regression, we determine the coefficients of the estimated regression plane by solving a set of three equations in three unknowns. As before, these are referred to as the

NORMAL EQUATIONS

$$\sum Y = na + b_1 \sum X_1 + b_2 \sum X_2$$
$$\sum X_1 Y = a \sum X_1 + b_1 \sum X_1^2 + b_2 \sum X_1 X_2$$
$$\sum X_2 Y = a \sum X_2 + b_1 \sum X_1 X_2 + b_2 \sum X_2^2$$

These equations may be obtained from the equation for a plane $Y = a + b_1 X_1 + b_2 X_2$. The first normal equation is found by summing each term of the plane equation, using the fact that $\sum a = na$. The second normal equation is obtained by multiplying every term in the plane equation by X_1 and summing the results. The third equation is found by multiplying every term by X_2 and summing.*

We will not introduce separate expressions for the regression coefficients here, because the resulting equations would be too complicated and cumbersome. Instead, we find a, b_1, and b_2 by calculating the required sums from the data for the various combinations of Y, X_1, and X_2 and substituting these sums into the normal equations, which are solved simultaneously.

ILLUSTRATION: PREDICTING SUPERMARKET PROFITS

In order to illustrate how to find the estimated multiple regression equation, we consider the problem of predicting profit Y for supermarkets in a large metropolitan area. As independent variables, we use the total sales X_1 of foods and X_2 of nonfoods. For simplicity of calculation, we use only the ten hypothetical observations shown in Table 11-1.

TABLE 11-1 Profit and Sales of Food and Nonfood Items

Supermarket Number	Profit (thousands of dollars) Y	Food Sales (tens of thousands of dollars) X_1	Nonfood Sales (tens of thousands of dollars) X_2
1	20	305	35
2	15	130	98
3	17	189	83
4	9	175	76
5	16	101	93
6	27	269	77
7	35	421	44
8	7	195	57
9	22	282	31
10	23	203	92

*This procedure is a mnemonic aid. Calculus was used to actually derive these equations.

One reason for splitting total sales into food and nonfood categories is that stores will differ significantly from each other in the nonfood items offered. Virtually all stores handle tobacco and cleaning agents. But some have liquor departments, offer lines of convenience hardware and small appliances, or handle clothing articles. The nonfood items typically have higher markups and move more slowly off the shelf. Thus, treating food and nonfood sales separately ought to provide a better prediction of a store's profit than total sales.

The intermediate calculations necessary to find the regression equation are shown in Table 11-2. The first eight columns contain the individual variable values and the squared and product terms. Column (9) contains the values for Y^2, which are not needed to obtain the regression coefficients but will be used later. Substituting the appropriate column totals, we obtain the following normal equations

$$191 = 10a + 2{,}270b_1 + 686b_2$$

$$48{,}690 = 2{,}270a + 594{,}832b_1 + 139{,}565b_2$$

$$12{,}569 = 686a + 139{,}565b_1 + 52{,}682b_2$$

Solving these equations simultaneously for the unknowns a, b_1, and b_2, the following solutions are obtained.

$$a = -23.074 \qquad b_1 = .1148 \qquad b_2 = .2349$$

The simultaneous solution of three normal equations by hand can be quite a chore. This task, as we will see later in this chapter, can be simplified by using a computer.

The above values for a, b_1, and b_2 provide the following estimated multiple regression equation.

$$\hat{Y} = -23.074 + .1148X_1 + .2349X_2$$

This equation may then be used to forecast the profit of a particular store. Suppose

TABLE 11-2 Intermediate Calculations for Obtaining Regression Coefficients

(1) Y	(2) X_1	(3) X_2	(4) X_1Y	(5) X_2Y	(6) X_1X_2	(7) X_1^2	(8) X_2^2	(9) Y^2
20	305	35	6,100	700	10,675	93,025	1,225	400
15	130	98	1,950	1,470	12,740	16,900	9,604	225
17	189	83	3,213	1,411	15,687	35,721	6,889	289
9	175	76	1,575	684	13,300	30,625	5,776	81
16	101	93	1,616	1,488	9,393	10,201	8,649	256
27	269	77	7,263	2,079	20,713	72,361	5,929	729
35	421	44	14,735	1,540	18,524	177,241	1,936	1,225
7	195	57	1,365	399	11,115	38,025	3,249	49
22	282	31	6,204	682	8,742	79,524	961	484
23	203	92	4,669	2,116	18,676	41,209	8,464	529
191	2,270	686	48,690	12,569	139,565	594,832	52,682	4,267
$= \sum Y$	$= \sum X_1$	$= \sum X_2$	$= \sum X_1Y$	$= \sum X_2Y$	$= \sum X_1X_2$	$= \sum X_1^2$	$= \sum X_2^2$	$= \sum Y^2$

that a new store is built that will have estimated sales of \$2,500,000 for foods and \$750,000 for nonfoods. To match the sample data, the food and nonfood sales are both expressed in increments of \$10,000, so that $X_1 = 250$ and $X_2 = 75$. The estimated store profit for these sales levels would be

$$\hat{Y} = -23.074 + .1148(250) + .2349(75)$$
$$= 23.244 \text{ (thousand dollars) or } \$23,244$$

We may interpret the value $b_1 = .1148$ as follows. For each \$10,000 increase in food sales there will be an estimated increase of .1148 thousand dollars, or \$114.80, in profits, holding the sales of nonfood items at any fixed level. Likewise, each additional \$10,000 in nonfood sales results in an estimated profit increase of $b_2 = .2349$ thousand dollars, or \$234.90, for any fixed amount of food sales. Thus the marginal contribution of nonfoods to profits is, dollar for dollar, slightly more than twice that of the foods. The result $a = -23.074$ signifies that \$23,074 of "fixed" costs, on the average, must be absorbed before a store can show a profit. These correspond to those expenses, such as rent, that continue whether or not the store is open. The \$23,074 figure may vary considerably from the actual fixed costs of any particular store, because of sampling error and due to different store characteristics. It also depends on (1) the linear model being appropriate and (2) the validity of extrapolation down to zero sales for both types of items.

ADVANTAGES OF MULTIPLE REGRESSION

Two interesting questions may be posed regarding the use of multiple rather than simple regression analysis. First, is the simultaneous analysis of two independent variables through multiple regression any improvement over that obtained through two separate simple regressions? Second, how can we show that the accuracy of predictions is improved by the use of multiple regression analysis? We will begin to answer these questions by continuing with our supermarket illustration.

Three two-dimensional diagrams for the supermarket data are shown in Figure 11-2. In Figure 11-2(a), profit is plotted against food sales. Food sales X_1 by itself might be a fairly reliable predictor of profit Y, since there is a high value of .76 for the sample correlation coefficient. Denoting this particular sample correlation coefficient by the double-subscripted symbol r_{Y1}, where $Y1$ indicates that the strength of association between the variables Y and X_1 is being measured, we have $r_{Y1} = .76$. A similar figure may be obtained for any pair of the three variables. Thus, analysis relating profit Y to nonfood sales X_2 provides another sample correlation coefficient, $r_{Y2} = -.29$. A cursory examination of this second relationship, shown in Figure 11-2(b), seems to indicate that nonfood sales have little effect on profits. Does this indicate that nonfood sales would be a poor predictor of a store's income? Two-variable analysis seems to contradict our previous finding that profit will increase by an estimated \$234.90 for each additional \$10,000 in nonfood sales. How might we explain this?

A comparison of food sales X_1 to nonfood sales X_2, as represented by the scatter diagram in Figure 11-2(c), shows a pronounced negative correlation between these two variables. We distinguish the sample correlation coefficient in this case from the others by using the subscript 12; here, $r_{12} = -.77$. Supermarkets having higher than average food sales tend to have lower than average nonfood sales,

FIGURE 11-2 Scatter diagrams for variable pairs using supermarket data.

whereas the reverse is true for stores with below average food sales. By specializing heavily in nonfood items, the operators having a low volume of food sales manage to survive and achieve profits in the face of competition from stores more successful at selling food. The two stores having annual food sales below $1.5 million have extraordinarily large profits, which are not very well explained by food sales alone. Their data points lie considerably above the regression line in Figure 11-2(a). The impact of nonfood sales is camouflaged by the interaction of food and nonfood sales.

This illustrates a general inadequacy in using simple regression to separately determine how a dependent variable relates to several independent variables. The same is true of correlation. Separate simple correlations of Y versus X_1 and Y versus X_2 seem to indicate that food sales would be a far better predictor of profit than nonfood sales. A two-variable analysis indicates that X_2 has a negligible correlation with Y of $r_{Y2} = -.29$. But it would be a blunder to discard X_2 because it shows such a small correlation with Y. This is because X_2 is highly negatively correlated with X_1, $r_{12} = -.77$, so that its influence on Y can be explained only by considering how Y relates to both X_1 and X_2 through multiple regression. The interactions between the predictor variables themselves must first be determined before a variable can be discarded. We will later present techniques of multiple regression and correlation analysis used to provide this information.

RESIDUALS AND THE STANDARD ERROR OF THE ESTIMATE

We have seen that the errors in making predictions from the regression line are smaller when the scatter of the data is less pronounced. The degree of such variation in Y can be expressed by the standard error of the estimate for values of Y. The same is true in multiple regression. The standard error of the estimate for values of Y about the regression *plane* is computed in the same way. This is determined from the following expression for the

STANDARD ERROR OF THE ESTIMATE

$$S_{Y \cdot 12} = \sqrt{\frac{\sum (Y - \hat{Y})^2}{n - 3}}$$

We use a different subscript notation, $Y \cdot 12$, to show that two independent variables X_1 and X_2 are being used to predict Y. As in simple regression, we find the standard error of the estimate by taking the square root of the mean squared deviations of observed Y values from the estimated regression plane. The divisor $n - 3$ is chosen because 3 degrees of freedom are lost in estimating the regression coefficients. This makes $S_{Y \cdot 12}^2$ an unbiased estimator of the variance of Y about the true regression plane.

As in simple regression, the vertical deviations $Y - \hat{Y}$ are referred to as **residuals**. This terminology reflects that the sum of the squared residuals represents the variation in Y left unexplained by the regression analysis. It is the unexplained variation in the evaluation that remains, and thus provides the residual. By including one more independent predictor variable in an expanded regression analysis, there may be a resulting reduction in the unexplained variation. The expanded regression would then provide a sum of the squared residuals that is smaller.

The predicted and residual values for the supermarket illustration are computed in Table 11-3. Notice that the residual values (vertical deviations) sum to zero (except for rounding errors). The least-squares procedure guarantees this outcome. The standard error of the estimate is

$$S_{Y \cdot 12} = \sqrt{\frac{132.2522}{10 - 3}} = 4.347 \text{ (thousand dollars)}$$

When performing the regression calculations by hand with a calculator, it may be simpler to use the following

SHORTCUT EXPRESSION FOR THE STANDARD ERROR

$$s_{Y \cdot 12} = \sqrt{\frac{\sum Y^2 - a\sum Y - b_1\sum X_1 Y - b_2 \sum X_2 Y}{n-3}}$$

because it does not require $\hat{Y}$ to be calculated for every data point.

Using the data in Table 11-2 and the regression constants found previously, we calculate the standard error of the estimate

$$s_{Y \cdot 12} = \sqrt{\frac{4{,}267 - (-23.074)(191) - .1148(48{,}690) - .2349(12{,}569)}{10 - 3}}$$

$$= 4.343 \text{ (thousand dollars)}$$

(Due to rounding this value differs slightly from the earlier result.)

This value may be compared to the corresponding standard error found in a simple regression for profit Y and food sales X_1. Using X_1 as the only independent variable, and then applying the procedures of Chapter 10 to the supermarket data, we find the regression line

$$\hat{Y}(X_1) = 3.891 + .0670X_1$$

The scatter of data about this regression *line* is summarized by the standard error of the estimate

$$s_{Y \cdot X_1} = 5.719 \text{ (thousand dollars)}$$

TABLE 11-3 Actual, Predicted, and Residual Values for Three-Variable Regression Analysis Using the Supermarket Data

Actual Profit Y	Predicted Value $\hat{Y}$	Residual Value $Y - \hat{Y}$	Squared Deviation $(Y - \hat{Y})^2$
20	20.1615	−0.1615	0.0261
15	14.8702	0.1298	0.0168
17	18.1199	−1.1199	1.2542
9	14.8684	−5.8684	34.4381
16	10.3665	5.6335	31.7363
27	25.8945	1.1055	1.2221
35	35.5924	−0.5924	0.3509
7	12.7013	−5.7013	32.5048
22	16.5815	5.4185	29.3601
23	21.8412	1.1588	1.3428
191	189.9974	0.0026	132.2522

Comparing this with the standard error of the estimate about the regression *plane*, $S_{Y \cdot 12} = 4.343$, we see that multiple regression provides a better interpretation of the data. As we noted earlier, the standard error expresses the amount of variation in Y that is left unexplained by regression analysis. Since $S_{Y \cdot 12}$ is smaller than $s_{Y \cdot X_1}$, our regression plane (incorporating both food and nonfood sales as *two* independent variables) explains more of the variation in Y than the regression line does (where food sales serves as the *single* independent variable and there is more unexplained variation). This indicates that all inclusion of nonfood sales data in the analysis will indeed provide better predictions of store profit.

ASSUMPTIONS OF MULTIPLE REGRESSION

The assumptions of linear multiple regression are similar to those of simple regression. The least-squares method provides a plane that is an estimate of

$$\mu_{Y \cdot 12} = A + B_1 X_1 + B_2 X_2$$

where $\mu_{Y \cdot 12}$ denotes the **conditional mean** of Y, given X_1 and X_2. The values of the true regression coefficients A, B_1, and B_2 remain unknown and are estimated by a, b_1, and b_2, respectively. For each combination of X_1 and X_2 there is a corresponding point on the true regression plane. The height of this point is $\mu_{Y \cdot 12}$, the mean of the corresponding population of Y.

The theoretical model expresses each observation in terms of the expression

$$Y = A + B_1 X_1 + B_2 X_2 + \varepsilon$$

where ε is the error term. Ordinarily, the ε's are assumed to be independent and normally distributed with mean 0 and standard deviation $\sigma_{Y \cdot 12}$. For any specified levels of X_1 and X_2, the Ys would then be normally distributed with mean $\mu_{Y \cdot 12}$ and standard deviation $\sigma_{Y \cdot 12}$.

CHALLENGES AND PITFALLS OF MULTIPLE REGRESSION ANALYSIS

There are several challenges associated with regression analysis involving several variables. It is a process fraught with pitfalls. A few issues and difficulties should be addressed.

VIOLATIONS OF THE UNDERLYING MODEL

Multiple regression analysis is subject to all of the potential complications discussed in Section 10-6 for simple regression. These include nonlinear relationships between variables, nonconstant variance in the error terms, outliers, and nonnormality in error terms. As in Chapter 10, *residual analysis* may be helpful in identifying some of the problem areas, and many of the same remedies apply in multiple regression. We will see that greater challenges are created by the existence of several variables and their interrelationships.

MULTICOLLINEARITY

A potential problem in multiple regression applications can arise when two independent variables are highly correlated. Business applications are especially prone to such high correlations. For example, consider retail sales and foot traffic or magazine advertising revenue and number of pages. In a three-variable situation, such a relationship would provide sample data that are scattered closely about a single line lying inside the least-squares regression plane. Although the estimated regression equation can be found with no special difficulty when X_1 and X_2 are highly correlated, a second set of sample observations may result in drastically different regression coefficients, even when the second line of scatter is nearly identical to the first one. Because many different regression planes can contain the same line, the regression exhibits **multicollinearity**.

The inherent instability of multicollinearity is reflected in imprecise regression coefficients that would vary widely from sample to sample. If the investigator is only interested in making predictions or estimating the conditional mean, multicollinearity presents no problem. But if the primary concern is in separate assessments of the effects of the independent variables, it may be better to evaluate X_1 and X_2 each in a separate study. In some cases, including a third independent variable will eliminate the problem created by the multicollinearity.

TIME-SERIES DATA

Some of the more interesting applications of regression involve data generated over time. This is epitomized by the problem economists face when they must use regression analysis to establish the mathematical forms of various relationships, such as those involving supply and demand curves. When data for evaluations are collected at regular intervals from monthly, quarterly, or annual reports, they are referred to as **time-series data**.

Time-series data may present special difficulties arising from a **serial correlation** between observations made in successive time periods. A serial correlation or **autocorrelation** exists whenever there is a tendency for similar values to follow the earlier number. For example, the following successive monthly seasonally adjusted unemployment rates show a serial correlation.

7.3   7.4   7.6   7.5   7.3   7.1   7.0   6.9   6.9   7.1   7.2   7.3

Notice that each successive monthly rate lies close to the preceding level, reflecting the inertia in the economy.

Serial correlations are common in time-series data. Difficulties arise when the error terms, or deviations $Y - \hat{Y}$, are serially correlated. Key assumptions of the underlying regression model are thereby violated, making the least-squares method inefficient and invalidating the inferences made. The problem might be alleviated by including another independent variable which is itself serially correlated. For example, a regression where the dependent variable is company profit and the independent variable is number of orders would involve a high serial correlation in error terms due to inflation (which raises unit prices, and thus, revenue and profits); inclusion of the consumer price index as a second independent variable might eliminate the difficulties.

Procedures exist for testing for serial correlation. A detailed discussion may be found in many of the references listed in the back of this book.

COMPUTATIONAL DEMANDS

Multiple regression analysis involves a substantially greater amount of computation than we encountered for simple regression in Chapter 10. It takes a great deal of patience and devotion to detail to successfully wade through those calculations by hand. The following example comprehensively illustrates all the steps involved in determining an estimated regression equation.

After working through one multiple regression problem by hand (or just carefully following all the steps in the example), the need for computer assistance becomes obvious. When four or more variables are involved a computer is almost mandatory. Section 11-3 describes in detail computer-assisted multiple regression analysis.

EXAMPLE: WEETEES PRODUCTION COSTS

Consider the problem of estimating the total cost Y of a production batch of WeeTees using quantity produced X_1 and grain price index X_2 as the independent variables. The following sample data apply.

Sample i	Total Cost (thousands of dollars) Y	Production Quantity (tons) X_1	Grain Price Index X_2
1	200	400	120
2	85	150	134
3	115	220	115
4	200	500	90
5	140	300	85
6	65	100	140
7	70	150	95
8	65	150	80
9	125	240	96
10	190	350	125

SOLUTION: The multiple regression procedure begins with the calculation of sums and sums of squares and products.

Y	X_1	X_2	$X_1 Y$	$X_1 X_2$	$X_2 Y$	X_1^2	X_2^2	Y^2
200	400	120	80,000	24,000	48,000	160,000	14,400	40,000
85	150	134	12,750	11,390	20,100	22,500	17,956	7,225
115	220	115	25,300	13,225	25,300	48,400	13,225	13,225
200	500	90	100,000	18,000	45,000	250,000	8,100	40,000
140	300	85	42,000	11,900	25,500	90,000	7,225	19,600
65	100	140	6,500	9,100	14,000	10,000	19,600	4,225
70	150	95	10,500	6,650	14,250	22,500	9,025	4,900
65	150	80	9,750	5,200	12,000	22,500	6,400	4,225
125	240	96	30,000	12,000	23,040	57,600	9,216	15,625
190	350	125	66,500	23,750	43,750	122,500	15,625	36,100
1,255	2,560	1,080	383,300	135,215	270,940	806,000	120,772	185,125
$= \sum Y$	$= \sum X_1$	$= \sum X_2$	$= \sum X_1 Y$	$= \sum X_2 Y$	$= \sum X_1 X_2$	$= \sum X_1^2$	$= \sum X_2^2$	$= \sum Y^2$

The appropriate values are placed in the normal equations.

$$1{,}255 = 10a + 2{,}560b_1 + 1{,}080b_2$$
$$383{,}300 = 2{,}560a + 806{,}000b_1 + 270{,}940b_2$$
$$135{,}215 = 1{,}080a + 270{,}940b_1 + 120{,}772b_2$$

To solve these normal equations, we eliminate all but one of the unknowns. We start by combining the first two equations to eliminate a.

$$-256(1,255 = 10a + 2,560b_1 + 1,080b_2)$$
$$383,300 = 2,560a + 806,000b_1 + 270,940b_2$$
$\Big\}\rightarrow$

$$-321,280 = -2,560a - 655,360b_1 - 276,480b_2$$
$$383,300 = 2,560a + 806,000b_1 + 270,940b_2$$
$$62,020 = 0a + 150,640b_1 - 5,540b_2$$

We next combine the first and the third equations, again eliminating a.

$$-108(1,255 = 10a + 2,560b_1 + 1,080b_2)$$
$$135,215 = 1,080a + 270,940b_1 + 120,772b_2$$
$\Big\}\rightarrow$

$$-135,540 = -1,080a - 276,480b_1 - 116,640b_2$$
$$135,215 = 1,080a + 270,940b_1 + 120,772b_2$$
$$-325 = 0a - 5,540b_1 + 4,132b_2$$

By combining the two resulting equations and eliminating b_2, we find the value of b_1.

$$4,132(62,020 = 150,640b_1 - 5,540b_1)$$
$$5,540(-325 = -5,540b_1 + 4,132b_2)$$
$\Big\}\rightarrow$

$$256,266,640 = 622,444,480b_1 - 22,891,280b_2$$
$$-1,800,500 = -30,691,600b_1 + 22,891,280b_2$$
$$254,466,140 = 591,752,880b_1 + 0b_2$$

$$b_1 = .430$$

We substitute b_1 into either of the equations having two variables to find the value of b_2.

$$62,020 = 150,640(.430) - 5,540b_2$$
$$62,020 = 64,775.2 - 5,540b_2$$
$$5,540b_2 = 2,755.2$$
$$b_2 = .497$$

We substitute b_1 and b_2 into one of the original equations with three variables to find the value of a.

$$1,255 = 10a + 2,560(.430) + 1,080(.497)$$
$$1,255 = 10a + 1,100.80 + 536.76$$
$$1,255 = 10a + 1,637.56$$
$$-10a = 382.56$$
$$a = -38.3$$

Substituting the values found for a, b_1, and b_2 into the estimated multiple regression equation, we get

$$\hat{Y} = -38.3 + .430X_1 + .497X_2$$

The predicted cost of WeeTees production runs can be made from the estimated regression equation. Consider the following.

Production Quantity (tons) X_1	Grain Price Index X_2	Predicted Cost (thousands of dollars) $\hat{Y}$
100	90	$\hat{Y} = -38.3 + .430(100) + .497(90) = 49.4$
150	110	$\hat{Y} = -38.3 + .430(150) + .497(110) = 80.9$
200	70	$\hat{Y} = -38.3 + .430(200) + .497(70) = 82.5$

EXERCISES

11-1 Determine the predicted level of Y for each of the following situations.
(a) $\hat{Y} = 10 + 2X_1 + 3X_2$ given $X_1 = 5$ and $X_2 = 10$.
(b) $\hat{Y} = -20 + 4X_1 + 5X_2$ given $X_1 = 1$ and $X_2 = .5$.
(c) $\hat{Y} = 14.67 + .23X_1 - .58X_2$ given $X_1 = 55$ and $X_2 = 27$.

11-2 Solve the following system of simultaneous equations.

$$5 = 2a + 1b_1 - 5b_2$$
$$2 = 1a + 4b_1 + 2b_2$$
$$-1 = 2a + 2b_1 - 2b_2$$

11-3 An economist wishes to predict the incomes of restaurants that are more than two years old using total floor space X_1 and number of employees X_2 as independent variables. The following data have been obtained for a sample of $n=5$ restaurants.

Income (thousands) of dollars) Y	Floor Space (thousands) of square feet) X_1	Number of Employees X_2
20	10	15
15	5	8
10	10	12
5	3	7
10	2	10

(a) Determine the estimated regression equation.
(b) State the meaning of the partial regression coefficients b_1 and b_2.

11-4 A college admissions director wishes to predict college GPA Y from the regression equation

$$\hat{Y} = .5 + .8X_1 + .003X_2$$

Using high school GPA X_1 and IQ score X_2 as independent variables, calculate the predicted college GPA for the following students.

	High School GPA X_1	IQ Score X_2
(a)	2.9	123
(b)	3.0	118
(c)	2.7	105
(d)	3.5	136

11-5 A Crunchola food processing manager wishes to predict the total cost Y of production runs from a least-squares regression. As independent variables she uses production quantity X_1 and wheat price index X_2. The following data apply.

Total Cost (thousands of dollars) Y	Production Quantity (tons) X_1	Wheat Price Index X_2
1,950	3,750	118
910	1,450	128
1,130	2,300	119
2,100	5,100	85
1,370	3,100	90
700	950	137
690	1,450	100
710	1,450	82
1,300	2,500	94
2,010	3,750	126

(a) Determine the estimated regression equation.

(b) By how much do these results indicate that total cost will increase if one additional ton is produced? If the wheat price index goes up one point?

11-6 The editor of a statistics journal wishes to predict the total typing hours Y for article drafts. As independent variables, she uses the number of words in the draft X_1 (tens of thousands) and an index X_2 for level of difficulty on a scale from 1 (least difficult) to 5 (most difficult). The following intermediate calculations have been obtained.

$$n=25 \qquad \sum Y = 200 \qquad \sum X_1 = 100 \qquad \sum X_2 = 75$$

$$\sum X_1 Y = 1,000 \qquad \sum X_2 Y = 800 \qquad \sum X_1^2 = 600$$

$$\sum X_2^2 = 325 \qquad \sum Y^2 = 3,800 \qquad \sum X_1 X_2 = 200$$

(a) Determine the equation for the regression plane $\hat{Y} = a + b_1 X_1 + b_2 X_2$.

(b) State the meaning of the values you obtain for b_1 and b_2.

11-7 A real estate appraiser wishes to predict the selling price of a home Y using building size X_1 and lot size X_2 as independent variables. The following data apply.

Price (thousands of dollars) Y	Building Size (hundreds of square feet) X_1	Lot Size (thousands of square feet) X_2
45	21	21
37	16	23
26	17	7
32	14	9
34	19	11
49	18	45
53	23	12
65	22	10
71	24	10
88	26	22

(a) Calculate the sums and the sums of squares and product terms.

(b) Express the normal equations, and solve them simultaneously to obtain the estimated multiple regression coefficients. Then, determine the estimated multiple regression equation.

(c) Compute the standard error of the estimate.

11-8 Refer to the intermediate calculations given in Exercise 11-6.

(a) Determine the equation for the estimated regression line $\hat{Y}(X_1) = a + bX_1$ using a *single* independent variable X_1.

(b) Compute $s_{Y \cdot X_1}$ using X_1 instead of X in the expression for $s_{Y \cdot X}$ on page 459. Then, compute $S_{Y \cdot 12}$ using the expression on page 515. Do you think more accurate predictions result if the variable X_2 is included than if X_1 is the sole predictor? Why?

11-3 MULTIPLE REGRESSION: COMPUTER APPLICATIONS

Multiple regression may involve more than two independent variables. For example, in predicting college GPA, we could also include the number of extracurricular high school activities, since this information is usually considered in making college admissions decisions. Including this third independent variable, denoted by X_3, would provide the regression equation

$$\hat{Y} = a + b_1X_1 + b_2X_2 + b_3X_3$$

To determine the regression coefficients, additional product sums involving X_3 must be computed and four normal equations must be solved simultaneously.

In multiple regression using X_1, X_2, and X_3, we compute the standard error of the estimate about the regression **hyperplane**. (Including Y, there are now four variables, and the regression surface can no longer be graphed in only three dimensions. Mathematicians call a four-dimensional plane a "hyperplane.") The standard error, denoted by $S_{Y \cdot 123}$, is calculated in the same way that we calculate $S_{Y \cdot 12}$, but with the extra term $-b_3 \sum X_3Y$ in the numerator. The denominator will be $n - 4$. The number of degrees of freedom will also be $n - 4$, and we calculate the prediction intervals as we did before, except using this reduced value.

When more predictor variables are added, we can expand the regression analysis by including X_4, X_5, and so on. When there are m total variables (one dependent and $m - 1$ independent), the number of degrees of freedom will be $n - m$, which is used as the denominator in computing the standard error and in finding $t_{\alpha/2}$ when constructing prediction intervals.

A computer application will now be discussed to illustrate multiple regression using three independent variables.

COMPUTER-ASSISTED MULTIPLE REGRESSION ANALYSIS

A computer generally provides greater levels of accuracy due to its superior capability of handling a large number of significant figures. It is not necessary for users to prepare their own computer programs to perform regression and correlation analysis. The widely available software packages vary considerably in format and type of output data, but they usually include determinations of the regression coefficients (a, b_1, b_2, and so on), standard errors, and correlation coefficients. These packages can be elaborate enough to include lower-dimensional regression equations for several variable combinations, values of the t statistics (used in making inferences regarding regression coefficients), and coefficients of partial determination (to be discussed in Section 11-5). The most complex programs provide inference-making computations that are too sophisticated to discuss here.

To explain the use of the computer, we will expand our supermarket illustration to include a third independent variable—the size of the store in thousands of square feet. Our previous sample data are augmented by including the ten observations for X_3 provided in Table 11-4.

A multiple regression run using the augmented supermarket data was performed and the computer printout in Figure 11-3 was generated. The top portion of the printout shows the data entered and the necessary commands for the program. Next, is the regression run, broken down into three parts. First, we find the information regarding the estimated regression equation; second, the analysis of variance (to be discussed in Section 11-4); and third, the printout provides the

TABLE 11-4 Sample Data for Supermarket Profits, Augmented

Supermarket Number	Food Sales (tens of thousands of dollars) X_1	Nonfood Sales (tens of thousands of dollars) X_2	Store Size (thousands of square feet) X_3	Profit (thousands of dollars) Y
1	305	35	35	20
2	130	98	22	15
3	189	83	27	17
4	175	76	16	9
5	101	93	28	16
6	269	77	46	27
7	421	44	56	35
8	195	57	12	7
9	282	31	40	22
10	203	92	32	23

```
MTB > Print c1-c4
```

ROW	Food X_1	Nonfood X_2	Size X_3	Profit Y
1	305	35	35	20
2	130	98	22	15
3	189	83	27	17
4	175	76	16	9
5	101	93	28	16
6	269	77	46	27
7	421	44	56	35
8	195	57	12	7
9	282	31	40	22
10	203	92	32	23

```
MTB > Name c5 = 'SRES1' c6 = 'FITS1' c7 = 'RESI1'
MTB > Regress c4 3 c1-c3 'SRES1' 'FITS1';
SUBC>    Residuals 'RESI1'.
```

The regression equation is
Profit = - 10.2 + 0.0270 Food + 0.0971 Nonfood + 0.525 Size

Predictor	Coef	Stdev	t-ratio	p
Constant	$-10.170\ a$	$3.473\ s_a$	-2.93	0.026
Food	$0.02704\ b_1$	$0.01204\ s_{b_1}$	2.25	0.066
Nonfood	$0.09705\ b_2$	$0.03015\ s_{b_1}$	3.22	0.018
Size	$0.52468\ b_3$	$0.05916\ s_{b_3}$	8.87	0.000

$s = 1.250$ R-sq = 98.5%   R-sq(adj) = 97.7%

$S_{Y\cdot 123}$ R^2

Analysis of Variance

SOURCE	DF	SS	MS	F	p
Regression	3	609.53 SSR	203.18 MSR	130.06	0.000
Error	6	9.37 SSE	1.56 MSE		
Total	9	618.90 $SSTO$			

SOURCE	DF	SEQ SS
Food	1	357.56
Nonfood	1	129.09
Size	1	122.88

```
MTB > Print c1 c4 c6 c7 c5.
```

ROW	Food	Profit	FITS1	RESI1	SRES1
1	305	20	19.8368	0.16315	0.15738
2	130	15	14.3987	0.60131	0.55938
3	189	17	17.1615	-0.16154	-0.13975
4	175	9	10.3322	-1.33221	-1.27938
5	101	16	16.2774	-0.27738	-0.34409
6	269	27	28.7111	-1.71110	-1.64730
7	421	35	34.8649	0.13509	0.18844
8	195	7	6.9303	0.06973	0.08087
9	282	22	21.4501	0.54987	0.72267
10	203	23	21.0369	1.96309	1.82476
	X_1	Y	$\hat{Y}$	$\varepsilon = Y - \hat{Y}$	

Note: Figure generated on an IBM PC using Minitab®.

FIGURE 11-3 Computer printout for the augmented supermarket data.

actual Y and predicted or fitted $\hat{Y}$ values—with residuals—computed for all of the observations.

Although the presentation may vary, most computer programs provide the same information as shown in Figure 11-3. The more important values are identified with annotated symbols added to the printout. The results indicate that store profit may be predicted from the estimated regression equation

$$\hat{Y} = -10.170 + .027X_1 + .097X_2 + .525X_3$$

We may interpret the values for the partial regression coefficients. The value $b_1 = .027$ indicates that a store's profit will increase by an estimated .027 thousand dollars or $27, for each additional $10,000 in food sales, holding other variables fixed. This is smaller than the value for b_1 found in the previous three-variable regression, but b_1 has a different meaning here. Instead of a single additional variable, two variables, both nonfood sales and store size, are accounted for and are being held constant. Likewise, $b_2 = .097$ indicates that holding store size and food sales constant, store profits will increase by an estimated $97 for each $10,000 in nonfood sales. The independent variable X_3, store size, has a partial regression coefficient of value $b_3 = .525$, indicating that a supermarket can increase its profits by an estimated $525 for each thousand square feet of additional floor space.

The substantial changes in the values a, b_1, and b_2 from the earlier multiple regression indicate that including store size X_3 as one of the independent variables should lead to better profit predictions. This improvement can be seen by comparing the standard error of the estimate of $S_{Y \cdot 123} = 1.250$ (shown in the computer printout) to the earlier one of 4.343. Including the additional variable X_3 for store size reduces the standard error of the estimate of Y considerably. This indicates that profit can be predicted with greater precision when store size is included as well as food and nonfood sales.

EXERCISES

11-9 An economist wishes to predict total spending for a sample of 10 families using income, family size, and additional savings as the three independent variables. The following data apply.

Family	Total Spending Y	Income X_1	Family Size X_2	Additional Savings X_3
A	$ 8,000	$10,000	3	$1,000
B	7,000	10,000	2	1,500
C	7,000	9,000	2	700
D	12,000	16,000	4	1,800
E	6,000	7,000	6	200
F	7,000	9,000	4	500
G	8,000	8,000	6	0
H	7,000	8,000	5	100
I	10,000	12,000	6	200
J	8,000	11,000	2	1,000

(a) Determine the coefficients for the estimated regression line $\hat{Y}(X_1) = a + bX_1$, and calculate $s_{Y \cdot X_1}$.
(b) Determine the coefficients for the estimated regression plane $\hat{Y} = a + b_1X_1 + b_2X_2$, and calculate $S_{Y \cdot 12}$.
(c) Does a comparison of the values of $S_{Y \cdot 12}$ and $s_{Y \cdot X_1}$ suggest that including family size X_2 as an independent variable improves total spending predictions? Explain.

11-10 *Computer exercise.* Refer to the data given in Exercise 11-9.
(a) Determine the coefficients for $\hat{Y} = a + b_1X_1 + b_2X_2 + b_3X_3$.
(b) Calculate the value of $S_{Y \cdot 123}$.
(c) Does a comparison of the values of $S_{Y \cdot 123}$ and $S_{Y \cdot 12}$ suggest that including additional savings as the third variable improves total spending predictions?

11-11 The Environmental Protection Agency wishes to predict the fuel consumption of one popular car model using speed, altitude, and passenger weight as the independent variables. The following data apply.

Trip	Fuel Consumption (mpg) Y	Average Speed (mph) X_1	Altitude (thousands of feet) X_2	Passenger Weight (hundreds of pounds) X_3
1	28	50	2	2
2	26	55	0	3
3	28	44	1	2
4	18	46	5	4
5	31	57	0	2
6	25	53	2	3
7	24	54	4	3
8	21	60	4	2
9	23	59	1	5
10	26	52	1	4

(a) Determine the coefficients for the estimated regression line $\hat{Y}(X_1) = a + bX_1$, and calculate $s_{Y \cdot X_1}$.
(b) Determine the coefficients for the estimated regression plane $\hat{Y} = a + b_1X_1 + b_2X_2$, and calculate $S_{Y \cdot 12}$.
(c) Does a comparison of the values of $S_{Y \cdot 12}$ and $s_{Y \cdot X_1}$ suggest that including altitude as a variable improves fuel consumption predictions? Explain.

11-12 *Computer exercise.* Refer to the data given in Exercise 11-11.
(a) Determine the coefficients for $\hat{Y} = a + b_1X_1 + b_2X_2 + b_3X_3$.
(b) Determine the value of $S_{Y \cdot 123}$.
(c) Does a comparison of the values of $S_{Y \cdot 123}$ and $S_{Y \cdot 12}$ suggest that including weight as the third variable improves fuel consumption predictions? Explain.

11-13 A VBM (Very Big Machines) systems programmer wishes to predict run times of payroll programs run on a particular software—hardware configuration. The following data have been obtained for 20 runs.

Run Time (minutes) Y	Required Memory (thousands of bytes) X_1	Amount of Output (thousands of lines) X_2	Amount of Input (thousands of lines) X_3
11.3	24	10	5
8.7	8	6	5
5.5	14	8	2
7.4	35	6	2
9.1	11	9	4
6.1	23	4	3
15.2	24	11	11
18.2	110	9	3
5.0	20	5	2
22.7	75	21	9
15.9	28	13	9
4.0	20	4	1
10.2	19	4	7
11.9	74	13	2
6.8	7	4	5
14.0	26	8	5
10.2	37	9	4
6.4	16	3	2
5.9	21	3	3
25.5	96	22	7

(a) Using required memory and amount of output as the independent variables and run time as the dependent variable, determine the equation for the estimated multiple regression equation.

(b) Using your regression plane from (a), compute the standard error of the estimate for run time.

11-14 *Computer exercise.* A Druid's Drayage truck dispatcher wishes to predict how many driver hours it will take to deliver less-than-truckload shipments over any one of a number of routes. Using four independent variables, he has collected the following 20 sample observations.

Driver Time (hours) Y	Distance (miles) X_1	Initial Load (tons) X_2	Deliveries X_3	Speed (mph) X_4
3.0	90	1.5	1	50
7.2	150	3.7	3	35
4.5	65	4.9	3	42
4.3	74	2.6	5	37
6.4	60	3.1	8	40
3.1	70	1.9	2	45
7.0	120	4.7	5	48
5.2	48	3.4	4	29
5.4	125	4.1	3	43
9.2	156	3.4	7	40
5.9	121	2.9	4	46
6.1	98	3.0	6	42
5.5	91	4.5	6	53
5.0	65	4.0	7	42
7.3	74	4.0	8	37

(continued on next page)

Driver Time (hours) Y	Distance (miles) X_1	Initial Load (tons) X_2	Deliveries X_3	Speed (mph) X_4
4.7	83	3.6	5	39
4.5	44	2.7	3	48
1.9	33	1.9	1	29
4.2	106	2.0	2	46
4.4	73	3.0	3	37

Determine the estimated multiple regression equation.

11-15 *Computer exercise.* Refer to the data given in Exercise 11-13. Include the amount of input X_3 as the third independent variable. Determine the estimated multiple regression equation.

11-4 INFERENCES IN REGRESSION ANALYSIS

Since the estimated multiple regression equation is derived from sample information, any conclusions based on it are subject to sampling error. As in simple regression, several types of inferences may be drawn. Most important of these are prediction intervals, testing for nonzero regression coefficients, and estimates of the coefficients.

PREDICTION INTERVALS IN MULTIPLE REGRESSION

The procedures used to construct prediction intervals to qualify estimates made from the regression plane are similar to those used in simple regression. In Chapter 10 we saw that the level of the single independent variable affects both the center and width of those intervals. In multiple regression analysis the levels of *all* the independent variables collectively establish the prediction intervals. Mathematically, the values of X_1, X_2, ... are elements of a *vector* and must be combined algebraically with a complex *matrix* to find the specific end points of the prediction interval for both a conditional mean $\mu_{Y \cdot 12 \ldots}$ and for an individual value Y_I. (A detailed discussion of the matrix algebra is beyond the scope of this book.)

Finding prediction intervals by hand using a calculator is a demanding task and is not ordinarily done—except to make approximations. Computer programs are available and should be used to properly handle this task.

To illustrate, we will use the supermarket data, augmented to include store size X_3 as the third independent predictor. Consider stores having food sales of $2,000,000, nonfood sales of $500,000, and size of 30,000 square feet. Thus (in $10,000 units), $X_1 = 200$, $X_2 = 50$, and $X_3 = 30$. The corresponding height of the regression plane is

$$\hat{Y} = -10.170 + .027(200) + .097(50) + .525(30) = 15.830 \text{ (thousand dollars)}$$

The computer printout in Figure 11-4 shows the results of a run using the augmented supermarket data. The top portion of the printout provides the 95% prediction intervals for $\mu_{Y \cdot 123}$ and Y_I given the above levels for the X's. Both of the intervals are centered at $\hat{Y} = 15.830$.

```
MTB > retrieve 'supermkt'
MTB > regress c4 3 c1-c3;
SUBC> predict 200 50 30.
```

```
The regression equation is
Profit = - 10.2 + 0.0270 Food + 0.0971 Nonfood + 0.525 Size
      .
      .
      .
      Fit   Stdev.Fit        95% C.I.          95% P.I.
   15.830       0.884   ( 13.666, 17.994)  ( 12.083, 19.577)
```

```
MTB > regress c4 3 c1-c3;
SUBC> predict c1-c3.
```

```
      .
      .
      .
      Fit   Stdev.Fit        95% C.I.          95% P.I.
   19.837       0.698   ( 18.128, 21.546)  ( 16.333, 23.341)
   14.399       0.638   ( 12.838, 15.959)  ( 10.964, 17.833)
   17.162       0.475   ( 15.998, 18.325)  ( 13.888, 20.435)
   10.332       0.691   (  8.640, 12.024)  (  6.836, 13.828)
   16.277       0.955   ( 13.940, 18.615)  ( 12.427, 20.128)
   28.711       0.695   ( 27.010, 30.413)  ( 25.211, 32.212)
   34.865       1.024   ( 32.359, 37.371)  ( 30.910, 38.819)
    6.930       0.905   (  4.716,  9.145)  (  3.154, 10.707)
   21.450       0.992   ( 19.023, 23.877)  ( 17.545, 25.355)
   21.037       0.636   ( 19.480, 22.594)  ( 17.604, 24.470)
```

Note: Figure generated on an IBM PC using Minitab®.

FIGURE 11-4 Portion of a computer printout for the augmented supermarket data.

The first prediction interval provides

$$13.666 \leq \mu_{Y \cdot 123} \leq 17.994 \text{ (thousand dollars)}$$

We are 95% confident that the mean profit of *all* stores having the given levels for the independent variables will lie between $13,666 and $17,994. The second prediction interval provides

$$12.083 \leq Y_I \leq 19.577 \text{ (thousand dollars)}$$

This interval is wider than the first and expresses 95% confidence that an individual store will have a profit that lies between $12,083 and $19,577.

The remaining information shown in Figure 11-4 is a portion of the output from a third run using the supermarket data. This optional segment provides the prediction interval sets for all observed levels of the X's. Notice that both the center and the width of these intervals vary, depending on the levels of the independent variables.

INFERENCES REGARDING REGRESSION COEFFICIENTS

The computed values of the intercept a and partial regression coefficients b_1, b_2, ... are statistical estimators of the true regression coefficients A, B_1, B_2, ... Ordinarily, confidence intervals for the B's are not constructed until the null hypothesis

$$H_0\colon B_1 = B_2 = \cdots = B_{m-1} = 0$$

has been tested. The regression results are statistically significant when the hypothesis is rejected. The procedure for making this determination is based on the *analysis of variance* approach (discussed in more detail in Chapters 17 and 18), which focuses on sums of squares.

Analogous to simple regression, the least-squares method minimizes the sum of the vertical deviations about the regression plane. Each deviation consists of an explained and unexplained component. Summing the squares of the individual components, the following relationship applies to the entire collection of observations.

$$\begin{array}{ccccc} \dfrac{\text{Total}}{\text{variation}} & = & \dfrac{\text{Explained}}{\text{variation}} & + & \dfrac{\text{Unexplained}}{\text{variation}} \end{array}$$

$$\sum [Y - \bar{Y}]^2 = \sum [\hat{Y} - \bar{Y}]^2 + \sum [Y - \hat{Y}]^2$$

$$SSTO = SSR + SSE$$

The **total sum of squares** $SSTO$ expresses the variation in observed Y's about their mean $\bar{Y}$ without regard to the regression relationship. Although not ordinarily computed by hand, the following expression applies.

$$SSTO = \sum [Y - \bar{Y}]^2$$

The **regression sum of squares** SSR summarizes the explained variation in estimated Y's about the sample mean. The following expression applies.

$$SSR = \sum [\hat{Y} - \bar{Y}]^2$$

The **error sum of squares** SSE expresses the unexplained variation in observed Y's about the estimated regression plane. The following expression applies.

$$SSE = \sum [Y - \hat{Y}]^2 = (n - m)\, S^2_{Y \cdot 12 \ldots}$$

The sums of squares in a multiple regression analysis are considered standard output for the popular computer software packages.

THE ANALYSIS OF VARIANCE APPROACH

To test the null hypothesis that all partial regression coefficients are equal to zero, we must compare the explained and unexplained variations in Y. This is accomplished by employing a composite test statistic based on the *means* of the squared deviations for the explained and unexplained variations. The first of these, the **regression mean square** *MSR*, is

$$MSR = \frac{SSR}{m - 1}$$

where m is the total number of variables in the regression analysis. The denominator $m-1$ is the number of degrees of freedom for the explained variation. The second mean, the **error mean square** *MSE*, is

$$MSE = \frac{SSE}{n - m} = S_{Y \cdot 12 \dots}^2$$

where $n - m$ is the number of degrees of freedom for the unexplained variation.

Recall that the sample variance is found by averaging the squared deviations about the central value. Both *MSR* and *MSE* are computed this way, and, thus, both of the mean squares are actually sample variances. Since these form the basis of the test, the procedure is called analysis of *variance* (even though the null hypothesis itself says nothing about variance).

The following expression provides the regression test statistic.

$$F = \frac{\text{Variance explained by regression}}{\text{Unexplained variance}} = \frac{MSR}{MSE}$$

The above quantity has the F distribution. That distribution allows us to find probabilities for getting the results achieved when the null hypothesis is true.

The value $F = 130.06$, from the printout in Figure 11-3, was computed for the augmented supermarket data during the multiple regression run. The corresponding prob. value is 0.000, indicating that those results are inconsistent with the null hypothesis, which must be *rejected*. The regression relationship found earlier is statistically very significant.

ESTIMATING REGRESSION COEFFICIENTS

After the null hypothesis that all Bs are equal to zero has been rejected, investigators will generally estimate the coefficients using a set of intervals applicable at a *collective* level of confidence. The following expression provides the $100(1 - \alpha)\%$.

BONFERRONI COLLECTIVE CONFIDENCE INTERVAL FOR A REGRESSION COEFFICIENT

$$B_k = b_k \pm t_{\alpha/2(m-1)} s_{b_k}$$

where the $n-m$ degrees of freedom apply.

Using the supermarket data given in Figure 11-3, the following intervals apply jointly at the 85% confidence level. The critical value $t_{.025} = 2.447$ is read from Appendix Table F using $10 - 4 = 6$ degrees of freedom.

$$B_1 = .027 \pm 2.447(.012)$$

or

$$-.002 \le B_1 \le .056 \qquad \text{(food sales)}$$

also

$$.024 \le B_2 \le .170 \qquad \text{(nonfood sales)}$$

$$.381 \le B_3 \le .669 \qquad \text{(store size)}$$

The first interval indicates that B_1, the profit obtained for \$10,000 of food sales, does not differ significantly from zero. Both nonfood sales and store size have partial regression coefficients (B_2 and B_3) and are significantly nonzero.

EXERCISES

11-16 *Computer exercise.*   Refer to Exercise 11-10 and to your answers.
(a) Construct the 95% prediction intervals for (1) the mean and (2) individual family spending when the income is \$10,000, the family size is 4, and additional savings is \$1,000.
(b) Using a collective confidence level of 97%, construct the interval estimates of the partial regression coefficients for (1) income, (2) size, and (3) additional savings.

11-17 *Computer exercise.*   Refer to Exercise 11-12 and to your answers.
(a) Construct the 95% prediction intervals for (1) the mean and (2) individual fuel consumption when the average speed is 50 mph, the altitude is 4 thousand feet, and the passenger weight is 2 hundred pounds.
(b) Using a collective confidence level of 97%, construct the interval estimates of the partial regression coefficients for (1) average speed, (2) altitude, and (3) passenger weight.

11-18 *Computer exercise.*   Refer to Exercise 11-14 and to your answers.
(a) Construct the 95% prediction intervals for (1) the mean and (2) individual driver time when the distance is 100 miles, the initial load is 4.0 tons, the number of deliveries is 5, and the speed is 50 mph.
(b) Using a collective confidence level of 96%, construct the interval estimates of the partial regression coefficients for (1) distance, (2) initial load, (3) number of deliveries, and (4) speed.

11-19 *Computer exercise.*   Refer to Exercise 11-15 and to your answers.
(a) Construct the 95% prediction intervals for (1) the mean and (2) run time when the required memory is 100 thousand bytes, there are 15 thousand lines of output and there are 10 thousand lines of input.
(b) Using a collective confidence level of 85%, construct the interval estimates of the partial regression coefficients for (1) required memory, (2) amount of output, and (3) amount of input.

11-5 MULTIPLE CORRELATION

COEFFICIENT OF MULTIPLE DETERMINATION

The concept of correlation can be extended to multiple variables. As we did in our earlier discussion of simple linear relationships, we will begin by describing the **coefficient of multiple determination** as an index of association. When a multiple regression involves only two independent variables, X_1 and X_2, this is denoted symbolically by $R_{Y \cdot 12}^2$, which represents the ratio of the variation in Y that is explained by the regression plane to the total variation, or

$$R_{Y \cdot 12}^2 = \frac{\text{Explained variation}}{\text{Total variation}} = 1 - \frac{\sum (Y - \hat{Y})^2}{\sum (Y - \overline{Y})^2}$$

The **multiple correlation coefficient** is defined as the square root of the coefficient of multiple determination, or $R_{Y \cdot 12} = \sqrt{R_{Y \cdot 12}^2}$. The sign of $R_{Y \cdot 12}$ is always considered positive.

A shorter, equivalent expression is used to calculate the

COEFFICIENT OF MULTIPLE DETERMINATION

$$R_{Y \cdot 12}^2 = 1 - \frac{S_{Y \cdot 12}^2}{s_Y^2} \left(\frac{n - m}{n - 1} \right)$$

As before, m represents the number of variables used.

To illustrate this computation, we will again use our earlier results from the multiple regression for store profit Y when food sales X_1 and nonfood sales X_2 are the only independent variables. The standard deviation in profit is

$$s_Y = \sqrt{\frac{\sum Y^2 - n\overline{Y}^2}{n - 1}} = \sqrt{\frac{4{,}267 - 10(19.1)^2}{9}} = 8.293$$

From before, we have $S_{Y \cdot 12} = 4.343$. Here, $m = 3$. Using these values we calculate

$$R_{Y \cdot 12}^2 = 1 - \frac{(4.343)^2}{(8.293)_2} \left(\frac{10 - 3}{10 - 1} \right) = .787$$

The interpretation of $R_{Y \cdot 12}^2 = .787$ is that an estimated 78.7% of the total variation in Y may be explained by knowledge of the regression plane and the values of X_1 and X_2. Only $100 - 78.7 = 21.3\%$ of the variation in Y is estimated due to other causes, such as chance, plus factors not explicitly considered—for example, store size, location, and advertising.

When the supermarket data were expanded to include an additional independent variable for store size, X_3, the estimated regression equation was recalculated to be $\hat{Y} = -10.170 + .027X_1 + .097X_2 + .525X_3$. As noted earlier, the standard error of the estimate for Y about this higher-dimensional regression hyperplane was significantly smaller than when store size was ignored. This indicates that, in this case, more of the total variation in Y may be explained by raising the number of regression variables. To see how far the total variation in Y that is explained by regression has risen, we obtain the coefficient of multiple determination when X_3 is included in the analysis. The computer printout in Figure 11-3 provides the value $R^2_{Y \cdot 123} = .985$. Thus, the total variation in Y that is explained by regression increases from 78.7% to 98.5% when store size X_3 is included as an additional independent variable. This further illustrates that expanding regression analysis to include more variables may increase the reliability of predictions.

We now consider a set of indexes helpful in determining whether or not it is worthwhile to include additional variables in the regression analysis.

PARTIAL CORRELATION

Let's begin by comparing the results of a simple regression analysis relating store profit Y to food sales X_1 alone. As we have seen, the equation for the estimated regression line is

$$\hat{Y}(X_1) = 3.891 + .0670X_1$$

and the simple coefficient of determination is $r^2_{Y1} = (.760)^2 = .578$. Suppose we now incorporate nonfood sales X_2 as a second independent variable. We have seen that better predictions for Y will result from doing this. To quantify the improvement achieved with a higher-dimensional regression analysis, we can calculate the proportional reduction in previously explained variation. This provides a further index of association, $r^2_{Y2 \cdot 1}$, called the **coefficient of partial determination**, that measures the correlation between Y and X_2 when the other independent variable X_1 is still considered but held constant. The subscript $Y2 \cdot 1$ indicates this.

COEFFICIENT OF PARTIAL DETERMINATION

$$r^2_{Y2 \cdot 1} = \frac{\text{Reduction in unexplained variation}}{\text{Previously unexplained variation}} = \frac{R^2_{Y \cdot 12} - r^2_{Y1}}{1 - r^2_{Y1}}$$

Substituting our earlier values, we obtain

$$r^2_{Y2 \cdot 1} = \frac{.787 - .578}{1 - .578} = .495$$

The difference, $R^2_{Y \cdot 12} - r^2_{Y1}$, represents the reduction in unexplained variation (which is also the increase in explained variation). The value $r^2_{Y2 \cdot 1} = .495$ tells us that 49.5% of the variation in store profit Y that was left unexplained by a simple regression with food sales X_1 alone can be explained by the regression obtained from including nonfood sales X_2.

In multiple regression analysis, the coefficient of partial determination or its square root, the **partial correlation coefficient**, provides an index of the correlation between two variables *after* the effects of all the other variables have been considered. Thus, the value .495 expresses the net association between store profit Y and nonfood sales X_2 when food sales X_1 are held constant but still accounted for.

The value $r^2_{Y2 \cdot 1} = .495$ may be compared to the *simple* coefficient of determination between Y and X_2, $r^2_{Y2} = (-.286)^2 = .082$. The former provides a truer impact of including X_2 in the multiple regression analysis than would be indicated by a simple correlation analysis using only X_2. When evaluating the potential merits of a predictor variable, the coefficients of partial determination (or the partial correlation coefficients) are sometimes employed in determining which independent variables to include (a superior method to using the simple counterpart coefficient). We can illustrate how the coefficient of partial determination may be used to do this.

In discussing a third independent variable X_3 (size of store), a multiple regression was run on the computer. The coefficient of partial determination may be found from

$$r^2_{Y3 \cdot 12} = \frac{\text{Reduction in unexplained variation}}{\text{Previously unexplained variation}} = \frac{R^2_{Y \cdot 123} - R^2_{Y \cdot 12}}{1 - R^2_{Y \cdot 12}}$$

Substituting the coefficients of multiple determination obtained from the previous two multiple regressions for the supermarket data, we have

$$r^2_{Y3 \cdot 12} = \frac{.985 - .787}{1 - .787} = .930$$

Thus, $r^2_{Y3 \cdot 12} = .930$ tells us that there is a 93.0% reduction in previously unexplained variation by including X_3. This additional variable has been quite effective in increasing the sharpness of the multiple regression analysis.

Table 11-5 shows how the amount of variation in Y that is explained by regression has increased through successive inclusions of additional variables. Note how the variation in Y is reduced from $s_Y = 8.293$, which was obtained when no regression was performed. Variation is expressed by the successive standard errors of the estimates of Y about the respective regression surfaces (line, plane, and hyperplane) shown in column (3). Paralleling the declining standard errors are increases in the proportion of variation explained by regression, shown in column (4). Column (5) shows the proportional reduction in previously unexplained variation in Y resulting from the additional variable.

The total explained variations in Y will not always be reduced by including additional variables. It is not always obvious that an additional factor will sharpen rather than cloud the predictive powers of regression analysis. Good common sense must be exercised in selecting variables for which there is a meaningful nonstatistical explanation of their influence on the dependent variable. Sales is one factor used to calculate profit, so it has a logical connection. Likewise, a larger store requires a greater investment in facilities and may be operated more efficiently than a smaller one, so store size can also be reasoned to have a direct relation to profits.

The supermarket coefficients of partial determination listed in Table 11-5 are what would apply if the successive Xs were added to the regression sequence in 1-2-3 order, according to their subscripts. But other sequences are possible. The tree in Figure 11-5 shows the various possible sequences for adding new variables

TABLE 11-5 How Explained Variation in Y Increases as Additional Variables Are Included

(1) Independent Variables Included	(2) Additional Variable	(3) Standard Error of Estimate (thousands of dollars)	(4) Proportion of Variation Explained	(5) Proportional Reduction in Previously Unexplained Variation
none	—	$s_Y = 8.293$	0.000	—
X_1	X_1	$s_{Y \cdot X_1} = 5.719$	$r_{Y1}^2 = .578*$	$\dfrac{.578 - 0}{1 - 0} = .578 = r_{Y1}^2$
X_1, X_2	X_2	$s_{Y \cdot 12} = 4.343$	$R_{Y \cdot 123}^2 = .787$	$\dfrac{.787 - .578}{1 - .578} = .495 = r_{Y2 \cdot 1}^2$
X_1, X_2, X_3	X_3	$s_{Y \cdot 123} = 1.250$	$R_{Y \cdot 123}^2 = .985$	$\dfrac{.985 - .787}{1 - .787} = .930 = r_{Y3 \cdot 12}^2$

*This value is the simple coefficient of determination calculated for the regression line $\hat{Y}(X_1) = 3.891 + .0670X_1$.

in obtaining the next higher-dimensional regression analysis. Altogether, the supermarket illustration involves three steps, each involving the choice of which remaining candidate should be added to the set of independent variables.

In Section 11-6 we will investigate how the coefficients of partial determination may be used in stepwise regression to select which variables to include in a regression analysis.

EXERCISES

11-20 An economist wishes to predict annual family spending Y using income X_1, size X_2, and annual savings X_3. The following intermediate calculations have been obtained for a sample of $n = 100$ families. All monetary figures are in thousands of dollars.

$$\bar{Y} = 10 \quad \bar{X}_1 = 12 \quad \bar{X}_2 = 5 \quad \bar{X}_3 = 1$$

$$\sum Y^2 = 11{,}400 \quad \sum X_1Y = 13{,}000 \quad \sum X_2Y = 6{,}000 \quad \sum X_3Y = 500$$

$$\text{Plane } A: \quad \hat{Y} = 1.7 + .4X_1 + .7X_2 \qquad (\text{excluding } X_3)$$

$$\text{Hyperplane } B: \quad \hat{Y} = 4.3 + .3X_1 + .6X_2 - .9X_3 \qquad (\text{including } X_3)$$

(a) Calculate $S_{Y \cdot 12}$ and $R_{Y \cdot 12}^2$. What percentage of the variation in Y is explained by regression plane A?

(b) If $S_{Y \cdot 123} = .722$ and $R_{Y \cdot 123}^2 = .964$, what percentage of the variation in Y is explained by regression hyperplane B?

(c) Has the inclusion of X_3 in the regression analysis reduced the standard error of the estimate of Y?

(d) Use the regression equations for planes A and B to determine the proportions of unexplained variation in Y. What proportional change in previously unexplained variation is achieved by adding X_3 to the analysis? Does this increase or decrease the unexplained variation?

1ST
VARIABLE
ADDED

2ND
VARIABLE
ADDED

3RD
VARIABLE
ADDED

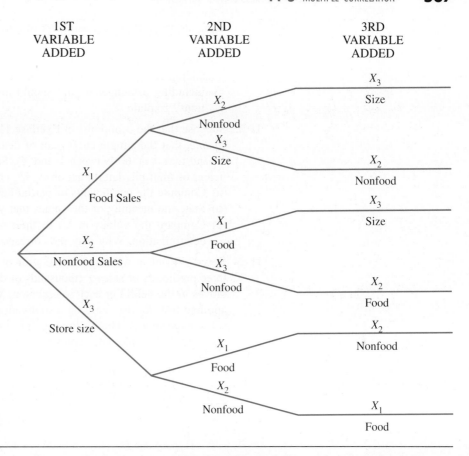

FIGURE 11-5 Tree diagram all of the regression sequences possible for adding predictor of supermarket sales.

11-21 Refer to the data given in Exercise 11-5. The following results have been obtained for predicting Crunchola production cost Y from quantity X_1 and wheat price index X_2.

$$r_{Y1}^2 = .9270 \qquad r_{Y2}^2 = .0052 \qquad R_{Y \cdot 12}^2 = .9715$$

(a) Compute the coefficient of partial determination $r_{Y2 \cdot 1}^2$ for production cost and wheat price index, holding production quantity constant.
(b) Compute the coefficient of partial determination $r_{Y1 \cdot 2}^2$ for production cost and quantity, holding wheat price index constant.

11-22 Refer to the data given in Exercise 11-11. The following regression results have been obtained for predicting fuel consumption Y from average speed X_1, altitude X_2, and passenger weight X_3.

$$s_Y = 3.742$$

$$s_{Y \cdot X_1} = 3.968 \qquad r_{Y1}^2 = .0003$$

$$s_{Y \cdot X_1} = 2.427 \qquad r_{Y2}^2 = .6261$$

$$S_{Y \cdot 12} = 2.522 \qquad R_{Y \cdot 12}^2 = .6465$$

$$S_{Y \cdot 123} = 1.794 \qquad R_{Y \cdot 123}^2 = .8467$$

Compute the following coefficient of partial determination.

(a) $r^2_{Y2 \cdot 1}$ (b) $r^2_{Y1 \cdot 2}$ (c) $r^2_{Y3 \cdot 12}$

(d) What is the percentage reduction in unexplained variation achieved by adding X_3 as the third independent variable? Does this suggest that including passenger weight should improve fuel consumption predictions? Explain.

11-23 Suppose that the economist in Exercise 11-20 has determined, *for another sample*, that the simple coefficient of determination is .50 between Y and X_1 and that it is .60 between Y and X_2. She has also found that the coefficient of multiple determination is .75, considering only X_1 and X_2.

(a) Compute the coefficients of partial determination $r^2_{Y1 \cdot 2}$ and $r^2_{Y2 \cdot 1}$.

(b) State the meaning of the values that you obtained in (a).

(c) Compare the values in (a) to their respective simple coefficients of determination. Why may the corresponding values differ?

11-24 Speed-E-Print, a wholesale distributor of business forms, has developed three predictors of sales Y (thousands of dollars) achieved by its representatives in the field. For each salesperson, X_1 represents the score on a sales aptitude test, X_2 the score on a motivation test, and X_3 the total years of sales experience. The following intermediate calculations have been obtained for sample data representing $n=30$ salespersons.

$$\bar{Y} = 50 \qquad \bar{X}_1 = 10 \qquad \bar{X}_2 = 5 \qquad \bar{X}_3 = 5$$

$$\sum Y^2 = 80,600 \quad \sum X_1 Y = 16,000 \quad \sum X_2 Y = 8,500 \quad \sum X_3 Y = 8,100$$

$$\text{Plane } A: \quad \hat{Y} = 10 + 3X_1 + 2X_2 \qquad \text{(excluding } X_3\text{)}$$

$$\text{Hyperplane } B: \quad \hat{Y} = 5 + 2X_1 + 1X_2 + 4X_3 \qquad \text{(including } X_3\text{)}$$

(a) Calculate $S_{Y \cdot 12}$ and $R^2_{Y \cdot 12}$. What percentage of the variation in Y is explained by the regression plane A?

(b) $R^2_{Y \cdot 123} = .964$. What percentage of the variation in Y is explained by the regression hyperplane B?

(c) Compute the coefficient of partial determination for adding X_3 to the analysis. What is the percentage reduction in previously unexplained variation achieved by adding X_3 as the third independent variable?

(d) Should years of sales experience be included in predictions of sales performance? Why?

11-6 FINDING A PREDICTIVE REGRESSION MODEL

In any data set comprising several variables, one will be the dependent variable Y whose value will be forecast from the known levels of one or more of the remaining variables. We now consider the problem of finding which variables in a data set might be used as independent predictor variables, serving as the Xs.

GOALS FOR A PREDICTIVE MODEL

There are two primary goals in establishing a predictive model.

1. Achieve a regression surface (line, plane, hyperplane) that explains a high proportion of variability in Y. One measure useful for this purpose is the coefficient of multiple determination.

2. Keep the regression equation simple. In a multiple regression, this is achieved by minimizing the number of predictors. Limiting the number of predictors gives stability to predictions made from different data sets.

Unfortunately, the two goals are contradictory, since the amount of variation left unexplained can only increase as each further independent predictor variable is brought into the next higher-dimensional analysis. Some trade-off must be made between achieving a high R^2 and finding a stable set of predictors.

SEARCHING FOR THE BEST PREDICTORS: ALL REGRESSIONS

To find the best predictors, all regressions might be performed. For the super-market illustration, the possibilities are listed in Table 11-6. A similar list of possibilities for a data set having four predictors would contain 15 separate predictor sets, each with a distinct regression equation. In general, for a data set having p possible predictors the number of possible different regressions would be

$$2^p - 1$$

With an 11-variable data set, excluding the Y there are $p = 10$ candidate predictors. The number of possible regressions would be

$$2^{10} - 1 = 1,023$$

When the number of candidate predictor variables is large, a prodigious amount of work would be necessary to complete all possible regressions. A streamlined procedure breaks the process of selecting predictors into steps.

STEPWISE REGRESSION

To minimize computational effort, statisticians add independent predictor variables to the predictor set one at a time. The process is called **stepwise regression**. The first step involves simple regression analyses; each analysis is performed

TABLE 11-6 All Possible Regressions for Supermarket Illustration

Predictor Set	Regression Equation	Coefficient of Determination
X_1	$\hat{Y} = 3.88 + .067X_1$	$r_{Y1}^2 = .578$
X_2	$\hat{Y} = 25.6 - .095X_2$	$r_{Y2}^2 = .082$
X_3	$\hat{Y} = .21 + .602X_3$	$r_{Y3}^2 = .958$
X_1, X_2	$\hat{Y} = -23.1 + .115X_1 + .235X_2$	$R_{Y.12}^2 = .786$
X_1, X_3	$\hat{Y} = .42 - .0038X_1 + .623X_3$	$R_{Y.13}^2 = .959$
X_2, X_3	$\hat{Y} = -3.76 + .0431X_2 + .634X_3$	$R_{Y.23}^2 = .972$
X_1, X_2, X_3	$\hat{Y} = -10.17 + .0270X_1 + .0971X_2 + .525X_3$	$R_{Y.123}^2 = .985$

separately with a different possible candidate as the single independent variable. This procedure is summarized in Figure 11-6. The decision tree in (a) shows the four choices, including the possibility of adding no predictor. Various criteria are employed for selecting the best predictor, which will be kept for future steps. For the supermarket illustration, the coefficient of partial determination is used to make this choice.

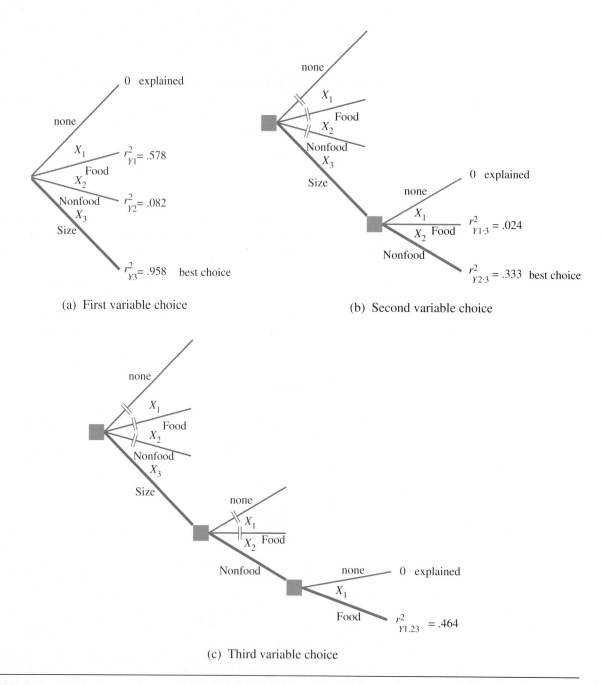

(a) First variable choice

(b) Second variable choice

(c) Third variable choice

FIGURE 11-6 Decision tree showing stepwise regression choices for selecting predictors of supermarket sales.

Of the three possible first Xs in Figure 11-6(a), the most promising is X_3 (store size) which has the greatest coefficient of $r_{Y3}^2 = .958$. (Since there are no independent variables to begin with, a coefficient of *partial* determination does not exist, and the respective *ordinary* coefficients of determination serve for making the first choice.) The first predictor variable added to the set is therefore X_3 (store size). The second step is shown in Figure 11-6(b), where either X_1 or X_2 can be chosen for the second predictor. (Again, it is possible to pick none, in which case the selection process would end.) The greatest coefficient of partial determination is $r_{Y2 \cdot 3}^2 = .333$, achieved by adding X_2 (nonfood sales). That variable gets picked as the second predictor.

The remaining choices are shown in Figure 11-6(c): to select *no more* predictors or to include X_1 (food sales) in the predictor set. The coefficient of partial determination is $r_{Y1 \cdot 23}^2 = .464$, indicating that including food sales as a predictor would bring about a major reduction in that variation in Y which is presently left unexplained by regression with the latest predictor set. The best choice is therefore to include X_1 (food sales) in the predictor set.

ILLUSTRATION: PERFORMANCE PREDICTORS FOR BASEBALL BATTER SUPERSTAR SALARY

Using batter superstar data from Table 10-2, a stepwise regression was performed in order to determine which of the following predictors to use for a regression model for forecasting salary Y.

X_4 = position code	X_9 = number of runs
X_5 = games played	X_{10} = fielding percentage
X_6 = number of at bats	X_{11} = number of home runs
X_7 = batting average	X_{12} = number of putouts
X_8 = runs batted in (RBI)	

This is summarized by the decision tree in Figure 11-7. Step 1 involves nine simple regression analyses, each using just one of the above Xs as the *single* independent variable. The largest coefficient of determination achieved is .081 from using X_8 (RBI). Step 2 then includes eight multiple regressions using X_8 plus one of each of the above as the *two* independent variables. Computing the coefficients of partial determination for each, the greatest value of .041 occurs with X_5 (games played), and that variable is added to the predictor set.

Step 3 repeats the process, this time including X_5 and X_8 along with just one of the remaining predictors in seven separate multiple regressions, each involving *three* independent variables. The maximum coefficient of partial determination is .101, found for the regression in which X_9 (number of runs) is the third independent variable. That variable joins X_5 and X_8 as the permanent predictors for Step 4. In that step, six separate multiple regressions were made with *four* independent variables (X_5, X_8, X_9, and one other). The coefficients of partial determination were all below .01, so that bringing a fourth predictor into the model would only reduce the remaining unexplained salary variation by less than 1%. Since little would be gained in predictive power by adding a fourth predictor, it was decided to terminate the steps at this point, adding no new variables to the predictor set.

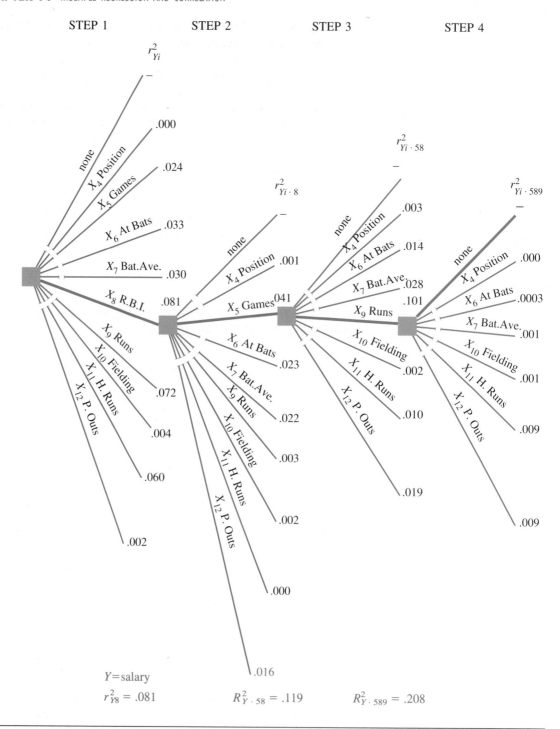

FIGURE 11-7 Decision tree showing stepwise regression choices for finding predictors of baseball batting superstar salaries.

Using the above predictors, the computer printout in Figure 11-8 is obtained. The regression equation (in thousands of dollars) is

$$\hat{Y} = 2{,}513 - 1.25X_5 + 1.13X_8 + 1.47X_9$$

The above regression equation might be used in making predictions about future player salaries. (Although the overall coefficient of determination is itself only $R^2_{Y \cdot 589} = .208$, which indicates that this model would be a very weak one.)

FINE-TUNING THE MODEL I: ELIMINATING OUTLIERS

Recall from Chapter 10 that outliers are data points that have unusually large residual values $Y - \hat{Y}$. In Figure 11-8 we see that there are four outliers—Joe

```
MTB > Regress c2 3 c5 c8 c9.
```

```
The regression equation is
Salary = 2513 - 1.25 Games + 1.13 RBI + 1.47 Runs

Predictor      Coef      Stdev      t-ratio        p
Constant     2513.3      170.0        14.78    0.000
Games       -1.2503     0.3995        -3.13    0.003
RBI          1.1338     0.4510         2.51    0.015
Runs         1.4667     0.5527         2.65    0.010

s = 517.0      R-sq = 20.8%      R-sq(adj) = 17.0%

Analysis of Variance

SOURCE        DF          SS           MS        F        p
Regression     3     4410688      1470230     5.50    0.002
Error         63    16838788       267282
Total         66    21249476

SOURCE        DF      SEQ SS
Games          1      516936
RBI            1     2011799
Runs           1     1881954

Unusual Observations
Obs.   Games    Salary      Fit  Stdev.Fit  Residual  St.Resid
  12    1024    3792.0   2758.9       90.2    1033.1      2.03R   Joe Carter
  17     874    2000.0   3124.0      151.8   -1124.0     -2.27R   Chili Davis
  36    1608    3250.0   3100.0      257.3     150.0      0.33 X  Rickey Henderson
  39     703    2100.0   3226.0      226.3   -1126.0     -2.42RX  Wally Joyner
  46     688    3750.0   2661.4       98.2    1088.6      2.14R   Kevin Mitchell
  60    1926    2225.0   2120.1      225.0     104.9      0.23 X  Ozzie Smith

R denotes an obs. with a large st. resid.
X denotes an obs. whose X value gives it large influence.
```

FIGURE 11-8 Minitab printout for final baseball batter regression model selected through stepwise regression.

Carter, Chili Davis, Wally Joyner, and Kevin Mitchell. The regression analysis indicates that each of these players, when compared with their peers, is either overpaid or underpaid by over a million dollars. Eliminating explainable outliers can sometimes result in an improved regression model.

After removing the data points for the above four players, a second regression analysis provides the regression equation

$$\hat{Y} = 2{,}574 - 1.85X_5 + 1.22X_8 + 2.39X_9$$

The new equation has a much lower partial regression coefficient for number of games X_5 and a greater one for number of runs X_9. The negative multiplier for X_5 reflects a pattern by owners to reward "new blood" and discount the value of veterans. The coefficient of 1.22 for X_8 indicates that an additional run batted in (RBI) should boost a superstar's salary by 1.22 thousand dollars. But the 2.39 coefficient for X_9 indicates that a player's own run justifies about twice the salary increase.

The coefficient of multiple determination for the new regression equation nearly doubles, to $R^2_{Y \cdot 589} = .367$, so that about 37% of the variation in a batting superstar's salary can be explained by the new regression equation. This is a big improvement.

The elimination of outliers may also be cause to change the predictors. A new stepwise regression with the reduced data set indicates that four further variables—home runs, fielding, batting average, and at bats, in that order—could be worthwhile predictors if added to the regression model. The expanded model is

$$\hat{Y} = 2{,}931 - 3.34X_5 + .285X_6 - 5.65X_7 + 2.36X_8$$
$$+2.63X_9 + 7.36X_{10} - 2.97X_{11}$$

The amount of salary variation explained by the above is a higher 44%, but this increase is a small one and does not seem to justify the further model complexity.

KINDS OF STEPWISE REGRESSION

Stepwise regression can be elaborate when done with a computer. One variation involves a backward procedure, in which all predictors are included as independent variables in a multiple regression of maximum dimension as the first step. Predictors are then *deleted* from the set in successive steps in a reverse process to the forward procedure described above. The forward procedure is elaborated in some programs, so that weaker members of the current predictive set might be deleted whenever a new variable is added.

A stepwise procedure can automatically screen predictors that do not improve the predictive worth of the evolving model. That might be done by excluding any candidate X for which the new regression would result in a low coefficient of partial determination. Another screening trigger would be to avoid variables too highly correlated with any of the current predictors.

STEPWISE REGRESSION WITH A COMPUTER

Stepwise regression is ordinarily done with computer assistance. Figure 11-9 shows the output from a Minitab stepwise regression run with the baseball super-

```
MTB > Stepwise c2 c4-c12;
SUBC>    FEnter 1;
SUBC>    FRemove 1.
```

```
STEPWISE REGRESSION OF  Salary  ON  9 PREDICTORS, WITH N =    67

     STEP        1        2        3
CONSTANT      2348     2496     2513

RBI           0.55     1.23     1.13
T-RATIO       2.39     2.62     2.51

Games                 -0.47    -1.25
T-RATIO               -1.66    -3.13

Runs                            1.47
T-RATIO                         2.65

S              548      541      517
R-SQ          8.09    11.90    20.76
```

FIGURE 11-9 Minitab printout of stepwise regression with baseball batting superstar data.

star batter data. The details of individual regressions are not provided, but those can be established in later regular regression runs.

The resulting set of predictors is listed in each step column. These are identical to the results achieved earlier. An equivalent criterion is used by the Minitab program for selecting predictors based on the F statistic. The steps continue until no new regression yields an F value greater than the screening level. The cutoff point was $F = 1.0$ in the current illustration. The t-ratio values shown in Figure 11-9 are the square roots of the computed F values.

Many assumptions concerning the *linearity* of the data are automatically made by such computer programs. As with any other application, in multiple regression analysis the computer does not eliminate the need for good judgment. Computer printouts must be thoroughly evaluated to determine if there is a meaningful explanation of why some variables are excluded and others are included. A variable may be rejected because it does not reduce the unexplained variation, but this may actually be due to a strong curvilinear relation between the variable and Y.

SELECTING SCREENING PARAMETERS

The decision when to terminate the stepwise regression is an arbitrary one. Termination always eliminates some further reduction in unexplained Y variation for the current data set. But too many predictors, yielding a model overly fine-tuned to one data set, can contribute to unstable predictions over time. Generally, the looser the cutoff specifications for screening parameters (r^2 or F), the greater will be the number of steps and predictors.

ILLUSTRATION: PREDICTING BASEBALL CARD PRICE FOR PITCHING SUPERSTARS

A second data set involving just *pitchers* was formed from the baseball superstar data in Table 10-2. A stepwise regression analysis was performed for predicting rookie baseball card price Y. As we shall see, this dependent variable for pitchers exhibits a much tighter relationship with players' performance statistics than did batter salaries. The following predictor candidates are used.

X_2 = salary X_8 = winning percentage

X_5 = games played X_9 = strikeouts

X_6 = innings pitched X_{10} = walks

X_7 = earned run average (ERA)

Figure 11-10 shows the results obtained.

```
MTB > Stepwise c3 c2 c5-c10;
SUBC>    FEnter 1;
SUBC>    FRemove 1;
SUBC>    Steps 5.
```

```
 STEPWISE REGRESSION OF Card Pr. ON  7 PREDICTORS, WITH N =    60

       STEP        1        2        3        4        5
   CONSTANT   -165.11  -105.60   -82.91    49.75   124.90

   Walks         0.389    0.797    0.474    0.534    0.558
   T-RATIO        9.59    10.55     5.43     5.62     5.78

   Innings               -0.181   -0.274   -0.254   -0.249
   T-RATIO               -5.97    -8.96    -7.75    -7.55

   S. Outs                         0.261    0.215    0.204
   T-RATIO                         5.28     3.73     3.52

   ERA                                       -42      -46
   T-RATIO                                 -1.50    -1.64

   Salary                                          -0.027
   T-RATIO                                          -1.26

   S             113      89.6     73.8     73.0     72.6
   R-SQ        61.32    76.20    84.11    84.74    85.17
```

FIGURE 11-10 Minitab printout of stepwise regression with baseball pitching superstar data.

Notice that five predictors are chosen, and that the coefficients of multiple determination R^2 for each successive regression (shown in the bottom row of the printout as percentages) are substantial. However, in steps 4 and 5 there is very little improvement. A tighter screening level for the F statistic should bring about an earlier stop to the search. A second computer run using a limit of 4.0 for the computed F terminated the predictor search after step 3.

The regression results using the three predictors are provided in Figure 11-11. The following regression equation is obtained.

$$\hat{Y} = -82.90 - .274X_6 + .261X_9 + .474X_{10}$$

The coefficient of multiple determination is quite substantial, $R^2_{Y \cdot 6910} = .841$,

```
MTB > Regress c3 3 c6 c9 c10.

The regression equation is
Card Pr. = - 82.9 - 0.274 Innings + 0.261 S. Outs + 0.474 Walks

Predictor       Coef        Stdev     t-ratio       p
Constant       -82.91       18.66      -4.44       0.000
Innings       -0.27358     0.03053     -8.96       0.000
S. Outs        0.26084     0.04938      5.28       0.000
Walks          0.47417     0.08726      5.43       0.000

s = 73.81        R-sq = 84.1%      R-sq(adj) = 83.3%

Analysis of Variance

SOURCE        DF         SS          MS         F        p
Regression     3      1615346      538448     98.83     0.000
Error         56       305092        5448
Total         59      1920437

SOURCE        DF       SEQ SS
Innings        1       570704
S. Outs        1       883768
Walks          1       160873

Unusual Observations
Obs. Innings   Card Pr.      Fit Stdev.Fit  Residual   St.Resid
  2    4837      60.00     153.87    50.45     -93.87    -1.74 X   Bert Blyleven
 13    1417       0.08     150.51    13.41    -150.43    -2.07R    Jose DeLeon
 30    1598       2.25     223.74    16.81    -221.49    -3.08R    Jimmy Key
 45    4990    1400.00    1175.80    67.44     224.20     7.47RX   Nolan Ryan

R denotes an obs. with a large st. resid.
X denotes an obs. whose X value gives it large influence.
```

FIGURE 11-11 Minitab printout applying selected regression model with baseball pitching superstar data.

signifying that the regression explains 84% of the variation in rookie baseball card price.

An interpretation of the above leads to some surprising conclusions.

FINE-TUNING THE MODEL II: FINDING A REGRESSION EQUATION THAT MAKES SENSE

The negative regression coefficient $-.274$ for the number of innings pitched X_6 indicates that veteran superstar pitchers' cards lose value as their careers get longer, about 25 cents per inning pitched. That does seem odd, since card prices generally rise as a player ages. The coefficient .261 for number of strikeouts X_9 gives added card value of \$.26 for each strikeout. Most interesting is the coefficient .474 for the number of walks X_{10}, which adds \$.474 to the value of a card for each walk. Walks are generally *bad* for pitching performance, and we should expect a predictive model to reflect that by assigning a *negative* regression coefficient for X_{10}. The model does not make a lot of sense.

Some of the explanation of the odd regression equation might be attributed to the *outliers*—especially Nolan Ryan, having a card value of \$1,400. Ryan has pitched much longer than the other superstar pitchers, and his long-term popularity is reflected in the price of his rookie baseball card. When Nolan Ryan is removed, a new stepwise regression with F limit of 4.0 leaves innings pitched X_6 out of the final predictor set.

The following regression equation applies.

$$\hat{Y} = -6.45 + .0227X_9 - .0247X_{10} \qquad \text{(without Nolan Ryan)}$$

This indicates that card prices will go up by about 2 cents for each strikeout and down by about the same for each walk. That is what we should intuitively expect. The coefficient of multiple determination, $R^2_{Y \cdot 910} = .775$, is somewhat smaller than before, so that less variation in Y gets explained by the regression equation. But removing Ryan gives the new model much better predictive accuracy, the standard error of the estimate dropping from \$73.81 to a much smaller $S_{Y \cdot 910} = $ \$4.15. Even better, the new model has simplicity and seems to make sense.

EXERCISES

11-25 Refer to the economist's family data in Exercise 11-9. Construct a tree showing all possible regression sequences that might be taken when adding successive predictor variables, one at a time, to obtain regression equations of successively higher dimensions for predicting total spending. Do not actually perform the regressions, and do not compute the coefficients of partial determination.

11-26 Refer to the economist's family data in Exercise 11-9 used to forecast total spending.
   (a) Determine the following estimated regression equations and compute the respective coefficients of determination.
   (1) $\hat{Y}(X_1) = a + bX_1$ (2) $\hat{Y}(X_2) = a + bX_2$ (3) $\hat{Y}(X_3) = a + bX_3$
   (b) As the first step in a stepwise regression, the best variable to include in the predictor set is X_1 (income). Why is this so?

(c) Perform the next stage of stepwise regression. To do this, first determine the following estimated regression equations.

$$(1)\ \hat{Y} = a + b_1X_1 + b_2X_2 \qquad (2)\ \hat{Y} = a + b_1X_1 + b_3X_3$$

Then compute the respective coefficients of multiple determination. Finally, calculate the respective coefficient of partial determination, assuming that X_1 was the predictor added in stage 1. The best stage-2 variable to add to the predictor set is X_2 (family size). Why is this so?

11-27 Consider the data given in Table 11-7 for first-basemen superstars. The following data apply for regressions for predicting salary from one or more Xs.

$$r^2_{Y5} = .598 \qquad R^2_{Y \cdot 56} = .841 \qquad R^2_{Y \cdot 567} = .842 \qquad R^2_{Y \cdot 5689} = .905$$

$$r^2_{Y6} = .680 \qquad R^2_{Y \cdot 57} = .637 \qquad R^2_{Y \cdot 589} = .841 \qquad R^2_{Y \cdot 5678} = .900$$

$$r^2_{Y7} = .170 \qquad R^2_{Y \cdot 58} = .838 \qquad R^2_{Y \cdot 578} = .848 \qquad R^2_{Y \cdot 5789} = .845$$

$$r^2_{Y8} = .735 \qquad R^2_{Y \cdot 68} = .752 \qquad R^2_{Y \cdot 568} = .898 \qquad R^2_{Y \cdot 58\ 10\ 11} = .841$$

$$r^2_{Y9} = .581 \qquad R^2_{Y \cdot 78} = .751 \qquad R^2_{Y \cdot 58\ 10} = .839 \qquad R^2_{Y \cdot 689\ 10} = .761$$

$$r^2_{Y10} = .020 \qquad R^2_{Y \cdot 8\ 10} = .741 \qquad R^2_{Y \cdot 689} = .755 \qquad R^2_{Y \cdot 678\ 11} = .783$$

$$R^2_{Y \cdot 79} = .595$$

(a) Ignoring any regression combinations not represented in the above, find the predictor variables selected in each stage of a stepwise regression that uses maximum coefficient of partial determination (regular determination in the first step) as the criterion for selection. Do this for (1) step 1 (single predictor), (2) step 2 (two predictors), (3) step 3 (three predictors), and (4) step 4 (four predictors).

(b) Do you think it is worthwhile to include four predictors? Explain.

11-28 *Computer exercise.* Consider the data given in Table 11-7 for first-basemen superstars.

(a) Perform a multiple regression analysis for predicting price of a player's rookie baseball card using games played, at bats, and runs batted in (RBI) as the only predictors. What is the regression equation and standard error?

(b) Determine for each player the predicted card value and calculate the residuals.

(c) An outlier may be identified as any data point having a residual that is in absolute value greater than twice the standard error of the estimate. The ninth player on the list, Kent Hrbek, is the only such player. Delete him from the data set and rerun the same regression. What is the new regression equation and standard error? Do you think that improved predictions might be made from the newest regression equation?

11-29 *Computer exercise.* Consider the data given in Table 11-7 for first-basemen superstars. In Exercise 11-28, multiple regression analysis is used to predict price of a player's rookie baseball card using games played, at bats, and runs batted in (RBI) as the only predictors.

(a) Determine the following correlation coefficients.
    (1) games played vs. RBI

TABLE 11-7 Data Set for First-Basemen Superstars

Player i	Salary	Card Price Y	Games Played X_5	At Bats X_6	Batting Average X_7	RBI X_8	Number of Runs X_9	Fielding Percent X_{10}	Home Runs X_{11}	Put-Outs X_{12}
8	2,400	3.00	761	2,717	279	426	408	953	98	1,219
18	3,792	15.00	1,024	3,941	262	646	541	982	175	3,467
19	3,400	20.00	1,773	6,109	270	1,060	1,011	986	38	7,016
20	3,775	5.00	736	2,700	302	447	452	992	117	6,588
29	3,275	12.00	830	3,032	262	518	427	992	166	6,951
40	2,100	.70	810	2,703	250	427	336	986	122	4,180
49	2,485	3.50	740	2,707	276	400	360	993	97	6,377
56	2,283	10.00	1,378	4,819	305	812	679	976	206	4,795
64	2,600	6.00	1,299	4,670	290	803	685	994	223	10,127
67	2,100	.80	703	2,657	286	422	759	994	93	6,061
75	3,420	30.00	1,117	4,416	317	759	655	995	169	8,769
79	2,750	1.00	578	1,944	278	305	348	993	125	4,161
80	2,875	3.00	623	2,173	253	429	355	993	156	4,913
86	2,562	45.00	2,135	7,997	294	1,373	1,210	993	379	17,030
88	2,038	.70	1,209	4,271	267	569	526	993	131	9,972

(2) games played vs. at bats

(3) at bats vs. RBI

(b) At bats is highly correlated with both games played and RBI. This indicates that at bats is not a strong predictor and could cause potential difficulties. Using all originally listed players, perform a multiple regression using just games played and RBI as the predictors. Provide the estimated regression equation and standard error of the estimate.

(c) Which model, the above or the one found in Exercise 11-28(a), would you prefer for making predictions of baseball card prices for future first-basemen superstars? Explain.

SUMMARY

1. **What is *multiple* regression and how does it differ from *simple* regression?**
Multiple regression incorporates two or more independent predictor variables. The method of least squares provides an *estimated regression plane* (or hyperplane) described by an **estimated multiple regression equation** of the form

$$\hat{Y} = a + b_1 X_1 + b_2 X_2 + \cdots + b_k X_k$$

The quality of predictions reached using the higher-dimensional regression plane is often greater than that obtained from a **simple regression** involving a single independent variable.

2. **How do we establish the multiple regression equation?**
The Y intercept a and **estimated partial regression coefficients** ($b_1, b_2, \ldots$) may be computed simultaneously solving a system of *normal equations*. In an $m = 3$ variable evaluation, so that there is a dependent variable Y and two

independent variables X_1 and X_2, the normal equations are

$$\sum Y = na + b_1 \sum X_1 + b_2 \sum X_2$$

$$\sum X_1 Y = a \sum X_1 + b_1 \sum X_1^2 + b_2 \sum X_1 X_2$$

$$\sum X_2 Y = a \sum X_2 + b_1 \sum X_1 X_2 + b_2 \sum X_2^2$$

The normal equations become more elaborate as m increases.

A computer is ordinarily used to perform a multiple regression analysis.

3. **What are the assumptions of regression analysis and the potential pitfalls?**
   The underlying theoretical assumptions are analogous to those for simple regression. One notable difficulty is **multicollinearity** which can cause instability in predictions. Another challenge arises from **serial correlation**, which might be alleviated by including an additional predictor variable.

4. **What inferences may be made with multiple regression analysis?**
   Multiple regression has analogous theoretical assumptions to those of simple regression and involves the same types of inferences, including prediction intervals for the conditional mean $\mu_{Y \cdot 12 \ldots}$ and an individual value Y_I and hypothesis tests and estimates of the partial regression coefficients. The necessary computations for these are often standard computer output. A **collective confidence level** is required for estimating the bs using simultaneous **Bonferroni intervals**.

5. **How do we assess the overall quality of a regression analysis?**
   The overall quality of the multiple regression analysis in explaining deviations in Y can be measured by the **coefficient of multiple determination**. **Partial correlation** is a useful concept, with the net contribution of one variable measured by the **coefficient of partial determination**. These statistics may be used in a **stepwise multiple regression** to determine which X predictors to include in the final evaluation.

6. **How can we find a predictive regression model?**
   Multiple regression analysis can be extended to include a search for best predictors that meet the dual goals of *explaining* a high proportion of variability in Y and achieving *simplicity*. The primary technique is **stepwise regression**, in which a series of regressions is performed in stages. The best predictor found at each step is added to the growing set of predictor variables. In a forward procedure, the new variable gives the greatest possible reduction in unexplained Y variation, and the respective *coefficients of partial determination* can be used for this purpose. Stepwise regression should be done with computer assistance, with criterion of choice varying among software packages. Ideally, the process should stop when a point of diminishing returns in improvement is reached. Some programs will drop variables from the predictive set as well. Regardless of how predictors are chosen, the final model should make sense, so that variables having coefficients of opposite sign to what is logical can be dropped. Predictive stability can be enhanced by not including a predictor that is highly correlated with other independent variables and through judicious elimination of outliers.

7. **How might dummy variables be used with multiple regression?**
   Multiple regression can be helpful in certain situations involving a *single* main predictor. When the sample data are placed into homogeneous groupings

according to some category, a second predictor or **dummy variable** may be used. Dummy variable techniques can be especially helpful when sample sizes are too small to obtain statistically reliable results through separate simple regressions.

REAL-LIFE STATISTICAL CHALLENGE

Multiple Regression and Correlation Applied to the Automobile Dream List

In Chapter 10 concepts of regression and correlation were used to analyze the list of 232 autos. We will now apply multiple regression and correlation testing methods to the list of "dream machines."

Again we consider what factors could determine mileage—weight of the vehicle, transmission type, driving skill, and engine size. With multiple regression we can assess the impact of several factors on gas mileage. The data we will work with are shown in Table 11-8. To simplify things we will compare gas mileage with engine size plus two dummy variables for size of the vehicle and transmission type. Size is categorized into either large and midsized or all others (two-seater, etc.). Transmission is either automatic (A or L) or manual (M). Large and midsized cars are assigned a value of 0 and small ones a value of 1. Automobiles with automatic transmissions are assigned a value of 0; those with manuals, a value of 1. The dependent variable is gas mileage and the three independent variables are engine size, model type and transmission type.

The multiple regression results for the samples are shown in Table 11-9. Observe how the results for each pair of independent variables compare to the result for the regression result when all three independent variables are used. The results are not really surprising—larger cars with bigger engines and automatic transmissions generally have lower mileage ratings.

Discussion Questions

1. Observations in two dimensions:
   (a) Plot a single scatter diagram comparing the data in Table 11-8 for larger (mid-size, large) versus smaller (compact, subcompact, minicompact) cars in terms of their respective engine displacements X and mileage ratings Y.
   (b) Determine the estimated regression equations for each group separately and plot these on your graph. Comment on what you observe.

2. With car size as a dummy variable, determine the estimated multiple regression using the data in Table 11-8. What do you think about making predictions from this equation rather than those found in (b)?

3. Using the data in Table 11-9 for the first regression, answer the following.
   (a) Calculate the 95 percent prediction interval for the conditional mean of Y when $X_1 = \bar{X}_1$, $X_2 = \bar{X}_2$, and $X_3 = \bar{X}_3$.
   (b) Calculate the 95 percent prediction interval for an individual value of Y given X when $X_1 = \bar{X}_1$, $X_2 = \bar{X}_2$, and $X_3 = \bar{X}_3$.

4. Refer again to Table 11-9. Which regression results do you prefer in making predictions of gasoline mileage? Discuss and substantiate.

TABLE 11-8 Data for a Sample of 1990 Automobiles Showing Mileage, Transmission Type, Engine Displacement (liters) and Highway Mileage per Gallon

Number	Type	Manu-facturer	Model	Trans-mission Type	Highway Mileage Miles/gallon	Engine Displacement in Liters	Dummy Variable Model	Dummy Variable Trans-mission
10026	Minicompact	Maserati	222E	M5	20	2.8	1	1
10053	Subcompact	Chevrolet	Camaro	M5	26	5.0	1	1
10088	Subcompact	Geo	Prizm	L3	29	1.6	1	0
10111	Subcompact	Mitsubishi	Eclipse	M5	32	1.8	1	1
10126	Subcompact	Subaru	XT	M5	31	1.8	1	1
10140	Compact	Chevrolet	Beretta	M5	28	3.1	1	1
10149	Compact	Isuzu	Stylus	M5	33	1.6	1	1
10151	Compact	Lexus	ES250	L4	25	2.5	1	0
10154	Compact	Mitsubishi	Galant	M5	29	2.0	1	1
10178	Mid-Size	BMW	750i	L4	18	5.0	0	0
10185	Mid-Size	Chevrolet	Lumina	L4	30	3.1	0	0
10186	Mid-Size	Chrysler	New Yorker	L4	26	3.3	0	0
10199	Mid-Size	Mazda	929	L4	23	3.0	0	0
10213	Mid-Size	Volvo	740	L4	26	2.3	0	0
10218	Large	Cadillac	Brougham	L4	21	5.7	0	0
		Sample	Average	26.47	2.97		
		Sample	St. Dev.	4.47	1.31		

Source: United States Environmental Protection Agency, 1989.

TABLE 11-9 Multiple Regression Results for 1990 Automobile Sample Data

	1st Regression	2nd Regression	3rd Regression	4th Regression
Y	mpg	mpg	mpg	mpg
Constant	32.34	31.86	31.89	24.00
Standard Error	3.40	3.26	3.39	4.24
R^2	.55	.54	.51	.23
n	15	15	15	15
m	4	3	3	3
X_1: **Displacement**	included	included	included	out
b_1	−2.23	−2.15	−2.11	—
X_2: **Transmission**	included	included	out	included
b_2	2.63	2.12	—	3.00
X_3: **Model**	included	out	included	included
b_3	−.76	—	1.43	3.46

REVIEW EXERCISES

11-30 A college admissions director wishes to predict college GPA Y of applicants using high school GPA X_1 and verbal SAT score X_2 as independent variables. The following data apply.

Student	College GPA Y	High School GPA X_1	Verbal SAT Score X_2
1	3.8	4.0	750
2	2.7	3.7	380
3	2.3	2.2	580
4	3.2	3.8	510
5	3.5	3.8	620
6	2.4	2.8	440
7	2.6	3.0	540
8	3.0	3.4	650
9	2.7	3.3	480
10	2.8	3.0	550

(a) Determine the estimated regression equation.
(b) Using your answer to (a), calculate the predicted college GPA for the following applicants.

	High School GPA X_1	SAT Score X_2
(1)	3.4	550
(2)	2.8	400
(3)	3.2	650
(4)	3.7	450

11-31 Refer to the data given in Exercise 11-30. The estimated regression equation for predicting college GPA Y using only high school GPA X_1 is

$$\hat{Y}(X_1) = .4957 + .7286X_1$$

The values of the standard error of the estimate and coefficient of determination are

$$s_{Y \cdot X_1} = .268 \qquad r_{Y1}^2 = .721$$

with the standard deviation in Y having value $S_Y = .478$. The standard error of the estimate when verbal SAT score X_2 is included as an independent variable is

$$S_{Y \cdot 12} = .110$$

(a) Compute the coefficient of multiple determination when both X_1 and X_2 are used to predict Y.
(b) Compute the coefficient of partial determination ($r_{Y2 \cdot 1}^2$) for adding SAT score X_2 to the regression analysis. What is the percentage reduc-

tion in unexplained variation in Y achieved by adding SAT score X_2 as the second independent variable? Does this suggest that including SAT score should improve college GPA predictions? Explain.

11-32 *Computer exercise.* A third independent variable, number of extracurricular activities X_3, is added to the college GPA prediction problem in Exercise 11-30. The following data apply.

Student	Number of Activities X_3
1	7
2	6
3	5
4	6
5	3
6	2
7	8
8	2
9	7
10	4

Determine the coefficients for $\hat{Y} = a + b_1X_1 + b_2X_2 + b_3X_3$.

11-33 (*Continuation of Exercise 11-32*):
(a) Calculate the value of $S_{Y \cdot 123}$.
(b) Compared to the value $S_{Y \cdot 12} = .110$, does a comparison of the values $S_{Y \cdot 123}$ and $S_{Y \cdot 12}$ suggest that including the number of high school activities improves college GPA predictions? Explain.
(c) Compute the coefficient of partial determination ($r^2_{Y3 \cdot 12}$) for including X_3 in the regression analysis. What is the percentage reduction in previously unexplained variation achieved by adding number of activities as the third independent variable?

11-34 *Computer exercise.* Suppose that the real estate appraiser in Exercise 11-7 also gathered data for the median neighborhood selling price to include as her third independent variable X_3. The following data (in thousands of dollars) apply.

Price Y	Median X_3
45	35
37	40
26	23
32	32
34	39
49	45
53	49
65	70
71	66
88	91

(a) You have been asked to run a higher-dimensional multiple regression for the appraiser. Determine the estimated multiple regression equation.

(b) The standard error of the estimate for selling price using the regression hyperplane is $S_{Y \cdot 123} = 3.912$. Does it appear that including the additional independent variable improves the regression analysis?

11-35 *Computer exercise.* The data set in Table 11-10 applies to baseball superstar third-basemen and shortstops.

(a) Determine the regression equation for predicting rookie baseball card price using runs batted in and number of home runs as independent variables.

(b) What is the proportion of variation in card price explained by the regression equation from (a)?

(c) Determine the regression equation for predicting salary using runs batted in and number of home runs as independent variables.

(d) What is the proportion of variation in salary explained by the regression equation from (c)?

(e) Which regression model, (a) or (c), would provide better predictions? Explain.

11-36 Figure 11-12 provides the results of a computer stepwise regression using the data in Table 11-10 to predict the price of a player's rookie baseball card.

(a) Do you think it would be worthwhile to use more than three predictors? Explain.

(b) If you were going to do a detailed regression analysis, which three predictors would you use?

11-37 *Computer exercise.* The data set in Table 11-10 applies to baseball superstar third baseman and shortstops.

(a) Determine the regression equation for predicting rookie baseball card price using number of games played, runs batted in, and number of home runs as independent variables.

TABLE 11-10 Data Set for Third-Basemen and Shortstop Superstars ($X_4 = 0$ for third basemen, $X_4 = 1$ for shortstop).

Player i	Salary	Card Price	Pos. X_4	Games X_5	At Bats X_6	Bat. Ave. X_7	RBI X_8	Runs X_9	Fielding X_{10}	Home Runs X_{11}	Put-Outs X_{12}
6	2,750	35.00	0	1,338	5,153	346	586	912	963	70	1,468
9	3,675	200.00	0	2,279	8,692	311	1,398	1,382	970	281	5,277
48	2,700	5.00	0	1,361	4,989	256	758	646	965	201	1,166
54	3,033	8.00	0	686	2,219	266	326	321	956	83	498
66	2,242	10.00	0	1,023	3,395	256	512	516	937	159	714
82	3,750	3.00	0	688	2,378	278	412	369	959	135	953
83	3,253	50.00	0	1,540	6,246	299	626	1,053	964	131	2,115
123	2,000	20.00	0	1,827	6,693	274	781	1,040	983	167	3,581
37	2,100	3.00	1	758	2,768	257	290	340	967	61	1,349
43	2,100	6.00	1	1,028	3,952	289	404	510	980	40	1,786
70	2,100	.80	1	572	2,125	293	221	314	970	38	846
98	2,433	18.00	1	1,476	5,655	274	828	871	977	225	4,469
110	2,225	45.00	1	1,926	7,019	256	600	910	978	19	3,237
119	2,200	50.00	1	1,835	6,702	288	810	1,009	977	152	2,880

```
MTB > Stepwise c3 c2 c4-c12;
SUBC>    FEnter 1;
SUBC>    FRemove 1.
```

```
 STEPWISE REGRESSION OF Card Pr. ON 10 PREDICTORS, WITH N =    14
```

STEP	1	2	3	4	5	6
CONSTANT	-54.34	-55.07	-23.42	-74.76	601.82	1235.50
RBI	0.142	0.201	0.425	0.360	0.383	0.347
T-RATIO	5.21	4.55	4.20	3.44	3.61	3.31
H.Runs		-0.28	-0.67	-0.62	-0.69	-0.71
T-RATIO		-1.63	-3.08	-2.98	-3.18	-3.43
Games			-0.091	-0.064	-0.063	-0.069
T-RATIO			-2.38	-1.60	-1.58	-1.81
Salary				0.019	0.014	0.015
T-RATIO				1.52	1.08	1.21
Fielding					-0.69	-1.35
T-RATIO					-1.06	-1.70
P.Outs						0.014
T-RATIO						1.34
S	29.7	27.8	23.3	21.9	21.8	20.7
R-SQ	69.32	75.32	84.25	87.48	89.02	91.27

FIGURE 11-12 Minitab stepwise regression results for baseball superstar data set in Table 11-10.

(b) What is the proportion of variation in card price explained by the regression equation from (a)?

(c) Determine a 95% prediction interval for a player who has played 1,000 games, having 1,000 RBIs and producing 300 home runs.

11-38 *Computer exercise.*   Refer to Exercise 11-37 and your answers to that problem.

(a) Add position as the fourth predictor variable. Determine the new regression equation for predicting rookie baseball card price.

(b) What is the proportion of variation in card price explained by the regression equation from (a)?

(c) Compute the coefficient of partial determination for adding position to the predictor set. What percentage reduction in previously unexplained variation is achieved by including position as the fourth predictor?

11-39 *Computer exercise.*   The data set in Table 11-11 applies to baseball superstar catchers and shortstops.

(a) Determine the regression equation for predicting rookie baseball card price using runs batted in and number of home runs as independent variables.

(b) What is the proportion of variation in card price explained by the regression equation from (a)?

(c) Determine the regression equation for predicting salary using runs batted in and number of home runs as independent variables.

(d) What is the proportion of variation in salary explained by the regression equation from (c)?

(e) Which regression model, (a) or (c), would provide better predictions? Explain.

11-40 *Computer exercise.* The data set in Table 11-11 applies to baseball superstar catchers and shortstops. Unlike those in other nonpitching positions, players in these two positions can be valued primarily on their fielding capabilities. Regression analysis may be used in reaching conclusions regarding the relationship between salary and defensive performance statistics and how salaries differ between catchers and shortstops.

(a) Determine the regression equation for predicting salary using position, fielding percentage, and number of putouts as independent variables.

(b) What is the proportion of variation in salary explained by the regression equation?

(c) Should fielding percentage be kept as a predictor? Using information contained in your computer printout, make a case for keeping or dropping this variable.

11-41 *Computer exercise.* Continuation of Exercise 11-40.

(a) Determine the regression equation for predicting salary using position and number of putouts as independent variables.

(b) What is the proportion of variation in salary explained by the regression equation?

(c) What is the interpretation of the regression coefficient for position? In using the regression equation from (a) to predict salary, who would we expect to make more, catchers or shortstops?

TABLE 11-11 Data Set for Catcher and Shortstop Superstars ($X = 0$ for catcher, $X = 1$ for shortstop).

Player i	Salary Y	Card Price	Pos. X_4	Games X_5	At Bats X_6	Bat. Ave. X_7	RBI X_8	Runs X_9	Fielding X_{10}	Home Runs X_{11}	Put-Outs X_{12}
45	2,455	150.00	0	2,278	8,055	272	1,231	1,220	987	354	10,660
89	2,417	30.00	0	1,656	6,066	257	947	765	991	285	8,166
90	2,350	2.50	0	1,350	4,676	273	528	500	989	89	7,668
104	2,183	7.00	0	1,205	3,680	262	382	340	987	57	7,017
37	2,100	3.00	1	758	2,768	257	290	340	967	61	1,349
43	2,100	6.00	1	1,028	3,952	289	404	510	980	40	1,786
70	2,100	.80	1	572	2,125	293	221	314	970	38	846
98	2,433	18.00	1	1,476	5,655	274	828	871	977	225	4,469
110	2,225	45.00	1	1,926	7,019	256	600	910	978	19	3,237
119	2,200	50.00	1	1,835	6,702	288	810	1,009	977	152	2,880

11-42 Consider populations comprising all statistics students. Using as sample data the master class data list developed in Exercise 1-19, perform the following regression and correlation operations. (Note: Be sure to show all your intermediate steps. You may use intermediate answers you developed in earlier chapters to avoid unnecessary effort. If needed, gather additional data.)

(a) Select two variables as the independent variables X_1 and X_2 and one as the dependent variable Y.

(b) Find the estimated regression equation.

(c) Determine the sample standard deviation and the standard error of the estimate for the dependent variable.

(d) Calculate the sample coefficient of multiple determination and the sample partial correlation coefficients.

(e) Predict the value of the dependent variable for four different sets of independent variable values.

(f) Demonstrate how to calculate the 95 percent prediction interval for the conditional mean of Y when $X_1 = \bar{X}_1$ and $X_2 = \bar{X}_2$.

(g) Demonstrate how to calculate the 95 percent prediction interval for an individual value of Y given $X_1 = \bar{X}_1$ and $X_2 = \bar{X}_2$.

11-43 Repeat Exercise 11-42 using your group's class data developed in Exercise 1-21.

11-44 *Comparing Commute Time and Distance to Work.* The following data are from a sample of graduate students who work in the Silicon Valley (San Jose, Calif.) and attend school at night.

Gender	Commute Time (Min.)	Distance (Kilometers)	Distance (Miles)
Male	20	8	5
Male	20	13	8
Male	35	21	13
Male	45	26	16
Male	25	24	15
Female	30	28	17
Male	20	20	12
Female	45	54	33
Female	30	28	17
Male	15	4	3
Female	10	8	5
Male	20	8	5
Female	35	31	19
Female	35	37	23
Female	25	18	11
Male	5	3	2

(a) Use gender as a dummy variable and calculate the estimated regression plane for predicting a student's commute time given the distance traveled to work.

(b) Compute the sample standard deviation and the standard error of the estimate for commute time.

(c) Compute the sample coefficient of multiple determination and the sample partial correlation coefficients.

(d) What is the predicted commute time for a female living 12 miles from the office?

11-45 Given your results in Exercises 11-42, 11-43, or 11-44, discuss the challenges and pitfalls you faced in carrying out these exercises.

11-46 Refer to Exercise 10-49 and your answers to that problem. Suppose homework (50 points possible) and quiz score (50 points possible) data are added to the original data, as shown below.

Student No.	Midterm	Homework	Quiz	Final Exam
42	43	31	25	24
61	36	26	23	34
86	65	40	34	49
24	89	48	41	87
37	82	48	38	73
13	90	50	46	95
51	43	15	21	10
31	75	33	32	75
18	87	41	37	86

(a) Select two variables as independent variables for predicting final exam grade.

(b) Find the estimated regression equation.

(c) Compute the sample standard deviation and the standard error of the estimate for the dependent variable.

(d) Calculate the sample coefficient of multiple determination and the sample partial correlation coefficients.

11-47 Refer to Exercise 11-46 and your answers to that problem.

(a) Add a third predictor variable. Determine the new estimated regression equation for predicting final exam grade.

(b) What is the proportion of variation in final exam grade explained by the regression equation in (a)?

(c) Compute the coefficient of partial determination for adding the third predictor variable.

(d) What percentage reduction in previously unexplained variation is achieved by including the third predictor?

11-48 Refer to Exercise 10-47 and your answers to that problem. Select a second independent variable to be used to predict the number of touchdowns (TD).

(a) Find the estimated regression equation.

(b) Compute the sample standard deviation and the standard error of the estimate for the dependent variable.

(c) Calculate the sample coefficient of multiple determination.

(d) Compute the coefficient of partial determination for adding the second predictor variable.

(e) What percentage reduction in previously unexplained variation is achieved by including the second predictor?

11-49 Refer to Exercise 11-48 and your answers to that problem.

(a) Add a third predictor variable. Determine the new estimated regression equation for predicting touchdowns.

(b) What is the proportion of variation in touchdowns explained by the regression equation in (a)?

(c) Compute the coefficient of partial determination for adding the third predictor variable.

(d) What percentage reduction in previously unexplained variation is achieved by including the third predictor?

CASE   Adventures in Regression Land

Cal Crunch, an economist for Million Bank, wonders about the quality of econometric investigations that are based largely on regression analysis. He wishes to explore various facets of multiple regression using his personal computer. Cal plans to submit his findings to his professor as an extra credit report for his MBA core statistics course.

Using his EasyStat software package, Cal generates the following data for a random sample of 25 heads of households using the U.S. census data for 1,000 Sacramento, California, homeowners. Although 14 variables are represented in the data base, Cal has decided to limit his investigations to the six variables listed in the table.

Income Y	Level of Education X_1	Home Value X_2	Age X_3	Mortgage Payment X_4	Sex* X_5
$ 5,705	16	$ 55,300	28	$285	1
20,005	16	88,900	39	398	0
24,005	14	61,400	34	202	0
16,425	15	55,000	38	344	0
33,005	14	86,000	37	317	0
19,810	04	30,300	56	087	0
40,005	20	90,000	53	152	0
28,005	13	69,600	51	115	0
50,585	19	111,400	58	263	0
9,885	18	41,800	30	098	1
22,005	14	61,600	49	419	0
9,745	16	45,300	30	312	1
20,005	16	53,000	29	258	0
14,520	15	57,400	22	415	1
22,010	22	112,400	40	900	0

(continued)

Income Y	Level of Education X_1	Home Value X_2	Age X_3	Mortgage Payment X_4	Sex* X_5
7,370	10	30,700	63	139	1
25,510	20	86,500	31	326	0
20,505	14	49,500	44	307	0
14,005	17	25,600	55	187	1
27,370	20	80,000	40	120	0
9,095	14	31,300	69	090	1
13,005	18	30,800	32	117	0
13,005	14	60,900	57	190	0
23,125	16	54,500	39	149	0
16,005	16	63,500	50	271	0

*Male = 0 and female = 1 for this variable.

   Cal then decides to determine the estimated multiple regression equation for predicting income using various Xs as independent predictor variables. To do this, he adapts the regression model to the above sample data. To conclude, Cal wishes to see how well that model will perform with different samples from the same population.
   You decide to accept Cal's invitation to join his study group and volunteer to answer the following questions.

QUESTIONS

Computer assistance should be available to answer the following questions.

1. Run a multiple regression to predict income from known levels of education and home value only.
   (a) Determine the estimated multiple regression equation.
   (b) What percentage of the variation in Y is explained by the multiple regression equation?
   (c) Determine the predicted levels of the conditional mean income using the following values for the independent predictor variables.

	Level of Education	Home Value
(1)	16	$100,000
(2)	10	50,000
(3)	12	75,000

2. Attempt to increase the percentage of explained variation in Y by including a third predictor variable. This will be done based on your results from three separate multiple regressions including successively

(a) age, (b) mortgage payment, and (c) sex as the new third independent variable. Determine the following for each multiple regression.
(1) The respective estimated multiple regression equation.
(2) The respective percentage of variation in Y that is explained by the multiple regression.
(3) The partial coefficient of determination for adding the respective third independent variable to the regression analysis.

3. Which of the above, if any, do you recommend for inclusion in further multiple regressions? Explain.

4. Run a multiple regression simultaneously using all five predictor variables for estimating income.
(a) Determine the estimated multiple regression equation.
(b) What percentage of the variation in Y is explained by the multiple regression equation?

5. To gain a different perspective on what variables to include in a multiple regression, consider dropping variables. To do this, use separate multiple regressions and, in each, drop just (a) education, (b) home value, (c) age, (d) mortgage payment, and (e) sex. Determine the following for each multiple regression.
(1) The respective estimated multiple regression equation.
(2) The respective percentage of variation in Y that is explained by the multiple regression.

6. If it is dropped, which potential independent variable appears to be (a) least damaging and (b) most damaging in the resulting regression's ability to explain variation in income?

7. Cal feels that three independent variables will provide more stable results in future multiple regressions. After perusing your answers and doing further experimentation, Cal decides to use home value, mortgage payment, and sex as the only independent predictor variables for income.
(a) Determine his final estimated regression equation.
(b) Calculate the coefficient of multiple determination.
(c) Determine the predicted mean income when the home value is $100,000, the mortgage payment is $400, and the homeowner is male.

8. Cal wishes to assess the overall quality of the regression procedure.
(a) Using your answers to Question 7, determine the Bonferroni interval estimates of the three partial regression coefficients (bs) using a collective confidence level of 94%.
(b) Using EasyStat, Cal generated 10 new separate random samples of $n = 25$ from the population data base. The following results were obtained. The predicted mean is based on $X_2 = 100,000$, $X_4 = 400$, and $X_5 = 0$.

Sample	Estimated Regression Line $\hat{Y} = a + b_2X_2 + b_4X_4 + b_5X_5$	Predicted Mean
1	$\hat{Y} = 18{,}339 - .010X_2 + 6.78X_4 - 10{,}389X_5$	$20{,}051
2	$\hat{Y} = 15{,}638 + .043X_2 + 3.66X_4 - 8{,}742X_5$	21,042
3	$\hat{Y} = 25{,}244 + .001X_2 - 13.49X_4 - 6{,}923X_5$	19,948
4	$\hat{Y} = 8{,}392 + .223X_2 + 5.97X_4 - 7{,}632X_5$	33,080
5	$\hat{Y} = 24{,}922 - .030X_2 - 4.18X_4 + 1{,}744X_5$	20,250
6	$\hat{Y} = 16{,}011 + .041X_2 + 9.90X_4 - 3{,}245X_5$	24,071
7	$\hat{Y} = 14{,}867 + .205X_2 - 21.57X_4 - 2{,}728X_5$	26,739
8	$\hat{Y} = 451 + .380X_2 + .41X_4 - 5{,}711X_5$	38,615
9	$\hat{Y} = 5{,}521 + .247X_2 + 3.21X_4 - 3{,}398X_5$	31,505
10	$\hat{Y} = 18{,}730 + .206X_2 - 13.78X_4 - 8{,}376X_5$	33,818

Using Cal's results and your answers to (a) and Question 7, what do you conclude regarding the following.
(1) Pitfalls in selecting independent predictor variables when the regression equation is adapted to one particular sample.
(2) Variability in predictions and in partial regression coefficients.

11-7　OPTIONAL TOPIC: DUMMY VARIABLE TECHNIQUES

It is sometimes necessary to determine how a dependent variable is related to quantitative independent random variables when there are nonhomogeneous factors influencing their interaction. Often such factors are qualitative in nature. For example, in printing a book, the cost of typesetting can be expressed by an equation involving the size of the book and the number of figures and tables. But this cost is also affected by the kind of book. A technical book using many special symbols and characters (like this one) requires a considerable amount of handwork and is, page for page, more expensive to set than a literary anthology. "Kind of book" can be viewed as a qualitative variable that influences composition cost. Although regression analysis requires all variables to be quantitative, qualititative variables may be incorporated into the framework of multiple regression through the introduction of dummy variables.

There are two major kinds of statistical studies where dummy variables may be used. Those made with sample data collected at a single point in time are sometimes referred to as **cross-sectional studies**. Studies made using observations collected over an extended time period use time-series data. In business and economics, time-series data are very important because observations of a dependent variable, such as consumption of electricity or gross national product, can only be obtained periodically. Often, time itself becomes the independent variable. Unavoidable historical heterogeneous influences, such as war or recession, may be treated as qualitative variables, and their effects must be identified somehow. Another important use for qualitative variables in time series is to identify seasonal influences and to relate them to the dependent variable.

USING A DUMMY VARIABLE

We illustrate the dummy variable technique in Figure 11-13 for data relating composition costs to total number of words for a hypothetical sample of textbooks. The books have been printed during one year by a firm under contract to various publishers. The data points for technical books are shown as crosses; the dots represent nontechnical texts. As we have noted, the technical books tend to be more costly, so that the crosses cluster higher than the dots. Two parallel lines have been constructed for the scatter diagram. The top one, fitting the data for the technical books, represents an upward shift in composition costs due to extensive hand typesetting.

These lines have been obtained by means of a linear least-squares *multiple* regression with two independent variables, word length X_1 and type of book X_2. X_2 is a **dummy variable** that takes on only two values, 1 or 0, depending on whether or not a book is technical. We may envision X_2 as a "switching" variable that is "on" when an observation is made for a technical book and "off" for an ordinary text. The estimated multiple regression equation is of the form

$$\hat{Y} = a + b_1X_1 + b_2X_2$$

where $X_2 = 0$ for nontechnical books and $X_2 = 1$ for technical books. This is the equation for a plane in three-dimensional space. However, we have restricted X_2 in such a way that only two parallel slices through the plane at $X_2 = 0$ and $X_2 = 1$ are possible. These are projected onto the X_1Y plane as the two estimated regression lines in Figure 11-13, the equations for which are

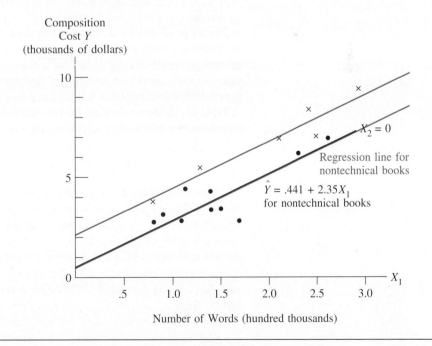

FIGURE 11-13 Multiple regression results using a dummy variable for typesetting cost illustration.

TABLE 11-12 Intermediate Calculations for Multiple Regression Using a Dummy Variable

Cost* Y	Length* X_1	X_2	$X_1 Y$	$X_2 Y$	$X_1 X_2$	X_1^2	X_2^2	Y^2
4.2	1.4	0	5.88	0	0	1.96	0	17.64
2.8	1.1	0	3.08	0	0	1.21	0	7.84
3.3	1.4	0	4.62	0	0	1.96	0	10.89
3.9	.8	1(T)	3.12	3.9	.8	.64	1	15.21
6.7	2.6	0	17.42	0	0	6.76	0	44.89
7.0	2.5	1(T)	17.50	7.0	2.5	6.25	1	49.00
9.3	2.9	1(T)	26.97	9.3	2.9	8.41	1	86.49
2.7	.8	0	2.16	0	0	.64	0	7.29
6.9	2.1	1(T)	14.49	6.9	2.1	4.41	1	47.61
2.8	1.2	0	3.36	0	0	1.44	0	7.84
5.4	1.3	1(T)	7.02	5.4	1.3	1.69	1	29.16
6.1	2.3	0	14.03	0	0	5.29	0	37.21
8.3	2.4	1(T)	19.92	8.3	2.4	5.76	1	68.89
3.3	1.5	0	4.95	0	0	2.25	0	10.89
3.1	.9	0	2.79	0	0	.81	0	9.61
75.8	25.2	6	147.31	40.8	12.0	49.48	6	450.46
$= \sum Y$	$= \sum X_1$	$= \sum X_2$	$= \sum X_1 Y$	$= \sum X_2 Y$	$= \sum X_1 X_2$	$= \sum X_1^2$	$= \sum X_2^2$	$= \sum Y^2$
	$\bar{Y} = 5.053$	$\bar{X}_1 = 1.680$	$\bar{X}_2 = .4$					

*Cost Y (thousands of dollars); length X_1 (hundreds of thousands of words).

$$\hat{Y} = a + b_1 X_1 + b_2 \quad \text{(technical books)}$$
$$\hat{Y} = a + b_1 X_1 \quad \text{(nontechnical books)}$$

The value of a is the Y intercept for nontechnical books. The value of b_1 is the incremental or variable cost per additional word for either type of book. The amount b_2 represents the additional estimated cost—here assumed to be fixed in nature—associated with setting the type for a technical book. Thus, the Y intercept for technical books is a total fixed cost estimated to be $a + b_2$.*

Table 11-12 shows the data for this example. Solving the corresponding normal equations, the following regression constants are obtained.

$$a = .441 \qquad b_1 = 2.35 \qquad b_2 = 1.66$$

The estimated regression equation is

$$\hat{Y} = .441 + 2.35 X_1 + 1.66 X_2$$

For the two values of X_2, the multiple regression equation provides

$$\hat{Y} = .441 + 2.35 X_1 \quad \text{(nontechnical books)}$$

and

$$\hat{Y} = .441 + 2.35 X_1 + 1.66$$

*A more general model would allow for different variable costs for technical books, which might be more realistic and would allow lines of different slope for the two types of tests.

or

$$\hat{Y} = 2.101 + 2.35X_1 \qquad \text{(technical books)}$$

We may interpret these lines as follows. The value $a = .441$ represents an estimated setup or fixed cost of \$441 applicable, on the average, to every book set in type. The partial regression coefficient value $b_1 = 2.35$, which is also the slope of each of the lines for the two kinds of books, is the estimated average variable cost of \$2,350 for each additional 100,000 words in length, or 2.35 cents per additional word. This applies to both technical and nontechnical books. The other partial regression coefficient, $b_2 = 1.66$, applies only to technical texts and indicates the estimated additional average fixed cost of handsetting special characters, \$1,660 per book, so that these books involve an average fixed cost estimated to be $\$441 + \$1,660 = \$2,101$ each.

The importance of treating kind of book as a separate variable is that this allows us to properly identify the relationship between composition cost and book length. Using the dummy variable X_2, we can treat the two kinds of books separately and yet still glean the common information that both types yield in relating book length to cost. We certainly should not ignore the kind of book in determining the relationship between these primary variables. Doing so can lead to very erroneous conclusions, as is shown in Figure 11-14, where a simple linear regression line relates Y to X_1. This line does not fit the data nearly as well as the two lines obtained for multiple regression, and the amount of scatter about this single line is substantially greater than that achieved for the parallel lines obtained for multiple regression analysis using a dummy variable.

But why can't we do just as well by making two separate linear regression analyses, splitting the observations into separate samples for technical and non-

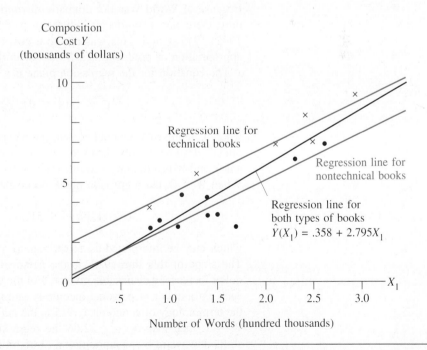

FIGURE 11-14 Linear least-squares regression and multiple regression using a dummy variable.

technical books? If the sample sizes are large, this would be more desirable than the above approach. Later in this section we will see how the dummy variable technique can be generalized through an interactive mode. Such a variation provides projected lines which may have different *slopes*. (That technique would permit technical and nontechnical books to have different variable costs if the raw data suggest it.)

USING A DUMMY VARIABLE WITH TIME SERIES

We have noted situations where regression analysis using dummy variables with time-series data may be advantageous. One of these involves isolation of the effect of nonhomogeneous influences—such as war and peace or recession and economic expansion—on the relationship between two or more variables. Such variables are characterized by the uncontrollability of the sampling experiment, so that observations can be collected only as they occur over time. The statistician or economist cannot make a large number of "peacetime-only" observations in order to determine a relationship between personal consumption expenditures and disposable personal income, for the data are available only with peacetime and war years intermingled. Separate analyses would be less reliable, because of the scarcity of observations, than a multiple regression analysis treating war as a dummy variable. The procedure for the latter is completely analogous to the one illustrated for textbook composition. A regression plane is fitted to the three-dimensional data array, with values for personal consumption expenditure and disposable personal income variables, and with the dummy variable taking the value 0 for peacetime and 1 for wartime.

Figure 11-15 shows the two projected regression lines obtained for the regression plane using disposable personal income and war to predict personal consumption expenditures for the United States, using data from 1935–1949. Because of World War II's dramatic disruptions of personal lives and the economy, there was a significantly different pattern of consumer spending during the 1942–1945 period. This was due to a host of factors, such as rationing and the appropriation of production facilities for military material.

The equation for the regression plane is

$$C = 1.49 + .915Y_D - 22.66W$$

where C represents personal consumption expenditures, Y_D is the traditional economist's designation for disposable income (taken here to be an independent variable), and W is a dummy variable ($W = 0$ for peacetime and $W = 1$ for wartime). When $W = 0$, the regression plane becomes the line

$$C = 1.49 + .915Y_D \qquad \text{(in peacetime)}$$

which may be interpreted as an estimate of the *aggregate consumption function*. The slope of this line, .915, is the personal consumption expenditure for each dollar increase in disposable income. For the economy as a whole, 91.5 cents from each extra dollar of personal income is estimated to be spent on consumption. In the terminology of economics, .915 is the *marginal propensity to consume*. When $W = 1$, then with $b_2 = -22.66$ the regression line (the consumption function) shifts downward by an amount of \$22.66 billion, reflecting a general drop in personal expenditures due to the shortage of many goods formerly purchased by indi-

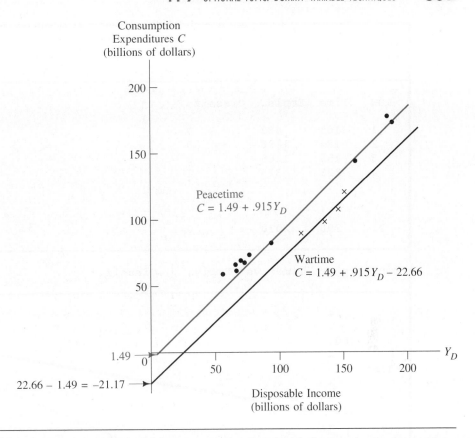

FIGURE 11-15 Multiple regression using a dummy variable for consumption function during wartime and peacetime.

viduals. Notice that this shifted regression line has the same slope, reflecting the fact that the marginal propensity to consume is the same as before.*

If the time-series data were expanded to include the 1950s and 1960s, the effects of two other wars, in Korea and Vietnam, would be much less pronounced. These wars were not as disruptive to consumer spending habits, since there were no major shortages or rationing. For this reason, a better fit to the time series could be obtained by treating these later war years like peacetime (so that perhaps the dummy variable, wartime *rationing*, would then be a better designation).

USING A DUMMY VARIABLE IN INTERACTIVE MULTIPLE REGRESSION

The preceding illustrations involve identical slopes for the individual regression lines projected onto the regression plane. The procedure may be generalized slightly to allow for a different slope under the settings of the dummy variable. To accomplish this, find the coefficients of the multiple regression equation

$$\hat{Y} = a + b_1 X_1 + b_2 X_2 + b_3 X_1 X_2$$

---

*As we have noted, this may not be realistic but it is a necessary consequence of the linear multiple regression model.

```
MTB > retrieve 'payroll'
MTB > print c1-c3
```

ROW	Time	Empls.	Classif.
1	105	483	0
2	184	1298	0
3	155	1105	0
4	225	325	1
.			
.			
.			
21	290	2010	0

```
MTB > lplot 'Time' vs 'Empls.', 'Classif.'
```

Note: Figure generated on an IBM PC using Minitab®.

FIGURE 11-16 Scatter diagram for the accounting service's payroll data.

where $X_2 = 0$ or 1 (dummy variable) and a third independent variable is expressed as

$$X_3 = X_1 X_2$$

Two lines result from the two-dimensional projections obtained for the above regression plane.

$$\hat{Y} = a + b_1 X_1 \qquad \text{(when } X_2 = 0)$$
$$\hat{Y} = (a + b_2) + (b_1 + b_3)X_1 \qquad \text{(when } X_2 = 1)$$

To illustrate the procedure, Figure 11-16 shows a computer-generated scatter diagram for data obtained from an accounting service. Each data point represent a sample payroll processed by the services. The dependent variable Y is payroll processing time (seconds) and the independent variable X_1 is number of employees. The dummy variable is X_2. The payrolls include a mixture of small and large firms, so that the data for firms with predominantly classified (hourly) employees ($X_2 = 1$) are plotted as A's and the firms with mostly unclassified (salaried) employees ($X_2 = 0$) are plotted as Z's. (The projection lines were added by hand after the estimated multiple regression equation was found.)

Figure 11-17 is the printout for a multiple regression run using the payroll data. The estimated regression equation is

$$\hat{Y} = 37.7 + .118X_1 + 163X_2 - .066X_1X_2$$

Using the above equation when $X_2 = 0$, the projected regression line is

$$\hat{Y} = 37.7 + .118X_1 \qquad \text{(unclassified employee payrolls)}$$

and, when $X_2 = 1$, the equation provides

$$\hat{Y} = (37.7 + 163) + (.118 - .066)X_1$$
$$= 200.7 + .052X_1 \qquad \text{(classified employee payrolls)}$$

These lines indicate that payrolls for classified employees have a fixed processing-time component that is about six times as long as that of the payrolls for unclassified employees. That may be attributable to the higher computational setup requirements for determining pay from hours worked for classified (largely hourly) employees. Computing basic pay for unclassified employees should be simpler, since they receive mainly a fixed salary. But the slope is less than half of the counterpart for classified payrolls. This may be due to the richer mix of benefits and salary perquisite items that are included for unclassified (largely white-collar) employees.

OPTIONAL EXERCISES

11-50 Six women and four men have taken a test that measures their manual dexterity and patience in handling tiny objects. Each has then gone through a week of intensive training as electronics assemblers, followed by a month at actual assembly, during which their productivity was measured by a relative index having values ranging from 0 to 10 (with 10 being the value for the most productive worker). The data in the table on page 573 (top) have been obtained.

(a) Plot a scatter diagram using different symbols for women and men.

(b) Using a dummy variable having value $X_2 = 1$ for women and $X_2 = 0$ for men, determine the coefficients of the equation $\hat{Y} = a + b_1X_1 + b_2X_2$ for the estimated regression plane. Plot the lines corresponding to $X_2 = 0$ and $X_2 = 1$ on your scatter diagram.

(c) State the meaning of the partial regression coefficients.

(d) Determine the estimated regression line obtained when the sex of the subjects is ignored. Plot the line on your scatter diagram.

```
MTB > let c4=c2*c3
MTB > name c4 'EmpxClas'
MTB > print c1-c4
```

ROW	Time	Empls.	Classif.	EmpxClas
1	105	483	0	0
2	184	1298	0	0
3	155	1105	0	0
4	225	325	1	325
5	203	52	1	52
6	210	125	1	125
7	56	210	0	0
8	99	355	0	0
9	220	378	1	378
10	208	224	1	224
11	64	106	0	0
12	81	425	0	0
13	231	515	1	515
14	315	2067	1	2067
15	285	1810	1	1810
16	125	844	0	0
17	135	771	0	0
18	199	94	1	94
19	75	186	0	0
20	50	409	0	0
21	290	2010	0	0

```
MTB > Regress c1 3 c2-c4.
```

The regression equation is
Time = 37.7 + 0.118 Empls. + 163 Classif. − 0.0659 EmpxClas

Predictor	Coef	Stdev	t-ratio	p
Constant	37.683	6.430	5.86	0.000
Empls.	0.117874	0.007404	15.92	0.000
Classif.	162.943	8.827	18.46	0.000
EmpxClas	−0.065930	0.009760	−6.75	0.000

$s = 13.74$ R−sq = 97.6%   R−sq(adj) = 97.1%

Note: Figure generated on an IBM PC using Minitab®.

FIGURE 11-17 Computer printout for the payroll data.

Subject	Productivity Index Y	Test Score X_1	Sex
A	5.2	5.8	F
B	6.0	8.5	M
C	6.5	8.2	F
D	2.0	3.5	F
E	2.7	6.5	M
F	10.0	9.5	F
G	6.4	9.8	M
H	6.6	9.2	M
I	3.5	4.0	F
J	4.0	5.5	F

11-51 The data in the following table have been obtained for personal savings and personal income (billions of dollars) for the time period 1935–1949.
(a) Plot the scatter diagram using dots for peacetime and crosses for wartime.
(b) Using a dummy variable having value $X_2 = 0$ for peacetime and $X_2 = 1$ for wartime, determine the estimated regression equation $\hat{Y} = a + b_1X_1 + b_2X_2$.
(c) Plot the two lines corresponding to wartime and peacetime on your scatter diagram.

Year	Personal Savings Y	Personal Income X_1	War Year
1935	2	60	
1936	4	69	
1937	4	74	
1938	1	68	
1939	3	73	
1940	4	78	
1941	11	96	
1942	28	123	yes
1943	33	151	yes
1944	37	165	yes
1945	30	171	yes
1946	15	179	
1947	7	191	
1948	13	210	
1949	9	207	

Source: *Economic Report of the President, February 1970.*

11-52 Refer to Exercise 11-50, and to your answers.
(a) Compute the average test scores separately for the men and the women. Then, compute the average productivity index for men and for women.
(b) Based on these averages, what conclusion can you draw with respect to the average test score results for the sample men as compared to

those for the women? Can the same conclusion be drawn for the productivity index?

(c) How do you reconcile your conclusion in (b) with the interpretation of the partial regression coefficient b_2?

11-53 A statistician used the following data to illustrate the cows–acres paradox.

Farm	Number of Cows Y	Number of Acres X_1	Primary Product
1	280	650	beef
2	250	400	beef
3	350	200	milk
4	370	350	milk
5	200	480	beef
6	420	340	milk
7	300	600	beef
8	320	130	milk
9	320	280	milk
10	250	450	beef

(a) Plot a scatter diagram using different symbols for farms whose main product is beef and for farms producing primarily milk.

(b) Determine the estimated regression equation expressing number of cows Y in terms of the single independent variable, number of acres X_1. Plot this line on your scatter diagram. Your line should indicate that Y (number of cows) decreases as X_1 (number of acres) increases. Explain.

(c) Using a dummy variable having value $X_2 = 0$ for beef and $X_2 = 1$ for milk, determine the estimated regression equation $\hat{Y} = a + b_1X_1 + b_2X_2$. Plot the lines corresponding to $X_2 = 0$ and $X_2 = 1$ on your graph. (In each case, a positive slope indicates that the predicted number of cows should be greater for larger acreages.)

11-54 Repeat Exercise 11-53 (a) and (b) using the interactive dummy-variable model.

11-55 Repeat Exercise 11-50 (a) and (b) using the interactive dummy-variable model.

CHAPTER 12

STATISTICAL QUALITY CONTROL

BEFORE READING THIS CHAPTER, MAKE SURE YOU UNDERSTAND:

The types of statistical data (Chapter 1).

How to describe and display data (Chapter 2).

How to summarize data (Chapter 3).

The basic concepts of statistical estimation (Chapter 9).

The basic concepts of hypothesis testing (Chapter 10).

AFTER READING THIS CHAPTER, YOU WILL UNDERSTAND:

About statistical quality control.

The basic types of control charts.

How to use a control chart to trigger remedial action.

About acceptance sampling and how to use it.

How acceptance sampling relates to hypothesis testing.

About sequential sampling and how to use it.

In recent years, **total quality management** has been growing in importance. This is largely due to the role quality plays in manufacturing, becoming increasingly significant with mushrooming international trade. Underlying the practice of total quality management are the same statistical procedures that have always been important in nonproduction applications—in services, retail, and transportation—as well as in the public sector. This chapter focuses on the two primary groupings of statistical methods for controlling quality.

An important area of statistical quality control focuses on production applications: the *creation* of end products, either goods or services. These applications involve the *process* by which the goods are created or services are rendered. Managers monitor such processes by means of **statistical controls**, which are applied continuously during various stages of production or service.

Acceptance sampling involves items or services supplied externally. The goal of acceptance sampling is to determine whether individual batches and shipments should be accepted or rejected. The procedures consider the existing *items* themselves. Any difficulties with their creation are not directly addressed.

The foundation has been laid in earlier chapters for understanding statistical quality control. The methods are based on familiar descriptive statistics, including the *sample mean*, *range*, *proportion*, and *standard deviation*. Parallel procedures apply to quantitative and qualitative data.

12-1 THE CONTROL CHART FOR QUALITATIVE DATA

Production applications are historically the main source of statistical quality control procedures. The methods help managers fine-tune production processes through early detection of problems, followed by quick remedies. Successfully employed, modern statistical controls prevent the creation of defective goods, perhaps avoiding the manufacture of thousands of items that would eventually be scrapped. At least as significant, statistical controls provide a framework that fosters the systematic search for improvements of both the end products and the processes whereby they are created.

Statistical control is achieved by establishing limits within which observed units should fall; corrective actions are generated automatically whenever too many items fall outside these bounds. A *sample* becomes the device that triggers those remedial actions. The limits must be wide enough to compensate for any *chance variation* that would be expected to arise naturally even under perfect circumstances. The limits cannot be so narrow that samples become "hairpin" triggers and generate false signals of nonexisting problems.

When a sample falls outside the prescribed limits, the control procedure flags the results to signal that the violators may arise from some *assignable cause*. Good follow-up action then involves a thorough search for the problem source. Common assignable causes include equipment malfunctions, operator errors, poor materials, and external disturbances. Appropriate remedies include adjusting equipment controls, improving the working atmosphere, changing suppliers, and stabilizing the plant environment.

The instrument used to accomplish this monitorship is the **control chart**. Control charts may be based either on quantitative data or on qualitative data. The following illustration demonstrates the latter.

ESTABLISHING CONTROL LIMITS FOR THE PROPORTION

ILLUSTRATION: DEFECTIVE DISKETTES

The quality assurance manager for a diskette manufacturer requested that a sample of $n = 1,000$ units be taken from each day's production run. There are many reasons why a diskette may prove unacceptable, such as poor casing, thin spots, or unevenness in ferrite layering. Rather than keeping track of each cause, the inspectors were asked to determine whether each sample diskette was defective or satisfactory. During the month of October, the data in Table 12-1 were obtained.

The data are plotted in Figure 12-1, with one dot representing each daily sample. Note that the dots oscillate around a central value. This is the **combined proportion defective** $\bar{P}$. The quantity is calculated by combining all 31 samples into one group, so that, for the composite sample, the combined proportion defective is

$$\bar{P} = \frac{\text{Combined number of defectives}}{\text{Combined sample size}} = \frac{2,126}{31,000} = .0686$$

In a general sense, sample proportions P generated under this procedure are random variables, each having a binominal distribution with parameters n and π. The true value of the population proportion π remains unknown. That parameter may be estimated from the sample results.

The procedure described here assumes that π remains *constant* or each successive sample observation as long as the process is *in control*.

As the scatter of the data in Figure 12-1 suggests, the observed Ps vary from

TABLE 12-1 Sample Data for Disk Production

Day	Number of Defectives	Proportion Defective P	Day	Number of Defectives	Proportion Defective P
10/01	52	.052	10/17	82	.082
2	81	.081	18	72	.072
3	76	.076	19	47	.047
4	48	.048	20	65	.065
5	66	.066	21	62	.062
6	115	.115	22	48	.048
7	122	.122	23	47	.047
8	61	.061	24	51	.051
9	144	.144	25	63	.063
10	65	.065	26	67	.067
11	73	.073	27	66	.066
12	51	.051	28	49	.049
13	68	.068	29	74	.074
14	47	.047	30	76	.076
15	52	.052	31	55	.055
16	81	.081		2,126	

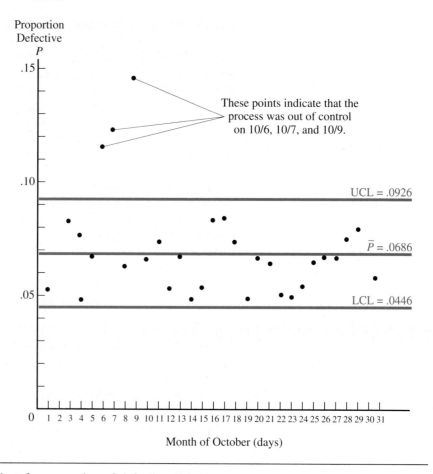

FIGURE 12-1 Preliminary control chart for proportion of defective diskettes.

one observation to the next. We summarize this variability in terms of the standard error of P, the theoretical value of which is

$$\sigma_P = \sqrt{\frac{\pi(1 - \pi)}{n}}$$

Using $\bar{P}$ as the estimator of π, the above quantity may be estimated from the expression

$$\sqrt{\frac{\bar{P}(1 - \bar{P})}{n}}$$

The above expression is used to establish the **control limits** that determine whether or not the process is in statistical control. For this purpose *3-sigma limits* are popular. That choice follows from a key property of the normal curve; that is, about 99.7% of the possible values will lie within $\mu \pm 3\sigma$. For large ns, since the normal distribution approximates the binomial, a similar percentage of possible values for P should fall within $\pi \pm 3\sigma_P$. It would be extremely rare for a sample P to fall outside those limits when π is the true level of the population proportion. Some investigators prefer to use the tighter *2-sigma limits*. About 95% of normally distributed values will fall within $\mu \pm 2\sigma$.

But the true value of π, and hence σ_P, remains unknown. Also, π may shift to abnormally high levels, at which time the process needs remedial action. The control chart is designed to detect those critical periods. Substituting $\bar{P}$ for π and using the estimated σ_P given above, we will use the following expressions to compute the

CONTROL LIMITS FOR THE PROPORTION DEFECTIVE

$$LCL = \bar{P} - SL\sqrt{\frac{\bar{P}(1 - \bar{P})}{n}}$$

$$UCL = \bar{P} + SL\sqrt{\frac{\bar{P}(1 - \bar{P})}{n}}$$

where SL denotes the desired sigma limits, LCL denotes the **lower control limit**, and UCL denotes the **upper control limit**. We define the process as "out of control" whenever the computed value of P lies above the UCL or below the LCL. If the computed value of the LCL is negative, that limit is set to zero.

Using the data from our diskette sampling illustration with $SL = 3$, we compute the following 3-sigma control limits.

$$LCL = .0686 - 3\sqrt{\frac{.0686(1 - .0686)}{1,000}}$$

$$= .0686 - 3(.0080)$$

$$= .0446$$

and

$$UCL = .0686 + 3(.0080)$$

$$= .0926$$

In Figure 12-1, these limits are represented by the colored horizontal lines on the control chart.

APPLYING THE CONTROL CHART

Note the three points in Figure 12-1 that lie above the UCL. These points are .115 (October 6), .122 (October 7), and .144 (October 9). We assume that the production process was out of control on those dates. Those problems went undetected until the above control limits were established. (Subsequent investigations show that key personnel were absent on those dates.)

Out-of-control data points ideally should be eliminated from the underlying data base before the control chart is used in actual production decisions. Figure 12-2 shows the revised control chart used to monitor diskette production during the following month of November. The recomputed value of the combined proportion defective is $\bar{P} = 1,745/28,000 = .0623$. The corresponding new control limits are LCL = .0394 and UCL = .0852.

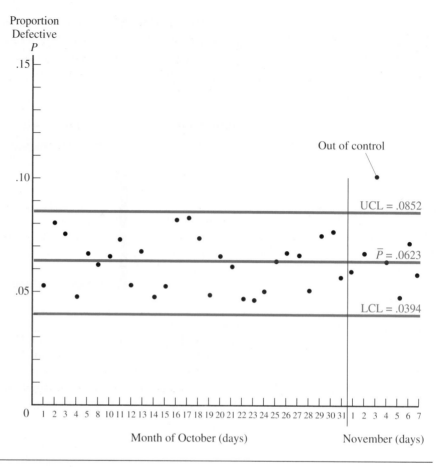

FIGURE 12-2 Final control chart for proportion of defective diskettes.

During the first week in November, the following observations were made.

Day	Proportion Defective P	Signaled Status
11/01	.058	in control
2	.071	in control
3	.098	out of control
4	.063	in control
5	.047	in control
6	.071	in control
7	.058	in control

The sample result for November 3 signaled that an abnormally high proportion of defective diskettes had been produced. A thorough investigation showed that the ferrite compound was contaminated by impurities. To avoid repetitions, improved storage was implemented for all critical materials.

FURTHER REMARKS

It may seem curious that an LCL even exists for the proportion defective. After all, are not low levels of P desirable? Usually, that is the case and zero is often set as the LCL, so that the statistical procedure becomes one-sided. But abnormally low levels of P may also arise from problems in need of fixing. Low Ps may result from much more expensive care than originally intended. Or, they may signify a breakdown in the inspection process itself, with too many defects going undetected. And, some undiscovered *improvement* to the process may be uncovered when investigating the cause for a low P.

The traditional 3-sigma limits are intended to provide an optimal balance between triggering excessive false alarms and letting a poor-quality operation continue undetected. A better balance may be achieved with narrower limits (say, 2-sigma) or with wider ones. The issue is analogous to the tradeoff between the Type I error (unnecessarily searching for nonexistent assignable causes when the violation is just due to chance) and the Type II error (letting an out-of-control process continue uncorrected).

EXERCISES

12-1 Determine the LCL and UCL for each of the following situations.

(a) $\bar{P} = .10$; $n = 500$ (c) $\bar{P} = .05$; $n = 1,000$
(b) $\bar{P} = .20$; $n = 100$ (d) $\bar{P} = .075$; $n = 200$

12-2 Ace Widgets obtained the following numbers of defectives in successive samples of 1,000 deluxe models removed at random from that day's production.

Day	Number of Defectives	Day	Number of Defectives
6/11	86	6/21	115
12	47	22	82
13	67	23	73
14	54	24	66
15	60	25	75
16	49	26	55
17	66	27	71
18	49	28	128
19	79	29	49
20	70	30	62

(a) Determine the 3-sigma control limits for the sample proportion defective. Plot your results and the above data on a chart.
(b) Identify any days on which the production process was out of control.
(c) Remove the violators from the data base and recompute the control limits. For each of the following numbers of defectives selected from a sample of $n = 1,000$, indicate whether the process is in control or out of control.
(1) 86   (2) 112   (3) 48   (4) 125   (5) 98

12-3 DanDee Assemblers obtained the following numbers of defectives in successive samples of 100 final assemblies removed at random from that day's production.

Day	Number of Defectives	Day	Number of Defectives
8/11	6	8/21	11
12	8	22	8
13	7	23	13
14	10	24	14
15	11	25	15
16	5	26	12
17	13	27	7
18	9	28	34
19	9	29	28
20	10	30	8

(a)–(b) Repeat Exercise 12-2.

(c) Remove the violators from the data base and recompute the control limits. For each of the following numbers of defectives selected from a sample of $n = 100$, indicate whether the process was found to be in control or out of control.

    (1) 5   (2) 29   (3) 7   (4) 10   (5) 17

12-4 Refer to the data in Table 12-1. Determine the 2-sigma control limits for the sample proportion. Indicate on which days the process was out of control.

12-5 Repeat Exercise 12-3 using 2-sigma control limits instead.

12-6 Refer to the diskette production illustration. Determine the probability that on any given day the process will be in control with the first set of limits when each of the following true population proportion defective applies. Use the normal approximation.

    (a) $\pi = .10$ (b) $\pi = .05$ (c) $\pi = .08$ (d) $\pi = .06$

12-2 CONTROL CHARTS FOR QUANTITATIVE DATA

Process quality may be assessed in terms of some *quantity*, such as service time, volume, weight, strength, or yield. Analogus to the *P*-chart described in Section 12-1, a control chart may be constructed for quantitative data. Since central tendency and variability are both important considerations in such evaluations, separate control charts monitor each.

The most common control charts are based on the *sample mean*. Control charts for monitoring variability may be based either on the *sample range* or the *sample standard deviation*. Anyone who has taken a statistics course should be familiar with the standard deviation, but for those with little statistical background, the underlying concepts may be hard to handle. Thus, it is more common to see control charts based on the sample range.

Statistical control procedures are more elaborate when using quantitative data. Since quantitative data provide a higher degree of information, the procedures are more sensitive than the *P*-charts. This allows for inspection schemes with smaller *n*s, which, in turn, permit quicker identification of assignable causes for process abnormalities. We will use the following example to illustrate the procedure.

ILLUSTRATION: MONITORING FILLING CONTROLS

As with others in the food processing business, Boxwell House must adhere to truth-in-labeling laws. Most critical are weights and measures of ingredients. Although it is unlikely that any particular one-pound jar of instant coffee will contain precisely 16 ounces, Boxwell House's objective is to come very close to that target.

To launch a quality control scheme for monitoring the contents weights, the Boxwell House superintendent requested that a sample of $n = 5$ jars be removed from production and the contents carefully weighed. Each half hour over a portion of a day's production operation the data in Table 12-2 were obtained. From the results given, the superintendent implemented a statistical control system designed to meet two objectives: (1) *mean* weight per jar should be close to the labeled 16 ounces and (2) *variability* in contents weights should not be excessive.

The procedure described here uses two triggers for corrective action. These are the computed values for the sample mean $\bar{X}$ and the sample range R. The data in Table 12-2 are used to establish control limits for these. During this initial phase, the filling process is assumed to be in control. Management chooses the tighter 2-sigma limits. These will provide them adequate protection against unnecessary corrections while allowing for earlier detection of problems.

The Boxwell House data are plotted in Figure 12-3. The chart in Figure 12-3(a) was constructed using the sample means $\bar{X}$ and serves to gauge shifts in the filling process mean μ. Chart (b) in Figure 12-3 was constructed using the sample ranges R and serves to detect shifts in the process variability.

The procedure for constructing the control charts in Figure 12-3 is similar to that used for the P-chart.

TABLE 12-2 Sample Contents Weights Data for One-Pound Jars of Instant Coffee

Sample	Contents Weight (ounces)					Mean $\bar{X}$	Range R	Standard Deviation s
1	15.75	16.12	16.22	15.87	16.22	16.036	0.47	.2146
2	16.23	16.35	16.11	16.48	15.90	16.214	0.58	.2229
3	15.88	15.95	16.07	16.33	16.05	16.056	0.45	.1714
4	16.67	15.60	16.22	15.65	15.71	15.970	1.07	.4635
5	15.56	15.82	15.95	15.76	15.82	15.782	0.39	.1421
6	16.20	16.35	16.05	15.90	16.11	16.122	0.45	.1678
7	15.88	16.22	16.35	15.71	15.88	16.008	0.64	.2663
8	16.10	16.25	16.05	16.11	15.90	16.082	0.35	.1262
9	15.70	15.55	16.08	16.21	15.72	15.852	0.66	.2792
10	16.15	16.16	16.34	15.88	15.80	16.066	0.54	.2215
11	16.22	16.08	16.07	15.55	15.72	15.928	0.67	.2805
12	15.66	15.78	16.22	15.85	15.91	15.884	0.56	.2096
13	16.44	15.71	15.93	16.12	16.10	16.060	0.73	.2687
14	16.21	16.34	16.05	15.87	15.61	16.016	0.73	.2872
15	15.55	15.78	15.82	15.60	16.24	15.798	0.69	.2725
16	16.05	16.22	16.28	15.90	15.85	16.060	0.43	.1896
17	16.10	16.08	15.70	15.82	16.12	15.964	0.42	.1916
18	15.67	15.91	15.88	16.10	15.84	15.880	0.43	.1543
19	15.95	15.81	16.12	16.07	15.64	15.918	0.48	.1960
20	16.04	16.29	16.18	15.76	15.99	16.052	0.53	.2014
						319.748	11.27	4.5267

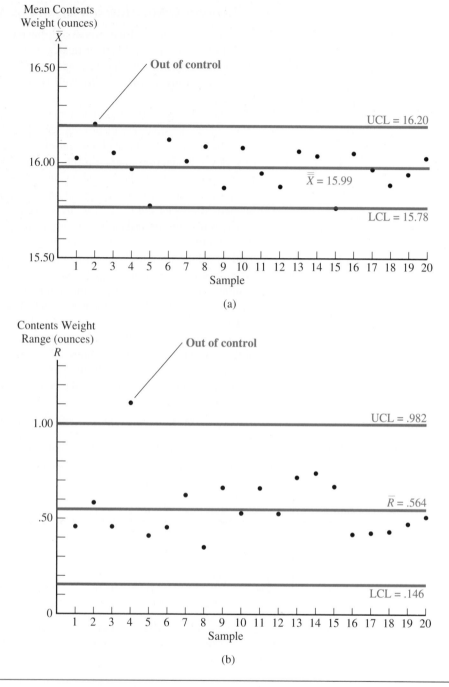

FIGURE 12-3 Two-sigma control charts for contents weights of jars of instant coffee

THE CONTROL CHART FOR THE SAMPLE MEAN

As with the P-chart, the sample results are pooled, so that an overall average, the **grand mean** $\bar{\bar{X}}$ is obtained. This value serves as the estimator of the underlying population mean. The computed value of $\bar{\bar{X}}$ establishes the center line of the

$\bar{X}$-chart, with individual sample means oscillating about this central value. For our instant coffee sample data we calculate

$$\bar{\bar{X}} = \frac{319.748}{20} = 15.99 \text{ ounces}$$

The process mean μ is estimated to be 15.99 ounces per jar of instant coffee, so that the center line of the $\bar{X}$-chart in Figure 12-3(a) is placed at a height of 15.99.

Two-sigma limits must be found to obtain the LCL and UCL for $\bar{X}$. Although earlier in this book we consistently used the sample standard deviation s to estimate the population standard deviation σ, the traditional quality control procedures are based instead on the sample range R. Using Rs to estimate σ proves to be easier from an operational point of view and provides nearly identical results.

Using the **overall mean range** R, the following expression computes the

ESTIMATED POPULATION STANDARD DEVIATION

$$\hat{\sigma} = \frac{\bar{R}}{d_R}$$

where the **range conversion constant** d_R is read from Appendix Table M.

For the Boxwell House data, the computed mean of the sample ranges is

$$\bar{R} = \frac{11.27}{20} = .5635$$

Using $n = 5$ as the individual sample size, we use Appendix Table M to find the range conversion constant $d_R = 2.326$. We then compute the estimated standard deviation to be

$$\hat{\sigma} = \frac{.5635}{2.326} = .242$$

To establish the SL-sigma control limits, the standard error of $\bar{X}$ is estimated by $\hat{\sigma}/\sqrt{n}$. The following expressions provide the

CONTROL LIMITS FOR THE SAMPLE MEAN

$$\text{LCL} = \bar{\bar{X}} - SL \frac{\hat{\sigma}}{\sqrt{n}} \qquad \text{UCL} = \bar{\bar{X}} + SL \frac{\hat{\sigma}}{\sqrt{n}}$$

For our instant coffee sample results, using $SL = 2$, the above expressions provide

$$\text{LCL} = 15.99 - 2\left(\frac{.242}{\sqrt{5}}\right) = 15.99 - .21 = 15.78 \text{ ounces}$$

$$\text{UCL} = 15.99 + .21 = 16.20 \text{ ounces}$$

The above are plotted as colored horizontal lines in Figure 12-3(a).

Referring to the sample data in Table 12-2, we see that sample 2 yields a mean exceeding the UCL. An investigation should be launched to determine the cause, such as a calibration error in the control settings.

THE CONTROL CHART FOR THE SAMPLE RANGE

An analogous procedure is used to find the control limits for successive Rs. The following expression computes the

ESTIMATED STANDARD ERROR OF THE SAMPLE RANGE

$$\hat{\sigma}_R = \bar{R}\,\frac{\sigma_w}{d_R}$$

where the **standard deviation conversion constant** σ_w expresses the ratio of the true level for σ_R to the actual population standard deviation σ. Like d_R, this quantity varies with n and is read from Appendix Table M.

Applying the above expression to the Boxwell House instant coffee data when $n = 5$, Appendix Table M provides a value for σ_w of .8641. Using this value and the quantity $d_R = 2.326$ found earlier, we compute the estimated standard error of R to be

$$\hat{\sigma}_R = .5635\left(\frac{.8641}{2.326}\right) = .209$$

The following expressions are used to compute the

CONTROL LIMITS FOR THE SAMPLE RANGE

$$\text{LCL} = \bar{R} - SL\,\hat{\sigma}_R \qquad \text{UCL} = \bar{R} + SL\,\hat{\sigma}_R$$

As with P, the LCL is set to zero whenever the computed lower limit is negative.

Returning to the Boxwell House instant coffee data, the following control limits (rounded to three figures) were obtained.

$$LCL = .564 - 2(.209) = .564 - .418 = .146 \text{ ounces}$$

$$UCL = .564 + .418 = .982 \text{ ounces}$$

These are plotted as colored horizontal lines in Figure 12-3(b), with the center line located at a height equal to the computed mean of the sample ranges, $\bar{R} = .564$.

Referring to the sample data in Table 12-2, we see that sample 4 yields a range exceeding the UCL. This is so even though the mean contents of that sample are nearly on target. But this finding is that those jars have contents that *vary* too much. An investigation should be launched to determine the cause, such as erratic controls.

CONTROL CHARTS FOR STANDARD DEVIATION

Although the range gives a quick and easy way to compute measure of variability, some investigators prefer control charts computed from the sample *standard deviation*. The following expressions are used to compute the

CONTROL LIMITS FOR THE STANDARD DEVIATION

$$LCL = \bar{s} - SL\hat{\sigma}_s \qquad UCL = \bar{s} + SL\hat{\sigma}_s$$

where

$\bar{s}$ = mean of sample standard deviations

$$\hat{\sigma}_s = \bar{s}\,(c_5/c_4).$$

The process begins with the calculation of standard deviations for each sample. These are then averaged to provide the mean of the sample standard deviations s. The standard error of s is found by multiplying s itself by the ratio of two constants of proportionality, c_4 and c_5. Appendix Table M gives levels for these parameters.

To illustrate, we continue with the coffee jar data from Table 12-2. There the sample standard deviations have been computed, giving us

$$\bar{s} = \frac{4.5267}{20} = .2263$$

For samples of size $n = 5$, Appendix Table M provides $c_4 = .940$ and $c_5 = .341$. Using 2-sigma limits as before, so that $SL = 2$, we compute the control limits:

$$LCL = .2263 - 2(.2263)\left(\frac{.341}{.940}\right) = .2263 - .1642 = .0621$$

$$UCL = .2263 + .1642 = .3905$$

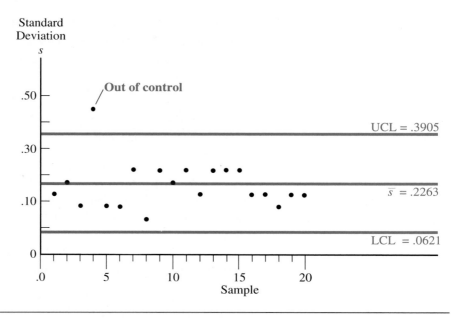

FIGURE 12-4 Two-sigma control chart for standard deviation using coffee jar data.

The above are used in constructing the control chart for s in Figure 12-4. Notice that the sample 4, as with the R chart, is out of control. The control chart for s generally provides the similar information to the R chart. Both should detect the same problems. Since the R chart involves statistics that are easier to compute, it is generally preferred.

IMPLEMENTING STATISTICAL CONTROL

The Boxwell House superintendent implemented the statistical control procedure over several days. From the first 300 half-hourly samples of one-pound jars, $\bar{X}$ exceeded the UCL three times and fell below twice. Assignable causes included defective control mechanisms, blocked laser beams, and lumps in the coffee granules. The latter problem was traced to excessive moisture in the holding vats— a problem remedied by repairing a broken dehumidifier. In three samples, the level of R exceeded the UCL. Assignable causes included oversized coffee crystals, a damaged timer, and operator error. The problem of oversized crystals was remedied by incorporating sifting into the final processing.

Most of the problems identified by the statistical controls were fixed immediately. The more permanent solutions led to further refinements in the filling process and to some improvements in the final product itself. Without the quality management capability provided by the control charts, the problems would have been discovered and corrected much later, and tens of thousands of undersized or oversized jars would have gone to market. The superintendent was so pleased with the success of the statistical controls that he implemented them in the roasting and separating processes for making the product itself.

12-7 For each of the following situations, determine the LCL and UCL for the (1) sample mean $\bar{X}$ and (2) sample range R. Use 3-sigma limits.

(a) $\bar{\bar{X}} = .20$; $\bar{R} = .050$; $n = 10$ (c) $\bar{\bar{X}} = .002$; $\bar{R} = .005$; $n = 4$
(b) $\bar{X} = 5.80$; $\bar{R} = .55$; $n = 5$ (d) $\bar{X} = 1.25$; $\bar{R} = .17$; $n = 7$

12-8 The Boxwell House superintendent obtained the following sample results during the initial phase of the control system for the coffee filling process.

Sample	Contents Weight (ounces)				
1	15.85	16.21	15.91	16.08	16.12
2	15.51	16.10	16.76	15.85	15.92
3	16.21	16.55	16.62	16.68	16.50
4	15.62	15.94	15.72	15.55	15.64
5	15.74	16.21	16.05	16.01	16.17

(a) Calculate the mean and range for each sample.
(b) Using the control limits in Figure 12-3, indicate, for each sample, whether the process is in control or out of control.

12-9 The Boxwell House superintendent introduced statistical controls for five-pound cans of ground coffee. The following sample data were obtained.

Sample	Contents Weight (pounds)			
1	4.85	5.27	5.35	5.09
2	4.62	4.35	4.55	4.62
3	4.95	5.11	5.12	4.88
4	4.69	4.80	5.20	5.15
5	5.64	5.75	5.41	5.64
6	4.78	5.21	5.09	4.85
7	4.22	5.05	5.55	4.84
8	5.12	5.07	5.05	4.95
9	5.11	5.08	4.91	4.89
10	4.79	5.10	5.17	4.95

(a) Calculate the mean and range for each sample. Then calculate the grand mean and overall mean range.
(b) Determine the 3-sigma control limits for $\bar{X}$ and construct the control chart, plotting the data point for each sample. Indicate which, if any, of the samples were generated when the process was out of control.
(c) Determine the control limits for R and construct the control chart, plotting the data point for each sample. Indicate which, if any, of the samples were generated when the process was out of control.
(d) Eliminate the samples where the process was found to be out of control in either (a) or (b). Determine revised control limits for (1) $\bar{X}$ and (2) R.

12-10 The following sample data were obtained for the thickness (millimeters) of aluminum sheets.

Sample	Thickness				
1	4.9	5.1	4.9	5.0	4.9
2	4.9	4.7	5.1	5.2	5.1
3	4.8	5.0	4.9	5.0	5.0
4	5.1	4.8	4.8	4.9	4.6
5	4.8	5.0	5.2	4.5	4.9
6	5.3	4.8	4.9	5.1	4.6
7	4.7	5.3	4.9	5.1	5.2
8	5.3	4.9	4.9	4.8	5.0
9	5.3	5.2	5.2	4.9	4.9
10	5.0	5.0	5.1	5.0	5.1
11	4.9	4.8	4.6	4.9	5.1
12	5.3	5.4	5.4	5.4	5.3
13	5.5	5.2	5.3	5.4	5.2
14	4.7	5.2	5.1	5.0	5.1
15	5.0	4.7	4.9	5.2	4.9
16	5.1	4.9	5.2	5.0	4.9
17	5.0	5.0	4.8	4.8	4.9
18	4.9	4.4	5.4	5.0	5.1
19	4.8	4.8	5.2	5.1	5.0
20	4.8	5.1	4.9	5.2	5.0
21	5.2	4.8	5.2	5.2	5.2
22	4.8	4.8	4.9	5.2	5.2
23	5.0	4.9	5.1	4.7	4.6
24	5.0	5.0	4.9	5.0	5.1
25	4.8	5.0	4.8	4.7	4.9

Repeat Exercise 12-9(a)–(d).

12-11 Assume that the control limits for the sample mean (page 586) apply to one-pound jars of Boxwell House instant coffee. Determine the probability that a particular sample mean $\overline{X}$ will flag the process as out of control when the true mean jar contents is represented by a population with the following values.

(a) $\mu = 16.1$; $\sigma = .3$ (c) $\mu = 16.0$; $\sigma = .25$
(b) $\mu = 15.8$; $\sigma = .2$ (d) $\mu = 15.6$; $\sigma = .4$

12-12 The following sample data for the contents of 12-ounce cans have been obtained over a 15-day period from a guava juice cannery.

Day 1:	11.78	12.21	12.16	Day 9:	11.55	12.02	12.85
Day 2:	11.87	12.13	12.11	Day 10:	12.08	12.02	12.19
Day 3:	12.21	11.58	12.02	Day 11:	11.87	11.94	11.75
Day 4:	12.06	12.10	12.13	Day 12:	11.73	12.21	12.34
Day 5:	12.56	12.78	12.44	Day 13:	12.17	12.10	12.33
Day 6:	11.95	11.67	12.22	Day 14:	11.88	12.25	12.23
Day 7:	12.16	12.05	12.30	Day 15:	12.05	12.25	12.17
Day 8:	11.88	12.05	12.31				

(a) Determine the 2-sigma control limits for the mean and plot the control chart.
(b) On which days (if any) was the process out of control?

12-13 Refer to the data in Exercise 12-12 for contents of 12-ounce guava juice cans.

(a) Determine the 2-sigma control limits for the range and plot the control chart.

(b) On which days (if any) was the process out of control?

12-14 Refer to the data in Exercise 12-12 for contents of 12-ounce guava juice cans.

(a) Determine the 2-sigma control limits for the standard deviation and plot the control chart.

(b) On which days (if any) was the process out of control?

12-3 ACCEPTANCE SAMPLING

The second major area of statistical quality control is acceptance sampling. The primary focus of these applications is to determine how to dispose of items that have already been provided by a supplier. The main consideration is the **lot**, which is the underlying statistical population with unknown parameters. A lot is either a production batch (such as subassemblies to be inserted into the main units), a shipment (such as logic chips for computer mother boards), or a grouping of rendered services (such as tax returns prepared by a CPA).

One of two actions may be taken in acceptance sampling: to *accept* the lot or to *reject* it. These actions are predicated on the assumption that the lot is *good* or *bad*. A rejected lot may be returned to the supplier (a typical action with raw materials), be scrapped or reworked (often the case with assembled units), or serve as the basis for extracting contractual penalties (the case with batches of already-rendered services).

Ordinarily, acceptance sampling is conducted when it is uneconomic or impractical to use census data. The underlying concepts of the procedure were encountered earlier, in Chapter 9, with the introduction of hypothesis testing. We will review some of those concepts here, in the context of quality control.

BASIC CONCEPTS OF ACCEPTANCE SAMPLING

The most commonly used acceptance plans are based on product attributes; that is, inspected items from a lot are classified as either *satisfactory* or *defective*. These designations apply even when the observations themselves are quantitative, so that a defective item may be so classified because it is too heavy, it could not meet a minimal strength, or it failed to survive an endurance test. A working definition of a good lot is one that has a low proportion of defectives π. Although the level of π remains unknown, various values are assumed when selecting statistical *decision rules*. As discussed earlier, although such rules are based on the sample proportion P, traditional acceptance sampling procedures are based on the number of sample defectives D. Decision rules are then distinguished by the pivotal level for the number of sample defectives. This is the **acceptance number**, denoted by C. The decision rule is of the form

$$Accept \text{ the lot if } D \leq C$$

$$Reject \text{ the lot if } D > C$$

The decision structure may be explained in terms of the more general hypothesis-testing procedures. The *null hypothesis* is that the lot is good, so that the true proportion of defectives is low and $\pi \leq \pi_0$, while the *alternative hypothesis* is that the proportion is high and $\pi > \pi_0$. The quantity π_0 is the **acceptable quality level** and serves as a benchmark for selecting an appropriate decision rule.

Accepting or rejecting the lot is analogous to accepting or rejecting the null hypothesis. Correct actions will be to accept good lots and reject bad ones. Of course, good lots may be rejected and bad lots may be accepted. These are analogous to the Type I and Type II errors.

PRODUCER'S AND CONSUMER'S RISK

The Type I error of a customer's rejecting a good lot is the most undesirable from the supplier's point of view. The probability for this error is referred to as the **producer's risk**. The Type II error of accepting a bad lot is least desired by the customer and is referred to as the **consumer's risk**. Of course the supplier wants to avoid both types of errors. There is no long-term advantage in having customers accept bad shipments, since they would then be stuck with excessive defectives and may switch suppliers.

THE PRODUCER'S RISK: SELECTING THE DECISION RULE

The decision rule, or choice of C, is determined in such a way that the Type I error probability meets the prescribed *significance level* α. The following expression applies.

$$\Pr[\textit{Reject } H_0 | H_0 \text{ true}] = \Pr[D > C | \pi = \pi_0] \leq \alpha$$

The binomial distribution is used to establish the level of C that achieves this specification. (Keep in mind that for lots of fixed size N and when sampling without replacement, the *hypergeometric distribution* provides the correct probabilities for D. But since that distribution is computationally so cumbersome, the binomial distribution is often used to *approximate* those probabilities, usually with accuracy.)

ILLUSTRATION: ACCEPTANCE SAMPLING IN A CANNERY

Yellow Giant uses acceptance sampling to determine whether incoming truckloads of fruits and vegetables should be accepted and emptied directly into washing bins or rejected and sent to a sorting area. Since the grower must pay for the labor involved, the penalty for rejecting a truckload is substantial.

Inspectors classify individual asparagus spears as satisfactory or defective, depending on ripeness, damage, infestation, and rot. Yellow Giant's acceptable quality level for the proportion π of defective asparagus is $\pi_0 = .01$. This level was negotiated with the growers and represents a reasonable quality standard. The contractual sampling scheme is based on a random sample of $n = 100$ spears from each truckload. The agreed acceptance number C guarantees the growers that no more than 5% of good loads (having a true π equal to π_0) will be incorrectly rejected, so that $\alpha = .05$. This level for α is also a negotiated target which reflects grower reluctance to have good shipments rejected unnecessarily. From Appendix Table C, the closest probability not exceeding .05 is

$$\Pr[D > 3] = 1 - .9816 = .0184$$

so that $C = 3$ is the asparagus acceptance number.

A different decision rule applies to sugar beets, for which the acceptable quality level is $\pi_0 = .05$. Using the same sample size and significance level, the closest binomial probability not exceeding .05 is

$$\Pr[D > 9] = 1 = .9718 = .0282$$

so that $C = 9$ is the sugar beet acceptance number.

Acceptance sampling procedures can be conveniently categorized in terms of where the rejection region lies. The preceding illustration provides an **upper-tailed test**. That terminology reflects that large values of D will result in rejection. Those values lie in the upper tail of the assumed sampling distribution for D. Although less common in acceptance samapling with the proportion, a **lower-tailed test** might apply.

DECISION RULES FOR ACCEPTANCE SAMPLING WITH THE PROPORTION

Lower-Tailed Test:

Accept if $D \geq C$
Reject if $D < C$

Upper-Tailed Test:

Accept if $D \leq C$
Reject if $D > C$

THE CONSUMER'S RISK

How robust are these decision rules for Yellow Giant's interests? The preceding acceptance numbers are always chosen so that the significance level target is met. That is, the focus is placed on the error of commission—rejecting a good batch. The errors of omission, accepting a poor quality batch—the consumer's risk—may be evaluated by computing Type II error probabilities for several levels of π.

Consider the earlier decision rule for asparagus. Appendix Table C provides the following values.

$$\Pr[accept|poor] = \Pr[D \leq 3|\pi = .05] = .2578$$

$$\Pr[accept|poor] = \Pr[D \leq 3|\pi = .10] = .0078$$

Note that as the true level of π increases, the probability for accepting the poorer-quality loads decreases dramatically. Thus the previously selected decision rules provide Yellow Giant fair protection from accepting bad shipments.

THE OPERATING CHARACTERISTIC CURVE

The number of ways for a batch to be of poor quality is infinite, however; so a graph is sometimes used to show all the possible probabilities for the Type II error. This graph is called the **operating characteristic curve**. Figure 12-5 shows the operating characteristic curve for the asparagus decision rule found above.

ACCEPTANCE SAMPLING WITH THE MEAN

For some products, it is more appropriate to measure the amount of a characteristic present and then decide if the amount is in an acceptable range. For example, product characteristics like weight, length, or diameter cannot be readily "eyeballed" for defects. For such characteristics, which are variables measurable on a continuous scale, acceptance plans are based on the mean. In all cases the sampling distribution for the mean is assumed to be a normal distribution centered at μ_0 and having standard deviation σ. Letting z_α and $z_{\alpha/2}$ denote the normal deviates corresponding to a tail area matching the desired significance level, the following expressions are used in establishing the

DECISION RULES FOR ACCEPTANCE SAMPLING WITH THE MEAN

Lower-Tailed Test:

Accept if $\bar{X} \geq \mu_0 - z_\alpha \sigma_{\bar{X}}$

Reject if $\bar{X} < \mu_0 - z_\alpha \sigma_{\bar{X}}$

Upper-Tailed Test:

Accept if $\bar{X} \leq \mu_0 + z_\alpha \sigma_{\bar{X}}$

Reject if $\bar{X} > \mu_0 + z_\alpha \sigma_{\bar{X}}$

Two-Sided Test:

Accept if $\mu_0 - z_{\alpha/2} \sigma_{\bar{X}} \leq \bar{X} \leq \mu_0 + z_{\alpha/2} \sigma_{\bar{X}}$

Reject if $\bar{X} < \mu_0 - z_{\alpha/2} \sigma_{\bar{X}}$
or if $\bar{X} > \mu_0 + z_{\alpha/2} \sigma_{\bar{X}}$

where the standard error of the sample mean is computed from

$$\sigma_{\bar{X}} = \frac{\sigma}{\sqrt{n}} \quad \text{or} \quad \sigma_{\bar{X}} = \frac{\sigma}{\sqrt{n}} \sqrt{\frac{N - n}{N - 1}}$$

LOWER-TAILED TEST

A lower-tailed test rejects lots having large values of the sample mean. To illustrate, we will continue with the coffee manufacturer illustrated earlier in the chap-

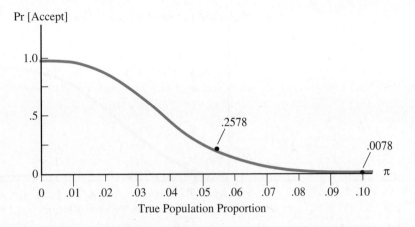

FIGURE 12-5 Operating characteristic curve for Yellow Giant asparagus.

ter. Boxwell House has two distribution channels for its product. The primary channel is regular grocery stores. Those retailers receive the highest quality outputs. A secondary channel is used to dispose of lots that are slightly underfilled. An in-house quality control department uses sample data in deciding, for every production batch, which channel will be used.

The decision will be made from a random sample of $n = 10$ jars selected from a completed batch of size $N = 1,000$. The sample mean will be computed and compared to a critical value. Batches having a sample mean lying below the critical value will be rejected (and subsequently sent to secondary distribution). Quality control policy allows for just a 5% chance of rejecting a batch when the true mean jar contents exactly meets the internal specifications of $\mu_0 = 16.10$ ounces. The contents are assumed to have a standard deviation of $\sigma = .25$ ounces.

The standard error of the sample mean is

$$\sigma_{\bar{X}} = \frac{\sigma}{\sqrt{n}} \sqrt{\frac{N-n}{N-1}} = \frac{.25}{\sqrt{10}} \sqrt{\frac{1,000-10}{1,000-1}} = .078$$

Since a small value for the sample mean will result in rejecting the batch, the test is lower-tailed. For an $\alpha = .05$, $z_{.05} = 1.64$. The decision rule is

Accept if $\bar{X} \geq 16.10 - 1.64(.078) = 16.10 - .13 = 15.97$

Reject if $\bar{X} < 15.97$

The operating characteristic curve for the above decision rule is given in Figure 12-6. The following sample values are obtained for a particular shipment.

15.7   16.3   15.8   15.6   16.1   16.0   15.9   15.6   15.9   16.2

The computed value for the sample mean is $X = 15.91$. Since this falls within the rejection regions, the batch must be *rejected*.

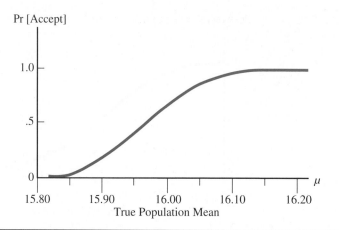

FIGURE 12-6 Operating characteristic curve for Boxwell House acceptance sampling decision rule.

UPPER-TAILED TEST

An upper-tailed test rejects lots having large values of the sample mean. To illustrate, consider a decision whether to accept or reject a batch of records digitized under contract. An acceptable quality level has been established at a true mean target level of $\mu_0 = 1.5$ errors per kilobyte. The decision for an $N = 2,500$ kilobyte batch will be based on a random sample of $n = 25$ one-kilobyte segments. An $\alpha = .10$ significance level is desired for incorrectly rejecting a good batch for which the target mean happens to be the true value. A standard deviation of $\sigma = .5$ errors per kilobyte is assumed to apply.

The following standard error and decision rule applies.

$$\sigma_{\bar{X}} = \frac{\sigma}{\sqrt{n}} \sqrt{\frac{N-n}{N-1}} = \frac{.5}{\sqrt{25}} \sqrt{\frac{2,500 - 25}{2,500 - 1}} = .10$$

Accept if $\bar{X} \le 1.5 + 1.28(.10) = 1.628$

Reject if $\bar{X} > 1.628$

The operating characteristic curve for this decision rule is given in Figure 12-7.

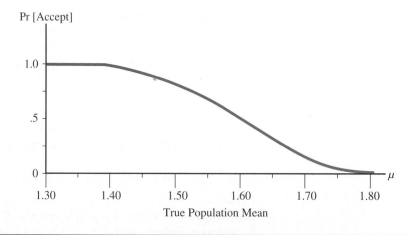

FIGURE 12-7 Operating characteristic curve for acceptance sampling decision rule for digitized records.

The following numbers of errors were detected in the sample segments.

7	8	0	2	1
3	2	1	0	1
0	1	2	2	1
4	3	9	6	3
0	1	1	1	0

The computed level for the sample mean is $X = 2.36$. Since this falls inside the rejection region, the batch must be *rejected*.

TWO-SIDED TEST FOR THE MEAN

When either large or small values give rise to rejection, the test is a two-sided one. For example, consider the experience of Million Bank, which accepts the system-wide teller daily cash count if a sample mean cash audit shows a mean reporting error that is accurate within ± some allowable deviation from the mean audit value. For example, suppose that the bank targets the mean error at $0 and assumes that the error standard deviation is $.50 per teller. There are 1,000 tellers altogether and the decision will be based on a sample audit of 10 tellers. An $\alpha = .05$ significance level is assumed.

The standard error and decision rule are computed below.

$$\sigma_{\bar{X}} = \frac{\sigma}{\sqrt{n}} \sqrt{\frac{N - n}{N - 1}} = \frac{\$.50}{\sqrt{10}} \sqrt{\frac{1,000 - 10}{1,000 - 1}} = \$.16$$

Accept if $\$0 - 1.96(.16) \leq \bar{X} \leq \$0 + 1.96(.16)$
  or if $-\$.31 \leq \bar{X} \leq \$.31$

Reject if $\bar{X} < -\$.31$
  or if $\bar{X} > \$.31$

Two-sided tests have a two-tailed operating characteristic curve, as shown in Figure 12-8.

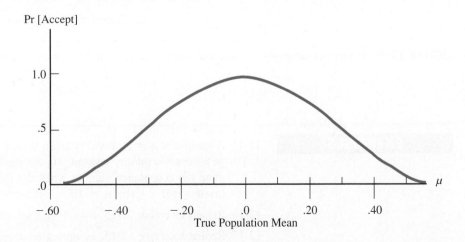

FIGURE 12-8 Operating characteristic curve for acceptance sampling decision rule for bank teller cash count errors.

SEQUENTIAL SAMPLING

The acceptance sampling process can be based on more than one sample, so that the procedure involves **sequential sampling**. A succession of samples is taken and a decision is made each time to (1) accept the lot, (2) reject the lot, or (3) continue sampling. The decision rule involves an **acceptance number** A_n and a **rejection number** R_n, where the subscript n represents the *cumulative* sample size. The chart in Figure 12-9 shows Yellow Giant's sequential sampling plan for truckloads of cherries. The results obtained from a particular load have also been plotted on the chart.

Sequential sampling schemes tend to be more efficient than single-sample plans. For specified Type I and Type II error probability targets, sequential sampling tends to use fewer sample observations. That advantage comes at a steep price—a far more elaborate procedure must be used. A detailed discussion of sequential sampling is beyond the scope of this book. The Selected References section of the book lists additional sources of information.

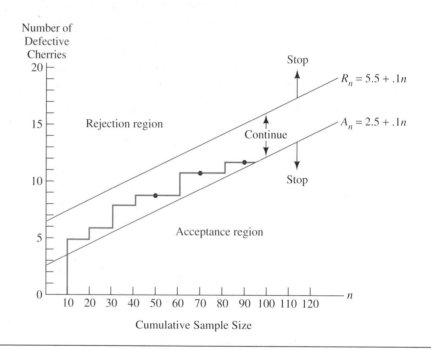

FIGURE 12-9 Sequential sampling scheme and sample results for Yellow Giant cherries.

12-15 A sample of $n = 50$ items is taken from a lot containing 10,000. Assuming an acceptable quality level of .10, use the binomial approximation to determine the acceptance number when the following values apply.
(a) $\alpha = .01$ (b) $\alpha = .05$ (c) $\alpha = .10$

12-16 Repeat Exercise 12-15, assuming a sample size of $n = 100$.

12-17 Repeat Exercise 12-15, assuming an acceptable quality level of .05.

12-18 Refer to the Yellow Giant acceptance sampling procedure for sugar beets. Determine the probability that a poor quality shipment will be accepted given that the true proportion defective is
(a) $\pi = .10$ (b) $\pi = .20$ (c) $\pi = .30$

12-19 A Midget Motors quality assurance inspector sets .10 as the acceptable quality level for outside-supplied spring locks. Each incoming shipment will be assessed using a random sample of $n = 20$.
(a) Assuming a significance level of .10, determine the acceptance number.
(b) Indicate for each of the following results whether the incoming shipment should be accepted or rejected.
   (1) $D = 1$ (2) $D = 3$ (3) $D = 5$

12-20 A Computronics purchasing manager has established .01 as the acceptable quality level for printed circuit boards. Incoming shipments are sampled by a thorough testing with $n = 100$ randomly selected boards.
(a) Assuming a significance level of .025, determine the acceptance number.
(b) Indicate for each of the following results whether the incoming shipment should be accepted or rejected.
   (1) $D = 4$ (2) $D = 2$ (3) $D = 7$ (4) $D = 3$

12-21 The guava juice cannery management in Exercise 12-12 must decide whether to redirect rejected shipments to secondary distribution. The decision will be made from a random sample of $n = 15$ cans selected from a completed batch of size $N = 2,000$. Management desires only a 5% chance of rejecting a batch when the true mean can contents have a true mean of 12.05 ounces when the standard deviation is assumed to be .15 ounces. The following sample values are obtained for a particular shipment.

11.7 12.1 11.8 11.6 12.1 12.0 11.9 12.1 12.0 11.9 11.8 12.1

(a) Find the decision rule for this test.
(b) Compute the sample mean. What action should be taken?
(c) Compute the probability of
   (1) accepting a shipment having a true mean of 12.0 ounces.
   (2) accepting a shipment having a true mean of 11.8 ounces.

12-22 Lilliput Telephone Company uses sample data to accept or reject the directory manuscript prepared by a contractor. The acceptable quality level for the true mean number of errors is 1.5 errors per thousand characters. The decision for an $N = 2,500$ thousand-character telephone book will be based on a random sample of 20 one-thousand character segments. An $\alpha = .05$ significance level is desired for incorrectly rejecting a good book having the acceptable quality level when the standard deviation is .3 errors per thousand characters. The following numbers of errors were detected in the sample segments.

6	0	2	3	4
1	2	2	2	5
5	4	2	3	1
3	2	0	1	3

(a) Find the decision rule for this test.
(b) Compute the sample mean. What action should be taken?
(c) Compute the probability of
   (1) accepting a book having a true mean error rate of 1.3.
   (2) accepting a book having a true mean error rate of 1.8.

12-23 A pharmaceutical house must guard against both overfilling and underfilling capsules. For a particular drug, pills should contain a mean active-ingredient weight of .1 milligram. The standard deviation is assumed to be .025 milligrams. A decision rule is needed to determine from a mean of 25 pills whether to accept or reject production of 5,000 pills each. An α = .05 significance level is desired for incorrectly rejecting a good batch. The following pill active-ingredient weights were measured for the sample.

.095	.102	.104	.105	.099
.101	.102	.097	.099	.101
.099	.100	.101	.098	.098
.103	.106	.096	.099	.110
.097	.103	.104	.095	.099

(a) Find the decision rule for this test.
(b) Compute the sample mean. What action should be taken?
(c) Compute the probability of
   (1) accepting a batch having a mean ingredient of .0990.
   (2) accepting a batch having a mean ingredient of .0995.
   (3) accepting a batch having a mean ingredient of .1010.

12-24 Consider the following numbers of defectives in successive samples of 10 items.

Sample	Number of Defectives
1	2
2	0
3	2
4	1
5	1
6	1
7	1
8	0
9	1
10	2

Determine for each of the following sequential sampling plans which of the above is the final set of observations. Indicate whether the lot should be accepted or rejected.

(a) $A_n = .05n$ (b) $A_n = .2n$ (c) $A_n = 1 + .1n$ (d) $A_n = 2 + .05n$
$R_n = 1 + .05n$ $R_n = 1 + .2n$ $R_n = 3 + .1n$ $R_n = 4 + .05n$

SUMMARY

1. What is statistical quality control?

There are two major areas of **statistical quality control**. When the major concern is the *process* of creating products or services, quality controls may be achieved using the **control chart**. The control chart graphically documents a procedure whereby sample data trigger remedial actions. The second type of statistical quality control is **acceptance sampling**.

2. What are the basic types of control charts?

For qualitative observations, the **P-chart** is used. Two charts are used for quantitative observations: the **$\bar{X}$-chart** for monitoring central tendency and the **R-chart** for assessing process variability.

3. How is a control chart used to trigger remedial action?

Control charts display a **lower control limit** LCL and an **upper control limit** UCL for the applicable statistic. Observations falling outside these limits correspond to times when the process is *out of control*. An essential feature of a successful quality control plan is the search for **assignable causes** for the unusually large or small observations that result. Since they are ordinarily based on *3-sigma* deviations, the LCL and UCL should be far enough apart that random causes alone will rarely trigger a search for nonexistent assignable causes.

4. What is acceptance sampling and how is it used?

Acceptance sampling places the focus on *items* already produced or *services* already rendered. There are two possible actions that may be taken when sampling the population or **lot**. It may be *accepted* or *rejected*. The *proportion defective*, the value of which remains unknown, is the primary issue. A pivotal level, the **acceptable quality level** π_0, is the focus in establishing a *decision rule*. The rule compares the number of sample defectives D to an **acceptance number** C. The lot must be *accepted* when $D \leq C$ and *rejected* otherwise.

5. How does acceptance sampling relate to hypothesis testing?

Acceptance sampling is a direct application of *hypothesis testing*. The procedure uses a specified **significance level** α, which establishes the level for C once the sample size is specified. The value of C represents an upper limit of the probability for the *Type I error* of rejecting a good shipment ($\pi = \pi_0$). That probability is referred to as the **producer's risk**. The *Type II error* of accepting a bad shipment ($\pi > \pi_0$) is also to be avoided. The corresponding probability is referred to as the **consumer's risk**.

6. What is sequential sampling and how is it used?

Ordinarily, acceptance sampling schemes are based on single samples. More elaborate procedures may involve **sequential sampling** where a succession of smaller-sized samples are taken, each resulting in either acceptance, rejection, or the choice to continue sampling.

REAL-LIFE STATISTICAL CHALLENGE

Designing Products to Last

For businesses to survive into the next century terms such as "quality control" and "total quality management" need to be more than faddish buzz-words. Genichi Taguchi, an engineer with Toyota Motor Cars of Japan, argues that "Quality is a virtue of design." From this premise a body of manufacturing quality assurance techniques has collectively become known as the Taguchi method.

SOME FEATURES OF THE TAGUCHI METHOD

The Taguchi method incorporates a number of statistical, financial analysis, and *heuristic* measures. (A heuristic measure uses rules of thumb to find solutions to answers.) We will examine four of these measures.

- Designing robustness into products.
- The "Quality Loss Function."
- Striving for consistent products, beginning with design through manufacturing and continuing beyond the plant into the field.
- Providing robust products that have a high internal and external signal-to-noise ratio.

PRODUCT ROBUSTNESS

Mr. Taguchi, in his article with Don Clausing published in the *Harvard Business Review*, puts forth the concept that the " 'robustness' of products is more a function of good design than of on-line control."* Over their useful lives products are subjected to greater variation in the field—due to dust, electrical conditions, and other factors. Therefore, measures to reduce product failure in the field should also reduce failures during manufacturing.

THE "QUALITY LOSS FUNCTION"

Taguchi makes use of a heuristic quality loss function (defined as the cost to fix a problem in the field after customers complain) shown as the formula

$$L = D^2 \times C$$

where D is the deviation from the target and C is the cost of the countermeasure to get back on target. For example, if it would cost a manufacturer $50 per unit as a countermeasure to get a product part on target, the quality loss function provides values of $50, $200, $450, and $800 at deviations of 1, 2, 3, and 4 from the target.

STRIVING FOR CONSISTENCY

In general, scattered deviations within specifications are more difficult to correct than consistent deviations outside of specifications. With scattered deviations, a number of factors may be interacting to create a product that eventually will fail or lead to customer dissatisfaction. Consistent error outside the target may be corrected by changing one or a few isolated factors rather than fixing many possible factors.

REAL-LIFE STATISTICAL CHALLENGE

HIGH SIGNAL-TO-NOISE RATIOS

Robust products have a high internal and external signal-to-noise ratio. The signal-to-noise ratio is a metaphor applied by Taguchi to all product behavior—not just electrical parts, for which the term has a precise physical definition.

The *signal* is what the product or service is trying to deliver. *Noise* is any interference internal or external to the product. Designers need to consider three factors in maximizing the ratio:

1. Determine the specific objective for developing the best signal-to-noise ratio.

2. Define feasible design options—physical characteristics such as dimensions and other physical characteristics.

3. Select the option that provides the greatest robustness.

The selection can be achieved through the process of multiple factor analysis (a set of techniques related to the multiple correlation concepts discussed in Chapter 11).

FURTHER CONSIDERATIONS

There are other elements to the Taguchi method that focus on cost/benefit trade-off issues and other financial measures.

The Taguchi method is one of many quality assurance techniques that have been used in a wide range of industries.[**] Nonmanufacturing and government and non-profit organizations may find adapting some of these "total quality methods" may lead to greater customer satisfaction and repeat business.

DISCUSSION QUESTIONS

1. If the cost of a countermeasure is $120 per unit, what will be the losses from not correcting at 2 and 3 deviations?

2. For the company where you work, how could robustness be enhanced for a product? For a service?

3. Traditional quality control, as described in this chapter, focuses on piecemeal improvements and corrections. Do you think that Taguchi's approach contradicts those methods?

REFERENCES

[*] Genichi Taguchi and Don Clausing, "Robust Quality," in *Harvard Business Review*, January–February 1990, pp 65–75.

[**] James B. Dilworth, "Total Quality Management," in *Operations Management: Design Planning and Control for Manufacturing and Services*. New York: McGraw-Hill, 1992, pp. 606–629.

REVIEW EXERCISES

12-25 Yellow Giant wishes to establish a control chart for the weights of canned foods. The data in the following table have been obtained over several days.

Day	Contents Weight (ounces)				
1	15.67	16.23	16.08	15.92	16.17
2	16.14	16.33	16.08	16.39	15.82
3	15.76	15.97	16.25	16.19	16.22
4	16.74	15.65	15.66	16.22	15.75
5	15.82	15.95	15.82	15.76	15.56
6	16.38	16.20	16.00	15.80	16.01
7	15.70	16.20	15.71	16.30	15.77
8	16.14	16.05	16.25	15.92	16.10
9	15.65	15.75	16.18	16.03	15.79
10	16.34	16.16	16.15	15.80	15.88

(a) Calculate the mean and range for each sample. Then calculate the grand mean and overall mean range.
(b) Determine Yellow Giant's control limits for $\bar{X}$ and R.
(c) For each of the following sample results, indicate whether the process is in control or out of control.

(1)	15.40	15.60	15.55	15.70	15.80
(2)	15.66	16.05	16.39	16.10	16.07
(3)	15.20	16.80	16.00	15.80	15.90
(4)	15.60	16.25	16.22	15.90	16.05

12-26 A Midget Motors inspector has established the following control limits for the amount of paint needed to cover a car.

$$\bar{X}: \quad \text{LCL} = 1.8 \text{ gallons} \qquad \text{UCL} = 2.2 \text{ gallons}$$
$$R: \quad \text{LCL} = 0.5 \text{ gallons} \qquad \text{UCL} = 0.8 \text{ gallons}$$

For each of the following sample results, indicate whether the painting process is (1) in control; (2) out of control because of the mean; (3) out of control because of the variability; or (4) out of control due to both the mean and variability.

(a)	1.6	2.2	2.1	1.8	(c)	2.0	1.3	2.7	1.9	
(b)	2.4	2.2	1.7	1.6	(d)	0.9	2.0	2.1	1.3	

12-27 Shirley Smart is responsible for quality control at Soft-WhereHaus. She wishes to determine an acceptance sampling plan for floppy disk drives.
(a) The following plans are being considered. Determine the acceptance number for each.
   (1) $\pi_0 = .01$; $n = 20$; $\alpha = .10$
   (2) $\pi_0 = .05$; $n = 50$; $\alpha = .05$
   (3) $\pi_0 = .10$; $n = 100$; $\alpha = .025$
(b) Using your answer to (a), determine the probability that a shipment will be accepted when the true proportion defective disk drives is .30.

12-28 Refer to Exercise 12-27. Suppose that Shirley Smart establishes an acceptable quality level of $\pi_0 = .05$ and a sample size $n = 100$.
(a) At a significance level of $\alpha = .02$, determine the acceptance number.

(b) Using your answer to (a), indicate for each of the following sample results whether she should accept or reject the shipment.
   (1) $D = 5$ (2) $D = 1$ (3) $D = 2$ (4) $D = 9$

12-29 An insurance company actuary uses control charts to determine when a region's rates need to be adjusted up or down. She maintains major fire claims data in 20 regions. During the past year the number of major structural damage claims per 1,000 homes was as follows.

Region	Number	Region	Number	Region	Number	Region	Number
1	5	6	11	11	3	16	4
2	2	7	7	12	3	17	8
3	8	8	6	13	6	18	14
4	7	9	13	14	9	19	33
5	6	10	11	15	17	20	2

(a) Determine the 2-sigma control limits and then plot the control chart for the proportion.
(b) On which regions (if any) is an adjustment indicated?

12-30 A rare-metals foundry casts precision 20-ounce gold ingots. The following sample data have been taken over a period of 10 days.

Day 1:	19.8	20.1	20.2	19.7	20.0
Day 2:	19.9	19.5	19.6	19.6	19.7
Day 3:	20.1	20.0	19.9	19.8	19.9
Day 4:	20.0	20.0	20.1	19.9	19.9
Day 5:	19.8	19.8	20.1	20.0	20.1
Day 6:	20.3	20.2	20.4	20.2	20.3
Day 7:	20.0	20.0	19.9	20.1	20.1
Day 8:	19.9	19.9	20.1	20.0	20.0
Day 9:	20.2	20.1	20.1	20.0	19.9
Day 10:	20.5	20.1	20.0	19.4	19.9

(a) Determine the 2-sigma control limits and then plot the control chart for the mean.
(b) On which days (if any) was the process out of control?

12-31 Refer to Exercise 12-30.
(a) Determine the 2-sigma control limits and then plot the control chart for the range.
(a) On which days (if any) was the process out of control?

12-32 The sample data in the following table were obtained from a production line that generates 14-pound bowling balls.

Sample	Weights				
1	14.05	14.09	14.04	14.20	14.01
2	14.07	13.91	13.97	14.03	14.11
3	13.82	14.17	14.04	13.91	13.86
4	13.66	14.14	14.06	14.16	13.91
5	13.62	13.85	14.15	14.07	13.90
6	14.11	14.16	14.02	13.87	13.99
7	14.06	13.81	13.90	13.79	14.21
8	13.87	13.94	14.13	14.26	13.84
9	13.91	14.05	14.20	13.92	13.88
10	14.07	13.93	13.86	14.09	14.18
11	13.98	13.94	14.10	13.95	13.98
12	14.04	14.13	13.89	13.77	13.96
13	14.18	13.79	14.10	14.14	14.08
14	13.87	14.08	14.12	13.88	13.91
15	13.82	14.11	14.22	14.16	14.05
16	14.22	14.27	14.21	14.28	14.22
17	13.77	14.08	14.16	14.23	13.97
18	13.76	14.11	14.28	13.81	14.12
19	14.13	14.21	14.07	13.95	13.82
20	14.06	14.15	14.23	14.07	13.96

(a) Find the preliminary 3-sigma control limits for the sample mean and construct the preliminary control chart, plotting the data point for each sample.

(b) Find the preliminary 3-sigma control limits for the sample range and construct the preliminary control chart, plotting the data point for each sample.

(c) Eliminate the samples where the process was found to be out of control in either (a) or (b). Determine the revised control limits for (1) $\bar{X}$ and (2) R. Indicate the revised 3-sigma control limits on your control charts.

12-33 The sample data in the following table were obtained from a wafer fabrication line which generates 4-inch circular wafers. Each sample consists of 100 wafers and the table contains the number of defective wafers in each sample.

Sample	Number Defective	Sample	Number Defective
1	18	21	15
2	16	22	19
3	23	23	23
4	7	24	16
5	14	25	30
6	12	26	16
7	19	27	18
8	4	28	21
9	12	29	25
10	21	30	16
11	15	31	23
12	24	32	15
13	19	33	6
14	16	34	22

(continued on next page)

Sample	Number Defective	Sample	Number Defective
15	13	35	13
16	28	36	15
17	14	37	9
18	20	38	24
19	17	39	19
20	13	40	19

(a) Find the preliminary 3-sigma control limits for the proportion of defective wafers and construct the preliminary control chart, plotting the data point for each sample.

(b) Eliminate the samples where the process was found to be out of control. Determine the revised 3-sigma control limits for the sample proportion. Indicate the revised control limits on your control chart.

12-34 Refer to Problem 12-33 and your answers to that problem. Determine the probability that for any given sample the process will be in control within your revised 3-sigma control limits when the following true population proportion defective applies. Use the normal approximation.
(a) $\pi = .15$ (b) $\pi = .20$

12-35 Refer to Problem 12-32 and your answers to that problem. Assume that the revised 3-sigma control limits for the sample mean apply to the 14-pound bowling balls. Determine the probability that a particular $\bar{X}$ will indicate that the process is out of control when the true weight of the bowling balls is represented by a population with the following parameters.
(a) $\mu = 13.9$, $\sigma = .10$ (b) $\mu = 14.06$, $\sigma = .15$

CASE   Billings, Kidd, and Hickock

Billings, Kidd, and Hickock is a large, multi-city, public accounting firm. The partners have several quality control concerns about the services the firm provides and those it procures from contractors.

Their first concern is with the accuracy of tax-return workups. A random sample of 100 files from each branch office has been selected, along with the computer input sheets. A detailed analysis yields the following numbers of returns that have major preparation errors.

Branch Office	Number of Errors	Branch Office	Number of Errors	Branch Office	Number of Errors
1	25	6	12	11	9
2	14	7	10	12	9
3	2	8	12	13	15
4	16	9	28	14	24
5	17	10	15	15	14

The firm prepares the payrolls for hundreds of medium-sized business clients. Each month, a sample of payrolls processed by the branch offices will be selected and each client employee's workup time will be determined. The following first month's data have been obtained.

Office	Workup Time per Employee (minutes)			
1	7.5	9.4	13.5	5.2
2	15.4	11.5	17.8	20.3
3	5.6	7.1	8.3	4.9
4	19.4	4.7	8.6	7.5
5	6.5	9.5	11.2	8.2
6	10.3	9.8	13.4	11.2
7	8.7	20.5	7.9	6.5
8	11.3	8.7	11.5	12.2
9	9.0	8.8	10.2	11.5
10	15.4	13.6	17.5	17.5
11	4.4	5.1	3.6	3.5
12	10.2	14.6	11.4	13.1
13	7.9	8.5	9.1	9.9
14	12.5	6.9	11.4	7.0
15	9.5	8.2	9.4	5.8

Billings, Kidd, and Hickock contracts out data transcription to a company that flies records to Jamaica, where the actual work is done. The firm needs to establish an acceptance sampling scheme and to negotiate terms with the contractor. The plan is to return for reprocessing any rejected batches of transcribed data, which the contractor will redo for free.

The firm has retained a statistical consultant to help evaluate the above issues.

QUESTIONS

1. A control chart will help to identify which branches are out of line with the firm's present standards for preparing tax returns. Using the sample error data, construct a *P*-chart. Indicate which, if any, branch offices appear to need remedial attention from the managing partner.

2. A control chart will also help to identify which employees are out of line with the standard workup time for processing payrolls. Construct an $\bar{X}$-chart and an *R*-chart for the given data. Identify which offices appear to violate the firm's suggested norms and state the form of those violations.

3. Discuss why the firm may be concerned with payroll $\bar{X}$'s that are too small as well as too large.

4. Discuss why the firm may expect a great deal of payroll processing variability and also what type of problem may be signaled by too little variability.

5. Discuss how the firm may reach an acceptable quality level for the error rate in transcribing data.

6. Discuss the key issues in setting the significance level and determining the sample size.

7. Suppose that $n = 100$ transactions are selected at random from each data-processed lot and that the acceptable quality level is an error rate of .01. At a significance level of .015, determine the acceptance number that the firm will propose to the contractor.

12-4 OPTIONAL TOPIC: CONTROL CHARTS WITH GIVEN STANDARDS

The control chart illustrations seen so far involve limits as computed from the sample data. In some applications management desires to see how well a current operation measures with respect to specified standards. The following expressions apply for computing the limits.

CONTROL CHART LIMITS USING SPECIFIED STANDARDS

Mean:

$$\text{LCL} = \mu_0 - SL\frac{\sigma_0}{\sqrt{n}} \qquad \text{UCL} = \mu_0 + SL\frac{\sigma_0}{\sqrt{n}}$$

Range:

$$\text{LCL} = d_R\sigma_0 - SL\sigma_w\sigma_0 \qquad \text{UCL} = d_R\sigma_0 + SL\sigma_w\sigma_0$$

Standard Deviation:

$$\text{LCL} = c_4\sigma_0 - SLc_5\sigma_0 \qquad \text{UCL} = c_4\sigma_0 + SLc_5\sigma_0$$

Proportion:

$$\text{LCL} = \pi_0 - SL\sqrt{\frac{\pi_0(1-\pi_0)}{n}} \qquad \text{UCL} = \pi_0 + SL\sqrt{\frac{\pi_0(1-\pi_0)}{n}}$$

where the following parameters apply:

μ_0 = standard for mean
σ_0 = specification for standard deviation
π_0 = standard for proportion

We will illustrate a control chart for the mean. Such a chart might apply, for example, if Boxwell House implements a new policy to ensure that nearly all jars of coffee meet labeling requirements. That might be achieved by filling them with slightly more than 16 ounces of coffee, so that a company standard might be $\mu_0 = 16.10$ ounces. A historical standard deviation, such as $\sigma_0 = .25$ ounces per jar, might also be assumed to apply.

Using $SL = 2$, the following control limits are computed.

$$\text{LCL} = 16.10 - 2\left(\frac{.25}{\sqrt{5}}\right) = 16.10 - .22 = 15.88$$

$$\text{UCL} = 16.10 + .22 = 16.32$$

These are shown in Figure 12-10, where the original data are again plotted. Notice that the center of the control chart is the standard of 16.10 ounces instead of the computed grand mean. Likewise, the control limits will be computed using the standard of $\sigma = .25$ ounces rather than the sample results. Notice that nearly all the sample means are below center, with several falling below the LCL. Management should use this chart to refine the coffee-filling process to meet the new standards. Current production predominantly undershoots the specifications, with several points out of control. Management must remedy the situation by adjusting controls to slightly increase jar contents.

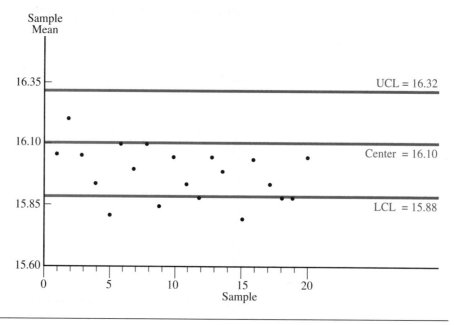

FIGURE 12-10 Two-sigma specified standards control chart for mean using coffee jar data.

OPTIONAL EXERCISES **12-36** Consider the sample data from Exercise 12-12 for the contents of 12-ounce guava juice cans. Company standards are that cans contain a mean of 12.10 ounces with a standard deviation of .10 ounce.

(a) Determine the 2-sigma control limits for the mean. Then plot the control chart.

(b) On which days (if any) was the process out of control?

12-37 Refer to Exercise 12-36.
  (a) Determine the 2-sigma control limits for the range. Then plot the control chart.
  (b) On which days (if any) was the process out of control?

12-38 Refer to Exercise 12-36 and your answers to that problem. The company wants to use the given data to establish standards for future controls. It was determined that on Days 2 and 10 the control valves malfunctioned. Eliminate the sample values for those days from the data base. Then use 2-sigma limits to determine
  (a) the central value, LCL, and UCL for the mean.
  (b) the central value, LCL, and UCL for the standard deviation.

SELECTED REFERENCES

The Role of Statistics

Careers in Statistics. The American Statistical Association (no date available).
Huff, Darrell. *How to Lie with Statistics.* New York: W. W. Norton, 1954.
Moroney, M. J. *Facts from Figures.* Baltimore: Penguin Books, 1952.
Reichmann, W. J. *Use and Abuse of Statistics.* New York: Oxford University Press, 1962.
Wallis, W. A. and H. V. Roberts. *The Nature of Statistics.* New York: The Free Press, 1965.

Probability

Feller, William. *An Introduction to Probability Theory and Its Applications,* Vol. 1, 3rd. ed.
    New York: John Wiley & Sons, 1968.
Hodges, J. L., Jr., and E. L. Lehmann. *Elements of Finite Probability.* San Francisco: Holden-
    Day, 1965.
Laplace, Pierre Simon, Marquis de. *A Philosophical Essay on Probabilities.* New York:
    Dover Publications, 1951.
Mosteller, F., R. Rourke, and G. Thomas, Jr. *Probability and Statistics.* Reading, Mass.:
    Addison-Wesley, 1961.
Parzen, Emanuel. *Modern Probability Theory and Its Applications.* New York: John Wiley &
    Sons, 1960.

Regression and Correlation Analysis

Ezekiel, Mordecai, and Karl A. Fox. *Methods of Correlation and Regression Analysis,* 3rd
    ed. New York: John Wiley & Sons, 1959.
Johnston, John. *Econometric Methods,* 2nd ed. New York: McGraw-Hill, 1971.
Neter, John, and William Wasserman. *Applied Linear Statistical Models,* 3rd ed. Homewood,
    Ill.: Richard D. Irwin, 1990.
Williams, E.J. *Regression Analysis.* New York: John Wiley & Sons, 1959.
Wonnacott, Ronald J., and Thomas H. Wonnacott, *Econometrics,* 2nd ed. New York: John
    Wiley & Sons, 1979.

Time Series Analysis and Index Numbers

Brown, Robert G. *Smoothing, Forecasting and Prediction of Discrete Time Series,* Engle-
    wood Cliffs, N.J.: Prentice-Hall, 1963.
Makridakis, S., and S. C. Wheelright. *Forecasting: Methods and Applications,* 2nd ed. New
    York: John Wiley & Sons, 1983.
    ———. *Interactive Forecasting: Univariate and Multivariate Methods,* 2nd ed. San Fran-
    cisco: Holden-Day, 1978.
McKinley, David H., Murray G. Lee, and Helene Duffy. *Forecasting Business Conditions.*
    The American Bankers Association, 1965.
Mudgett, Bruce D. *Index Numbers,* New York: John Wiley & Sons, 1951.
Spencer, Milton H., Colin G. Clark, and Peter W. Hoguet. *Business and Economic Forecast-
    ing: An Econometric Approach.* Homewood, Ill.: Richard D. Irwin, 1965.

Analysis of Variance and Design of Experiments

Cochran, William G., and Gertrude M. Cox. *Experimental Designs,* 2nd ed. New York: John Wiley & Sons, 1957.

Cox, David R. *Planning of Experiments.* New York: John Wiley & Sons, 1958.

Guenther, W. C. *Analysis of Variance.* Englewood Cliffs, N.J.: Prentice-Hall, 1964.

Mendenhall, William. *An Introduction to Linear Models and the Design and Analysis of Experiments.* Belmont, Calif.: Wadsworth, 1968.

Neter, John, and William Wasserman. *Applied Linear Statistical Models,* 3rd ed. Homewood, Ill.: Richard D. Irwin, 1990.

Scheffé, Henry. *The Analysis of Variance.* New York: John Wiley & Sons, 1959.

Nonparametric Statistics

Bradley, James V. *Distribution-Free Statistical Tests.* Englewood Cliffs, N.J.: Prentice-Hall, 1968.

Conover, W. J. *Practical Nonparametric Statistics,* 2nd ed. New York: John Wiley & Sons, 1980.

Gibbons, Jean D. *Nonparametric Statistical Inference.* New York: McGraw-Hill, 1970.

Hájek, Jaroslav, *Nonparametric Statistics.* San Francisco: Holden-Day, 1969.

Kraft, Charles H., and Constance van Eeden. *A Nonparametric Introduction to Statistics.* New York: Macmillan, 1968.

Noether, Gottfried E. *Introduction to Statistics: A Nonparametric Approach,* 2nd ed. Boston: Houghton Mifflin, 1976.

Siegel, Sidney. *Nonparametric Statistics for the Behavioral Sciences.* New York: McGraw-Hill, 1956.

Statistical Quality Control

Deming, W. E. *Some Theory of Sampling.* New York: Dover, 1984.

Dodge, H. F., and H. G. Romig. *Sampling Inspection Tables—Single and Double Sampling,* 2nd ed. New York: John Wiley & Sons, 1959.

Enrick, N. L. *Quality Control and Reliability,* 5th ed. New York: The Industrial Press, 1966.

Grant, Eugene L., and Richard S. Leavenworth. *Statistical Quality Control,* 5th ed. New York: McGraw-Hill, 1979.

Juran, J. M. (ed.). *Quality Control Handbook,* 4th ed. New York: McGraw-Hill, 1988.

Wadsworth, Harrison M., Kenneth S. Stephens, and B. Blanton Godfrey. *Modern Methods for Quality Control and Improvement.* New York: John Wiley & Sons, 1986.

Decision Theory and Utility

Chernoff, Herman, and L. E. Moses. *Elementary Decision Theory.* New York: Dover, 1986.

Jones, J. Morgan. *Introduction to Decision Theory.* Homewood, Ill.: Richard D. Irwin, 1977.

Luce, R.D., and H. Raiffa. *Games and Decisions.* New York: John Wiley & Sons, 1957.

Miller, David W., and M. K. Starr. *Executive Decisions and Operations Research,* 2nd ed. Englewood Cliffs, N.J.: Prentice-Hall, 1969.

Morris, W. T. *Management Science: A Bayesian Introduction.* Englewood Cliffs, N.J.: Prentice-Hall, 1968.

Pratt, J. W., H. Raiffa, annd R. Schlaifer. *Introduction to Statistical Decision Theory.* New York: McGraw-Hill, 1965.

Raiffa, H. *Decision Analysis: Introductory Lectures on Choices Under Uncertainty.* New York: Random House, 1986.

Schlaifer, R. *Analysis of Decisions Under Uncertainty.* New York: McGraw-Hill, 1969.

———. *Introduction to Statistics for Business Decisions.* Melbourne, Florida: Robert E. Krieger Publishing Co., Inc., 1982.

Statistical Tables

Beyer, William H. (ed.). *Handbook of Tables for Probability and Statistics,* 2nd ed. Cleveland, Ohio: The Chemical Rubber Co., 1968.

Burington, Richard S., and Donald C. May. *Handbook of Probability and Statistics with Tables,* 2nd ed. New York: McGraw-Hill, 1970.

Fisher, Ronald A., and F. Yates. *Statistical Tables for Biological, Agricultural and Medical Research,* 6th ed. London: Longman Group, 1978.

National Bureau of Standards. *Tables of the Binomial Distribution.* Washington, D.C.: U.S. Government Printing Office, 1950.

Owen, D. B. *Handbook of Statistical Tables.* Reading, Mass.: Addison-Wesley, 1962.

Pearson, E. S., and H. O. Hartley, eds. *Biometrika Tables for Statisticians,* 3rd ed. Monticello, N.Y.: Lubrecht & Cramer, 1976.

The Rand Corporation. *A Million Random Digits with* 100,000 *Normal Deviates.* New York: The Free Press, 1955.

APPENDIX

TABLE A Four-Place Common Logarithms

N	0	1	2	3	4	5	6	7	8	9	1	2	3	4	5	6	7	8	9
														Proportional Parts					
10	0000	0043	0086	0128	0170	0212	0253	0294	0334	0374	4	8	12	17	21	25	29	33	37
11	0414	0453	0492	0531	0569	0607	0645	0682	0719	0755	4	8	11	15	19	23	26	30	34
12	0792	0828	0864	0899	0934	0969	1004	1038	1072	1106	3	7	10	14	17	21	24	28	31
13	1139	1173	1206	1239	1271	1303	1335	1367	1399	1430	3	6	10	13	16	19	23	26	29
14	1461	1492	1523	1553	1584	1614	1644	1673	1703	1732	3	6	9	12	15	18	21	24	27
15	1761	1790	1818	1847	1875	1903	1931	1959	1987	2014	3	6	8	11	14	17	20	22	25
16	2041	2068	2095	2122	2148	2175	2201	2227	2253	2279	3	5	8	11	13	16	18	21	24
17	2304	2330	2355	2380	2405	2430	2455	2480	2504	2529	2	5	7	10	12	15	17	20	22
18	2553	2577	2601	2625	2648	2672	2695	2718	2742	2765	2	5	7	9	12	14	16	19	21
19	2788	2810	2833	2856	2878	2900	2923	2945	2967	2989	2	4	7	9	11	13	16	18	20
20	3010	3032	3054	3075	3096	3118	3139	3160	3181	3201	2	4	6	8	11	13	15	17	19
21	3222	3243	3263	3284	3304	3324	3345	3365	3385	3404	2	4	6	8	10	12	14	16	18
22	3424	3444	3464	3483	3502	3522	3541	3560	3579	3598	2	4	6	8	10	12	14	15	17
23	3617	3636	3655	3674	3692	3711	3729	3747	3766	3784	2	4	6	7	9	11	13	15	17
24	3802	3820	3838	3856	3874	3892	3909	3927	3945	3962	2	4	5	7	9	11	12	14	16
25	3979	3997	4014	4031	4048	4065	4082	4099	4116	4133	2	3	5	7	9	10	12	14	15
26	4150	4166	4183	4200	4216	4232	4249	4265	4281	4298	2	3	5	7	8	10	11	13	15
27	4314	4330	4346	4362	4378	4393	4409	4425	4440	4456	2	3	5	6	8	9	11	13	14
28	4472	4487	4502	4518	4533	4548	4564	4579	4594	4609	2	3	5	6	8	9	11	12	14
29	4624	4639	4654	4669	4683	4698	4713	4728	4742	4757	1	3	4	6	7	9	10	12	13
30	4771	4786	4800	4814	4829	4843	4857	4871	4886	4900	1	3	4	6	7	9	10	11	13
31	4914	4928	4942	4955	4969	4983	4997	5011	5024	5038	1	3	4	6	7	8	10	11	12
32	5051	5065	5079	5092	5105	5119	5132	5145	5159	5172	1	3	4	5	7	8	9	11	12
33	5185	5198	5211	5224	5237	5250	5263	5276	5289	5302	1	3	4	5	6	8	9	10	12
34	5315	5328	5340	5353	5366	5378	5391	5403	5416	5428	1	3	4	5	6	8	9	10	11
35	5441	5453	5465	5478	5490	5502	5514	5527	5539	5551	1	2	4	5	6	7	9	10	11
36	5563	5575	5587	5599	5611	5623	5635	5647	5658	5670	1	2	4	5	6	7	8	10	11
37	5682	5694	5705	5717	5729	5740	5752	5763	5775	5786	1	2	3	5	6	7	8	9	10
38	5798	5809	5821	5832	5843	5855	5866	5877	5888	5899	1	2	3	5	6	7	8	9	10
39	5911	5922	5933	5944	5955	5966	5977	5988	5999	6010	1	2	3	4	5	7	8	9	10
40	6021	6031	6042	6053	6064	6075	6085	6096	6107	6117	1	2	3	4	5	6	8	9	10
41	6128	6138	6149	6160	6170	6180	6191	6201	6212	6222	1	2	3	4	5	6	7	8	9
42	6232	6243	6253	6263	6274	6284	6294	6304	6314	6325	1	2	3	4	5	6	7	8	9
43	6335	6345	6355	6365	6375	6385	6395	6405	6415	6425	1	2	3	4	5	6	7	8	9
44	6435	6444	6454	6464	6474	6484	6493	6503	6513	6522	1	2	3	4	5	6	7	8	9
45	6532	6542	6551	6561	6571	6580	6590	6599	6609	6618	1	2	3	4	5	6	7	8	9
46	6628	6637	6646	6656	6665	6675	6684	6693	6702	6712	1	2	3	4	5	6	7	7	8
47	6721	6730	6739	6749	6758	6767	6776	6785	6794	6803	1	2	3	4	5	5	6	7	8
48	6812	6821	6830	6839	6848	6857	6866	6875	6884	6893	1	2	3	4	4	5	6	7	8
49	6902	6911	6920	6928	6937	6946	6955	6964	6972	6981	1	2	3	4	4	5	6	7	8
50	6990	6998	7007	7016	7024	7033	7042	7050	7059	7067	1	2	3	3	4	5	6	7	8
51	7076	7084	7093	7101	7110	7118	7126	7135	7143	7152	1	2	3	3	4	5	6	7	8
52	7160	7168	7177	7185	7193	7202	7210	7218	7226	7235	1	2	2	3	4	5	6	7	7
53	7243	7251	7259	7267	7275	7284	7292	7300	7308	7316	1	2	2	3	4	5	6	6	7
54	7324	7332	7340	7348	7356	7364	7372	7380	7388	7396	1	2	2	3	4	5	6	6	7
N	0	1	2	3	4	5	6	7	8	9	1	2	3	4	5	6	7	8	9

TABLE B
Random Numbers

12651	61646	11769	75109	86996	97669	25757	32535	07122	76763
81769	74436	02630	72310	45049	18029	07469	42341	98173	79260
36737	98863	77240	76251	00654	64688	09343	70278	67331	98729
82861	54371	76610	94934	72748	44124	05610	53750	95938	01485
21325	15732	24127	37431	09723	63529	73977	95218	96074	42138
74146	47887	62463	23045	41490	07954	22597	60012	98866	90959
90759	64410	54179	66075	61051	75385	51378	08360	95946	95547
55683	98078	02238	91540	21219	17720	87817	41705	95785	12563
79686	17969	76061	83748	55920	83612	41540	86492	06447	60568
70333	00201	86201	69716	78185	62154	77930	67663	29529	75116
14042	53536	07779	04157	41172	36473	42123	43929	50533	33437
59911	08256	06596	48416	69770	68797	56080	14223	59199	30162
62368	62623	62742	14891	39247	52242	98832	69533	91174	57979
57529	97751	54976	48957	74599	08759	78494	52785	68526	64618
15469	90574	78033	66885	13936	42117	71831	22961	94225	31816
18625	23674	53850	32827	81647	80820	00420	63555	74489	80141
74626	68394	88562	70745	23701	45630	65891	58220	35442	60414
11119	16519	27384	90199	79210	76965	99546	30323	31664	22845
41101	17336	48951	53674	17880	45260	08575	49321	36191	17095
32123	91576	84221	78902	82010	30847	62329	63898	23268	74283
26091	68409	69704	82267	14751	13151	93115	01437	56945	89661
67680	79790	48462	59278	44185	29616	76531	19589	83139	28454
15184	19260	14073	07026	25264	08388	27182	22557	61501	67481
58010	45039	57181	10238	36874	28546	37444	80824	63981	39942
56425	53996	86245	32623	78858	08143	60377	42925	42815	11159
82630	84066	13592	60642	17904	99718	63432	88642	37858	25431
14927	40909	23900	48761	44860	92467	31742	87142	03607	32059
23740	22505	07489	85986	74420	21744	97711	36648	35620	97949
32990	97446	03711	63824	07953	85965	87089	11687	92414	67257
05310	24058	91946	78437	34365	82469	12430	84754	19354	72745
21839	39937	27534	88913	49055	19218	47712	67677	51889	70926
08833	42549	93981	94051	28382	83725	72643	64233	97252	17133
58336	11139	47479	00931	91560	95372	97642	33856	54825	55680
62032	91144	75478	47431	52726	30289	42411	91886	51818	78292
45171	30557	53116	04118	58301	24375	65609	85810	18620	49198
91611	62656	60128	35609	63698	78356	50682	22505	01692	36291
55472	63819	86314	49174	93582	73604	78614	78849	23096	72825
18573	09729	74091	53994	10970	86557	65661	41854	26037	53296
60866	02955	90288	82136	83644	94455	06560	78029	98768	71296
45043	55608	82767	60890	74646	79485	13619	98868	40857	19415
17831	09737	79473	75945	28394	79334	70577	38048	03607	06932
40137	03981	07585	18128	11178	32601	27994	05641	22600	86064
77776	31343	14576	97706	16039	47517	43300	59080	80392	63189
69605	44104	40103	95635	05635	81673	68657	09559	23510	95875
19916	52934	26499	09821	87331	80993	61299	36979	73599	35055
02606	58552	07678	56619	65325	30705	99582	53390	46357	13244
65183	73160	87131	35530	47946	09854	18080	02321	05809	04898
10740	98914	44916	11322	89717	88189	30143	52687	19420	60061
98642	89822	71691	51573	83666	61642	46683	33761	47542	23551
60139	25601	93663	25547	02654	94829	48672	28736	84994	13071

SOURCE: The Rand Corporation. *A Million Random Digits with 100,000 Normal Deviates*. New York: The Free Press, 1955. Reproduced with permission of The Rand Corporation.

TABLE C
Cumulative
Values for the
Binomial
Probability
Distribution

$\Pr[R \leq r]$

		$n = 1$						
r	r/n	π .01	.05	.10	.20	.30	.40	.50
0	.00	0.9900	0.9500	0.9000	0.8000	0.7000	0.6000	0.5000
1	1.00	1.0000	1.0000	1.0000	1.0000	1.0000	1.0000	1.0000

		$n = 2$						
r	r/n	π .01	.05	.10	.20	.30	.40	.50
0	.00	0.9801	0.9025	0.8100	0.6400	0.4900	0.3600	0.2500
1	.50	0.9999	0.9975	0.9900	0.9600	0.9100	0.8400	0.7500
2	1.00	1.0000	1.0000	1.0000	1.0000	1.0000	1.0000	1.0000

		$n = 3$						
r	r/n	π .01	.05	.10	.20	.30	.40	.50
0	.00	0.9703	0.8574	0.7290	0.5120	0.3430	0.2160	0.1250
1	.33	0.9997	0.9927	0.9720	0.8960	0.7840	0.6480	0.5000
2	.67	1.0000	0.9999	0.9990	0.9920	0.9730	0.9360	0.8750
3	1.00	1.0000	1.0000	1.0000	1.0000	1.0000	1.0000	1.0000

		$n = 4$						
r	r/n	π .01	.05	.10	.20	.30	.40	.50
0	.00	0.9606	0.8145	0.6561	0.4096	0.2401	0.1296	0.0625
1	.25	0.9994	0.9860	0.9477	0.8192	0.6517	0.4752	0.3125
2	.50	1.0000	0.9995	0.9963	0.9728	0.9163	0.8208	0.6875
3	.75	1.0000	1.0000	0.9999	0.9984	0.9919	0.9744	0.9375
4	1.00	1.0000	1.0000	1.0000	1.0000	1.0000	1.0000	1.0000

		$n = 5$						
r	r/n	π .01	.05	.10	.20	.30	.40	.50
0	.00	0.9510	0.7738	0.5905	0.3277	0.1681	0.0778	0.0313
1	.20	0.9990	0.9774	0.9185	0.7373	0.5282	0.3370	0.1875
2	.40	1.0000	0.9988	0.9914	0.9421	0.8369	0.6826	0.5000
3	.60	1.0000	1.0000	0.9995	0.9933	0.9692	0.9130	0.8125
4	.80	1.0000	1.0000	1.0000	0.9997	0.9976	0.9898	0.9688
5	1.00				1.0000	1.0000	1.0000	1.0000

TABLE C
(*continued*)

					$n = 10$			
	π	.01	.05	.10	.20	.30	.40	.50
r	r/n							
0	.00	0.9044	0.5987	0.3487	0.1074	0.0282	0.0060	0.0010
1	.10	0.9957	0.9139	0.7361	0.3758	0.1493	0.0464	0.0107
2	.20	0.9999	0.9885	0.9298	0.6778	0.3828	0.1673	0.0547
3	.30	1.0000	0.9990	0.9872	0.8791	0.6496	0.3823	0.1719
4	.40	1.0000	0.9999	0.9984	0.9672	0.8497	0.6331	0.3770
5	.50	1.0000	1.0000	0.9999	0.9936	0.9526	0.8338	0.6230
6	.60	1.0000	1.0000	1.0000	0.9991	0.9894	0.9452	0.8281
7	.70				0.9999	0.9984	0.9877	0.9453
8	.80				1.0000	1.0000	0.9983	0.9893
9	.90						0.9999	0.9990
10	1.00						1.0000	1.0000

					$n = 20$			
	π	.01	.05	.10	.20	.30	.40	.50
r	r/n							
0	.00	0.8179	0.3585	0.1216	0.0115	0.0008	0.0000	0.0000
1	.05	0.9831	0.7358	0.3917	0.0692	0.0076	0.0005	0.0000
2	.10	0.9990	0.9245	0.6769	0.2061	0.0355	0.0036	0.0002
3	.15	1.0000	0.9841	0.8670	0.4114	0.1071	0.0160	0.0013
4	.20	1.0000	0.9974	0.9568	0.6296	0.2375	0.0510	0.0059
5	.25	1.0000	0.9997	0.9887	0.8042	0.4164	0.1256	0.0207
6	.30	1.0000	1.0000	0.9976	0.9133	0.6080	0.2500	0.0577
7	.35	1.0000	1.0000	0.9996	0.9679	0.7723	0.4159	0.1316
8	.40	1.0000	1.0000	0.9999	0.9900	0.8867	0.5956	0.2517
9	.45	1.0000	1.0000	1.0000	0.9974	0.9520	0.7553	0.4119
10	.50				0.9994	0.9829	0.8725	0.5881
11	.55				0.9999	0.9949	0.9435	0.7483
12	.60				1.0000	0.9987	0.9790	0.8684
13	.65					0.9997	0.9935	0.9423
14	.70					1.0000	0.9984	0.9793
15	.75						0.9997	0.9941
16	.80						1.0000	0.9987
17	.85							0.9998
18	.90							1.0000

TABLE C
(*continued*)

r	r/n	π .01	.05	.10	.20	.30	.40	.50
					n = 50			
0	.00	0.6050	0.0769	0.0052	0.0000	0.0000	0.0000	0.0000
1	.02	0.9106	0.2794	0.0338	0.0002	0.0000	0.0000	0.0000
2	.04	0.9862	0.5405	0.1117	0.0013	0.0000	0.0000	0.0000
3	.06	0.9984	0.7604	0.2503	0.0057	0.0000	0.0000	0.0000
4	.08	0.9999	0.8964	0.4312	0.0185	0.0002	0.0000	0.0000
5	.10	1.0000	0.9622	0.6161	0.0480	0.0007	0.0000	0.0000
6	.12	1.0000	0.9882	0.7702	0.1034	0.0025	0.0000	0.0000
7	.14	1.0000	0.9968	0.8779	0.1904	0.0073	0.0001	0.0000
8	.16	1.0000	0.9992	0.9421	0.3073	0.0183	0.0002	0.0000
9	.18	1.0000	0.9998	0.9755	0.4437	0.0402	0.0008	0.0000
10	.20	1.0000	1.0000	0.9906	0.5836	0.0789	0.0022	0.0000
11	.22	1.0000	1.0000	0.9968	0.7107	0.1390	0.0057	0.0000
12	.24	1.0000	1.0000	0.9990	0.8139	0.2229	0.0133	0.0002
13	.26	1.0000	1.0000	0.9997	0.8894	0.3279	0.0280	0.0005
14	.28	1.0000	1.0000	0.9999	0.9393	0.4468	0.0540	0.0013
15	.30	1.0000	1.0000	1.0000	0.9692	0.5692	0.0955	0.0033
16	.32				0.9856	0.6839	0.1561	0.0077
17	.34				0.9937	0.7822	0.2369	0.0164
18	.36				0.9975	0.8594	0.3356	0.0325
19	.38				0.9991	0.9152	0.4465	0.0595
20	.40				0.9997	0.9522	0.5610	0.1013
21	.42				0.9999	0.9749	0.6701	0.1611
22	.44				1.0000	0.9877	0.7660	0.2399
23	.46					0.9944	0.8438	0.3359
24	.48					0.9976	0.9022	0.4439
25	.50					0.9991	0.9427	0.5561
26	.52					0.9997	0.9686	0.6641
27	.54					0.9999	0.9840	0.7601
28	.56					1.0000	0.9924	0.8389
29	.58						0.9966	0.8987
30	.60						0.9986	0.9405
31	.62						0.9995	0.9675
32	.64						0.9998	0.9836
33	.66						0.9999	0.9923
34	.68						1.0000	0.9967
35	.70							0.9987
36	.72							0.9995
37	.74							0.9998
38	.76							1.0000

TABLE C
(*continued*)

		π							
			.01	.05	.10	.20	.30	.40	.50
r	r/n								
0	.00		0.3660	0.0059	0.0000	0.0000	0.0000	0.0000	0.0000
1	.01		0.7358	0.0371	0.0003	0.0000	0.0000	0.0000	0.0000
2	.02		0.9206	0.1183	0.0019	0.0000	0.0000	0.0000	0.0000
3	.03		0.9816	0.2578	0.0078	0.0000	0.0000	0.0000	0.0000
4	.04		0.9966	0.4360	0.0237	0.0000	0.0000	0.0000	0.0000
5	.05		0.9995	0.6160	0.0576	0.0000	0.0000	0.0000	0.0000
6	.06		0.9999	0.7660	0.1172	0.0001	0.0000	0.0000	0.0000
7	.07		1.0000	0.8720	0.2061	0.0003	0.0000	0.0000	0.0000
8	.08		1.0000	0.9369	0.3209	0.0009	0.0000	0.0000	0.0000
9	.09		1.0000	0.9718	0.4513	0.0023	0.0000	0.0000	0.0000
10	.10		1.0000	0.9885	0.5832	0.0057	0.0000	0.0000	0.0000
11	.11		1.0000	0.9957	0.7030	0.0126	0.0000	0.0000	0.0000
12	.12		1.0000	0.9985	0.8018	0.0253	0.0000	0.0000	0.0000
13	.13		1.0000	0.9995	0.8761	0.0469	0.0001	0.0000	0.0000
14	.14		1.0000	0.9999	0.9274	0.0804	0.0002	0.0000	0.0000
15	.15		1.0000	1.0000	0.9601	0.1285	0.0004	0.0000	0.0000
16	.16		1.0000	1.0000	0.9794	0.1923	0.0010	0.0000	0.0000
17	.17		1.0000	1.0000	0.9900	0.2712	0.0022	0.0000	0.0000
18	.18		1.0000	1.0000	0.9954	0.3621	0.0045	0.0000	0.0000
19	.19		1.0000	1.0000	0.9980	0.4602	0.0089	0.0000	0.0000
20	.20		1.0000	1.0000	0.9992	0.5595	0.0165	0.0000	0.0000
21	.21		1.0000	1.0000	0.9997	0.6540	0.0288	0.0000	0.0000
22	.22		1.0000	1.0000	0.9999	0.7389	0.0479	0.0001	0.0000
23	.23		1.0000	1.0000	1.0000	0.8109	0.0755	0.0003	0.0000
24	.24					0.8686	0.1136	0.0006	0.0000
25	.25					0.9125	0.1631	0.0012	0.0000
26	.26					0.9442	0.2244	0.0024	0.0000
27	.27					0.9658	0.2964	0.0046	0.0000
28	.28					0.9800	0.3768	0.0084	0.0000
29	.29					0.9888	0.4623	0.0148	0.0000
30	.30					0.9939	0.5491	0.0248	0.0000
31	.31					0.9969	0.6331	0.0398	0.0001
32	.32					0.9984	0.7107	0.0615	0.0002
33	.33					0.9993	0.7793	0.0913	0.0004
34	.34					0.9997	0.8371	0.1303	0.0009
35	.35					0.9999	0.8839	0.1795	0.0018

n = 100

TABLE C
(continued)

r	r/n	π	.01	.05	.10	.20	.30	.40	.50
							n = 100		
36	.36					0.9999	0.9201	0.2386	0.0033
37	.37					1.0000	0.9470	0.3068	0.0060
38	.38						0.9660	0.3822	0.0105
39	.39						0.9790	0.4621	0.0176
40	.40						0.9875	0.5433	0.0284
41	.41						0.9928	0.6225	0.0443
42	.42						0.9960	0.6967	0.0666
43	.43						0.9979	0.7635	0.0967
44	.44						0.9989	0.8211	0.1356
45	.45						0.9995	0.8689	0.1841
46	.46						0.9997	0.9070	0.2421
47	.47						0.9999	0.9362	0.3086
48	.48						0.9999	0.9577	0.3822
49	.49						1.0000	0.9729	0.4602
50	.50							0.9832	0.5398
51	.51							0.9900	0.6178
52	.52							0.9942	0.6914
53	.53							0.9968	0.7579
54	.54							0.9983	0.8159
55	.55							0.9991	0.8644
56	.56							0.9996	0.9033
57	.57							0.9998	0.9334
58	.58							0.9999	0.9557
59	.59							1.0000	0.9716
60	.60								0.9824
61	.61								0.9895
62	.62								0.9940
63	.63								0.9967
64	.64								0.9982
65	.65								0.9991
66	.66								0.9996
67	.67								0.9998
68	.68								0.9999
69	.69								1.0000

SOURCE: From *Management Science for Business Decisions* by Lawrence L. Lapin, copyright © 1980 by Harcourt Brace Jovanovich, Inc. Reproduced by permission of the publisher.

TABLE D
Areas Under the
Standard Normal
Curve

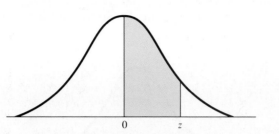

0   z

The following table provides the area between the mean and normal deviate
value z.

Normal Deviate z	.00	.01	.02	.03	.04	.05	.06	.07	.08	.09
0.0	.0000	.0040	.0080	.0120	.0160	.0199	.0239	.0279	.0319	.0359
0.1	.0398	.0438	.0478	.0517	.0557	.0596	.0636	.0675	.0714	.0753
0.2	.0793	.0832	.0871	.0910	.0948	.0987	.1026	.1064	.1103	.1141
0.3	.1179	.1217	.1255	.1293	.1331	.1368	.1406	.1443	.1480	.1517
0.4	.1554	.1591	.1628	.1664	.1700	.1736	.1772	.1808	.1844	.1879
0.5	.1915	.1950	.1985	.2019	.2054	.2088	.2123	.2157	.2190	.2224
0.6	.2257	.2291	.2324	.2357	.2389	.2422	.2454	.2486	.2518	.2549
0.7	.2580	.2612	.2642	.2673	.2704	.2734	.2764	.2794	.2823	.2852
0.8	.2881	.2910	.2939	.2967	.2995	.3023	.3051	.3078	.3106	.3133
0.9	.3159	.3186	.3212	.3238	.3264	.3289	.3315	.3340	.3365	.3389
1.0	.3413	.3438	.3461	.3485	.3508	.3531	.3554	.3577	.3599	.3621
1.1	.3643	.3665	.3686	.3708	.3729	.3749	.3770	.3790	.3810	.3830
1.2	.3849	.3869	.3888	.3907	.3925	.3944	.3962	.3980	.3997	.4015
1.3	.4032	.4049	.4066	.4082	.4099	.4115	.4131	.4147	.4162	.4177
1.4	.4192	.4207	.4222	.4236	.4251	.4265	.4279	.4292	.4306	.4319
1.5	.4332	.4345	.4357	.4370	.4382	.4394	.4406	.4418	.4429	.4441
1.6	.4452	.4463	.4474	.4484	.4495	.4505	.4515	.4525	.4535	.4545
1.7	.4554	.4564	.4573	.4582	.4591	.4599	.4608	.4616	.4625	.4633
1.8	.4641	.4649	.4656	.4664	.4671	.4678	.4686	.4693	.4699	.4706
1.9	.4713	.4719	.4726	.4732	.4738	.4744	.4750	.4756	.4761	.4767
2.0	.4772	.4778	.4783	.4788	.4793	.4798	.4803	.4808	.4812	.4817
2.1	.4821	.4826	.4830	.4834	.4838	.4842	.4846	.4850	.4854	.4857
2.2	.4861	.4864	.4868	.4871	.4875	.4878	.4881	.4884	.4887	.4890
2.3	.4893	.4896	.4898	.4901	.4904	.4906	.4909	.4911	.4913	.4916
2.4	.4918	.4920	.4922	.4925	.4927	.4929	.4931	.4932	.4934	.4936
2.5	.4938	.4940	.4941	.4943	.4945	.4946	.4948	.4949	.4951	.4952
2.6	.4953	.4955	.4956	.4957	.4959	.4960	.4961	.4962	.4963	.4964
2.7	.4965	.4966	.4967	.4968	.4969	.4970	.4971	.4972	.4973	.4974
2.8	.4974	.4975	.4976	.4977	.4977	.4978	.4979	.4979	.4980	.4981
2.9	.4981	.4982	.4982	.4983	.4984	.4984	.4985	.4985	.4986	.4986
3.0	.49865	.4987	.4987	.4988	.4988	.4989	.4989	.4989	.4990	.4990
4.0	.49997									

SOURCE: © 1977 by Harcourt Brace Jovanovich, Inc., and reproduced with their permission from
Statistical Analysis for Decision Making, 2nd ed., by Morris Hamburg.

Normal Deviates for Statistical Estimation

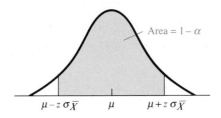

Reliability or Confidence Level $1 - \alpha$	Normal Deviate $z_{\alpha/2}$
.80	1.28
.90	1.64
.95	1.96
.98	2.33
.99	2.57
.998	3.08
.999	3.27

Critical Normal Deviates for Hypothesis Testing

One-Sided Tests

Two-Sided Tests

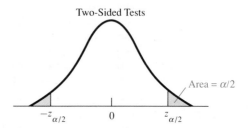

Significance Level α	Normal Deviate z_{α}		Significance Level α	Normal Deviate $z_{\alpha/2}$
.10	1.28		.10	1.64
.05	1.64		.05	1.96
.025	1.96		.025	2.24
.01	2.33		.01	2.57
.005	2.57		.005	2.81
.001	3.08		.001	3.27

The following table provides the values of t_α that correspond to a given upper tail area α and a specified number of degrees of freedom.

Degrees of Freedom	Upper Tail Area α									
	.4	.25	.1	.05	.025	.01	.005	.0025	.001	.0005
1	0.325	1.000	3.078	6.314	12.706	31.821	63.657	127.32	318.31	636.62
2	.289	.816	1.886	2.920	4.303	6.965	9.925	14.089	22.327	31.598
3	.277	.765	1.638	2.353	3.182	4.541	5.841	7.453	10.214	12.924
4	.271	.741	1.533	2.132	2.776	3.747	4.604	5.598	7.173	8.610
5	0.267	0.727	1.476	2.015	2.571	3.365	4.032	4.773	5.893	6.869
6	.265	.718	1.440	1.943	2.447	3.143	3.707	4.317	5.208	5.959
7	.263	.711	1.415	1.895	2.365	2.998	3.499	4.029	4.785	5.408
8	.262	.706	1.397	1.860	2.306	2.896	3.355	3.833	4.501	5.041
9	.261	.703	1.383	1.833	2.262	2.821	3.250	3.690	4.297	4.781
10	0.260	0.700	1.372	1.812	2.228	2.764	3.169	3.581	4.144	4.587
11	.260	.697	1.363	1.796	2.201	2.718	3.106	3.497	4.025	4.437
12	.259	.695	1.356	1.782	2.179	2.681	3.055	3.428	3.930	4.318
13	.259	.694	1.350	1.771	2.160	2.650	3.012	3.372	3.852	4.221
14	.258	.692	1.345	1.761	2.145	2.624	2.977	3.326	3.787	4.140
15	0.258	0.691	1.341	1.753	2.131	2.602	2.947	3.286	3.733	4.073
16	.258	.690	1.337	1.746	2.120	2.583	2.921	3.252	3.686	4.015
17	.257	.689	1.333	1.740	2.110	2.567	2.898	3.222	3.646	3.965
18	.257	.688	1.330	1.734	2.101	2.552	2.878	3.197	3.610	3.922
19	.257	.688	1.328	1.729	2.093	2.539	2.861	3.174	3.579	3.883
20	0.257	0.687	1.325	1.725	2.086	2.528	2.845	3.153	3.552	3.850
21	.257	.686	1.323	1.721	2.080	2.518	2.831	3.135	3.527	3.819
22	.256	.686	1.321	1.717	2.074	2.508	2.819	3.119	3.505	3.792
23	.256	.685	1.319	1.714	2.069	2.500	2.807	3.104	3.485	3.767
24	.256	.685	1.318	1.711	2.064	2.492	2.797	3.091	3.467	3.745
25	0.256	0.684	1.316	1.708	2.060	2.485	2.787	3.078	3.450	3.725
26	.256	.684	1.315	1.706	2.056	2.479	2.779	3.067	3.435	3.707
27	.256	.684	1.314	1.703	2.052	2.473	2.771	3.057	3.421	3.690
28	.256	.683	1.313	1.701	2.048	2.467	2.763	3.047	3.408	3.674
29	.256	.683	1.311	1.699	2.045	2.462	2.756	3.038	3.396	3.659
30	0.256	0.683	1.310	1.697	2.042	2.457	2.750	3.030	3.385	3.646
40	.255	.681	1.303	1.684	2.021	2.423	2.704	2.971	3.307	3.551
60	.254	.679	1.296	1.671	2.000	2.390	2.660	2.915	3.232	3.460
120	.254	.677	1.289	1.658	1.980	2.358	2.617	2.860	3.160	3.373
∞	.253	.674	1.282	1.645	1.960	2.326	2.576	2.807	3.090	3.291

SOURCE: E. S. Pearson and H. O. Hartley, *Biometrika Tables for Statisticians*, Vol. I. London: Cambridge University Press, 1966. Partly derived from Table III of Fisher and Yates, *Statistical Tables for Biological, Agricultural and Medical Research*, published by Longman Group Ltd., London (previously published by Oliver & Boyd, Edinburgh, 1963). Reproduced with permission of the authors and publishers.

TABLE G
F Distribution

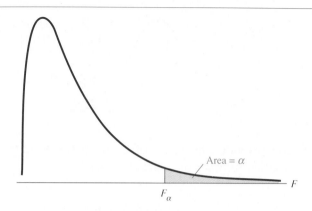

The following table provides the values of F_α that correspond to a given upper tail area α and a specified degrees of freedom pair. The values of $F_{.05}$ are in lightface type, while those for $F_{.01}$ are given in boldface type. The number of degrees of freedom for the *numerator* mean square is indicated at the head of each *column*, while the number of degrees of freedom for the *denominator* mean square determines which *row* is applicable.

Degrees of Freedom for Denominator	Degrees of Freedom for Numerator											
	1	2	3	4	5	6	7	8	9	10	11	12
1	161	200	216	225	230	234	237	239	241	242	243	244
	4,052	**4,999**	**5,403**	**5,625**	**5,764**	**5,859**	**5,928**	**5,981**	**6,022**	**6,056**	**6,082**	**6,106**
2	18.51	19.00	19.16	19.25	19.30	19.33	19.36	19.37	19.38	19.39	19.40	19.41
	98.49	**99.01**	**99.17**	**99.25**	**99.30**	**99.33**	**99.34**	**99.36**	**99.38**	**99.40**	**99.41**	**99.42**
3	10.13	9.55	9.28	9.12	9.01	8.94	8.88	8.84	8.81	8.78	8.76	8.74
	34.12	**30.81**	**29.46**	**28.71**	**28.24**	**27.91**	**27.67**	**27.49**	**27.34**	**27.23**	**27.13**	**27.05**
4	7.71	6.94	6.59	6.39	6.26	6.16	6.09	6.04	6.00	5.96	5.93	5.91
	21.20	**18.00**	**16.69**	**15.98**	**15.52**	**15.21**	**14.98**	**14.80**	**14.66**	**14.54**	**14.45**	**14.37**
5	6.61	5.79	5.41	5.19	5.05	4.95	4.88	4.82	4.78	4.74	4.70	4.68
	16.26	**13.27**	**12.06**	**11.39**	**10.97**	**10.67**	**10.45**	**10.27**	**10.15**	**10.05**	**9.96**	**9.89**
6	5.99	5.14	4.76	4.53	4.39	4.28	4.21	4.15	4.10	4.06	4.03	4.00
	13.74	**10.92**	**9.78**	**9.15**	**8.75**	**8.47**	**8.26**	**8.10**	**7.98**	**7.87**	**7.79**	**7.72**
7	5.59	4.74	4.35	4.12	3.97	3.87	3.79	3.73	3.68	3.63	3.60	3.57
	12.25	**9.55**	**8.45**	**7.85**	**7.46**	**7.19**	**7.00**	**6.84**	**6.71**	**6.62**	**6.54**	**6.47**
8	5.32	4.46	4.07	3.84	3.69	3.58	3.50	3.44	3.39	3.34	3.31	3.28
	11.26	**8.65**	**7.59**	**7.01**	**6.63**	**6.37**	**6.19**	**6.03**	**5.91**	**5.82**	**5.74**	**5.67**
9	5.12	4.26	3.86	3.63	3.48	3.37	3.29	3.23	3.18	3.13	3.10	3.07
	10.56	**8.02**	**6.99**	**6.42**	**6.06**	**5.80**	**5.62**	**5.47**	**5.35**	**5.26**	**5.18**	**5.11**
10	4.96	4.10	3.71	3.48	3.33	3.22	3.14	3.07	3.02	2.97	2.94	2.91
	10.04	**7.56**	**6.55**	**5.99**	**5.64**	**5.39**	**5.21**	**5.06**	**4.95**	**4.85**	**4.78**	**4.71**
11	4.84	3.98	3.59	3.36	3.20	3.09	3.01	2.95	2.90	2.86	2.82	2.79
	9.65	**7.20**	**6.22**	**5.67**	**5.32**	**5.07**	**4.88**	**4.74**	**4.63**	**4.54**	**4.46**	**4.40**
12	4.75	3.89	3.49	3.26	3.11	3.00	2.92	2.85	2.80	2.76	2.72	2.69
	9.33	**6.93**	**5.95**	**5.41**	**5.06**	**4.82**	**4.65**	**4.50**	**4.39**	**4.30**	**4.22**	**4.16**
13	4.67	3.80	3.41	3.18	3.02	2.92	2.84	2.77	2.72	2.67	2.63	2.60
	9.07	**6.70**	**5.74**	**5.20**	**4.86**	**4.62**	**4.44**	**4.30**	**4.19**	**4.10**	**4.02**	**3.96**
14	4.60	3.74	3.34	3.11	2.96	2.85	2.77	2.70	2.65	2.60	2.56	2.53
	8.86	**6.51**	**5.56**	**5.03**	**4.69**	**4.46**	**4.28**	**4.14**	**4.03**	**3.94**	**3.86**	**3.80**

TABLE G
(*continued*)

Degrees of Freedom for Denominator	____Degrees of Freedom for Numerator____											
	14	16	20	24	30	40	50	75	100	200	500	∞
1	245	246	248	249	250	251	252	253	253	254	254	254
	6,142	6,169	6,208	6,234	6,258	6,286	6,302	6,323	6,334	6,352	6,361	6,366
2	19.42	19.43	19.44	19.45	19.46	19.47	19.47	19.48	19.49	19.49	19.50	19.50
	99.43	99.44	99.45	99.46	99.47	99.48	99.48	99.49	99.49	99.49	99.50	99.50
3	8.71	8.69	8.66	8.64	8.62	8.60	8.58	8.57	8.56	8.54	8.54	8.53
	26.92	26.83	26.69	26.60	26.50	26.41	26.30	26.27	26.23	26.18	26.14	26.12
4	5.87	5.84	5.80	5.77	5.74	5.71	5.70	5.68	5.66	5.65	5.64	5.63
	14.24	14.15	14.02	13.93	13.83	13.74	13.69	13.61	13.57	13.52	13.48	13.46
5	4.64	4.60	4.56	4.53	4.50	4.46	4.44	4.42	4.40	4.38	4.37	4.36
	9.77	9.68	9.55	9.47	9.38	9.29	9.24	9.17	9.13	9.07	9.04	9.02
6	3.96	3.92	3.87	3.84	3.81	3.77	3.75	3.72	3.71	3.69	3.68	3.67
	7.60	7.52	7.39	7.31	7.23	7.14	7.09	7.02	6.99	6.94	6.90	6.88
7	3.52	3.49	3.44	3.41	3.38	3.34	3.32	3.29	3.28	3.25	3.24	3.23
	6.35	6.27	6.15	6.07	5.98	5.90	5.85	5.78	5.75	5.70	5.67	5.65
8	3.23	3.20	3.15	3.12	3.08	3.05	3.03	3.00	2.98	2.96	2.94	2.93
	5.56	5.48	5.36	5.28	5.20	5.11	5.06	5.00	4.96	4.91	4.88	4.86
9	3.02	2.98	2.93	2.90	2.86	2.82	2.80	2.77	2.76	2.73	2.72	2.71
	5.00	4.92	4.80	4.73	4.64	4.56	4.51	4.45	4.41	4.36	4.33	4.31
10	2.86	2.82	2.77	2.74	2.70	2.67	2.64	2.61	2.59	2.56	2.55	2.54
	4.60	4.52	4.41	4.33	4.25	4.17	4.12	4.05	4.01	3.96	3.93	3.91
11	2.74	2.70	2.65	2.61	2.57	2.53	2.50	2.47	2.45	2.42	2.41	2.40
	4.29	4.21	4.10	4.02	3.94	3.86	3.80	3.74	3.70	3.66	3.62	3.60
12	2.64	2.60	2.54	2.50	2.46	2.42	2.40	2.36	2.35	2.32	2.31	2.30
	4.05	3.98	3.86	3.78	3.70	3.61	3.56	3.49	3.46	3.41	3.38	3.36
13	2.55	2.51	2.46	2.42	2.38	2.34	2.32	2.28	2.26	2.24	2.22	2.21
	3.85	3.78	3.67	3.59	3.51	3.42	3.37	3.30	3.27	3.21	3.18	3.16
14	2.48	2.44	2.39	2.35	2.31	2.27	2.24	2.21	2.19	2.16	2.14	2.13
	3.70	3.62	3.51	3.43	3.34	3.26	3.21	3.14	3.11	3.06	3.02	3.00

TABLE G
(continued)

Degrees of Freedom for Denominator	Degrees of Freedom for Numerator											
	1	2	3	4	5	6	7	8	9	10	11	12
15	4.54	3.68	3.29	3.06	2.90	2.79	2.70	2.64	2.59	2.55	2.51	2.48
	8.68	**6.36**	**5.42**	**4.89**	**4.56**	**4.32**	**4.14**	**4.00**	**3.89**	**3.80**	**3.73**	**3.67**
16	4.49	3.63	3.24	3.01	2.85	2.74	2.66	2.59	2.54	2.49	2.45	2.42
	8.53	**6.23**	**5.29**	**4.77**	**4.44**	**4.20**	**4.03**	**3.89**	**3.78**	**3.69**	**3.61**	**3.55**
17	4.45	3.59	3.20	2.96	2.81	2.70	2.62	2.55	2.50	2.45	2.41	2.38
	8.40	**6.11**	**5.18**	**4.67**	**4.34**	**4.10**	**3.93**	**3.79**	**3.68**	**3.59**	**3.52**	**3.45**
18	4.41	3.55	3.16	2.93	2.77	2.66	2.58	2.51	2.46	2.41	2.37	2.34
	8.28	**6.01**	**5.09**	**4.58**	**4.25**	**4.01**	**3.85**	**3.71**	**3.60**	**3.51**	**3.44**	**3.37**
19	4.38	3.52	3.13	2.90	2.74	2.63	2.55	2.48	2.43	2.38	2.34	2.31
	8.18	**5.93**	**5.01**	**4.50**	**4.17**	**3.94**	**3.77**	**3.63**	**3.52**	**3.43**	**3.36**	**3.30**
20	4.35	3.49	3.10	2.87	2.71	2.60	2.52	2.45	2.40	2.35	2.31	2.28
	8.10	**5.85**	**4.94**	**4.43**	**4.10**	**3.87**	**3.71**	**3.56**	**3.45**	**3.37**	**3.30**	**3.23**
21	4.32	3.47	3.07	2.84	2.68	2.57	2.49	2.42	2.37	2.32	2.28	2.25
	8.02	**5.78**	**4.87**	**4.37**	**4.04**	**3.81**	**3.65**	**3.51**	**3.40**	**3.31**	**3.24**	**3.17**
22	4.30	3.44	3.05	2.82	2.66	2.55	2.47	2.40	2.35	2.30	2.26	2.23
	7.94	**5.72**	**4.82**	**4.41**	**3.99**	**3.76**	**3.59**	**3.45**	**3.35**	**3.26**	**3.18**	**3.12**
23	4.28	3.42	3.03	2.80	2.64	2.53	2.45	2.38	2.32	2.28	2.24	2.20
	7.88	**5.66**	**4.76**	**4.26**	**3.94**	**3.71**	**3.54**	**3.41**	**3.30**	**3.21**	**3.14**	**3.07**
24	4.26	3.40	3.01	2.78	2.62	2.51	2.43	2.36	2.30	2.26	2.22	2.18
	7.82	**5.61**	**4.72**	**4.22**	**3.90**	**3.67**	**3.50**	**3.36**	**3.25**	**3.17**	**3.09**	**3.03**
25	4.24	3.38	2.99	2.76	2.60	2.49	2.41	2.34	2.28	2.24	2.20	2.16
	7.77	**5.57**	**4.68**	**4.18**	**3.86**	**3.63**	**3.46**	**3.32**	**3.21**	**3.13**	**3.05**	**2.99**
26	4.22	3.37	2.89	2.74	2.59	2.47	2.39	2.32	2.27	2.22	2.18	2.15
	7.72	**5.53**	**4.64**	**4.14**	**3.82**	**3.59**	**3.42**	**3.29**	**3.17**	**3.09**	**3.02**	**2.96**
27	4.21	3.35	2.96	2.73	2.57	2.46	2.37	2.30	2.25	2.20	2.16	2.13
	7.68	**5.49**	**4.60**	**4.11**	**3.79**	**3.56**	**3.39**	**3.26**	**3.14**	**3.06**	**2.98**	**2.93**
28	4.20	3.34	2.95	2.71	2.56	2.44	2.36	2.29	2.24	2.19	2.15	2.12
	7.64	**5.45**	**4.57**	**4.07**	**3.76**	**3.53**	**3.36**	**3.23**	**3.11**	**3.03**	**2.95**	**2.90**
29	4.18	3.33	2.93	2.70	2.54	2.43	2.35	2.28	2.22	2.18	2.14	2.10
	7.60	**5.52**	**4.54**	**4.04**	**3.73**	**3.50**	**3.33**	**3.20**	**3.08**	**3.00**	**2.92**	**2.87**
30	4.17	3.32	2.92	2.69	2.53	2.43	2.34	2.27	2.21	2.16	2.12	2.09
	7.56	**5.39**	**4.51**	**4.02**	**3.70**	**3.47**	**3.30**	**3.17**	**3.06**	**2.98**	**2.90**	**2.84**
32	4.15	3.30	2.90	2.67	2.51	2.40	2.32	2.25	2.19	2.14	2.10	2.07
	7.50	**5.34**	**4.46**	**3.97**	**3.66**	**3.42**	**3.25**	**3.12**	**3.01**	**2.94**	**2.86**	**2.80**
34	4.13	3.28	2.88	2.65	2.49	2.38	2.30	2.23	2.17	2.12	2.08	2.05
	7.44	**5.29**	**4.42**	**3.93**	**3.61**	**3.38**	**3.21**	**3.08**	**2.97**	**2.89**	**2.82**	**2.76**
36	4.11	3.26	2.86	2.63	2.48	2.36	2.28	2.21	2.15	2.10	2.06	2.03
	7.39	**5.25**	**4.38**	**3.89**	**3.58**	**3.35**	**3.18**	**3.04**	**2.94**	**2.86**	**2.78**	**2.72**
38	4.10	3.25	2.85	2.62	2.46	2.35	2.26	2.19	2.14	2.09	2.05	2.02
	7.35	**5.21**	**4.34**	**3.86**	**3.54**	**3.32**	**3.15**	**3.02**	**2.91**	**2.82**	**2.75**	**2.69**

Degrees of Freedom for Denominator	Degrees of Freedom for Numerator											
	14	16	20	24	30	40	50	75	100	200	500	∞
15	2.43	2.39	2.33	2.29	2.25	2.21	2.18	2.15	2.12	2.10	2.08	2.07
	3.56	**3.48**	**3.36**	**3.29**	**3.20**	**3.12**	**3.07**	**3.00**	**2.97**	**2.92**	**2.89**	**2.87**
16	2.37	2.33	2.28	2.24	2.20	2.16	2.13	2.09	2.07	2.04	2.02	2.01
	3.45	**3.37**	**3.25**	**3.18**	**3.10**	**3.01**	**2.96**	**2.89**	**2.86**	**2.80**	**2.77**	**2.75**
17	2.33	2.29	2.23	2.19	2.15	2.11	2.08	2.04	2.02	1.99	1.97	1.96
	3.35	**3.27**	**3.16**	**3.08**	**3.00**	**2.92**	**2.86**	**2.79**	**2.76**	**2.70**	**2.67**	**2.65**
18	2.29	2.25	2.19	2.15	2.11	2.07	2.04	2.00	1.98	1.95	1.93	1.92
	3.27	**3.19**	**3.07**	**3.00**	**2.91**	**2.83**	**2.78**	**2.71**	**2.68**	**2.62**	**2.59**	**2.57**
19	2.26	2.21	2.15	2.11	2.07	2.02	2.00	1.96	1.94	1.91	1.90	1.88
	3.19	**3.12**	**3.00**	**2.92**	**2.84**	**2.76**	**2.70**	**2.63**	**2.60**	**2.54**	**2.51**	**2.49**
20	2.23	2.18	2.12	2.08	2.04	1.99	1.96	1.92	1.90	1.87	1.85	1.84
	3.13	**3.05**	**2.94**	**2.86**	**2.77**	**2.69**	**2.63**	**2.56**	**2.53**	**2.47**	**2.44**	**2.42**
21	2.20	2.15	2.09	2.05	2.00	1.96	1.93	1.89	1.87	1.84	1.82	1.81
	3.07	**2.99**	**2.88**	**2.80**	**2.72**	**2.63**	**2.58**	**2.51**	**2.47**	**2.42**	**2.38**	**2.36**
22	2.18	2.13	2.07	2.03	1.98	1.93	1.91	1.87	1.84	1.81	1.80	1.78
	3.02	**2.94**	**2.83**	**2.75**	**2.67**	**2.58**	**2.53**	**2.46**	**2.42**	**2.37**	**2.33**	**2.31**
23	2.14	2.10	2.04	2.00	1.96	1.91	1.88	1.84	1.82	1.79	1.77	1.76
	2.97	**2.89**	**2.78**	**2.70**	**2.62**	**2.53**	**2.48**	**2.41**	**2.37**	**2.32**	**2.28**	**2.26**
24	2.13	2.09	2.02	1.98	1.94	1.89	1.86	1.82	1.80	1.76	1.74	1.73
	2.93	**2.85**	**2.74**	**2.66**	**2.58**	**2.49**	**2.44**	**2.36**	**2.33**	**2.27**	**2.23**	**2.21**
25	2.11	2.06	2.00	1.96	1.92	1.87	1.84	1.80	1.77	1.74	1.72	1.71
	2.89	**2.81**	**2.70**	**2.62**	**2.54**	**2.45**	**2.40**	**2.32**	**2.29**	**2.23**	**2.19**	**2.17**
26	2.10	2.05	1.99	1.95	1.90	1.85	1.82	1.78	1.76	1.72	1.70	1.69
	2.86	**2.77**	**2.66**	**2.58**	**2.50**	**2.41**	**2.36**	**2.28**	**2.25**	**2.19**	**2.15**	**2.13**
27	2.08	2.03	1.97	1.93	1.88	1.84	1.80	1.76	1.74	1.71	1.68	1.67
	2.83	**2.74**	**2.63**	**2.55**	**2.47**	**2.38**	**2.33**	**2.25**	**2.21**	**2.16**	**2.12**	**2.10**
28	2.06	2.02	1.96	1.91	1.87	1.81	1.78	1.75	1.72	1.69	1.67	1.65
	2.80	**2.71**	**2.60**	**2.52**	**2.44**	**2.35**	**2.30**	**2.22**	**2.18**	**2.13**	**2.09**	**2.06**
29	2.05	2.00	1.94	1.90	1.85	1.80	1.77	1.73	1.71	1.68	1.65	1.64
	2.77	**2.68**	**2.57**	**2.49**	**2.41**	**2.32**	**2.27**	**2.19**	**2.15**	**2.10**	**2.06**	**2.03**
30	2.04	1.99	1.93	1.89	1.84	1.79	1.76	1.72	1.69	1.66	1.64	1.62
	2.74	**2.66**	**2.55**	**2.47**	**2.38**	**2.29**	**2.24**	**2.16**	**2.13**	**2.07**	**2.03**	**2.01**
32	2.02	1.97	1.91	1.86	1.82	1.76	1.74	1.69	1.67	1.64	1.61	1.59
	2.70	**2.62**	**2.51**	**2.42**	**2.34**	**2.25**	**2.20**	**2.12**	**2.08**	**2.02**	**1.98**	**1.96**
34	2.00	1.95	1.89	1.84	1.80	1.74	1.71	1.67	1.64	1.61	1.59	1.57
	2.66	**2.58**	**2.47**	**2.38**	**2.30**	**2.21**	**2.15**	**2.08**	**2.04**	**1.98**	**1.94**	**1.91**
36	1.98	1.93	1.87	1.82	1.78	1.72	1.69	1.65	1.62	1.59	1.56	1.55
	2.62	**2.54**	**2.43**	**2.35**	**2.26**	**2.17**	**2.12**	**2.04**	**2.00**	**1.94**	**1.90**	**1.87**
38	1.96	1.92	1.85	1.80	1.76	1.71	1.67	1.63	1.60	1.57	1.54	1.53
	2.59	**2.51**	**2.40**	**2.32**	**2.22**	**2.14**	**2.08**	**2.00**	**1.97**	**1.90**	**1.86**	**1.84**

TABLE G
(continued)

Degrees of Freedom for Denominator	Degrees of Freedom for Numerator											
	1	2	3	4	5	6	7	8	9	10	11	12
40	4.08	3.23	2.84	2.61	2.45	2.34	2.25	2.18	2.12	2.08	2.04	2.00
	7.31	**5.18**	**4.31**	**3.83**	**3.51**	**3.29**	**3.12**	**2.99**	**2.88**	**2.80**	**2.73**	**2.66**
42	4.07	3.22	2.83	2.59	2.44	2.32	2.24	2.17	2.11	2.06	2.02	1.99
	7.27	**5.15**	**4.29**	**3.80**	**3.49**	**3.26**	**3.10**	**2.96**	**2.86**	**2.77**	**2.70**	**2.64**
44	4.06	3.21	2.82	2.58	2.43	2.31	2.23	2.16	2.10	2.05	2.01	1.98
	7.24	**5.12**	**4.26**	**3.78**	**3.46**	**3.24**	**3.07**	**2.94**	**2.84**	**2.75**	**2.68**	**2.62**
46	4.05	3.20	2.81	2.57	2.42	2.30	2.22	2.14	2.09	2.04	2.00	1.97
	7.21	**5.10**	**4.24**	**3.76**	**3.44**	**3.22**	**3.05**	**2.92**	**2.82**	**2.73**	**2.66**	**2.60**
48	4.04	3.19	2.80	2.56	2.41	2.30	2.21	2.14	2.08	2.03	1.99	1.96
	7.19	**5.08**	**4.22**	**3.74**	**3.42**	**3.20**	**3.04**	**2.90**	**2.80**	**2.71**	**2.64**	**2.58**
50	4.03	3.18	2.79	2.56	2.40	2.29	2.20	2.13	2.07	2.02	1.98	1.95
	7.17	**5.06**	**4.20**	**3.72**	**3.41**	**3.18**	**3.02**	**2.88**	**2.78**	**2.70**	**2.62**	**2.56**
55	4.02	3.17	2.78	2.54	2.38	2.27	2.18	2.11	2.05	2.00	1.97	1.93
	7.12	**5.01**	**4.16**	**3.68**	**3.37**	**3.15**	**2.98**	**2.85**	**2.75**	**2.66**	**2.59**	**2.53**
60	4.00	3.15	2.76	2.52	2.37	2.25	2.17	2.10	2.04	1.99	1.95	1.92
	7.08	**4.98**	**4.13**	**3.65**	**3.34**	**3.12**	**2.95**	**2.82**	**2.72**	**2.63**	**2.56**	**2.50**
65	3.99	3.14	2.75	2.51	2.36	2.24	2.15	2.08	2.02	1.98	1.94	1.90
	7.04	**4.95**	**4.10**	**3.62**	**3.31**	**3.09**	**2.93**	**2.79**	**2.70**	**2.61**	**2.54**	**2.47**
70	3.98	3.13	2.74	2.50	2.35	2.32	2.14	2.07	2.01	1.97	1.93	1.80
	7.01	**4.92**	**4.08**	**3.60**	**3.29**	**3.07**	**2.91**	**2.77**	**2.67**	**2.59**	**2.51**	**2.45**
80	3.96	3.11	2.72	2.48	2.33	2.21	2.12	2.05	1.99	1.95	1.91	1.88
	6.95	**4.88**	**4.04**	**3.56**	**3.25**	**3.04**	**2.87**	**2.74**	**2.64**	**2.55**	**2.48**	**2.41**
100	3.94	3.09	2.70	2.46	2.30	2.19	2.10	2.03	1.97	1.92	1.88	1.85
	6.90	**4.82**	**3.98**	**3.51**	**3.20**	**2.99**	**2.82**	**2.69**	**2.59**	**2.51**	**2.43**	**2.36**
125	3.92	3.07	2.68	2.44	2.29	2.17	2.08	2.01	1.95	1.90	1.86	1.83
	6.84	**4.78**	**3.94**	**3.47**	**3.17**	**2.95**	**2.79**	**2.65**	**2.56**	**2.47**	**2.40**	**2.33**
150	3.91	3.06	2.67	2.43	2.27	2.16	2.07	2.00	1.94	1.89	1.85	1.82
	6.81	**4.75**	**3.91**	**3.44**	**3.13**	**2.92**	**2.76**	**2.62**	**2.53**	**2.44**	**2.37**	**2.30**
200	3.89	3.04	2.65	2.41	2.26	2.14	2.05	1.98	1.92	1.87	1.83	1.80
	6.76	**4.71**	**3.88**	**3.41**	**3.11**	**2.90**	**2.73**	**2.60**	**2.50**	**2.41**	**2.34**	**2.28**
400	3.86	3.02	2.62	2.39	2.23	2.12	2.03	1.96	1.90	1.85	1.81	1.78
	6.70	**4.66**	**3.83**	**3.36**	**3.06**	**2.85**	**2.69**	**2.55**	**2.46**	**2.37**	**2.29**	**2.23**
1,000	3.85	3.00	2.61	2.38	2.22	2.10	2.02	1.95	1.89	1.84	1.80	1.76
	6.66	**4.62**	**3.80**	**3.34**	**3.04**	**2.82**	**2.66**	**2.53**	**2.43**	**2.34**	**2.26**	**2.20**
∞	3.84	2.99	2.60	2.37	2.21	2.09	2.01	1.94	1.88	1.83	1.79	1.75
	6.64	**4.60**	**3.78**	**3.32**	**3.02**	**2.80**	**2.64**	**2.51**	**2.41**	**2.32**	**2.24**	**2.18**

Degrees of Freedom for Denominator	Degrees of Freedom for Numerator											
	14	16	20	24	30	40	50	75	100	200	500	∞
40	1.95	1.90	1.84	1.79	1.74	1.69	1.66	1.61	1.59	1.55	1.53	1.51
	2.56	**2.49**	**2.37**	**2.29**	**2.20**	**2.11**	**2.05**	**1.97**	**1.94**	**1.88**	**1.84**	**1.81**
42	1.94	1.89	1.82	1.78	1.73	1.68	1.64	1.60	1.57	1.54	1.51	1.49
	2.54	**2.46**	**2.35**	**2.26**	**2.17**	**2.08**	**2.02**	**1.94**	**1.91**	**1.85**	**1.80**	**1.78**
44	1.92	1.88	1.81	1.76	1.72	1.66	1.63	1.58	1.56	1.52	1.50	1.48
	2.52	**2.44**	**2.32**	**2.24**	**2.15**	**2.06**	**2.00**	**1.92**	**1.88**	**1.82**	**1.78**	**1.75**
46	1.91	1.87	1.80	1.75	1.71	1.65	1.62	1.57	1.54	1.51	1.48	1.46
	2.50	**2.42**	**2.30**	**2.22**	**2.13**	**2.04**	**1.98**	**1.90**	**1.86**	**1.80**	**1.76**	**1.72**
48	1.90	1.86	1.79	1.74	1.70	1.64	1.61	1.56	1.53	1.50	1.47	1.45
	2.43	**2.40**	**2.28**	**2.20**	**2.11**	**2.02**	**1.96**	**1.88**	**1.84**	**1.78**	**1.73**	**1.70**
50	1.90	1.85	1.78	1.74	1.69	1.63	1.60	1.55	1.52	1.48	1.46	1.44
	2.46	**2.39**	**2.26**	**2.18**	**2.10**	**2.00**	**1.94**	**1.86**	**1.82**	**1.76**	**1.71**	**1.68**
55	1.88	1.83	1.76	1.72	1.67	1.61	1.58	1.52	1.50	1.46	1.43	1.41
	2.43	**2.35**	**2.23**	**2.15**	**2.06**	**1.96**	**1.90**	**1.82**	**1.78**	**1.71**	**1.66**	**1.64**
60	1.86	1.81	1.75	1.70	1.65	1.59	1.56	1.50	1.48	1.44	1.41	1.39
	2.40	**2.32**	**2.20**	**2.12**	**2.03**	**1.93**	**1.87**	**1.79**	**1.74**	**1.68**	**1.63**	**1.60**
65	1.85	1.80	1.73	1.68	1.63	1.57	1.54	1.49	1.46	1.42	1.39	1.37
	2.37	**2.30**	**2.18**	**2.09**	**2.00**	**1.90**	**1.84**	**1.76**	**1.71**	**1.64**	**1.60**	**1.56**
70	1.84	1.79	1.72	1.67	1.62	1.56	1.53	1.47	1.45	1.40	1.37	1.35
	2.35	**2.28**	**2.15**	**2.07**	**1.98**	**1.88**	**1.82**	**1.74**	**1.69**	**1.63**	**1.56**	**1.53**
80	1.82	1.77	1.70	1.65	1.60	1.54	1.51	1.45	1.42	1.38	1.35	1.32
	2.32	**2.24**	**2.11**	**2.03**	**1.94**	**1.84**	**1.78**	**1.70**	**1.65**	**1.57**	**1.52**	**1.49**
100	1.79	1.75	1.68	1.63	1.57	1.51	1.48	1.42	1.39	1.34	1.30	1.28
	2.26	**2.19**	**2.06**	**1.98**	**1.89**	**1.79**	**1.73**	**1.64**	**1.59**	**1.51**	**1.46**	**1.43**
125	1.77	1.72	1.65	1.60	1.55	1.49	1.45	1.39	1.36	1.31	1.27	1.25
	2.23	**2.15**	**2.03**	**1.94**	**1.85**	**1.75**	**1.68**	**1.59**	**1.54**	**1.46**	**1.40**	**1.37**
150	1.76	1.71	1.64	1.59	1.54	1.47	1.44	1.37	1.34	1.29	1.25	1.22
	2.20	**2.12**	**2.00**	**1.91**	**1.83**	**1.72**	**1.66**	**1.56**	**1.51**	**1.43**	**1.37**	**1.33**
200	1.74	1.69	1.62	1.57	1.52	1.45	1.42	1.35	1.32	1.26	1.22	1.19
	2.17	**2.09**	**1.97**	**1.88**	**1.79**	**1.69**	**1.62**	**1.53**	**1.48**	**1.39**	**1.33**	**1.28**
400	1.72	1.67	1.60	1.54	1.49	1.42	1.38	1.32	1.28	1.22	1.16	1.13
	2.12	**2.04**	**1.92**	**1.84**	**1.74**	**1.64**	**1.57**	**1.47**	**1.42**	**1.32**	**1.24**	**1.19**
1,000	1.70	1.65	1.58	1.53	1.47	1.41	1.36	1.30	1.26	1.19	1.13	1.08
	2.09	**2.01**	**1.89**	**1.81**	**1.71**	**1.61**	**1.54**	**1.44**	**1.38**	**1.28**	**1.19**	**1.11**
∞	1.69	1.64	1.57	1.52	1.46	1.40	1.35	1.28	1.24	1.17	1.11	1.00
	2.07	**1.99**	**1.87**	**1.79**	**1.69**	**1.59**	**1.52**	**1.41**	**1.36**	**1.25**	**1.15**	**1.00**

SOURCE: Reprinted by permission from *Statistical Methods* by George W. Snedecor and William G. Cochran, 7th ed. © 1980 by Iowa State University Press, Ames, Iowa 50010.

TABLE H
Chi-Square
Distribution

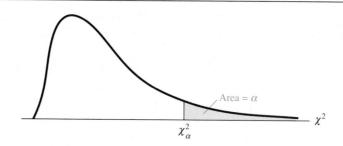

The following table provides the values of χ_α^2 that correspond to a given upper tail area α and a specified number of degrees of freedom.

Degrees of Freedom	Upper Tail Area α						
	.30	.20	.10	.05	.02	.01	.001
1	1.074	1.642	2.706	3.841	5.412	6.635	10.827
2	2.408	3.219	4.605	5.991	7.824	9.210	13.815
3	3.665	4.642	6.251	7.815	9.837	11.345	16.268
4	4.878	5.989	7.779	9.488	11.668	13.277	18.465
5	6.064	7.289	9.236	11.070	13.388	15.086	20.517
6	7.231	8.558	10.645	12.592	15.033	16.812	22.457
7	8.383	9.803	12.017	14.067	16.622	18.475	24.322
8	9.524	11.030	13.362	15.507	18.168	20.090	26.125
9	10.656	12.242	14.684	16.919	19.679	21.666	27.877
10	11.781	13.442	15.987	18.307	21.161	23.209	29.588
11	12.899	14.631	17.275	19.675	22.618	24.725	31.264
12	14.011	15.812	18.549	21.026	24.054	26.217	32.909
13	15.119	16.985	19.812	22.362	25.472	27.688	34.528
14	16.222	18.151	21.064	23.685	26.873	29.141	36.123
15	17.322	19.311	22.307	24.996	28.259	30.578	37.697
16	18.418	20.465	23.542	26.296	29.633	32.000	39.252
17	19.511	21.615	24.769	27.587	30.995	33.409	40.790
18	20.601	22.760	25.989	28.869	32.346	34.805	42.312
19	21.689	23.900	27.204	30.144	33.687	36.191	43.820
20	22.775	25.038	28.412	31.410	35.020	37.566	45.315
21	23.858	26.171	29.615	32.671	36.343	38.932	46.797
22	24.939	27.301	30.813	33.924	37.659	40.289	48.268
23	26.018	28.429	32.007	35.172	38.968	41.638	49.728
24	27.096	29.553	33.196	36.415	40.270	42.980	51.179
25	28.172	30.675	34.382	37.652	41.566	44.314	52.620
26	29.246	31.795	35.563	38.885	42.856	45.642	54.052
27	30.319	32.912	36.741	40.113	44.140	46.963	55.476
28	31.391	34.027	37.916	41.337	45.419	48.278	56.893
29	32.461	35.139	39.087	42.557	46.693	49.588	58.302
30	33.530	36.250	40.256	43.773	47.962	50.892	59.703

SOURCE: From Table IV of Fisher and Yates, *Statistical Tables for Biological, Agricultural and Medical Research*, published by Longman Group Ltd., London (previously published by Oliver & Boyd, Edinburgh, 1963). Reproduced with permission of the authors and publishers.

y	e^y	e^{-y}	y	e^y	e^{-y}
0.00	1.0000	1.000000	3.00	20.086	.049787
0.10	1.1052	.904837	3.10	22.198	.045049
0.20	1.2214	.818731	3.20	24.533	.040762
0.30	1.3499	.740818	3.30	27.113	.036883
0.40	1.4918	.670320	3.40	29.964	.033373
0.50	1.6487	.606531	3.50	33.115	.030197
0.60	1.8221	.548812	3.60	36.598	.027324
0.70	2.0138	.496585	3.70	40.447	.024724
0.80	2.2255	.449329	3.80	44.701	.022371
0.90	2.4596	.406570	3.90	49.402	.020242
1.00	2.7183	.367879	4.00	54.598	.018316
1.10	3.0042	.332871	4.10	60.340	.016573
1.20	3.3201	.301194	4.20	66.686	.014996
1.30	3.6693	.272532	4.30	73.700	.013569
1.40	4.0552	.246597	4.40	81.451	.012277
1.50	4.4817	.223130	4.50	90.017	.011109
1.60	4.9530	.201897	4.60	99.484	.010052
1.70	5.4739	.182684	4.70	109.95	.009095
1.80	6.0496	.165299	4.80	121.51	.008230
1.90	6.6859	.149569	4.90	134.29	.007447
2.00	7.3891	.135335	5.00	148.41	.006738
2.10	8.1662	.122456	5.10	164.02	.006097
2.20	9.0250	.110803	5.20	181.27	.005517
2.30	9.9742	.100259	5.30	200.34	.004992
2.40	11.023	.090718	5.40	221.41	.004517
2.50	12.182	.082085	5.50	244.69	.004087
2.60	13.464	.074274	5.60	270.43	.003698
2.70	14.880	.067206	5.70	298.87	.003346
2.80	16.445	.060810	5.80	330.30	.003028
2.90	18.174	.055023	5.90	365.04	.002739
3.00	20.086	.049787	6.00	403.43	.002479

TABLE I
Exponential
Functions

TABLE J
Cumulative Probability Values for the Poisson Distribution

λt					$Pr[X \leq x]$					
x	1.0	2.0	3.0	4.0	5.0	6.0	7.0	8.0	9.0	10.0
0	0.3679	0.1353	0.0498	0.0183	0.0067	0.0025	0.0009	0.0003	0.0001	0.0000
1	0.7358	0.4060	0.1991	0.0916	0.0404	0.0174	0.0073	0.0030	0.0012	0.0005
2	0.9197	0.6767	0.4232	0.2381	0.1247	0.0620	0.0296	0.0138	0.0062	0.0028
3	0.9810	0.8571	0.6472	0.4335	0.2650	0.1512	0.0818	0.0424	0.0212	0.0103
4	0.9963	0.9473	0.8153	0.6288	0.4405	0.2851	0.1730	0.0996	0.0550	0.0293
5	0.9994	0.9834	0.9161	0.7851	0.6160	0.4457	0.3007	0.1912	0.1157	0.0671
6	0.9999	0.9955	0.9665	0.8893	0.7622	0.6063	0.4497	0.3134	0.2068	0.1301
7	1.0000	0.9989	0.9881	0.9489	0.8666	0.7440	0.5987	0.4530	0.3239	0.2202
8		0.9998	0.9962	0.9786	0.9319	0.8472	0.7291	0.5926	0.4557	0.3328
9		1.0000	0.9989	0.9919	0.9682	0.9161	0.8305	0.7166	0.5874	0.4579
10			0.9997	0.9972	0.9863	0.9574	0.9015	0.8159	0.7060	0.5830
11			0.9999	0.9991	0.9945	0.9799	0.9466	0.8881	0.8030	0.6968
12			1.0000	0.9997	0.9980	0.9912	0.9730	0.9362	0.8758	0.7916
13				0.9999	0.9993	0.9964	0.9872	0.9658	0.9262	0.8645
14				1.0000	0.9998	0.9986	0.9943	0.9827	0.9585	0.9165
15					0.9999	0.9995	0.9976	0.9918	0.9780	0.9513
16					1.0000	0.9998	0.9990	0.9963	0.9889	0.9730
17						0.9999	0.9996	0.9984	0.9947	0.9857
18						1.0000	0.9999	0.9993	0.9976	0.9928
19							0.9999	0.9997	0.9989	0.9965
20							1.0000	0.9999	0.9996	0.9984
21								1.0000	0.9998	0.9993
22									0.9999	0.9997
23									1.0000	0.9999
24										0.9999
25										1.0000

λt	\multicolumn{10}{c}{$Pr[X \le x]$}								
x	11.0	12.0	13.0	14.0	15.0	16.0	17.0	18.0	19.0	20.0
0	0.0000	0.0000	0.0000	0.0000	0.0000	0.0000	0.0	0.0	0.0	0.0
1	0.0002	0.0001	0.0000	0.0000	0.0000	0.0000	0.0000	0.0000	0.0000	0.0
2	0.0012	0.0005	0.0002	0.0001	0.0000	0.0000	0.0000	0.0000	0.0000	0.0000
3	0.0049	0.0023	0.0011	0.0005	0.0002	0.0001	0.0000	0.0000	0.0000	0.0000
4	0.0151	0.0076	0.0037	0.0018	0.0009	0.0004	0.0002	0.0001	0.0000	0.0000
5	0.0375	0.0203	0.0107	0.0055	0.0028	0.0014	0.0007	0.0003	0.0002	0.0001
6	0.0786	0.0458	0.0259	0.0142	0.0076	0.0040	0.0021	0.0010	0.0005	0.0003
7	0.1432	0.0895	0.0540	0.0316	0.0180	0.0100	0.0054	0.0029	0.0015	0.0008
8	0.2320	0.1550	0.0998	0.0621	0.0374	0.0220	0.0126	0.0071	0.0039	0.0021
9	0.3405	0.2424	0.1658	0.1094	0.0699	0.0433	0.0261	0.0154	0.0089	0.0050
10	0.4599	0.3472	0.2517	0.1757	0.1185	0.0774	0.0491	0.0304	0.0183	0.0108
11	0.5793	0.4616	0.3532	0.2600	0.1847	0.1270	0.0847	0.0549	0.0347	0.0214
12	0.6887	0.5760	0.4631	0.3585	0.2676	0.1931	0.1350	0.0917	0.0606	0.0390
13	0.7813	0.6815	0.5730	0.4644	0.3632	0.2745	0.2009	0.1426	0.0984	0.0661
14	0.8540	0.7720	0.6751	0.5704	0.4656	0.3675	0.2808	0.2081	0.1497	0.1049
15	0.9074	0.8444	0.7636	0.6694	0.5681	0.4667	0.3714	0.2866	0.2148	0.1565
16	0.9441	0.8987	0.8355	0.7559	0.6641	0.5660	0.4677	0.3750	0.2920	0.2211
17	0.9678	0.9370	0.8905	0.8272	0.7489	0.6593	0.5640	0.4686	0.3784	0.2970
18	0.9823	0.9626	0.9302	0.8826	0.8195	0.7423	0.6549	0.5622	0.4695	0.3814
19	0.9907	0.9787	0.9573	0.9235	0.8752	0.8122	0.7363	0.6509	0.5606	0.4703
20	0.9953	0.9884	0.9750	0.9521	0.9170	0.8682	0.8055	0.7307	0.6472	0.5591
21	0.9977	0.9939	0.9859	0.9711	0.9469	0.9108	0.8615	0.7991	0.7255	0.6437
22	0.9989	0.9969	0.9924	0.9833	0.9672	0.9418	0.9047	0.8551	0.7931	0.7206
23	0.9995	0.9985	0.9960	0.9907	0.9805	0.9633	0.9367	0.8989	0.8490	0.7875
24	0.9998	0.9993	0.9980	0.9950	0.9888	0.9777	0.9593	0.9317	0.8933	0.8432
25	0.9999	0.9997	0.9990	0.9974	0.9938	0.9869	0.9747	0.9554	0.9269	0.8878
26	1.0000	0.9999	0.9995	0.9987	0.9967	0.9925	0.9848	0.9718	0.9514	0.9221
27		0.9999	0.9998	0.9994	0.9983	0.9959	0.9912	0.9827	0.9687	0.9475
28		1.0000	0.9999	0.9997	0.9991	0.9978	0.9950	0.9897	0.9805	0.9657
29			1.0000	0.9999	0.9996	0.9989	0.9973	0.9940	0.9981	0.9782
30				0.9999	0.9998	0.9994	0.9985	0.9967	0.9930	0.9865
31				1.0000	0.9999	0.9997	0.9992	0.9982	0.9960	0.9919
32					0.9999	0.9999	0.9996	0.9990	0.9978	0.9953
33					1.0000	0.9999	0.9998	0.9995	0.9988	0.9973
34						1.0000	0.9999	0.9997	0.9994	0.9985
35							0.9999	0.9999	0.9997	0.9992
36							1.0000	0.9999	0.9998	0.9996
37								1.0000	0.9999	0.9998
38									1.0000	0.9999
39										0.9999
40										1.0000

SOURCE: From *Management Science for Business Decisions* by Lawrence L. Lapin, copyright © 1980 by Harcourt Brace Jovanovich, Inc. Reproduced by permission of the publisher.

TABLE K
Critical Values
for Studentized
Range

Parameter for Denominator	$q_{.90}$ Parameter for Numerator								
	2	3	4	5	6	7	8	9	10
1	8.93	13.4	16.4	18.5	20.2	21.5	22.6	23.6	24.5
2	4.13	5.73	6.77	7.54	8.14	8.63	9.05	9.41	9.72
3	3.33	4.47	5.20	5.74	6.16	6.51	6.81	7.06	7.29
4	3.01	3.98	4.59	5.03	5.39	5.68	5.93	6.14	6.33
5	2.85	3.72	4.26	4.66	4.98	5.24	5.46	5.65	5.82
6	2.75	3.56	4.07	4.44	4.73	4.97	5.17	5.34	5.50
7	2.68	3.45	3.93	4.28	4.55	4.78	4.97	5.14	5.28
8	2.63	3.37	3.83	4.17	4.43	4.65	4.83	4.99	5.13
9	2.59	3.32	3.76	4.08	4.34	4.54	4.72	4.87	5.01
10	2.56	3.27	3.70	4.02	4.26	4.47	4.64	4.78	4.91
11	2.54	3.23	3.66	3.96	4.20	4.40	4.57	4.71	4.84
12	2.52	3.20	3.62	3.92	4.16	4.35	4.51	4.65	4.78
13	2.50	3.18	3.59	3.88	4.12	4.30	4.46	4.60	4.72
14	2.49	3.16	3.56	3.85	4.08	4.27	4.42	4.56	4.68
15	2.48	3.14	3.54	3.83	4.05	4.23	4.39	4.52	4.64
16	2.47	3.12	3.52	3.80	4.03	4.21	4.36	4.49	4.61
17	2.46	3.11	3.50	3.78	4.00	4.18	4.33	4.46	4.58
18	2.45	3.10	3.49	3.77	3.98	4.16	4.31	4.44	4.55
19	2.45	3.09	3.47	3.75	3.97	4.14	4.29	4.42	4.53
20	2.44	3.08	3.46	3.74	3.95	4.12	4.27	4.40	4.51
24	2.42	3.05	3.42	3.69	3.90	4.07	4.21	4.34	4.44
30	2.40	3.02	3.39	3.65	3.85	4.02	4.16	4.28	4.38
40	2.38	2.99	3.35	3.60	3.80	3.96	4.10	4.21	4.32
60	2.36	2.96	3.31	3.56	3.75	3.91	4.04	4.16	4.25
120	2.34	2.93	3.28	3.52	3.71	3.86	3.99	4.10	4.19
∞	2.33	2.90	3.24	3.48	3.66	3.81	3.93	4.04	4.13

SOURCE: E. S. Pearson and H. O. Hartley, *Biometrika Tables for Statisticians*, Vol. I. London: Cambridge University Press, 1966. Partly derived from J. Pachares. Reproduced with permission of the authors and publishers.

The following table provides the critical values D_α corresponding to an upper tail probability α of the test statistic D. The following relationship holds

$$\alpha = \Pr[D \geq D_\alpha]$$

TABLE L
Critical Values of
D for Kolmogorov-
Smirnov
Goodness-of-Fit
Test

n	α = .10	α = .05	α = .025	α = .01	α = .005
1	.90000	.95000	.97500	.99000	.99500
2	.68377	.77639	.84189	.90000	.92929
3	.56481	.63604	.70760	.78456	.82900
4	.49265	.56522	.62394	.68887	.73424
5	.44698	.50945	.56328	.62718	.66853
6	.41037	.46799	.51926	.57741	.61661
7	.38148	.43607	.48342	.53844	.57581
8	.35831	.40962	.45427	.50654	.54179
9	.33910	.38746	.43001	.47960	.51332
10	.32260	.36866	.40925	.45662	.48893
11	.30829	.35242	.39122	.43670	.46770
12	.29577	.33815	.37543	.41918	.44905
13	.28470	.32549	.36143	.40362	.43247
14	.27481	.31417	.34890	.38970	.41762
15	.26588	.30397	.33760	.37713	.40420
16	.25778	.29472	.32733	.36571	.39201
17	.25039	.28627	.31796	.35528	.38086
18	.24360	.27851	.30936	.34569	.37062
19	.23735	.27136	.30143	.33685	.36117
20	.23156	.26473	.29408	.32866	.35241
21	.22617	.25858	.28724	.32104	.34427
22	.22115	.25283	.28087	.31394	.33666
23	.21645	.24746	.27490	.30728	.32954
24	.21205	.24242	.26931	.30104	.32286
25	.20790	.23768	.26404	.29516	.31657
26	.20399	.23320	.25907	.28962	.31064
27	.20030	.22898	.25438	.28438	.30502
28	.19680	.22497	.24993	.27942	.29971
29	.19348	.22117	.24571	.27471	.29466
30	.19032	.21756	.24170	.27023	.28987
31	.18732	.21412	.23788	.26596	.28530
32	.18445	.21085	.23424	.26189	.28094
33	.18171	.20771	.23076	.25801	.27677
34	.17909	.20472	.22743	.25429	.27279
35	.17659	.20185	.22425	.25073	.26897
36	.17418	.19910	.22119	.24732	.26532
37	.17188	.19646	.21826	.24404	.26180
38	.16966	.19392	.21544	.24089	.25843
39	.16753	.19148	.21273	.23786	.25518
40	.16547	.18913	.21012	.23494	.25205

SOURCE: Reprinted by permission from L. H. Miller, "Table of Percentage Points of Kolmogorov Statistics," *Journal of the American Statistical Association*, 51 (1956), pages 111–121.

Sample Size *n*	Conversion Constant for Range d_R	Standard Deviation Ratio σ_w	Constants of Proportionality	
			c_4	c_5
2	1.128	.8525	.798	.603
3	1.693	.8884	.886	.463
4	2.059	.8798	.921	.389
5	2.326	.8641	.940	.341
6	2.534	.8480	.952	.308
7	2.704	.8332	.959	.282
8	2.847	.8198	.965	.262
9	2.970	.8078	.969	.246
10	3.078	.7971	.973	.232
11	3.173	.7873	.975	.220
12	3.258	.7785	.978	.210

SOURCE: Values for d_R were obtained from American Society of Testing Materials, *A.S.T.M. Manual on Quality Control of Materials,* Philadelphia, 1951. Values for σ_w were obtained from E. S. Pearson and H. O. Hartley, *Biometrika Tables for Statisticians,* Vol. I, Cambridge University Press, 1966. Reproduced with permission of the authors and publishers. Values for c_4 and c_5 were taken from Harrison M. Wadsworth, Kenneth S. Stephens, and A. Blanthon Godfrey, *Modern Methods for Quality Control,* Wiley, 1986. Reproduced with permission.

ANSWERS TO EVEN-NUMBERED EXERCISES

1-2 Answers will vary.

1-4 Answers will vary.

1-6 (a) ordinal (b) nominal (c) interval (d) ratio (e) interval

1-8 Answers will vary.

1-10 (a)

slipper, hat	hat, dog	dog, thimble
slipper, dog	hat, thimble	dog, car
slipper, thimble	hat, car	thimble, car
slipper, car		

(b)

slipper, hat, dog	slipper, thimble, car
slipper, hat, thimble	hat, dog, thimble
slipper, hat, car	hat, dog, car
slipper, dog, thimble	hat, thimble, car
slipper, dog, car	dog, thimble, car

1-12 Answers will vary.

1-14 (a) deductive (c) deductive
        (b) inductive (d) inductive

1-16 Answers will vary.

1-18 Answers will vary.

1-20 Answers will vary.

2-2 (a)

0.	4 7 3 7 6 3 5 8
1.	6 2 8 8 2 0 5 2 5 1 8
2.	9 8 6 6 2 9 6 0 9 7 2 1 9 9 9 3 9 0 9 2 7 4 4
3.	8 1 4 7 0 7 3 4 6 2 2 6 7 3 9 6 1 4 6 8 5 3 9 6 6 2 3 1 4
4.	4 0 2 0 1 0 8 5 0 0
5.	0 9 4 8 4

(b)

Class Interval (inches)	Frequency
0.0–under 1.0	8
1.0–under 2.0	11
2.0–under 3.0	23
3.0–under 4.0	29
4.0–under 5.0	10
5.0–under 6.0	5
	86

2-4 (a)

Class Interval	Frequency	Class Interval	Frequency
$ 3,000–under 5,000	4	$15,000–under 17,000	2
5,000–under 7,000	6	17,000–under 19,000	1
7,000–under 9,000	13	19,000–under 21,000	0
9,000–under 11,000	13	21,000–under 23,000	1
11,000–under 13,000	7	23,000–under 25,000	1
13,000–under 15,000	1	25,000–under 27,000	1
			50

2-6 (a)

Class Interval (inches)	Frequency
58–under 59	2
59–under 60	2
60–under 61	4
61–under 62	7
62–under 63	7
63–under 64	12
64–under 65	9
65–under 66	4
66–under 67	2
67–under 68	1
	50

2-8

Letter	Frequency	Letter	Frequency	Letter	Frequency
a	20	j	0	s	7
b	2	k	0	t	22
c	7	l	5	u	4
d	8	m	1	v	3
e	26	n	20	w	5
f	3	o	17	x	0
g	6	p	2	y	2
h	9	q	1	z	0
i	14	r	16		200

2-10 (a) ambiguous designations   (c) some values not included
(b) overlapping intervals

2-14

	(a)	(b)
Class Interval (mpg)	Relative Frequency	Cumulative Frequency
14.0–under 16.0	.09	9
16.0–under 18.0	.13	22
18.0–under 20.0	.24	46
20.0–under 22.0	.38	84
22.0–under 24.0	.16	100

2-16

	(a)	(b)
Consecutive Days Absent	Relative Frequency	Cumulative Relative Frequency
0–under 5	.620	.620
5–under 10	.162	.782
10–under 15	.102	.884
15–under 20	.064	.948
20–under 25	.024	.972
25–under 30	.006	.978
30–under 60	.022	1.000
	1.000	

2-18

		(a)	(b)	(c)
Number of Shares (thousands)	Cumulative Relative Frequency	Relative Frequency	Frequency [(a) × 1,000)]	Cumulative Frequency
0–under 5	.36	.36	360	360
5–under 10	.63	.63 − .36 = .27	270	630
10–under 15	.81	.81 − .63 = .18	180	810
15–under 20	.90	.90 − .81 = .09	90	900
20–under 25	.97	.97 − .90 = .07	70	970
25–under 30	1.00	1.00 − .97 = .03	30	1,000
		1.00	1,000	

2-20 Answers will vary.

2-22

Major	Marital Status		Total
	Single	Married	
Electrical	10	19	29
Mechanical	27	28	55
Civil	6	10	16
Total	43	57	100

There is a lower tendency for mechanical engineers to be married than with other majors.

2-28 Out of control days are 3, 4, 5, 6, and 9.

2-30 (b) A peak in average fuel consumption was reached in 1970. It remained steady until 1978, when it declined dramatically.

2-32

Major	Sex		Total
	Male	**Female**	
Electrical	19	10	29
Mechanical	35	20	55
Civil	14	2	16
Total	68	32	100

2-34

	(a)	(c)	(d)
Class Interval (inches)	Frequency	Relative Frequency	Cumulative Relative Frequency
61.5–under 62.5	1	.02	.02
62.5–under 63.5	1	.02	.04
63.5–under 64.5	1	.02	.06
64.5–under 65.5	2	.04	.10
65.5–under 66.5	3	.06	.16
66.5–under 67.5	2	.04	.20
67.5–under 68.5	5	.10	.30
68.5–under 69.5	5	.10	.40
69.5–under 70.5	7	.14	.54
70.5–under 71.5	7	.14	.68
71.5–under 72.5	6	.12	.80
72.5–under 73.5	3	.06	.86
73.5–under 74.5	3	.06	.92
74.5–under 75.5	2	.04	.96
75.5–under 76.5	1	.02	.98
76.5–under 77.5	1	.02	1.00
	50	1.00	

(f) (1) .54   (2) .96   (3) .16

2-36 (a)

Sex	Frequency
male	220
female	130
	350

(c)

Occupation	Frequency
blue collar	155
white collar	173
professional	22
	350

(b)

Marital Status	Frequency
married	171
single	179
	350

2-38 (a)

Sex	Marital Status		Total
	Single	Married	
Male	96	124	220
Female	83	47	130
Total	179	171	350

(b)

Marital Status	Occupation			Total
	Blue Collar	White Collar	Professional	
Single	67	104	8	179
Married	88	69	14	171
Total	155	173	22	350

(c)

Sex	Occupation			Total
	Blue Collar	White Collar	Professional	
Male	130	75	15	220
Female	25	98	7	130
Total	155	173	22	350

2-40 Answers will vary.

2-42 (b)

	1991			2100		
Country	Relative Frequency	Cumulative Relative Frequency		Country	Relative Frequency	Cumulative Relative Frequency
1. China	.298	.298		1. India	.233	.233
2. India	.222	.520		2. China	.224	.457
3. U.S.	.065	.585		3. Nigeria	.072	.529
4. Indonesia	.047	.632		4. Indonesia	.051	.580
5. Brazil	.040	.672		5. Pakistan	.045	.625
6. Russia	.038	.710		6. U.S.	.044	.669
7. Japan	.032	.742		7. Bangladesh	.042	.711
8. Nigeria	.032	.774		8. Brazil	.042	.753
9. Pakistan	.030	.804		9. Mexico	.028	.781
10. Bangladesh	.030	.834		10. Russia	.026	.807
11. Mexico	.022	.856		11. Ethiopia	.025	.832
12. Germany	.021	.877		12. VietNam	.024	.856
13. VietNam	.017	.894		13. Iran	.023	.879
14. Philippines	.016	.910		14. Zaire	.020	.899
15. Thailand	.015	.925		15. Japan	.018	.917
16. Iran	.015	.940		16. Philippines	.018	.935
17. Turkey	.015	.955		17. Tanzania	.017	.952
18. Italy	.015	.970		18. Kenya	.017	.969
19. U.K.	.015	.985		19. Burma	.016	.985
20. France	.015	1.000		20. Egypt	.016	1.001

(c)

Continent	1991 Population	Relative Frequency	2100 Population	Cumulative Relative Frequency
Asia/Europe	3,254,400,000	.841	5,049,400,000	.720
N. America	338,500,000	.087	504,200,000	.072
S. America	153,300,000	.040	293,200,000	.042
Africa	122,500,000	.032	1,167,500,000	.166
	3,868,700,000	1.000	7,014,300,000	1.000

2-44   Answers will vary.

3-2   Choose CompuQuick.

3-4 $\bar{X} = 26.18$ hours

3-6   (a)

A	B	C	D	E
30.2%	17.4%	13.5%	32.5%	22.8%

(b) 23.28%   (c) B, C, and E

3-8   (b) $\bar{X} = 24.0\%$ (c) $\bar{X} = 23.28\%$, above by .72%

3-10   2.893 inches

3-12   (a) 2.75   (b) 2   (c) 2

3-14 $2,129

3-16   Answers will vary.

3-18   3.050 inches

3-20   (a) .1   (b) 1.25   (c) 2.50   (d) 6.50   (e) 8

3-22   (a)

```
0. | 3 3 4 5 6 7 7 8
1. | 0 1 2 2 2 5 5 6 8 8 8
2. | 0 0 1 2 2 2 3 4 4 6 6 6 7 7 8 9 9 9 9 9 9 9 9
3. | 0 1 1 1 2 2 2 3 3 3 3 4 4 4 4 5 6 6 6 6 6 6 7 7 7 8 8 9 9
4. | 0 0 0 0 0 1 2 4 5 8
5. | 0 4 4 8 9
```

(b) (1) .94   (2) 2.075   (3) 3.050   (4) 3.7   (5) 4.26

3-24   (a) 10   (b) 4   (c) 3   (d) 7   (e) 5

3-26   (a) $Q_{.25} = 415$ $Q_{.50} = 485$ $Q_{.75} = 555$

3-28   (a) 184.30   (b) 13.58

3-30 Answers will vary.

3-32 (a) 1,643 (b) 111,480.1 (c) 333.9

3-34 140

3-36 (a) (1) 5.6 (2) 1.625

3-38 (a) 2.75 (b) .63

3-40 Population is normally distributed.

3-42 (a) 1.615 (b) 1.271

3-44 (a) .30 (b) .35 (c) .575 (d) .875

3-46 Answers will vary.

3-48 (a) .10 (b) .04 (c) .03 (d) .07 (e) .04 (f) .05

3-50 (a) 450 (b) 573 (c) 165

3-52 (a) 126.2 (b) 124.86 (c) 385.41 (d) 19.63

3-54 (a) $\bar{X} = 77.615$; $s^2 = 208.55$ (b) $\bar{X} = 78.077$; $s^2 = 176.30$
(c) $-.461$

3-56 (c) (1) 77.62 (2) 14.44
(d) (1) 57.40 (2) 73.50 (3) 89.00
(e) 78.50
(f) (1) 66 (2) 15.50

3-58 Answers will vary.

3-60 Answers will vary.

3-62 $\bar{X} = 551.3$ $s = 202.9$ 74%

3-64 (a) $\bar{X} = 2,860$ $s = 589.91$
(c) 407.5 (d) 13 or 18
(e) .833

3-66 (a) $\bar{X} = 33,230,342.8$ $s = 17,250,300.5$

4-2 Answers will vary.

4-4 Answers will vary.

4-6 Answers will vary.

4-8 Answers will vary.

4-10 (a) convenience   (c) random
       (b) judgment   (d) judgment or convenience

4-12 Answers will vary.

4-14 A judgment-convenience sample applies.

4-16 Solti, Maag, Abbado, Rowicki, Bloomfield, Krips, Prêtre, Frühbeck de Burgos, Newman, Schippers

4-18 Beecham, Dragon, Golschmann, Karajan, Krips, Pedrotti, Rignold, Scherchen, Stein, Svetlanov

4-20 Answers will vary.

4-22 Answers will vary.

4-24 Answers will vary.

4-26 Answers will vary.

5-2 1/38

5-4 (a) 1/20   (b) 1/10

5-6 (a) .140   (b) .400   (c) .260   (d) .200

5-8 (a) 24/72   (b) 5/72   (c) 11/72   (d) 6/72   (e) 7/72

5-10

Occupation	Family Income			Marginal Probability
	Low	Medium	High	
Homemaker	.04	.13	.03	.20
Blue-collar	.08	.20	.07	.35
White-collar	.03	.31	.06	.40
Professional	0	.01	.04	.05
Marginal Probability	.15	.65	.20	1.00

5-12

Sex	Major				Marginal Probability
	Accounting	Finance	Marketing	Management	
Male	10/72	14/72	10/72	6/72	40/72
Female	6/72	10/72	10/72	6/72	32/72
Marginal Probability	16/72	24/72	20/72	12/72	1

5-14 (a)

Sex	Marital Status		Marginal Probability
	Married	Unmarried	
Male	3/35	17/35	20/35
Female	5/35	10/35	15/35
Marginal Probability	8/35	27/35	1

(b) (1) 3/35   (2) 5/35   (3) 10/35   (4) 17/35

5-16 (a) equally likely outcomes
(b) .03125 for each

5-18 (a)

Sex	Marital Status		Marginal Probability
	Married	Unmarried	
Man	.35	.15	.50
Woman	.35	.15	.50
Marginal Probability	.70	.30	1.00

(b)

Sex	Marital Status		Marginal Probability
	Married	Unmarried	
Man	.30	.20	.50
Woman	.40	.10	.50
Marginal Probability	.70	.30	1.00

5-20 (a) 31/42   (b) 41/42   (c) 41/42   (d) 11/42   (e) 41/42   (f) 1

5-22 (a) .97   (b) .83   (c) .27   (d) .02

5-24 (a) $.90 \times (1 - .95) = .045$

(b)

Action	Quality		Marginal Probability
	Good (G)	Bad (B)	
Accept (A)	.895	.005	.900
Reject (R)	.055	.045	.100
Marginal Probability	.950	.050	1.00

(c) (1) 5.5%   (2) 89.5%   (3) .5%
(d) Pr[incorrect] = .005 + .055 = .060

5-28 Pr[good] = .90

(a)

Shipment Quality	Inspector Action		Marginal Probability
	Accept	Reject	
Good	.855	.045	.900
Bad	.010	.090	.100
Marginal Probability	.865	.135	1.000

(b) .055

5-30 (a) .288   (b) .200   (c) .0625   (d) .0714

5-32 (a) (1) .40   (2) .80   (3) .32
     (b) (1) .60   (2) .90   (3) .54

5-34 (a) 13/26   (b) 12/20   (c) 13/26   (d) 4/12   (e) 20/40   (f) 16/28

5-36 (a) (1) .60   (2) .40
     (b) (1) .360   (2) .320

(c)

Result	Direction		Marginal Probability
	L	R	
H	.216	.128	.344
O	.384	.272	.656
Marginal Probability	.600	.400	1.000

$\Pr[H \ and \ L] = .60 \times .36 = .216$
$\Pr[H \ and \ R] = .40 \times .32 = .128$

(d) (1) .372   (2) .628

5-38 (a) (1) 1/52   (2) 0
     (b) (1)   (2) 0

5-42 (a) (1) 3/52   (2) 22/52
     (b) (1) 2/52   (2) 28/52
     (c) (1) 4/52   (2) 12/52
     (d) (1) 5/52   (2) 28/52

5-44 (a) .48   (b) .51   (c) .36   (d) .50

5-46 (a) (1) .299   (2) .205   (3) .266

5-48 (a)

Highest Degree	Academic Assignment			Marginal Probability
	Teaching	Research	Admin.	
Doctorate	14/64	11/64	8/64	33/64
Master	5/64	8/64	18/64	31/64
Marginal Probability	19/64	19/64	26/64	1

(b) not independent
(c) (1) .161   (2) .258   (3) .581
(d) (1) .579   (2) .421

5-50 (a) .729   (b) .2916   (c) .40951

5-52 (a) 1/4   (b) 1/2   (c) 3/10   (d) 1/5   (e) 9/20   (f) 3/10

5-54 (a) (1) 11/20   (2) 3/4   (3) 4/5
(b) (1) 3/5   (2) 9/20   (3) 3/5

5-56

Discipline	Employment Status		Marginal Probability
	Full-time	Part-time	
Accounting	7/71	7/71	14/71
Finance	8/71	6/71	14/71
Management	10/71	8/71	18/71
Marketing	14/71	11/71	25/71
Marginal Probability	39/71	32/71	1

5-58 (a) (1) .05   (2) .01   (3) .90

(b)

Quality	Inspector Action		Marginal Probability
	Accept	Reject	
Good	.891	.009	.900
Bad	.005	.095	.100
Marginal Probability	.896	.104	1.000

(c) .014

5-60   (a)

Marital Status	Sex		Marginal Probability
	Male	Female	
Single	2/10	1/10	3/10
Married	3/10	1/10	4/10
Divorced	1/10	1/10	2/10
Widowed	0	1/10	1/10
Marginal Probability	6/10	4/10	1

(b) (1) 3/10   (2) 5/10   (3) 7/10   (4) 7/10

5-62   (b) .467

5-64   (a) (1) .729   (2) .243   (3) .027   (4) .001
(b) (1) .028   (2) .999   (3) .271

5-68   Answers will vary.

5-70   (a)

Country	Medal			Marginal Probability
	Gold	Silver	Bronze	
Germany	10/171	10/171	6/171	26/171
Unified Team	9/171	6/171	8/171	23/171
Austria	6/171	7/171	8/171	21/171
Norway	9/171	6/171	5/171	20/171
Italy	4/171	6/171	4/171	14/171
U.S.	5/171	4/171	2/171	11/171
Others	14/171	19/171	23/171	56/171
Marginal Probability	57/171	58/171	56/171	1

(b) 10/57
(c) 5/11

5-72   (a)

Mileage	Car Type		Marginal Probability
	Two Seater	Minicompact	
10–under 20	4/36	3/36	7/36
20–under 30	15/36	7/36	22/36
30–under 40	5/36	1/36	6/36
40 and above	1/36	0	1/36
Marginal Probability	25/36	11/36	1

5-72 (a) *Continued*

Pr[minicompact *or* 30–under 40] = 16/36
Pr[10–under 20 *and* two-seater] = 1/9
Pr[two-seater|40 and above] = 1

(b) Pr[mileage < 20] = 7/36
Pr[mileage > 26] = 11/36
Pr[18 ≤ mileage ≤ 27] = 26/36
Pr[mileage > 25|two seater] = 8/25
Pr[two seater|mileage < 30] = 19/29
Pr[mileage ≥ 30|minicompact] = 1/11

5-74 (a) One possibility:

Int	TD 12-16	17-21	22-26	Marginal Probability
6-10	1/12	0	1/12	2/12
11-15	3/12	2/12	1/12	6/12
16-20	2/12	1/12	1/12	4/12
Marginal Probability	6/12	3/12	3/12	1

(b) .50   (c) .33

5-76 (a)

Winning League	Number of Games 4	5	6	7	Marginal Probability
National	2/30	2/30	2/30	8/30	14/30
American	2/30	4/30	4/30	6/30	16/30
Marginal Probability	4/30	6/30	6/30	14/30	1

(b) .57   (c) .67

6-2

Cost	Probability
$2,200	.09
2,400	.15
2,600	.06
2,700	.21
2,900	.35
3,100	.14
	1.00

6-4 (b) (1) .729 (3) .027 (5) .271
(2) .243 (4) .001 (6) .999

6-6 (b) (1) .72398 (3) .02295 (5) .27600
(2) .25254 (4) .00051 (6) .99947

6-8 (a)

w	Pr[W = w]
−$1	20/36
1	14/36
2	1/36
3	1/36
	1

6-10 (a) .99   (b) .969900   (c) .985

6-12 (a) 2.1   (b) 1.2690   (c) 1.136

6-14 (a) $155.25 for High-Volatility Engineering
$103.50 for Stability Power

6-16 (a) (1) 2.52   (2) 2.25   (3) 1.50

(b)

x	Pr[X = x]
0	.08
1	.16
2	.32
3	.20
4	.12
5	.08
6	.04

(c) (1) 2.52   (2) 2.2496   (3) 1.50

6-18

Possible Mean $\bar{x}$	Corresponding Possibilities	Pr[$\bar{X}$ = $\bar{x}$]
950	(R,P)(R,A)	2/10
1,000	(A,P)	1/10
1,050	(R,D)(R,J)	2/10
1,100	(A,D)(A,J)(P,D)(P,J)	4/10
1,200	(D,J)	1/10
		1

6-20 (a)

$\bar{x}$	Pr[$\bar{X}$ = $\bar{x}$]
900	1/25
950	4/25
1,000	4/25
1,050	4/25
1,100	8/25
1,200	4/25
	1

(b) (1) 1.060   (2) 7,200   (3) 84.85

6-22 (a) 24   (b) 720   (c) 5,040   (d) 40,320

6-24 (a) (1) .1642   (2) .2734   (3) .0078   (4) .2734
(b) same answers as in (a)

6-26 (a) .16807   (b) .00243   (c) .3087

6-28 .05

6-30 (a) .1390   (c) .7822   (e) .0009
      (b) .1224   (d) .0848   (f) .3105

6-32	r/5	Pr[P = r/5]	Pr[P ≤ r/5]
	.0	.00243	.00243
	.2	.02835	.03078
	.4	.13230	.16308
	.6	.30870	.47178
	.8	.36015	.83193
	1.0	.16807	1.00000
		1.00000	

6-34 0.0000 (rounded)

6-36 (a) .0565   (c) .8744   (e) .25000
      (b) .0710   (d) .5956   (f) .8534

6-38 (a) .63396   (b) .86738   (c) .95245   (d) .99408

6-40	Cost	Probability
	$2,400	.09
	2,900	.15 + .21 = .36
	3,100	.06
	3,400	.35
	3,600	.14
		1.00

6-42 (a) .03125   (b) .03125   (c) .31250

6-44 (a) .4096   (b) .1536   (c) .9586   (d) .0588

6-46 (a)

Possible Mean Age $\bar{x}$	Corresponding Possibilities	Pr[$\bar{X} = \bar{x}$]
19.5	(H,M)	1/10
20.0	(H,J)	1/10
20.5	(J,M)	1/10
21.0	(H,T)	1/10
21.5	(C,H)(M,T)	2/10
22.0	(C,M)(J,T)	2/10
22.5	(C,J)	1/10
23.5	(C,T)	1/10
		1

(b) (1) 21.40   (2) 1.29   (3) 1.14
(c) 1.85   (d) 1.31

6-48 (a)

Proportion	Applicable Combinations	Probability
0	(Bob, Don)(Bob, Eve)(Don, Eve)	3/10
.5	(Ann, Bob)(Ann, Don)(Ann, Eve)	
	(Bob, Cal)(Cal, Don)(Cal, Eve)	6/10
1.0	(Ann, Cal)	1/10
		1

(b)

Range	Applicable Combinations	Probability
0	(Ann, Cal)(Bob, Eve)	2/10
1	(Ann, Bob)(Ann, Don)(Ann, Eve)	
	(Bob, Cal)(Cal, Don)(Cal, Eve)	6/10
2	(Bob, Don)(Don, Eve)	2/10
		1

6-50 (a) (1) 15/100   (3) 14/99   (5) 85/99
　　　　　(2) 85/100   (4) 15/99   (6) 84/99
　　　(b) (1) 13/98   (4) 15/98   (7) 84/98
　　　　　(2) 14/98   (5) 85/98   (8) 83/98
　　　　　(3) 14/98   (6) 84/98

6-52 Answers will vary.

6-54 Answers will vary.

6-56 (a) Answers will vary.
　　　(b) E(R) = 2   Var(R) = 1   SD(R) = 1

6-58 (a) Population: 25, 15, 23, 19
　　　　　$\mu = 20.5$ $\sigma^2 = 14.75$ $\sigma = 3.84$

(b)

$\bar{x}$	$\Pr[\bar{X} = \bar{x}]$
15	1/16
16	0
17	2/16
18	0
19	3/16
20	2/16
21	2/16
22	2/16
23	1/16
24	2/16
25	1/16

(c) $E(\bar{X}) = 20.5$
　　$Var(\bar{X}) = 7.375$
　　$SD(\bar{X}) = 2.72$
(d) $Var(\bar{X}) = \sigma^2/2$

6-60 $\Pr[X = 0] = .006738$ $\Pr[X = 5] = .018316$

6-62 (a) .018316   (b) .018316

6-64 (a) .1755   (b) .0067   (c) .0138   (d) .7419

6-66 (a) .904837   (b) .090484   (c) .004524

7-2 (a) .4332   (c) .2420   (e) .0968   (g) .97585
        (b) .1915   (d) .0062   (f) .9861   (h) .0606

7-4 (a) .2734   (c) .0668   (e) .3085   (g) .0928
        (b) .4772   (d) .0668   (f) .9772   (h) .1026

7-6 86.92 inches

7-8 (a) .01   (b) .10   (c) .50   (d) 2.00   (e) 10.00

7-10 (a) (1) 1.60   (2) .4714
         (b) (1) .80   (2) .7888
         (c) (1) .566   (2) .9232
         (d) (1) .358   (2) .9948

7-12 (a) (1) .0749   (2) .2242   (3) .1631   (4) .0668
         (b) (1) 6.698"   (2) 7.055"   (3) 7.925"   (4) 8.282"

7-14 (a) .9876   (b) .7888   (c) .4714   (d) .2434

7-16 (a) .0456   (b) .83995   (c) .16005

7-18 .1814

7-20 (a) .0490
         (b) .0207
         (c) (1) .0495   (2) .0043

7-22 (a) .0027   (b) .0011

7-24 (a) .9050   (b) .7888   (c) .6826

7-26 (a) .0207   (b) .0036

7-28 (a) .0062   (b) .1587

7-30 .00135

7-32 (a) .4525   (c) 0 (approximately)   (e) .9734
         (b) .0475   (d) 0 (approximately)

7-34 (a) .0228   (b) .0062

7-36 Anwers will vary.

7-38 Anwers will vary.

7-40 (a) $\mu = 16.70$ $\sigma = 6.70$
         (b) $\sigma_{\bar{X}} = 3.35$
             Answers will vary.
         (c) Answers will vary.

7-42 (a) 47.7 and 75.1
(b) .8502   (c) .1841

7-44 (a) .4545   (b) .0170   (c) .0055   (d) .8810

7-46 (a) .9742 for Chilean   (b) .9566 for Chilean   (c) No
   .4746 for Bolivian   .9556 for Bolivian
   .9652 for Arizonian   .9556 for Arizonian

8-2 (a) \$14,800   (b) \$11,708   (c) .6   (d) .1

8-4 (a) 5   (b) 1.94   (c) No

8-6 $15.9 \pm .10$ ounces

8-8 Ratings constitute the population.

8-10 (16.71, 27.13)

8-12 (a) 1.812   (b) 2.650   (c) 2.080   (d) 2.358

8-14 (a) $\$8.00 \pm 4.12$
(b) $\$15.03 \pm .40$ minutes
(c) 27.30 ± 1.43 pounds

8-16 $\$73,249 \pm 14,817$

8-18 (a) $t_{.005} = 2.704$; $\mu = 52,346 \pm 1,113$ miles

8-20 (a) 3 ± 1.43 (b) negligible

8-22 (.20640, .23627)

8-24 (a) $.2 \pm .025$ (b) $.04 \pm .0086$ (c) $.01 \pm .0087$

8-26 (a) $.5 \pm .013$ (b) $.4 \pm .10$

8-28 (a) $.04 \pm .038$ (b) .0013

8-30 (a) 661   (b) 385
(c) 166; it is one-fourth as large.
(d) 2,642; it increases by a factor of 4.

8-32 (a) 4^{11} (b) \$30,000   (c) 40%   (d) .01

8-34 (a) .8414   (b) 1.39

8-36 (a) 385   (b) 350; 35

8-38 1,246 + 22.7

8-40 5.4 ± .08 gallons

8-42 (a) $43,150   (b) 135,113,880   (c) .5

8-44 (a) 83.7 ± 14.43   (b) 83.7 ± 9.92   (c) 83.7 ± 8.00
(d) 83.7 ± 16.48

8-46 3.5 ± .02

8-48 76,400 ± 1,040

8-50 Answers will vary.

8-52 Answers will vary.

8-54 Answers will vary.

8-56 (a) e = $4 σ = 6.70 z = 1.65
n = 8
(b) Answers will vary.

8-58 Answers will vary.

8-60 1.5 ± 1.41 mph

8-62 .128 ± .69 sec

8-64 (a) $40,400   (b) $46,550   (c) $46,850

8-66 Answers will vary.

8-68 Answers will vary.

9-2 (a) (1) correct   (2) Type II error   (3) correct   (4) Type I error
(b) (1) Type II error   (2) correct   (3) Type I error   (4) correct
(c) (1) Type I error   (2) correct   (3) correct   (4) Type II error

9-4 (a) Type I error: Adopt the new process when it is no improvement.
Type II error: Don't adopt the new process when it is an improvement.
(b) Type I error: Sign the contract when output will not increase.
Type II error: Don't sign the contract when output will increase.
(c) Type I error: Lobby for the new law when it does not meet greater approval.
Type II error: Don't lobby for the new law when it does meet greater approval.

9-6 α = .0918 β = .0228

9-8 $\alpha = .0294$ $\beta = .0023$
Both α and β decrease (are smaller).

9-10 $t_{.05} = 1.711$ $t = 1.67$ *Accept H_0*

9-12   (a) (1) $H_0{:}\mu = 16$ ounces $H_A{:}\mu \neq 16$ ounces
   (2) $\bar{X}$ or z *(recurring decision)*
   (3) *Accept H_0*   if $15.88 \leq \bar{X} \leq 16.12$ $(-19.6 \leq z \leq 1.96)$
      Reject H_0 otherwise.
   (b) (1) *Accept H_0*   (Take no action.)
   (2) *Reject H_0*   (Take remedial action.)

9-14 $z_{.005} = 2.57$ $z = 3.5$ *Reject H_0.*

9-16   *Reject H_0*   (adjust).

9-18   (a) $t_{.01} = 2.423$
   Accept H_0 if $t \geq -2.423$.
   Reject H_0 if $t < -2.423$.
   (b) $t = -3.12$ *Reject H_0.*

9-20   (a) $H_0{:}\mu = 1''$
   (b) $\bar{X}$ or z
   (c) *Accept H_0*   if $.9974'' \leq \bar{X} \leq 1.0026''$ $(-2.57 \leq z \leq 2.57)$
      Reject H_0   otherwise.
   (d) (1) *Reject H_0*   (2) *Accept H_0.*

9-22   (a) $H_0{:}\mu \geq 2$ days   (b) $t = -5.00$
   Accept H_0 if $t \geq -1.711$.   *Reject H_0 and use new formulation.*
   Reject H_0 if $t < -1.711$.

9-24   (a) $H_0{:}\mu \leq \$5.00$ $H_A{:}\mu > \$5.00$
   (b) $\$5.12$
   Accept H_0 if $\bar{X} \leq \$5.12$.
   Reject H_0 if $\bar{X} > \$5.12$.
   (c) (1) *Reject H_0*   (2) *Accept H_0*   (3) *Accept H_0*   (4) *Reject H_0*

9-26   (a) (1) ship   (2) render
   (b) $\alpha = .01$
   Accept H_0   if $\bar{X} \geq 513.35$ $(z \geq -2.33)$.
   Reject H_0   otherwise.
   (c) (1) *Accept H_0*   (2) *Accept H_0*   (3) *Accept H_0*   (4) *Reject H_0*

9-28   (a) $z = 5.79$ 0.0000
   (b) rejected

9-30   (a) $\bar{X} = 53.87$ $s = 7.76$
   (b) accept

9-32 (a) Upper-tailed
      (b) (1) accepted   (2) accepted   (3) rejected

9-34 rejected

9-36 accepted

9-38 (a) *Reject H_0*   (b) *Reject H_0*   (c) *Reject H_0*

9-40 (a) $H_0{:}\mu \leq 10$ minutes
         $H_A{:}\mu > 10$ minutes
      (b) *Accept H_0* if $\bar{X} \leq 10.47$ minutes $(z \leq 2.33)$
         Reject H_0 if $\bar{X} > 10.47$ minutes $(z > 2.33)$
      (c) (1) *Reject H_0*   (2) *Accept H_0*   (3) *Accept H_0*

9-42 (a) $H_0{:}\mu = .5''$
      (b) *t*
      (c) *Accept H_0* if $-2.617 \leq t \leq 2.617$.
         Reject H_0 if $t < -2.617$.
             or if $t > 2.617$.
      (d) (1) *Reject H_0* and correct for undersizing.
         (2) *Reject H_0* and correct for oversizing.

9-44 Change design.

9-46 *Accept H_0* and don't take corrective action.

9-48 (a) $H_0{:}\mu \leq 86$
         Accept H_0 if $t \leq 1.711$.
         Reject H_0 if $t > 1.711$.
      (b) *Accept H_0* and keep present procedure.

9-50 Answers will vary.

9-52 Answers will vary.

9-54 *Reject H_0* and conclude exam is hard enough.

9-56 Answers will vary.

9-58 $t = 1.152$ *Accept H_0*

9-60 $t = 4.20$ *Reject H_0*

9-62 (a) $-.52$ hours $\leq \mu_A - \mu_B \leq .12$ hours   (b) *Accept H_0*

10-2 (a) \$258 billion   (b) \$446 billion   (c) \$634 billion

10-4

Dependent Variable	Independent Variable
(a) Time deposits	Employee income
(b) Income	Stock purchases
(c) Savings	Wages

10-6 .791

10-8 (a) correlation (b) regression (c) regression (d) both

10-10 (b) $\hat{Y}(X) = 22.405 + 3.619X$

10-12 (a) $\hat{Y}(X) = 20.03 + .412X$
(c) (1) 102.4 (2) 164.2 (3) 184.8

10-14 (a) $\hat{Y}(X) = 1,980 + .4062X$ (b) $\hat{Y}(X) = 15.07 + .06053X$

10-16 (b) $\hat{Y}(X) = 31.0 + 1.42X$
(c) (1) 8.50 (2) 5.484

10-18 (b) $\hat{Y}(X) = 30.4 + 5.64X$

10-20 (a)

(1) Number of Components X	(2) Simulated Actual Time Y	(3) Theoretical Time $\mu_{Y.X}$	(4) Estimated Time $\hat{Y}(X)$	(5) Error Term $\epsilon = Y - \mu_{Y.X}$	(6) Residual $Y - \hat{Y}(X)$
5	49.2	60.5	58.6	−11.3	−9.4
7	81.6	70.7	69.9	10.9	11.7
10	83.0	86.0	86.8	−3.0	−3.8
12	86.7	96.2	98.1	−9.5	−11.4
13	122.7	101.3	103.7	21.4	19.0
15	114.0	111.5	115.0	2.5	−1.0
16	121.3	116.6	120.6	4.7	.7
20	136.2	137.0	143.2	−.8	−7.0
22	152.5	147.2	154.5	5.3	−2.0
25	174.7	162.5	171.4	12.2	3.3

(b) No (c) No

10-22 (a) $1,600 \pm 41.38$ and ± 211.00
(b) $2,275 \pm 139.82$ and ± 249.71
(c) $2,950 \pm 270.29$ and ± 340.39

10-24 (a) $\$44.12 \pm 20.16$ (b) $\$54.98 \pm 42.61$

10-26 (a) (1) (34.95, 46.88) (2) (40.79, 49.54) (3) (47.45, 57.05)
(b) (1) (26.93, 54.90) (2) (31.78, 58.55) (3) (38.72, 65.78)

10-28 (a) $\hat{Y}(X) = 16.83 + 8.769X$ (b) positive (d) .998

10-30 (a) 99.8% (b) .999

10-32 (a)

Observation i	Distance X	Charge Y	Predicted $\hat{Y}(X)$	Residual $Y - \hat{Y}(X)$
1	14	68	73.0714	−5.0714
2	23	105	105.6429	−0.6429
3	9	40	54.9762	−14.9762
4	17	79	83.9286	−4.9286
5	10	81	58.5952	22.4048
6	22	95	102.0238	−7.0238
7	5	31	40.9500	−9.5000
8	12	72	65.8333	6.1667
9	6	45	44.1190	0.8810
10	16	93	80.3095	12.6905

10-34 (a) (1) .972   (2) +.986

10-36 (a) $\hat{Y}(X) = 2.486 + .129X$
(b) (1) .556   (2) .438
(c) (1) .449   (2) .670
(d) (1) 3.13   (2) 2.74   (3) 3.00   (4) 3.78

10-38 (a) 12,500 ± 1,209.3 bales   (b) 10,000 ± 1,263.0 bales
(c) 15,000 ± 1,263.0 bales

10-40 (a) \$80,000 ± 79.20   (b) \$80,000 ± 1,052

10-42 Answers will vary.

10-44 Answers will vary.

10-46 (a) $\hat{Y}(X) = 10.8 + 1.19X$
(b) $s_Y = 11.434$ (c) $s_{Y \cdot X} = 6.1$
(c) $r^2 = .734$ $r = .857$
(d) 25.08

10-48 Answers will vary.

10-50 (a) $\hat{Y}(X) = 352.49 + .337X$
(b) $s_Y = 4.427$ $s_{Y \cdot X} = 3.34$
(c) $r^2 = .49$ $r = .70$

10-52 (a) 27 ± 7.25.   (b) rejected   (c) $t = 10.457$ *rejected*

11-2 $a = -8.17$ $b_1 = 4.250$ $b_2 = -3.417$

11-4 (a) 3.189   (b) 3.254   (c) 2.975   (d) 3.708

11-6 (a) $\hat{Y} = -26 + 4X_1 + 6X_2$

11-8 (a) $\hat{Y}(X_1) = 4 + X_1$ (b) $s_{Y \cdot X1} = 9.325$ $S_{Y \cdot 12} = 3.02$

11-10 (a) $\hat{Y} = 4.2 + .7668X_1 + 192.9X_2 - .634X_3$ (b) 422.7   (c) yes

11-12 (a) $\hat{Y} = 36.6584 - .0670X_1 - 1.6525X_2 - 1.6013X_3$

(b) 1.79   (c) yes

11-14 $\hat{Y} = 1.5045 + .030X_1 + .250X_2 + .444X_3 - .038X_4$

11-16 (a) (1) ($7,299, 8,321)   (2) ($6,656, 8,964)

(b) (1) .767 ± .350   (2) 192.9 ± 514.9   (3) −.634 ± 1.980

11-18 (a) (1) (5.186, 6.392)   (2) (4.216, 7.362)

(b) (1) .0297 ± .0145   (2) .2504 ± .5664

(3) .4436 ± .2469   (4) −.03802 ± .7527

11-20 (a) $S_{Y.12} = 1.759$ $R^2_{Y.12} = .786$ 78.6%

(b) 96.4%   (c) Yes   (d) $r^2_{Y3.12} = .465$

11-22 (a) .646   (b) .055   (c) .566   (d) 56.6%

11-24 (a) $S_{Y.12} = 4.714$ $R^2_{Y.12} = .893$ 89.3%   (b) 96.4%

(c) .664   66.4%

11-26 (a) (1) $\hat{Y}(X_1) = 1,667 + .6333\ X_1$ (2) $\hat{Y}(X_2) = 7,538.4 + 115.4\ X_1$

$r^2_{Y1} = .8595$ $r^2_{Y2} = .0124$

(3) $\hat{Y}(X_3) = 7,099 + 1.287X_3$

$r^2_{Y3} = .202$

(b) X_1

(c) (1) $\hat{Y} = -58.82 + .6765X_1 + 323.5X_2$

$r^2_{Y2.1} = .665$

(2) $\hat{Y} = 444.84 + .8410X1 - 1.2218X3$

$r^2_{Y3.1} = .637$

11-28 (a) $\hat{Y} = -9.082 - .09552X_2 + .020944\ X_6 + .06411X_8$

$S_{Y.568} = 4.584$

Player	Card Pr. Y	Games X_5	At Bats X_6	RBI X_8	Predicted	Residual $Y - \hat{Y}$
8	3.0	761	2,717	426	2.4408	0.5592
18	15.0	1,024	3,941	646	17.0578	−2.0578
19	20.0	1,773	6,109	1,060	17.4589	2.5411
20	5.0	736	2,700	447	5.8192	−0.8192
29	12.0	830	3,032	518	8.3452	3.6548
40	0.7	810	2,703	427	−2.4689	3.1689
49	3.5	740	2,707	400	2.5705	0.9295
56	10.0	1,378	4,819	812	12.2736	−2.2736
64	6.0	1,299	4,670	803	16.1223	−10.1223
67	0.8	703	2,657	422	6.4681	−5.6681
75	30.0	1,117	4,416	759	25.3669	4.6331
79	1.0	578	1,944	305	−4.0254	5.0254
80	3.0	623	2,173	429	4.4218	−1.4218
86	45.0	2,135	7,997	1,373	42.4881	2.5119
88	0.7	1,209	4,271	569	1.3611	−0.6611

(c) $\hat{Y} = -9.14 - .0905X_5 + .0183X_6 + .0729\ X_8$

$S_{Y.568} = 3.405$

11-30 (a) $\hat{Y} = -.412 + .631X_1 + .00223X_2$
(b) (1) 2.96 (2) 2.25 (3) 3.06 (4) 2.93

11-32 $\hat{Y} = -.386 + .637X_1 + .002X_2 - .007X_3$

11-34 (a) $\hat{Y} = -16.563 + 1.518X_1 + .1554X_2 + .6847X_3$
(b) Yes

11-36 (a) No (b) X_8, X_{11}, X_5

11-38 (a) $\hat{Y} = -17.5 - .0899X_5 + .426X_8 - .706X_{11} - 9.4X_4$
(b) .850
(c) .045 4.5% reduction

11-40 (a) $\hat{Y} = 253 + 308X_4 + 1.49X_{10} + .07487X_{12}$
(b) .841
(c) Drop fielding.

11-42 Answers will vary.

11-44 (a) $X_1 =$ distance $X_2 =$ gender (male $= 0$, female $= 1$)
    $\hat{Y} = 10.8 + 1.37X_1 - 5.20X_2$
(b) $s_Y = 11.434$ $S_{Y\cdot12} = 5.872$
(c) $R^2_{Y\cdot12} = .771$ $r^2_{Y1} = .734$ $r^2_{Y2} = .105$
    $r^2_{Y1\cdot2} = .771$ $r^2_{Y2\cdot1} = .139$
(d) 21.99

11-46 Answers will very.

11-48 Answers will vary.

11-50 (b) $\hat{Y} = -4.443 + 1.1609X_1 + 2.5804X_2$
(d) $\hat{Y}(X_1) = -.686 + .8477X_1$

11-52 (a) $\bar{X} = 8.5$ (men) $\bar{X} = 6.08$ (women)
    $\bar{Y} = 5.42$ $\bar{Y} = 5.2$
(b) Men have higher test scores and productivity.

11-54 (b) $\hat{Y} = 138.8 + .277X_1 + 138.6X_2 + .075X_1X_2$

12-2 (a) LCL $= .046$ UCL $= .094$
(b) 6/21 and 6/28
(c) LCL $= .041$ UCL $= .087$
(d) (1) in control (2) out (3) in (4) out (5) in

12-4 LCL $= .0526$ UCL $= .0846$
out of control on 10/01, 4, 6, 7, 9, 12, 14, 15, 19, 22, 23, 24, 28

12-6 (a) .2177 (c) .9292
(b) .7823 (d) .9798

12-8 (a,b)

Sample	$\bar{X}$	R
1	16.034	.36 in control
2	16.028	1.25 out of control (R)
3	16.512	.47 out of control ($\bar{X}$)
4	15.694	.39 in control
5	16.036	.47 in control

12-10 (a)

Sample	$\bar{X}$	R	Sample	$\bar{X}$	R
1	4.96	.2	14	5.02	.5
2	5.00	.5	15	4.94	.5
3	4.94	.2	16	5.02	.3
4	4.84	.5	17	4.90	.2
5	4.88	.7	18	4.96	1.0
6	4.94	.7	19	4.98	.4
7	5.04	.6	20	5.00	.4
8	4.98	.5	21	5.12	.4
9	5.10	.4	22	4.98	.2
10	5.04	.1	23	4.86	.5
11	4.86	.5	24	5.00	.2
12	5.36	.1	25	4.84	.3
13	5.32	.3			

$$\bar{\bar{X}} = 5.00 \quad \bar{R} = .42$$

12-12 (a) LCL = 12.38   UCL = 11.83   (b) Day 5

12-14 (a) LCL = .42   UCL = 0   (b) Day 9

12-16 (a) 17   (b) 15   (c) 14

12-18 (a) .4513   (b) .0023   (c) 0

12-20 (a) 4
(b) (1) accepted   (2) accepted   (3) rejected   (4) accepted

12-22 (a) *Accept*   if $\bar{X} \leq 1.61$
Reject   if $\bar{X} > 1.61$
(b) $\bar{X} = 2.55$ *Reject*
(c) (1) 1   (2) .0023

12-24 (a) n = 10   reject   (c) n = 20   accept
(b) n = 30   accept   (d) n = 10   accept

12-26

	$\bar{X}$	R
(a)	1.93	.6 (1)
(b)	1.98	.8 (1)
(c)	1.98	1.4 (3)
(d)	1.58	1.2 (4)

12-28 (a) 10   (b) accepted for (1)–(4)

12-30 (a) LCL = 19.84   UCL = 20.12
           (b) Days 2 and 6

12-32 (a) LCL = 13.826   UCL = 14.219
           (b) LCL = 0   UCL = .72
           (c) (1) LCL = 13.806   UCL = 14.216
               (2) LCL = 0   UCL = .751

12-34 (a) .9942   (b) .9330

12-36 (a) LCL = 11.98   UCL = 12.22
           (b) Days 3, 5, 6, and 11

12-38 (a) Center = 12.11   LCL = 11.82   UCL = 12.40
           (b) Center = .22   LCL = 0   UCL = .45

CREDITS

The author is indebted to the following for permission to reprint from copyrighted material.

INDEX